D0239734

THE GREAT BOOK
OF HUMOUR

He eyed my glass in a wolfish sort of way

See page 765

THE
GREAT BOOK
of
HUMOUR

Edited by
J. M. PARRISH *and*
JOHN R. CROSSLAND

ODHAMS PRESS LTD.
LONG ACRE, LONDON, W.C.2

Copyright, 1935

Printed in Great Britain

INTRODUCTION

"FOR what do we live, but to make sport for our neighbours and laugh at them in our turn?" asked Jane Austen's irrepressible Mr. Bennett. We may contend that Mr. Bennett's attitude towards his responsibilities enabled him to support his philosophy more confidently than ours can do. But we will most of us admit that there would be something less to live for if our fellows did not make sport for us, and we for our fellows.

A sense of humour is regarded by some of the wisest and most illustrious as a pricelsss gift; it seems to be a pretty universal opinion that Life, even with Love, is incomplete without Laughter; and the man who takes either himself or others too seriously is usually an object of commiseration.

Which brings us to one reason—and perhaps the best and most important reason—why we derive such tonic enjoyment from the funny story—the type of story that is close to life itself. For with what keen pleasure we recognize in the characters involved the little foibles of our friends, our relatives, our neighbours, and—if we are true humorists—of ourselves; the comical inconsistencies of our society—its laws, prejudices, habits, and reactions.

The latest incomprehensible knot tied in the already tangled red tape of officialdom, that has provided exercise for our wit over the morning paper; the idiosyncrasies of the man next door, of our colleagues at the office; the little inconsequences of husband or wife; the bewildering, charming inconsistencies of youth in love; the exquisite naïveté of the very young; the Cockney wit that spontaneously entertains us in bus or tram; the rustic wisdom we meet with in country inn or on the beach; the comic ingenuity of repartee and action that distinguishes the men who follow invisible pathways across the high seas or trace the coastline; all these and a myriad other aspects of kaleidoscopic life have caught the fancy of famous writers belonging to every age.

They are mirrored for our delight in the challenging paradox of Chesterton; in the smooth raillery of Belloc; in the cheery boisterousness of Wodehouse; in the rollicking fantasy of Twain;

7

in the scintillating wit of Wilde ; in the retributive satire of Bennett ; in the enchanting sympathy of Locke ; in the sly solidarity of Priestley ; in the delicate charm of Lucas ; in the hilarious humanity of Jacobs ; in the joyous contemplation of Milne ; in the crispness of O. Henry ; in the audacious burlesque of Leacock.

A glittering array of names, although only a few of those that have been chosen to bear each other company in this cavalcade of mirth—names that have added much Laughter to Life and Love and not a little Wisdom. For there is little real humour that has not Wisdom and Truth for its sponsors. How could we laugh at our own mistakes and at our oddities if we were not a little wiser than our folly ?

Laughter, then, is Wisdom. Laughter is a fleeting but invigorating holiday from the stress of life, which we may take almost as often as we need it. Laughter brings us friends, and helps us to understand them and to keep them. Laughter is a tonic—and who would not prefer to go for their restorative to their bookshelf rather than to the medicine chest ?

We are proud, then, to offer you so many delicious doses of this stimulating elixir, with such a variety of flavours—sparkling satire, rich irony, fully-spiced wit, pungent burlesque, bubbling farce, sharp-tanged paradox.

The authors of these stories have found laughter everywhere ; they have found it on the wharves of dockland and at the seaside bungalow ; among the elect of our Universities and in our pompous clubs ; in the drowsy countryside of England and Ireland, and in the dusty French village ; on the high seas and on the coastal steamer ; in the forbidding archives wherein are written the shalt and shalt-nots of our indefatigable law-makers ; in the hunting-field, in the East End of London, in Mayfair, in a department store, and in a one-man shop.

Many of the characters we shall recognize, with keen apprecia-tion, as reflections of those that jostle us in our particular corner of the world. Surely we have met Mr. Lucas's well-intentioned but somewhat misguided church workers ? We know, do we not, the members of Mr. Alan's amateur dramatic club ? Un-doubtedly we have acquaintance with small persons as involun-tarily wayward as Wee MacGreegor, as attractively sincere as the Bastable family, so that our hearts warm towards them, and we chuckle sympathetically over their escapades. And we can hardly fail to learn a little of the art of living by accompanying the lovable Aristide Pujol on one of his exploits.

We leave the people and the surroundings with whom we are familiar and wing our way on flights of the authors' fancy to China, to the New World and Rip Van Winkle's mountains.

We find our heroes in situations sublimely ridiculous, yet brought about by much the same motives as expedite the adventures of the Cockney Educated Evans, the inimitable Jeeves, the hapless Mr. Caudle—ambition, the tender emotions, a desire to appear more important than merit justifies, or to escape from the monotonous and inevitable. We laugh heartily at Mr. Caudle because his only refuge is to bury his head in the bedclothes and thump his pillow (as ours would probably be). Rip Van Winkle manages to escape the unpleasant tongue for ever by means denied to us, but, given the scolding wife, how stimulating to see her defeated in this wholly unanswerable fashion ! Whilst we appreciate the story of a diffident youth's efforts to win fame and fortune in London for their fidelity to life as we know it, yet it does us good to see the restrictions that would hamper him swept aside by the simple-minded Seng Heng on a similar quest in China.

The Comic Muse has led the authors into a rich variety of scene and circumstance ; the reader may select a meeting place with her at random, according to taste or mood ; perhaps he will begin by an entertaining train journey with " the fellow traveller " ; afterwards he will find himself in Mayfair, and must eventually arrive on board a very amateur yotsman's yot ; he will find pleasant entertainment over the Border with Wee MacGreegor, and in the Five Towns ; it is but a page or two and he is in China, chuckling over one of the ingenious Kai Lung's anecdotes ; he arrives back in England in time to take part in a strange adventure in Kensington, and afterwards at a popular seaside resort ; he goes with the Caudles to Margate, and then bridges the gulf of ages in order to learn the astonishing secret of roast pig ; he is admitted to the very exclusive Problem Club, and permitted to overhear a most entertaining conversation at a party in New York ; he attends Sheridan's famous " Rehearsal," and goes to the races in rural Ireland ; then he has a rendezvous with Educated Evans in the East End before sailing the high seas with princes and magnates and some other queer birds ; he is privileged to share in both sides of a young man's double life, and to learn why it is so essential to be earnest ; and he finds his way, inevitably, to the incomparable Jeeves.

Each of the authors who has been given a place in this book being " a fellow of infinite jest, of most excellent fancy," we feel that in this anthology we are offering not only a companion fitted to share joyous and care-free moments, but, when required, a formidable rival to the most efficacious set of vitamins ever recommended for imparting a rosy complexion to the world.

ILLUSTRATIONS

CONTENTS

ACKNOWLEDGMENTS

The Editors wish to express their thanks for permission to include in this volume stories by the following authors :

A. J. ALAN, *The Cabmen's Shelter* : to Charles Lavell, Esq.

ALPHA OF THE PLOUGH, *A Fellow Traveller* (from *Leaves in the Wind*) : to Messrs. J. M. Dent & Sons Ltd.

MICHAEL ARLEN, *The Man with the Broken Nose* (from *These Charming People*) : to the Author.

ANTHONY ARMSTRONG, *How to Yot* (from *How to Do It*) : to the Author and to Messrs. Methuen & Co. Ltd.

F. E. BAILEY, *Look this Way, Baby !* : to the Author.

" BARTIMEUS," *The Leg-Puller* : to the Author.

J. J. BELL, *Green Paint* (from *Wee MacGreegor*) : to the Author's Executors.

HILAIRE BELLOC, *The Joke* (from *This and That and the Other*) : to the Author and to Messrs. Methuen & Co. Ltd.

ARNOLD BENNETT, *The Burglary* : to the Author's Executors.

GEORGE A. BIRMINGHAM, *A Lunatic at Large* (from *Lady Bountiful*) : to the Author and to Messrs. Christophers.

ERNEST BRAMAH, *The Probation of Sen Heng* : to the Author.

G. K. CHESTERTON, *The Eccentric Seclusion of the Old Lady* (from *The Club of Queer Trades*) : to Messrs. Harper & Bros.

AGATHA CHRISTIE, *The Rajah's Emerald* : to the Author.

WALTER DE LA MARE, *The Orgy* (from *On the Edge*) : to the Author and to Messrs. Faber & Faber Ltd.

JEFFERY FARNOL, *The Divine Phyllidia* : to the Author.

J. S. FLETCHER, *Provisions of Partnership* : to the Author's Executors.

THOMAS HARDY, *Tony Kytes, the Arch-Deceiver* (from *Life's Little Ironies*) : to the Author's Executors and to Messrs. Macmillan & Co. Ltd.

O. HENRY, *Tobin's Palm* : to Messrs. Hodder & Stoughton Ltd., and to Messrs. Doubleday Doran, Inc.

A. P. HERBERT, *The Human Hen* (from *More Misleading Cases*) : to the Author and to Messrs. Methuen & Co. Ltd.

W. W. JACOBS, *The Dreamer* : to the Author.

17

HERBERT JENKINS, *The Summer Camp for Tired Workers* : to the Author's Executors and to Messrs. Herbert Jenkins Ltd.

STEPHEN LEACOCK, *Gertrude the Governess* (from *Nonsense Novels*) : to the Author and to Messrs. John Lane The Bodley Head Ltd.

W. J. LOCKE, *The Adventure of the Pig's Head* (from *The Joyous Adventures of Aristide Pujol*) : to the Author's Executors and to Messrs. John Lane The Bodley Head Ltd.

E. V. LUCAS, *The Christmas Decorations* (from *Character and Comedy*) : to the Author and to Messrs. Methuen & Co. Ltd.

DENIS MACKAIL, *Say it with Cheese* : to the Author.

A. A. MILNE, *Winter Sport* (from *Once a Week*) : to the Author and to Messrs. Methuen and Co. Ltd.

NEIL MUNRO, *A New Cook* (from *In Highland Harbours with Para Handy*) : to the Author's Trustees and to Messrs. William Blackwood & Sons Ltd.

E. NESBIT, *The Conscience-Pudding* : to Messrs. Ernest Benn Ltd.

BARRY PAIN, *The Giraffe Problem* : to the Author's Executors.

DOROTHY PARKER, *The Sexes* : to the Viking Press, Inc.

G. W. PECK, *A Bad Boy Begins his Diary* (from *A Bad Boy's Diary*) : to Messrs. W. Foulsham & Co. Ltd.

EDEN PHILLPOTTS, *The Matchmaker* : to the Author.

J. B. PRIESTLEY, *The Taxi and the Star* : to the Author.

W. PETT RIDGE, *Retiring Inspector* : to the Author's Executors and to Messrs. Hodder & Stoughton Ltd.

SAKI, *Esmé* (from *The Chronicles of Clovis*) : to the Author's Executors and to Messrs. John Lane The Bodley Head Ltd.

E. Œ. SOMERVILLE AND MARTIN ROSS, *Occasional Licenses* (from *Some Experiences of an Irish R.M.*) : to Messrs. Longmans, Green & Co. Ltd.

MARK TWAIN, *The Stolen White Elephant* : to Messrs. Chatto & Windus.

EDGAR WALLACE, *A Souvenir* (from *More Educated Evans*) : to Messrs. Edgar Wallace Ltd.

H. G. WELLS, *A Deal in Ostriches* : to the Author.

OSCAR WILDE, *The Importance of Being Earnest* : to Captain V. B. Holland.

P. G. WODEHOUSE, *The Ordeal of Young Tuppy* (from *Very Good, Jeeves*) : to the Author and to Messrs. Herbert Jenkins Ltd.

A. J. ALAN, *a welcome voice to listeners and no more than a name to countless other admirers, is the most mysterious figure in modern fiction. He keeps the secret of his identity well, whilst as a spinner of yarns—humorous, fantastic, or mysterious—he becomes ever more popular. Here is the transcript of a story taken down in shorthand as he told it over the air. It is one of his gayest tales.*

THE CABMEN'S SHELTER

HAVE you ever noticed that the most difficult and troublesome jobs you have to do are always shoved on to you by some one else? Things you would never dream of tackling on your own account. Well, I have—and I'm going to tell you about a time when I got properly landed.

It was about three years ago. There was a man I knew called Martin. I didn't know him at all well—he was a member of my club, and we had occasional cocktails together, as one does, but that was about all—quite a nice beast.

Well, one evening he rang me up on the telephone and said he was in terrible trouble and might he come round and see me. I said, " Certainly ; how much do you want ? " However, it wasn't a question of money, apparently—something much worse ; he'd tell me about it presently—and he came straight along.

I sat him down in a chair and gave him something to drink, and then he told me all about it. He'd apparently got a friend who lived in the country—a Mrs. Wilson. This good lady was by way of being a leading light in her own particular county, and she'd taken it into her head to get up an entertainment in aid of a local charity.

According to Martin, the whole neighbourhood round about was fairly seething with talent. There were any amount of people who knew they could play and sing and recite, and who meant to, so the first hour of the entertainment was to take the form of a concert.

That wasn't the worst.

There was also in the district, in the actual process of being formed, an amateur dramatic club. Mrs. Wilson had somehow been blackmailed into allotting the last two hours of her programme to this amateur dramatic club. They were to do their first play.

I agreed that it all sounded pretty deadly, but what was his, Martin's, particular trouble ?

He then confessed that in a very weak moment he'd promised to write the play that these people were going to act.

I said :

" Well, have you written it ? "

And he said :

" No, that's the milk in the coco-nut ! When I said I would, I hadn't tried ; and now I've tried, I find I can't."

I said :

" Well, it's something to have found that out. Lots don't—ever. But why not tell Mrs. Thing—Mrs. Wilson—that you can't manage it ? "

Oh no ; that wouldn't do at all—there were reasons—or rather *a* reason. In fact, he was rather mashed on Miss Wilson, and wanted to get engaged to her, and if he backed out it would ruin his chances.

I asked him how far he had got—er—with the play. He told me he'd got the plot all worked out, but when it came to writing down the things the characters were to say to each other, he'd sort of stuck. Would it bore me very much to help him just write the words in ? That was exactly how he put it.

I said it wouldn't bore me a bit, but that he'd lose his young woman for certain if I did. He agreed to risk it, and began to unfold the plot. Very original the plot was. I must tell you about it. Martin won't mind.

In the first act, the heroine's father turns down the hero as a prospective son-in-law because he hasn't any money. The hero thereupon finds a piece of parchment covered with hieroglyphics in an old box belonging to his grandfather.

An erudite friend of the hero's translates these hieroglyphics, and finds that they give an account of some sacrificial rites practised by the Chocky Wocky Indians in Central South America.

These rites consisted of chucking vast quantities of rubies, emeralds, diamonds, and what-not into a sacred lake on the top of a mountain. Position of lake conveniently stated, and colour blue on plan (but no information as to how the lake got on to the top of the mountain).

As this wasteful business had been taking place once a month for about ten million years, the idea was that the aforesaid lake might be worth dredging.

The hero puts his last fiver on a horse, which, of course, wins at 100 to 1, and with his money he fits out an expedition to go out to South America. What did I think of that for a first act?

I said it was simply great, but wasn't everything going too smoothly? There surely ought to be a villain to steal a copy of the—agenda. That would introduce exciting complications in the second act, and make it last longer. My amendment was agreed to without a division, and incorporated in the general scheme.

The second act occurred on the banks of the lake, and was full of incident. First of all, there was the problem of dredging. I suggested draining the lake. Why not drill a hole in the bottom of it, and let the water run through into the mountain?

Martin didn't approve of that. He'd been a civil engineer. He said it would be more scientific to draw it off through a trench.

When this engineering work is nearly finished, the villain happens along with an expedition of his own; there's a scrap, and they're driven off, leaving the hero's party up to their knees in jewels.

Then the Chocky Wocky Indians turn up in force and capture them. The officer in charge takes a very serious view of the hero's operations and says it's a job for the Queen Goddess to settle.

According to him, this lady is a sort of cross between She, Cleopatra, and the Queen of Sheba. She is white, marvellously beautiful, and all that, and apparently wears nothing but rubies and emeralds.

I couldn't help warning Martin not to make the piece too expensive to dress or there'd be nothing left for the charity. He said he'd thought of that. They'd only be imitation jewels.

Well, the second act closes with the hero and his party being marched off to the Queen Goddess's Palace.

You can imagine the last act. A scene of barbaric splendour. There's a sort of trial. The lady first of all sentences the hero to a sticky death; then she relents and wants to marry him instead, but he, being a hero, is obliged to refuse—got a young woman at home, and so on—and things are looking very bleak for him when the heroine and her father turn up with a rescue party and all ends happily.

Martin said, " What do you think of that for a plot? " and for the life of me I couldn't tell him. (He *was* my guest for the moment.)

I said :

" I'm not sure, but I think it's a masterpiece. Let's get it on to paper *at once*." So we did.

We finished the whisky at three o'clock and the first act at five past. We wrote the second act the next night and finished the play the night after. We might have taken a little longer, only it was due to be performed in three weeks' time.

I admit it was very lightly constructed, but it was only meant to last for one night.

I didn't worry about stage directions, because it struck me that the producer, whoever he was, might do that. Martin wanted to know what a producer was. He seemed to think he was the man who produced the money.

I explained that this idea was not usually borne out in actual practice—judging from the ones I knew—but that they had their uses all the same. He wondered whether the idea of producing the show would appeal to me at all. Of course, I didn't know as much as I do now, or I shouldn't have let myself in.

As it was he carted me down to Mrs. Wilson's two days later.

I must say they were all charming people, but a little too rich. Huge house in the middle of a park, lots of cars, swimming-bath, squash court, and so on. It was all rather oppressive until one got used to it.

One couldn't help wondering why they troubled to get up an entertainment for the charity at all. It would have been so much easier to write the cheque and have done with it. But no, they wanted to act.

I asked what the charity was that the whole thing was for. They told me it was to build a cabmen's shelter at the local railway station. The joke was that the cabmen said they didn't want a shelter. If it rained they could go into the station and shelt. However, Mrs. Wilson said they'd got to have one, and that settled it.

The first evening they collected the amateur dramatic club and I read the play to it. It went quite well. Then we allotted the parts—nineteen of 'em. That took some time—not that it mattered who played what.

The next thing was to get the play typed. Mrs. Wilson put her secretary at my entire disposal. I thanked her very much. I thanked her still more after I'd seen the secretary. My word ! She was very handsome. She was rather of the Diana type— not Diana anybody—just Diana. The Greek lady, in fact—and she knew her job. I don't know what her name was. She was always called Bar. Her initials were B. A. R. That may have had something to do with it. She finished the entire typing of that play in three days, and we put in the stage directions as she went along. Martin rather faded out about now. I think the detail bored him, and Miss Wilson didn't, so Bar and I agreed to run the show ourselves. Martin was delighted. We wrote him a part to keep him quiet. He was Walla Walla, Chief of the Chocky Wocky Indians.

Then we got on with the business. On the evening of the third day we had just a run through to give the company a slight idea of the hang of the thing. Then we sent them home to learn their parts. Vain hope. At the first rehearsal the only people who knew their lines were the ones who had nothing to say, and *they* wouldn't stop talking.

We gave them a week more to get word perfect in, and then they had to put a shilling in a box every time they dried up. But that soon had to be stopped. At the rate money was coming in they'd have been able to build the cabmen's shelter of platinum. There'd have been no need to give the performance at all.

The prompter went down with clergyman's throat. However, after a time they began to put their backs into it. They were quite a cheery crowd. All except one young man. He caused the only breeze we had.

He was rather dreadful. He was tall and thin and wore Oxford trousers. His fingers were stained up to the elbow with cigarette juice. His hair was long and smarmed back with vaseline, and it looked exactly like straw. Any drowning man would have clutched at it on sight.

But it wasn't only that. He made puns. Of course, as long as he only made them in his own spare time it didn't matter so much ; one could pretend not to notice. But when he insisted on introducing one into his lines in the play, I—er—demurred.

Well, he resented some remark of mine, and threw up his part. You've heard of actors throwing up their parts, haven't you ? Well, they don't ; they throw them down and stamp on them. At least, he did. Perhaps that proved he wasn't an actor. I picked up the part and gave it to his successor, and we bore his loss with Christian fortitude.

I hadn't said so very much to him either, only that real people don't make puns.

Well, we had a fairly strenuous time of it, what with rehearsals every day, and all the arrangements to make for *the night*.

The scenery and dresses had to be hired from London, but as far as possible we managed the properties ourselves.

We had a certain amount of trouble with the supply of

precious stones which had to be fished up out of the lake.
Broken glass might have *looked* all right, but there were difficulties
in the way of handling it with the necessary " abandon " which
made us turn it down in favour of something blunter.

However, I happened to be going past the local chemist one
day, and I saw in the window a large jar of bright green lozenges.
I went in and bought his entire stock. He also kept them in
bright red, and I bought them too. He told me they were very
good for colds—they were very good for rubies and emeralds
too.

The great day dawned—before I was up.

The performance was to take place in an enormous marquee
on the lawn, and it and the scenery were coming across from
Birmingham by road. The contractors had guaranteed that
everything would be up and ready for use by noon.

But instead of the tent being *up* by twelve o'clock, there
wasn't a sign of it. Every one started having fits and fusing all
the telephone wires, and eventually a convoy of lorries and an
army of men rolled up and things began to move.

The prime mover was a perfectly splendid person called
Charlie. He was about five feet square, and he wore a bowler
hat on the back of his head. He was fairly clean-shaven except
for a cigarette which was permanently stuck to his lower lip.
He had a wonderful vocabulary. If he'd been in the Navy he'd
have been an admiral. Actually he had been a dockyard
rigger.

He never took his hands out of his pockets, but he did the work
of ten men. He put up that tent—verbally. Several of our
women strolled up to watch, but it cramped his style so much
that the work slowed down visibly. I had to shoo them away.
To give you an instance : there was a pole left lying somewhere
where he didn't want it, and he lifted up his voice and said so.
Several of his minions sprang forward to do his bidding, but I
swear that spar began to move before they got to it. In fact,
Charlie was *it*.

The marquee was up by 2.30, with the stage and chairs complete. We finished our dress rehearsal at five, and it wasn't too
depressing on the whole. When it was over the company were
told to go away for a change of thought and not to show up till
it was time to dress.

Well, eight o'clock came. The tent fairly bulged with
humanity. Every seat was sold, some of them twice over.

The concert from eight to nine went with great vim and *éclat*.
There were several encores, and, of course, it ran well over its

time. Then, after a short interval, came our overture. Oh yes, we were doing the thing in style.

Our orchestra consisted of a piano, 'cello, and fiddle. The piano was down in the body of the hall, so to speak, but the 'cellist and the fiddler were performing on the stage itself behind the curtain.

They were having an averagely thin time, too, because what with the roar of conversation from the audience, and the noise of the scene being set for act one all over them, they couldn't hear each other, much less the piano.

When they were half-through the overture, some one knocked over a chair. This made rather the same noise as the signal for sending the curtain up, and it duly went up. This wouldn't have mattered, but our instrumentalists had already done their respective turns in the concert, and were also performing in our play.

Owing to the concert having finished late and mopped up some of the interval, these two wretched men had only got a certain way with their dressing. The fiddler was, frankly, in his trousers and vest ; and when I say vest, I mean vest, not waist-coat. He bolted for the wings like a good 'un. The 'cellist took cover behind his 'cello.

The whole thing only lasted about ten seconds, but it was by far and away the best turn of the evening. The audience yelled themselves hoarse. But we couldn't give an encore.

I'm not going to worry you with an account of our play. It began astoundingly well. People didn't forget their lines—much—and they remembered quite a lot of the things they'd been told to do.

By the middle of the second act I was beginning to toy with the idea that we *might* get through without any serious hitch.

I'm not saying there hadn't been any small ones, because there had. For instance, you may remember that there were two battles in the second act. There were several casualties in these engagements, and one of the corpses, who was lying in full view of the audience, was attacked by a fit of coughing. If he'd had more experience he might have pretended he wasn't quite killed, and used it, but unfortunately he was such a perfect gent that he put his hand in front of his mouth each time. It was a pity.

There had been one or two other things like that, but all obviously accidents, and no one's fault.

Well, as I say, I was standing in the wings, just beginning to hope, when Bar came up to me quietly and said :

" Come outside ! I've got some dreadful news for you."

So we went out, and she told me that the Rifford Cottage Hospital had just rung up to say that Miss Saxon, our Queen Goddess, was there. She'd skidded—in her car—and tried to push a tree down.

Nothing very serious, luckily—a broken collar-bone and general shake-up—but as a Queen Goddess she was *na poo*.

It's hardly necessary to explain that this was just about the worst thing that could have happened. The whole play had been leading up to her. Without her, there simply couldn't *be* a last act. Unless—of course——

I said :

" Look here, Bar, you've worked like a nigger to make this show a success. You know the part backwards. *Are* you going to let it go down the drain at the very last moment ? "

And she said :

" I suppose not ; but you can *see* me in that frock ? "

Of course, that *was* the trouble. We *should* be able to.

You see, even on Miss Saxon, who was somewhat petite, the dress was distinctly daring, but on Bar, who was the proper size, and a good six inches taller, it was going to be positively foolhardy.

It wasn't that we'd wanted to do anything in the least risqué, but it was simply that the leopard skin—hearthrug—that the frock had been made out of, wouldn't run to it.

Bar said :

" I shall get the sack if I wear it."

I said :

" Not you ; but the county looks like getting it's money's worth."

You see, you can't put a flounce on a leopard skin. It's got to remain leopard skin—*tout court* (however *court*).

All this was settled on the way to the ladies' dressing-room, at the double. There was another trouble, too, and a very serious one. There was a wonderful network of rubies and emeralds which the Queen Goddess had to wear over her neck and shoulders, and the Saxon girl had taken it home with her to alter, as it didn't hang quite right. So another had to be improvised.

I pushed Bar into the dressing-room and went to hunt for anything that looked like jewellery. There was no one in the house, and I burgled it completely in ten minutes. But it was a waste of time. All the people who had anything were wearing it in the marquee. You can't look splendidly barbaric in a gold locket and a couple of rows of seed pearls (at least, you can, but it wouldn't do !), which was all I could find. So I left 'em where they were—in the Tweenie's dressing-case.

However, you may remember that we'd got a large quantity of red and green lozenges from the village chemist. Well, there were a whole lot left over, and I found them.

Then I knocked at the door of the dressing-room, and asked Bar whether she'd got into the dress yet, and she said :

" Yes, just." So I went in.

She said :

" Is it at all possible, do you think ? "

I said :

" It's simply wonderful ; sit down and keep still." And I got hold of some one's make-up box and made her up—to look as wicked as sin. Jezebel wouldn't have stood a chance with her.

When the job was done, I told her to look in the glass.

She said :

" No one will ever speak to me after this."

I said :

" They will if you don't wash it off."

Then there was the question of the mantle of precious stones. First of all, I drew a network of lines all over her neck and shoulders, back and front, with an eyebrow pencil. After that I took alternate lozenges of green and red, and stuck them on to the intersections of the black lines. They looked very fine.

Of course, we didn't know each other very well, so she sat with her tongue out, and I moistened the precious stones and " *appliqué-d* " them on.

After she'd " *mouillé-d* " about twenty, she began to droop a bit. She said :

" Do you know there's something funny about those jujubes. I wish you'd taste one." So I did, and there was no doubt about it—ipecac. I asked her if matters had gone too far, and she said : " No, but they soon might have ! " After that I dipped them in a glass of water, but it seemed rather pedantic, somehow.

By this time the second act was over, and all the women trooped into the dressing-room and wanted to know what we were doing. We said :

" Go away, we're trying to save the situation."

I went in front of the curtain before it went up on the last act, and announced that Miss Saxon had been unavoidably detained, but that Miss—well—Bar, in fact, had undertaken to play the part at a moment's notice. I didn't crave their indulgence, because I knew she wouldn't need it.

And she didn't.

She went through without a single slip—er—yes. She even managed to take two curtains at the end, but then her courage failed her. She said she didn't think they were only applauding her acting. Some women are never satisfied.

From what they told me afterwards, she spent the next two hours in a very hot bath, soaking off my handiwork.

That is the end of the story. The cabmen's shelter was duly built. I saw it only the other day. There's never any one in it. The cabmen still prefer the station. It's got a refreshment-room.

ALPHA OF THE PLOUGH (1865–   ),
*journalist and biographer, as well as essayist
of unusual charm, has written under his own
name of A. G. Gardiner a number of important books on the affairs of the day. This
delightful essay is one of a collection published under the title of " Leaves in the
Wind," which were written as a diversion
from strenuous war-time work and anxieties.*

A FELLOW-TRAVELLER

I DO not know which of us got into the carriage first. Indeed,
I did not know he was in the carriage at all for some time.
It was the last train from London to a Midland town—a
stopping train, an infinitely leisurely train, one of those trains
which give you an understanding of eternity. It was tolerably
full when it started, but as we stopped at the suburban stations
the travellers alighted in ones and twos, and by the time we
had left the outer ring of London behind I was alone—or, rather,
I thought I was alone.

There is a pleasant sense of freedom about being alone in a
carriage that is jolting noisily through the night. It is liberty
and unrestraint in a very agreeable form. You can do anything
you like. You can talk to yourself as loud as you please and
no one will hear you. You can have that argument out with
Jones and roll him triumphantly in the dust without fear of a
counter-stroke. You can stand on your head and no one will
see you. You can sing, or dance a two-step, or practise a golf
stroke, or play marbles on the floor without let or hindrance.
You can open the window or shut it without provoking a protest.
You can open both windows or shut both. Indeed, you can go
on opening them and shutting them as a sort of festival of
freedom. You can have any corner you choose and try all of
them in turn. You can lie at full length on the cushions and
enjoy the luxury of breaking the regulations and possibly the
heart of D.O.R.A. herself. Only D.O.R.A. will not know that
her heart is broken. You have escaped even D.O.R.A.

On this night I did not do any of these things. They did
not happen to occur to me. What I did was much more ordinary.
When the last of my fellow-passengers had gone I put down my
paper, stretched my arms and my legs, stood up, and looked

29

out of the window on the calm summer night through which I was journeying, noting the pale reminiscence of day that still lingered in the northern sky ; crossed the carriage and looked out of the other window ; lit a cigarette, sat down and began to read again. It was then that I became aware of my fellow-traveller. He came and sat on my nose. . . . He was one of those wingy, nippy, intrepid insects that we call, vaguely, mosquitoes. I flicked him off my nose, and he made a tour of the compartment, investigated its three dimensions, visited each window, fluttered round the light, decided that there was nothing so interesting as that large animal in the corner, came and had a look at my neck.

I flicked him off again. He skipped away, took another jaunt round the compartment, returned, and seated himself impudently on the back of my hand. It is enough, I said ; magnanimity has its limits. Twice you have been warned that I am some one in particular, that my august person resents the tickling impertinences of strangers. I assume the black cap. I condemn you to death. Justice demands it, and the court awards it. The counts against you are many. You are a vagrant; you are a public nuisance ; you are travelling without a ticket ; you have no meat coupon. For these and many other mis-demeanours you are about to die. I struck a swift, lethal blow with my right hand. He dodged the attack with an insolent ease that humiliated me. My personal vanity was aroused. I lunged at him with my hand, with my paper ; I jumped on the seat and pursued him round the lamp ; I adopted tactics of feline cunning, waiting till he had alighted, approaching with a horrible stealthiness, striking with a sudden and terrible swiftness.

It was all in vain. He played with me, openly and ostenta-tiously, like a skilful matador finessing round an infuriated bull. It was obvious that he was enjoying himself, that it was for this that he had disturbed my repose. He wanted a little sport, and what sport like being chased by this huge, lumbering windmill of a creature, who tasted so good and seemed so helpless and so stupid ? I began to enter into the spirit of the fellow. He was no longer a mere insect. He was developing into a personality, an intelligence that challenged the possession of this compart-ment with me on equal terms. I felt my heart warming towards him and the sense of superiority fading. How could I feel superior to a creature who was so manifestly my master in the only competition in which we had ever engaged ? Why not be magnanimous again ? Magnanimity and mercy were the noblest attributes of man. In the exercise of these high qualities I could recover my prestige. At present I was a ridiculous figure, a thing for laughter and derision. By being merciful I could reassert the moral dignity of man and go back to my corner with honour. I withdraw the sentence of death, I said, returning to my seat. I cannot kill you, but I can reprieve you. I do it.

I took up my paper and he came and sat on it. Foolish fellow, I said, you have delivered yourself into my hands. I have but to give this respectable weekly organ of opinion a smack on both covers and you are a corpse, neatly sandwiched between an article on " Peace Traps " and another on " The Modesty of Mr. Hughes." But I shall not do it. I have reprieved you, and I will satisfy you that when this large animal says a thing he means it. Moreover, I no longer desire to kill you. Through knowing you better I have come to feel—shall I say ?—a sort of affection for you. I fancy that St. Francis would have called you " little brother." I cannot go so far as that in Christian charity and civility. But I recognize a more distant relationship. Fortune has made us fellow-travellers on this summer night. I have interested you and you have entertained me. The obligation is mutual and it is founded on the fundamental fact that we are fellow-mortals. The miracle of life is ours in common and its mystery too. I suppose you don't know anything about your journey. I'm not sure that I know much about mine. We are really, when you come to think of it, a good deal alike —just apparitions that are and then are not, coming out of the night into the lighted carriage, fluttering about the lamp for a while and going out into the night again. Perhaps . . .

" Going on to-night, sir ? " said a voice at the window. It was a friendly porter giving me a hint that this was my station. I thanked him and said I must have been dozing. And seizing my hat and stick I went out into the cool summer night. As I closed the door of the compartment I saw my fellow-traveller fluttering round the lamp. . . .

MICHAEL ARLEN (1895–   ) *is one of the few novelists whose short stories equal in artistry his longer works. His famous novel, "The Green Hat," brought him to the summit of his literary career, a position in which his later novels and his sparkling stories of Mayfair life, of which one is given here, have the more firmly entrenched him.*

THE MAN WITH THE BROKEN NOSE

" EVER been to the National Gallery ? " asked George Tarlyon.

It was an offensive question to ask a grown man, but I answered it.

" Ah ! " said Tarlyon.

" I can't help thinking," said Tarlyon, " that you did Madam Tussaud's the same afternoon. . . ."

" If you want to know, it was the Tower, St. Paul's, and the National Gallery that I did on the same afternoon. My mother took me."

" Of course, I can't compete with your mother," said Tarlyon ; " but I will take you—now. Waiter—the bill, please."

It was a day in July, and we were sitting over luncheon at the Café Royal. It was very warm for the time of the year. I don't know if I have mentioned it, but I am something in the City. There was, if you remember, a slump in the City in the summer of 1922. I was in that slump. And so, what with one thing and another, I sighed. . . .

" Come on," said Tarlyon firmly. " One must not neglect art. And two certainly mustn't." Poor, silly man !

We walked from the Café Royal to Trafalgar Square, which is an untidy walk on a glaring afternoon in July. And then we walked about the Gallery ; we looked at paintings with that rapt look which can see All Round and Into a thing ; and we stood before " Musidora Bathing her Feet."

" What a masterpiece," Tarlyon sighed, " if only she hadn't got three legs ! " I could not at first see Musidora's third leg, but after he had pointed it out to me I could see nothing else but that ghostly third leg dangling over her knee between the other two.

" You see," he explained, " Gainsborough painted one leg badly, and so he painted it out and fitted another—but Musidora's third leg came back. Say what you like, there is something displeasing about a woman with an exaggerated number of legs, though some people rather like that kind of thing, saying that a woman can't have too many. . . ."

It was as we turned away, talking loftily about legs, that we were confronted by a tall and dark young man.

" Sir," he addressed Tarlyon, " I would be obliged if you would tell me in which gallery hang the pictures by Manet ? "

One wondered why he didn't ask one of the many uniformed men who are strewn about the Gallery for the purpose of being asked that kind of thing.

" You are quite sure," Tarlyon put frankly to him, " that you do not mean Monet ? "

" Manet," said the dark stranger, and looked as though he meant it.

" Well, then, you're in luck," said Tarlyon ; " for we, too, were just about to view the Manets. We are partial to Manet. This way."

We followed him like lambs. Tarlyon's knowledge as to where the Manets were took the form of trying every gallery in which the Manets were not. We repassed Gainsborough's three-legged lady, Tarlyon commenting. The dark stranger walked silently but firmly. He was a tall young man of slight but powerful build ; his nose, which was of the patrician sort, would have been shapely had it not once been broken in such a way that for ever after it must noticeably incline to one side ; and, though his appearance was that of a gentleman, he carried himself with an air of determination and assurance which would, I thought, make any conversation with him rather a business. There was any amount of back-chat in his dark eyes. His hat, which was soft and had the elegance of the well-worn, he wore cavalierly. Shoes by Lobb.

At last a picture rose before our eyes, a large picture, very blue. Now who shall describe that picture which was so blue, blue even to the grass under the soldiers' feet, the complexion of the soldiers' faces and the rifles in the soldiers' hands ? Over against a blue tree stood a man, and miserably blue was his face, while the soldiers stood very stiffly with their backs to us, holding their rifles in a position which gave one no room to doubt but that they were about to shoot the solitary man for some misdemeanour. He was the loneliest looking man I have ever seen.

" Manet," said Tarlyon.

G.B.H.   2

The dark young stranger was absorbed ; he pulled his hat a little lower over his left eye, so that the light should not obtrude on his vision. . . .

"Come on," I whispered to Tarlyon, for we seemed to be intruding—so that I was quite startled when the stranger suddenly turned from the picture to me.

"You see, sir," he said gravely, "I know all about killing. I have killed many men. . . ."

"Army Service Corps ? " inquired Tarlyon.

"No, sir," snapped the stranger. "I know nothing of your Corps. I am a Zeytounli."

"Please have patience with me," I begged the stranger. "What is a Zeytounli ? "

He regarded me with those smouldering dark eyes ; and I realized vividly that his nose had been broken in some argument which had cost the other man more than a broken nose.

"Zeytoun," he said, "is a fortress in Armenia. For five hundred years Zeytoun has not laid down her arms, but now she is burnt stones on the ground. The Zeytounlis, sir, are the hill-men of Armenia. I am an Armenian."

"Oh, I'm so sorry," Tarlyon murmured.

"Why ? " snarled the Armenian.

"Well, you've been treated pretty badly, haven't you ? " said Tarlyon. "All these massacres and things. . . ."

The stranger glared at him, and then he laughed at him. I shall remember that laugh. So will Tarlyon. Then the stranger raised a finger, and, very gently, he tapped Tarlyon's shoulder.

"Listen," said he. "Your manner of speaking bores me. Turks have slain many Armenians. Wherefore Armenians have slain many Turks. You may take it from me that, by sticking to it year in and year out for five hundred years, Armenians have in a tactful way slain more Turks than Turks have slain Armenians. That is why I am proud of being Armenian. And you would oblige me, gentlemen, by informing your countrymen that we have no use for their discarded trousers, which are anyway not so good in quality as they were, but would be grateful for some guns. And you would still further oblige me by trying, in future, not to talk nonsense about Armenians. Adieu, gentlemen. You will probably hear of me again. I am in England on public business."

He left us.

"I didn't know," I murmured, "that Armenians were like that. I have been misled about Armenians. And he speaks English very well. . . ."

"Hum," said Tarlyon thoughtfully. "But no one would say he was Armenian if he wasn't, would he?"

"Also," said I, "he is the most aggressive young man I have ever met. Manet indeed!"

"So would you be aggressive, if you had been massacred and made an atrocity of ever since you were a slip of a boy, and had spent your holidays being chased round Lake Van by roaring Turks and hairy Kurds with scimitars dripping with the blood of Circassian children?"

"Oh, not Circassian!" I pleaded, for I have always been very sentimental about Circassian woman; but Tarlyon insisted that they generally died young and that they were a fat race. . . .

II

THIS is what actually happened, towards midnight of that very day, within a stone's-throw of Claridge's Hotel, in Brook Street, Mayfair. George Tarlyon and I had been of the same company for dinner and then bridge at a house in Brook Street. Towards midnight a gap in the bridge allowed us to slip away, which we did. Tarlyon had parked his car outside Claridge's, and thither we walked.

Now Brook Street at that hour is undecided between a state of coma and one of glittering abandon; which means that the deathly silence is every now and then shattered by rich automobiles hurling themselves and lovely ladies all covered in pearls and chrysoprase into the bosom of Grosvenor Square. Claridge's, of course, hath music, so that youth may dance. But of pedestrians along Brook Street there are less than a few . . . and of young men in gent's evening wear running furiously after limousines there is a noticeable scarcity. He simply tore past us, that young man, in the middle of the road, a few yards behind a swiftly going car. The car stopped towards Grosvenor Square, and somehow the young man seemed to disappear. We were more than fifty yards away, and could not determine whether it was a man or a woman who emerged from the car and entered the house, but it looked like a fat little man. Then the car slid away. The pursuing young man had disappeared.

"He can't have been doing it for fun," said Tarlyon.

"Perhaps he's gone to have a bath," I suggested. For it was a very warm night, and running after motor-cars must have been a wet business.

"We'll see," said Tarlyon. We retraced our steps up Brook

Street, and passed the house into which the occupant of the
car had disappeared. It was a house like another, dark and
silent ; and as it stood almost at the corner we went round the
corner into Grosvenor Square ; at least, we were rounding the
corner when a young man in a great hurry collided into us.

" Ah ! " said Tarlyon.

" Sorry," said the stranger. I was right about the running
—it had made his face very wet.

" So it's you ! " said Tarlyon.

" Good evening, gentlemen," said the Armenian, with a
sort of furious courtesy. " If you will excuse me, I am in a
hurry." He made to pass us.

" We noticed it," said Tarlyon. " In fact, we noticed
nothing else."

" Damn ! " snapped the Armenian. " So you saw me
running ? "

" So did he," I murmured, looking up Brook Street. A
policeman was sauntering towards us.

" If you don't want to be asked any questions by the arm
of the law," Tarlyon suggested, " you had better take a turn
round the square with us."

" I won't move," the stranger muttered passionately. " I
have found him at last—I won't move."

" But neither will he," I soothed him. " He's gone into the
house. . . ."

" Did you see him go in ? "

We nodded.

" Ah, but His Excellency is clever ! " said the Armenian
viciously.

We grabbed hold of him and hauled him round the
square.

" Now," said Tarlyon, " what's all this Excellency nonsense ? "

" *He* doesn't think it's nonsense," the young man muttered
grimly.

" Look here," I said, " either this is a plot or it is not a plot.
In either case you'll look rather an idiot, so——"

" You'd better confide in us," Tarlyon finished. " We,
being English, have great sympathy with oppressed peoples——"

" I have noticed it," said the Armenian grimly. He was
obviously a well-educated young man.

We had him walking between us, and he never even pretended that he liked our company.

" I suppose," said Tarlyon cattishly, " you've got bombs all
over you."

" Sir ! " snapped the Armenian.

" Sir to you," said Tarlyon.

" I was merely going to say," said the Armenian, " that in my opinion you are a fool. Do I look the kind of man to carry bombs ? I favour the revolver."

" Oh, do you ? " said I. Sarcastic I was, you understand. He looked at me with those large, devilish eyes.

" And one shot," he said gently, " is always enough. . . ."

I gave up.

" And where," asked Tarlyon reasonably, " does His Excellency come in ? "

" He won't come in anywhere after to-night. His Excellency is going to die." And with that the Armenian suddenly stopped in his unwilling stride, and looked from one to the other of us. His broken nose made fantasy of his dark face, but I remember thinking that it must once have been a handsome enough face of its kind, for not even a broken nose made him quite ugly. He was as tall as Tarlyon, but slighter ; his was a dangerous thinness. He addressed Tarlyon. He did not seem to have a very high opinion of me.

" Sir," he said—an Armenian habit, I suppose, that " sir "— " you have intruded your company on me, but I have accepted you. I have trusted you. I have treated you as gentlemen, being by nature an optimist, and I take it for granted that you will neither betray me nor try to deter me. You will understand the vigour of my purpose when I say that a young girl is concerned in this, that I have sworn a vow, and that if you were in my position you would do what I am going to do. Goodnight, gentlemen. I hope we will meet again when I am less occupied with more important business."

" Hold on," cried Tarlyon. " What on earth were you chasing that car for ? And who the devil is His Excellency ? We'd like to know, you see, so as to be able to pick him out from among the other murders in to-morrow's papers."

" Achmed Jzzit Pasha, the Young Turk," said the Armenian softly.

" Ah ! " said George Tarlyon. " I see. Enver Pasha, Djemal Pasha, Talaat Pasha, and Achmed Jzzit Pasha, of the Committee of Union and Progress. I see. Talaat Pasha has already been killed, hasn't he ? "

" Four of us," said the Armenian sombrely, " set out from Armenia last year, and each of us had a mission of revenge. One of us—you will remember ?—shot and killed Talaat Pasha in a street in Berlin some months ago. Djemal Pasha was lately

slain in Syria. Enver Pasha has fled to Bokhara. A murder has
been arranged, and will shortly take place in Bokhara. And I,
the fourth, have at last found Achmed Jzzit, the foulest murderer
of all. There is not an Armenian in the world who would not
shoot Achmed Jzzit Pasha on sight if he had the chance—but
Armenians who come to Western countries only too soon acquire
nasty Western habits of money-grubbing and forget the glory
there is in killing. But I, a Zeytounli, have never forgotten
it. . . ."

"You speak English very well," I remarked. "Were you
educated at an English public-school ? "

"That, sir, is a matter of opinion. But even an English
public-school could not make me forget that I am an Armenian,
and that an Armenian's first business is to kill Turks ; failing
Turks, he may, of course, kill Kurds or ravish Circassian
maidens——"

"Oh, not Circassians ! " I pleaded.

"Well, Albanian," he allowed. "During the War I fought
through the siege of Zeytoun, and then as an irregular under
Andranik ; and since the War I have pursued Achmed Jzzit
Pasha—and to-night I have found him ! He has been here in
London for some months, but under an assumed name, for he
knows that he is marked by the Dashnakists [1] and the Hencha-
kists,[1] and he is afraid. It is my present business to cure him of
his fear for ever." And with a wrench his arms were free of our
gently restraining hands and he was off down the square. But
Tarlyon was swift, very swift ; I panted up just as he was
again " intruding himself" on the Armenian.

"You don't seem to realize," breathed Tarlyon, "that you
can't enter a house in Brook Street, kill a Pasha, and get away——"

"I don't care if I get away or not," the other broke in
fiercely. "Besides, my friend who killed Talaat in Berlin was
acquitted. And I cannot believe that your English juries are
as thick-headed as you would have me think. So will you please
excuse me, sir ? "

It was marvellous what venom that broken-nosed young
man could put into a simple question !

"I've taken rather a fancy to you," murmured Tarlyon,
"and I hate to think of your going off murdering Pashas.
Come and have a drink instead, there's a good fellow."

"If I tell you," snapped the Armenian, "that there is a girl
in that house, and that I must rescue that girl, then you will
perhaps see your way to minding your own business."

[1] Armenian Revolutionary Societies.

"Has the Pasha got your girl?" I asked kindly.

"She is my sister, O fool," he said wearily. "And do you think I can allow my little sister to stay in that loathsome old creature's house one night more than I can help?"

"Collar him," said Tarlyon to me; and I grabbed the young man's other arm, though I didn't in the least want to, and again we began hauling him round the square. As I walked close to him I could feel a solid bulky thing in his hip-pocket, and I did not like the feeling.

"Now," said Tarlyon, very business-like, "what's all this about your sister?"

The Armenian almost screamed with impatience.

"Have I not told you all along that if you were in my position you would do exactly what I am going to do? Must I explain to you that my little sister was carried away by that old lecher before my eyes? Must I tell you how Zeytoun on the hill was at last shelled to dust by the batteries of two Army Corps under Achmed Jzzit Pasha, and how the Turks entered the smoking town and gave no quarter to man, woman, or child? Must I, just to satisfy your wanton and asinine curiosity, ravage my heart with retailing how my father and mother were bayoneted before my eyes, and how I escaped only because those Turkish swine thought me already dead? Must I tell you how my little sister was carried away to the harem of Achmed Jzzit Pasha, who, on beholding her, swore a mighty swear that he would not rest from disembowelling Christians until he had ravished her? Did she give way? The slaying went on, day by day and night by night, so that a count of the leaves of the trees in your puny but not unattractive Green Park would make but a fraction of the number of the dead bodies that to this day lie rotting in the plain of Mush. An expert killer was Achmed Jzzit Pasha; and whether or not the natural blood-lust of the illiterate Osmanli was heightened by his oath to ravish my sister I do not know, but I do know that there has not been such a tale of dead Christians since Timur passed through the land to meet Bajazet. And that is the man who holds my sister in that house, while you detain me here with the vain questions and idiotic comments peculiar to the high-minded people of your patrician land. I followed him to Paris, but he escaped me. I found him in Bournemouth, but again I withheld my hand while I planned some way of rescuing Anaïs—fool that I was! But the idea in my head was that I must first get the girl to some place of safety—and then to come back, slay him, and pay whatever is the penalty in your country for killing a loathsome animal. But now I have realized that there is no other way of rescuing Anaïs but by killing him first. Always, wherever he goes, he keeps her locked in a room next to his, and thus it must be in this house. Bestial fancies seethe in his brain, wherefore he sleeps lightly. And while the night is dwindling, here I stand satisfying your idle curiosity. You really must excuse me now, gentlemen."

"But hold on!" cried Tarlyon. "Why kill the wretched man at all? Why not rescue your sister with the charming name and let the Pasha go on being a Pasha until he dies a horrible death by reason of those bestial fancies which you mentioned? He won't dare come after her—and I don't see much point in getting your sister back if you have got to swing for it more or less at once. Eh, Ralph?"

"Quite right," said I. "Come and have a drink instead."

"This is no time for drink," snapped the Armenian. "The night is dwindling—and how can I desist from killing him when, as I have told you, I cannot get into her room without awaking him? And it stands to reason that as soon as I see him I shall also see red, and kill—as I must, by reason of my vow and by order of the Dashnakists. As I have told you, I would have preferred to have got Anaïs out of the house first, but that seems impossible. . . ."

Tarlyon opened his mouth, and closed it. I knew what was passing in Tarlyon's mind, and I thought I would let it pass, so that he might think again. But then he re-opened his mouth, and this is what he said :

"My friend and I," he said, "might perhaps consider giving you a little assistance, if in return you gave us a promise——"

"I promise nothing!"

"Drat the boy!" said Tarlyon. "What I wish to point out is that, if my friend and I help you to get your sister out of that house, you must drop this killing business. We will contrive some way of keeping His Excellency quiet while you rescue your sister—but you must give us your word of honour, or some efficient substitute, that you will not come back and murder the wretched Pasha. Now, I want no back-chat about it—either you will or you will not."

"But I am bound to the Dashnakists!" cried the Armenian ; rather regretfully, I thought.

"Blast the Dashnakists!" said Tarlyon. "Yes or no?"

"I promise," said the Armenian suddenly.

My native common sense now got the better of me.

"You seem to take it for granted that we just walk into the house. How do we get in?"

" This cuts windows like a knife," said the Armenian, showing us in the palm of his hand a glittering little thing like a toy dagger. " An Argentine invention."

" The matter will be further facilitated," said Tarlyon, " by our first getting my car, which is opposite Claridge's, and driving in it to the front door. My reason for this step is that no police-man would dare suspect anything wrong in a house while a Rolls-Royce is standing outside it. Especially, Ralph, when your manly appearance is decorating the driving-seat. . . ."

" I shall be in the house," I said firmly. Not that I wanted to be—but one always says those things, and one always says them firmly.

" Perhaps that would be better," said the Armenian. " It will certainly take the two of you to keep His Excellency quiet while I break in the first locked door I see and get Anaïs. And a Rolls-Royce car is, I understand, even more impressive empty than when some one is in it—people make it seem possible."

III

WE got the car and drove bravely to the house. We passed two policemen at the corner of Davies Street, but they were not interested in us. I must say burglary is easy when one has a large and rich car to do it from. . . .

Like all Mayfair houses, this had a tradesmen's entrance ; through a little gate on the right of the few steps to the front door, down some steps, and into a little area where was the kitchen door and a window.

" Wait in the car," said the dark young man, and vanished down to the area. We heard a very faint scratching, one little wicked word, a little more scratching ; and then the lights blazed up through the glass above the front door, and it was opened. The Armenian stood in the lighted doorway as though he owned the house. I admired him.

Tarlyon's first words when we were in the hall of the house were : " Give me your gun, you charming atrocity."

The Armenian surrendered his revolver without a word ; he only sighed. Then he marshalled us.

" Very quiet," he whispered. " And very quick. We must try the upstairs rooms, to see which is his bedroom. One touch on the door will wake him, so you must muffle him at once, else he will rouse the servants. In the meanwhile I will find my sister ; then I will take her straight out of the house, and we will await you in the car. I will blow your horn twice, to show that I am awaiting you. It will be kind of you, then, to drive us to Mr. Ritz's hotel in Piccadilly, where, perhaps, with your influence, we may get my sister a lodging for the night. But, remember, keep a tight hold on Achmed Jzzit until I blow the horn—muffle him straightway and let him not open his mouth, else he will bring the whole neighbourhood down on us. Let us begin."

We began with a bit of luck—or so it seemed. Having tiptoed up to the first landing, the very first door we touched held the lightly sleeping Pasha. We knew he was there by the howl that followed our touching the door-knob—indeed, he was a light sleeper, that man of bestial fancies ! But we gave him no time to make a real noise ; we leapt into the room ; I switched on the light, Tarlyon leapt on bed and Pasha, I leapt after Tarlyon, and in a second we held him, making smothered howling noises under the bedclothes. We had not even had time to see if he was young or old, but the shape of him suggested that he was older than most people. His was, however, an active and restless shape. We were very gentle with him, almost too gentle, for once a distinct howl issued from somewhere under the sheets.

" Steady," said George Tarlyon to the restless shape.

" You'll throttle yourself," said George Tarlyon.

To prevent him from doing that we, with a sudden and well-concerted movement, unscrewed his head and muffled him with a handkerchief. We looked upon his face for the first time.

" You're a nasty, cruel old man," said George Tarlyon.

Achmed Jzzit Pasha looked all that the Armenian had said he was, and more. A fierce old face it was that looked murder at us. His eyes, under white, bushy eyebrows, were frantic and furious, and never for a second did he cease to struggle. I thought of that fine old Turkish warrior of the last century, the man of Plevna, Osman Pasha ; this old man is of the same breed, I thought.

We had so far heard nothing of the Armenian ; but that Achmed Jzzit Pasha realized that we two were only accessories was evident, for not even his struggling with us concealed the fact that he was listening, listening intently.

A slight noise, as of a drawer hastily banged, came from the next room. It was only a small noise, but it had a mighty effect on the old slayer of men. His eyes simply tore at us, his fat little body heaved frantically, he bit my finger in trying to howl—he went quite mad, that violent old Turk. I admonished him severely :

" It's only little Anaïs packing up to go away with her brother," I told him ; but that old Turk knew not resignation nor repentance, and still we had gently to battle with him.

" He's an infernally long time about it," grumbled Tarlyon at last—and at that very moment the horn outside blew twice. We welcomed it.

" Now," said Tarlyon to the heaving old man, " we are about to release you. Your girl has flown, so it's too late for you to make a noise. So don't." And for form's sake he showed the revolver, though I never saw a man who looked less likely to use it. " You may not realize it," he added severely, " but we have saved your life. After the first shock has worn off you will thank two disinterested men for having saved you from the wrath of an Armenian."

With another sudden and well-concerted movement we let go. The Pasha did not make a noise. It was evident he realized that it was too late to make a noise. But in the next few seconds he revealed, for a Turk, an astonishing knowledge of the baser words and idioms of the English language. Then he leapt out of bed, a funny little creature in pink flannel pyjamas, and rushed out of the room. Breathless, we found him in the next room.

Now I have very little acquaintance with girls' bedrooms, but a glance was sufficient to show me that no girl alive could have a bedroom like that. There was no bed in it, and very little else ; just a thing like a tallboy, but made of steel, or so it looked ; and that, if I may say so, had certainly been ravished. . . .

Then the old man really began to howl, and we hadn't the heart to stop him. He howled himself back to the bedroom, and we followed him, looking and feeling like all the things he said we were.

" But aren't you Achmed Jzzit Pasha ? " I pleaded. But the life had suddenly gone out of him ; he sat on the edge of the bed.

" My name is Wagstaffe," he said weakly, " and I have the finest collection of Roman coins in the country. Or rather, I had. My son, Michael Wagstaffe, has them now—thanks to you two idiots ! "

Tarlyon had an idea which took him to the window ; I had the same idea, and followed him. We looked down upon the face of Brook Street, and behold ! it was empty. Never was a Rolls-Royce car with lamps alight so invisible. We went back to Mr. Wagstaffe on the edge of the bed.

" We are sorry," I muttered, but he seemed not to hear us. George Tarlyon is usually a fine up-standing fellow, and some people have thought him handsome, but now he looked as though he had seen horrid spectres after dining entirely on *pâté de foie gras*.

Mr. Wagstaffe was whispering, almost to himself : " Two years ago, when I drove him out of the house, he swore that one day he would steal my coins. And now he has stolen my coins. I always knew he would keep his word, for he is a devil. And he always knew that, come what might, I would not prosecute my son for a thief . . . My Roman coins ! " And Mr. Wagstaffe wept.

We explained our position to him. We gave him a brief outline of the facts. We begged him to understand. We pointed out that if his son really had been an Armenian and if he had really been Achmed Jzzit Pasha we had undoubtedly saved his life. I couldn't help thinking that he ought to be grateful to us, but I didn't say that.

He seemed to find a little solace in our discomfiture.

" Ah, he's a clever boy, Michael," sighed Mr. Wagstaffe. " He is always on the look-out for what he calls the Mugs. I gather that you two gentlemen are Mugs—the same, perhaps, as what are known in America as Guys. But I, his father, can assure you that he is not an Armenian ; nor has he ever been nearer to Armenia than the Bankruptcy Court, but he has been there twice. He calls himself the cavalier of the streets, but when he is up to any of his tricks he disguises himself as an Armenian—the disguise consisting merely of his saying he is an Armenian. It's so simple, he says, for the Mugs believe him at once, on the ground that no one would say he was an Armenian if he wasn't. I have only been back from America a week, and he must have been searching all London for me. He probably saw me at the theatre this evening, and was going to raid my house alone when you two intelligent gentlemen got in his way. But he is not a bad boy really—he's got ideas, that's what it is ; and also Mugs have an irresistible fascination for him. Take your case, for instance. I have no doubt but that he will be ready to return me my coins in exchange for a cheque—though, of course, that depends on the cheque. And I can see, gentlemen, that you are eager to show your regret for breaking into my house and assaulting my person by offering to pay the cheque yourselves. I thank you ; though, indeed, it is the least you can do, and an infinitely more convenient way of settling the matter than wearisome arguments in a police court—provided, of course, that housebreaking and assault are matters for argument. I have never yet heard they were. . . ."

I giggled. I simply couldn't help it.

He leapt out of bed, a funny little figure in pink flannel pyjamas

Helena sat up "ed," a funny little figure in Jack Pearse's pyjamas.

" That's all very well," said Tarlyon, " but what about my car ? "

" What is the matter with your car ? " asked Mr. Wagstaffe gently.

" There's so damn little the matter with it," snapped Tarlyon, " that it's probably half-way down the Dover road by now."

" Ah," said Mr. Wagstaffe wearily. " I see. Cars have an irresistible fascination for Michael. I see. I am sorry. Was it a good car ? "

" Pity," said Mr. Wagstaffe. " A great pity. He may, of course, return it. He may. You cannot, of course, compel him to, for it would be difficult for you, in your position, to put the police on him. But he may return it on his own. Michael is not a bad boy, really. He will, I am sure, communicate with me as to what I will offer for the return of my coins. I will then give him the cheque you have so kindly promised to post to me to-night, and perhaps he will soften also as regards your car and return it to you. Naturally, he will expect your cheque to approximate to the value of your car—say, half its value. Michael is something of an expert about the value of cars. That's why I said it was a pity, sir, a pity that your car was not a cheap car. But I am sure you will have no difficulty in finding a taxi-cab home. They are so abundant in Grosvenor Square that my sleep is often disturbed by them. . . ."

The rest of the story is not at all interesting. George Tarlyon's car was finally returned, and George Tarlyon is sorry that Mr. Michael Wagstaffe's nose is already broken.

ANTHONY ARMSTRONG (1897–   ),
*the author of that phenomenally successful play,
" Ten Minute Alibi," is very versatile ,
humour, romance, detection, plays, and com-
mentaries upon affairs of the day all provide
material for his enterprising pen. As " A. A,"
he is a regular contributor to " Punch,"
and some of his dissertations have been
collected in a volume entitled " How to Do
It," from which this little " treatise " is taken.*

HOW TO YOT

As one experienced in the best of all summer sports, I feel
well qualified to say a few words about Yatching—I
mean, Yahcting—dammit, Yotting. These hints are intended only for beginners on the broads and rivers ; the professional Yotter may pay little, if any, attention to them.

On arrival at the quayside you will find your yot tied up
there. The observant man will at once notice that it has a sharp
and a blunt end. Normally the direction of motion is usually
towards the sharp end—except when strong tides are running
when the boat will probably move sideways. At the blunt end
is a rudder. This occupies the attention of one of the crew and
gives him the pleasant impression of directing the course of the
yot. Actually it has very little to do with it, unless he moves it
rapidly back and forth, in which case the boat will move slowly
forwards. This should, however, be done only in the entire
absence of wind, and when time is no object.

In the middle of the yot is a mast upon which are gracefully
draped sails. The sails are kept spread out by means of gaffs and
booms at the top and bottom. The gaff is smaller than the
boom ; on the other hand, being at the top, it has farther to
fall when the sails are let down, and therefore hurts more. The
idea of the sails is, of course, that the wind, impinging thereon,
drives the yot on a headlong course in various directions, which
with luck will include the one desired.

Many ropes are hung about the mast. These are for hoisting
the sails which on arrival will be found unhoisted. A short
series of experiments will show you which ropes hoist which
sails ; but don't give up if some ropes do not appear to hoist
anything. It may just be that you are standing on the sail concerned. In this case, you should either get off and try again or

48

else pull much harder. The former course is recommended as being less dangerous for non-swimmers.

When you have hoisted your sails you must untie the yot from the quayside. This should always be done ; it makes for quicker and brighter yotting, and quaysides hardly ever float. It is preferable, if there is a wind, to get on board before untying. Nothing then remains but to enjoy yourself for the remainder of the day ; though it is advisable not to decide definitely upon your destination for the night till you have actually reached it.

On preparing to spend the night by a river bank, first tie the yot to the river bank and then tie the river bank to the yot. This prevents what we yotman call " night-driftage," which means that on waking next morning you probably have to do your previous day's journey all over again. Then you should take down the sails. This is easy : simply untie all the ropes you can see and gravity does the rest.

To make snug for the night you must realize that the cabin top lifts up. To find the cabin top go into the cabin and you will discover it immediately, about a couple of feet lower than you expected. Then come outside again and try to lift it up properly, this time with your hands. So far, so good. If it doesn't come down with a run in the middle of the night, it will stay up, and I cannot say fairer than that.

All you have to do after this is to take your " Secundus " stove, play with it for three-quarters of an hour till it catches fire at every pore, throw it into the water, eat your cold beef, and go to bed.

In the morning get up at once and bale out the cabin. Then go on deck and see if you can tell what things have

(a) Been washed overboard during high tide,
(b) Been commandeered by ships that pass in the night,
(c) Been eaten by cows that ditto.

Next, while you are waiting for the tide to rise again and float you off the expanse of mud which you do not remember noticing the night before, you may as well have breakfast and make ship-shape—though I have never yet been able to discover exactly what the latter expression means. Every ship I have so far been on board has retained the same shape throughout the voyage—except one which got a little bent about the sharp end owing to my forgetting at a critical moment that the tiller and the rudder worked opposite ways.

By the time you have done this the tide will be ready to float you off and you may hoist sails again, untie the boat and repeat as before.

Armed with this knowledge you should be able to enjoy a holiday that is both pleasant and full of incident : but for those who are really keen, I can dispense yet a few more hints. They deal with the more difficult operations, such as lowering the mast, " quanting," reefing, anchoring, and so on.

Now, lowering the mast is a particularly nasty thing which frequently has to be done, owing to a culpable lack of foresight displayed by bridge builders on the Norfolk rivers. There are two ways of doing it— the hurried and the unhurried.

In the hurried method the main thing is to get the mast down before the bridge-arch does it for you ; and owing to your mis-calculation of the strength of the tide and wind, you generally have about one and a quarter minutes for it. Now at the sharp end of the boat, which may or may not be the front end at the time, there is a rope called the forestay which holds the mast up. Using either your fingers or a pocket knife, undo this within one and a quarter minutes, and there you are ! Have I made my-self clear ?

The unhurried method aims at less expenditure of energy. Tie up near a lot of other yachts and let one of you take hold of your jib-halyard and say, " Is this the forestay ? " To which the other will reply, " No, that's your mainbrace." If you continue to say things like this often and loud enough, you will soon have, human nature being what it is, five or six people taking your mast down for you and explaining to you how to do it.

In putting the mast up again care should be taken not to stand on any of the ropes which are going up with it, nor should you let your belt or the slack of your braces get hitched up on the end of the mast itself—particularly if the fellow who is pulling on the forestay is rather deaf and very strong.

Quanting (when your mast is down) is like punting except that the pole is too heavy to lift quickly out of the water, the yacht is too unwieldy to answer to your thrusts, and the river is too deep for the length of pole. Hence it follows you should always quant *with* the tide. In the total absence of river bottom the pole may be used to fend yourself off other craft lying at anchor. Fend off, if possible, on good strong woodwork. Don't try and do it on a port-hole ; the pole may go right through and out at the opposite one, which leads to a difficult situation, if not to your hurriedly changing yachts.

Taking in a reef is a thing that often has to be done. All I know about taking in a reef is that it costs about one shilling to any old salt on the bank. This is over-all charge, not one shilling per reef.

Anchoring, again, is rather difficult. You have two kinds of anchor on your yacht. One is a heavy weight for anchoring in mid-stream, and great care should be taken not to drop it on the cabin top. Make certain too before you let it go overboard that your dinghy is not alongside. This latter error will not affect your anchoring, of course, but it will affect the dinghy. Even greater care should be taken to tie the end of the anchor cable somewhere on to the yacht, *before* you put it over, as yachts usually carry only one.

The other kind of anchor is in the shape of a hook, and is for anchoring on to any convenient object ashore. If possible, objects selected should be both immovable and inanimate. It is therefore not advisable to throw it ashore in the manner of a grapnel and trust to luck. You may catch a cow grazing on the far side of a bank, or even a member of a picnic party. Avoid hooking the lower part of windmill sails, as it is apt eventually to make you giddy.

Finally, no set of hints for beginners is complete without instructions on how to revive the apparently drowned. It is of course no use practising this unless the patient *is* apparently drowned ; so that, should your companion (or even a complete stranger) fall into the water, it is quite futile to pull him out and attempt restoration, until he has reached the condition of needing it. In stubborn cases you may even have to fend him off with your foot or push him under once more with the boathook.

When you are at last satisfied that he is in a suitable state for restoration, haul him out and go through his pockets. In many cases this will bring him to at once. If it doesn't, lay him on the deck and go and get a barrel to roll him on. But if this is likely to take too long—for some yachtsmen prefer to carry their food in bottles rather than in the cask—you must try another method. Lay him reverently out face upwards and seize his elbows from behind. Pull them up towards you and then on down again to his sides at the rate of about fifteen times a minute. Or is it fifteen times a second ; for the moment I quite forget ? If he opens his eyes, speaks, breathes, swears, and otherwise shows signs of life, he is alive, and you may congratulate yourself on your masterly presence of mind. If, however, he has not moved by the time you are tired of working his arms, you may take it that he is dead and may eat his sandwiches. It is all really quite simple.

F. E. BAILY (1887–   ), *writer of serials, short stories, articles, and verse, whose sprightly dissertations upon love and marriage are a popular feature of modern magazines, was Editor of " The Royal" before and after the War, from which he was invalided home. He is the husband of May Edginton, novelist and journalist, with whom he occasionally has an entertaining skirmish in print.*

LOOK THIS WAY, BABY!

GEORGE ATKINSON sat on the front lawn of his uncle', bungalow at Goldensands, caressing a stone turtles which represented art in the midst of Nature, and waiting for a yellow-haired girl in a horizon-blue riding shirt and tan Jodhpores to ride past on a chestnut horse, leading a bay. George deduced from the colour of the riding shirt that the girl's eyes were blue. He considered her a very pretty girl, and from the expression of hatred and contempt on her face whenever he caught her eye, so did she.

The girl usually rode past at 10 a.m. It was now 9.52 a.m., which gave George a few minutes in which to settle his inside, throw back his shoulders, and put on the stern, relentless expression proper to a he-man. Unfortunately the yellow-haired girl had the effect of making his heart jump up into his throat in a disturbing manner.

The bungalow of George's uncle, a Mr. Richard Bolt, was called " Such Fun " in the frivolous manner of the speculative builders who develop Goldensands. It had a red tiled roof and white walls and a verandah, and a hard tennis court at the back, and a garage shaped like something out of a fairy tale. The architecture of the bungalow itself did sudden and unexpected things and the inside walls were made of a sort of stout cardboard, so that you could hear distinctly if the person in the next room to yours opened his eyes. Down the road and round to the right stood another bungalow with a thatched roof and a flagstaff and two toy cannon, called " Oh, I Say ! " It was there that the yellow-haired girl lived with her mother.

George himself looked very beautiful in extremely pale grey flannel trousers, the exact shade of the inside of an angel's wing, a tennis shirt open at the neck with sleeves rolled up, and white

shoes with brown strappings. His thick dark locks offered themselves hatless to the breeze and not one hair strayed from its
place owing to a liberal application of Ososticki, which is
blizzard-proof and yet cannot soil the most delicate cushion.

Gently fondling the stone turtle and waiting for the girl to
ride past, George brooded on the tragedy of life.

Right in the forefront he felt constrained to put Uncle
Richard. Mr. Bolt, though fifty, always had been and still
remained a man of iron. Rising with the lark, he splashed
singing through his cold bath and compelled George, fortified
only by a cup of tea, to play many sets of extremely hard tennis
before breakfast. It was only the fact that Mr. Bolt insisted on a
lapse of one and a half hours between breakfast and his morning
swim which permitted George to see the golden-haired girl ride
past. At 11 a.m. precisely, Mr. Bolt and George would stroll
down to the sea in bathing suits and bath-gowns, and Mr. Bolt
uttering a war-cry, would fling his short, stocky form into the
waves and disappear in the general direction of the United
States, using the Australian crawl. Long after George, who was
tall and slight, had emerged from the sea, Mr. Bolt would return,
jeering heartily at the effete new generation, and proceed at a
brisk trot to " Such Fun," where, having changed, he would carry
George off to play golf, strictly forbidding the use of caddies.

Between tea and dinner, Mr. Bolt liked half a dozen more
sets of tennis, and after dinner, George enjoyed a little leisure
because Mr. Bolt considered George's bridge so dreadful that
he refused to let it bring disgrace on the family. Therefore,
after dinner, an admiral, a general, and a stockbroker, all retired,
came into " Such Fun " and George went out. He walked
across a field where he could watch the twinkling lights of " Oh,
I Say ! " and imagine how the slender fingers of the yellow-
haired girl were twiddling the knobs of a portable wireless, or
how her equally slender legs danced to the music of a portable
gramophone. George would have liked very much to shoot the
men she danced with.

From his left, along the grass verge of the road, came a thud-
thud of trotting hoofs. George pulled himself together and
focussed his eyes for their daily feast.

He saw her approach riding the offside horse, leading the
near and keeping to the right-hand side of the road. This is
against accepted practice in these matters, but George approved
because it brought her almost up against the garden fence.
Some day, he hoped, the fidgety chestnut would prance right
over the fence and enable George to say : " Don't mention it ;

it doesn't matter in the least," and so start a friendship ripening into love to which only death would put an end.

Grasping the turtle's head in a vice-like grip from sheer emotion, George let his gaze wander over the girl. Her golden head was bare ; she looked straight ahead, featuring the usual scorn and contempt. Even the Jodhpores could not disguise the fact that she had simply divine legs, and the horizon-blue riding shirt outlined her figure in the most charming fashion.

The chestnut as usual had its ears back and was fidgeting from side to side. The bay, a placid animal, turned its pleasant silly face towards its friend with the expression of a church-warden taking the collection.

"Oh, Arthur," the bay seemed to be saying, "why will you always ruin the doings like this ? What you need is a little more poise, dear old boy. There's no necessity to shy at that man's white shirt. It won't bite you."

The girl wheeled her horses half right along a field path and disappeared, and George's day was over. He had only the memory of that little tip-tilted nose and ruthlessly lip-sticked mouth to carry him through a weary twenty-four hours. He wished he knew her Christian name. The surname was Wright, for the milkman had told him so. George sat on, murmuring fatuously : "Muriel Wright, Angela Wright, Pamela Wright, Geraldine Wright, Diana Wright," and last, with a faint blush over his tanned features : "Diana Atkinson." Then all the happiness drained from his expression, he pushed the stone turtle aside irritably and lit a cigarette. He realized with a pang he had not the means to support even a mere ordinary girl, let alone an angel on horseback.

Mr. Bolt, who manufactured a certain very superior car which he christened "The Greyhound" and sold for a thousand pounds a chassis, had kindly allowed George to serve his time in the shops. "After all, he is poor Annie's boy," Mr. Bolt had told himself a little sadly, being accustomed to charge a whacking premium for this kind of thing. And when George's five long years were up he spoke manfully, as befits a twenty-three year old who considers himself one of the only three men in England who know how to use a file, and said :

"Now, Uncle Richard, I will repay all your goodness to me. Here are the drawings for the £80 car the public is waiting for. It will sell in millions. All you need to do is to put down £250,000 capital and leave the rest to me."

Unfortunately Mr. Bolt had merely replied with a few coarse expressions picked up in the engine sheds of a well-known railway during his hard-working youth. "When I was your age," Mr. Bolt continued, " I'd got over your sort of moonshine. My foreman was knocking my head off every day because he said he'd either teach me how to hold a somethinged spanner or kill me."

" Well, Uncle Richard, I played cricket in my dinner hour at the Greyhound works with an axle shaft for a bat while somebody bowled at me with a crown-wheel, until I taught the chaps rugger and elected myself referee just to save my own life."

" We make fifty cars a year, and the profit on each is £250, and that suits me very well, because my needs are simple, not being troubled with a wife," Mr. Bolt ended. " You can go to work at the service station and try and not get in the way and I'll pay you six pounds a week and stand you a summer holiday."

Somehow, sitting on the lawn of " Such Fun," George could not see himself keeping a golden-haired sylph and supplying her with horizon-blue riding shirts and fretful chestnuts on six pounds a week. Besides, she drove about in a super-charged hyper-sports Greyhound, while George himself could only afford a fifth-hand mass-produced vehicle. True he had rebuilt it until the designer would never have known his own child, but even without a windscreen it had never exceeded 61·1416 miles an hour, by speedometer.

When George had finished his second cigarette, Mr. Bolt emerged from the French window of " Such Fun," dressed in bathing suit and bath-gown.

" What are you doing, George, composing poetry or what ? " called Mr. Bolt heartily. " Why, you aren't even undressed. Do you know the time ? Ho, for the briny ! You can drive us down in that flying mangle of yours this morning if you like. I know how you hate walking. Now, when I was your age——"

George went and undressed, not wishing to hear what his uncle did at George's age, and drove his uncle and himself down to the beach, while Mr. Bolt said uncomplimentary and technical things about the flying mangle. They then plunged into the main, from which, as usual, George emerged the first, and took a lonely sunbath. All around he saw the beach thronged with beautiful damsels in backless bathing suits, beach pyjamas, and other attractive looking soft goods, but they only wearied him. He could think of nothing except a golden head above a blue riding shirt whose owner sat immovably on a restless chestnut. Presently he got up and strolled towards his car. Perhaps Uncle Richard's criticisms had contained some truth. Perhaps the mixture was a shade too rich.

But when he reached it he saw a sleek and slender hyper-sports Greyhound drawn up alongside. In it sat the golden-haired girl wearing a horizon-blue bathing suit that clung damply and a blue and white wrap. Beside her a woman of charm and tact, whom George took to be her mother, smoked a cigarette and gazed into the far distance while the girl treated the self-starter in a fashion which made George's engineering blood boil. Unfortunately nothing happened. Not one sputter came from the engine.

Mustering up a frank, courageous smile to disguise the sinking feeling which afflicted him, George began :

" Excuse me, but won't she start ? Can I help you ? "

The girl took her foot off the starter switch and gazed at him as though he were a certified lunatic.

" She doesn't appear to be starting, does she," said her icy voice. The blue eyes raked the flying mangle scornfully. " Do you," the voice went on, " know very much about cars ? "

Forbearing to reply " I probably helped to assemble yours," because love is kind, George lifted the bonnet and answered gently : " It's about a thousand to one the arm of the contact breaker is sticking," and proceeded to examine that component. He nodded gravely, helped himself to the tool kit, dealt with the trouble, and said :

" Now give her a buzz over."

Once more a little sandalled foot pressed the starter. This time a muffled roar answered, and the exhaust pipe began to give out what enthusiasts refer to as a healthy note. The woman of tact and charm removed the cigarette from her lips and remarked :

" I think that was most awfully clever, don't you, Sally ? "

So her name was Sally ! Well, he would never have guessed in a million years, but he quite realized it couldn't possibly have been anything else.

" Awf'ly," Sally agreed with a faint bleak smile. " Thank you most frightfully, Mr.—er——"

She thrust the gear-lever into first, spun the car as it were on a sixpence, and shot away down the cliff road. George gazed after her in a deep reverie.

" Sally," he murmured ; " Sally Wright " ; and then, with a blush deepening the tan of his face : " Sally Atkinson."

II

HE met her next in the establishment of Mr. Grits the grocer, who is also a baker and purveyor of wines and spirits. It was but eleven-thirty of a lovely summer morning, and by rights George should have been cleaving the billows in company with his uncle. Unfortunately, owing to severe pressure on his fleet of transport, two horse vans of quaint design and a carrier bicycle which has never been oiled since 1897, Mr. Grits's deliveries become greatly in arrears during the summer season, so that you either fetch it yourself or go without. Mr. Bolt had gone without in the matter of whisky on the previous evening, and excused George from bathing parade in order that a fresh supply might be guaranteed.

As one enters Mr. Grits's premises a vast cloud of flies of every kind, from the common house-fly to the more spectacular bluebottle, rise from the cakes, pastries and jam tarts lying in profusion on the counter, and a swarm of disturbed wasps buzz angrily. Brushing the insects from his eyes, George perceived Sally in a strategic position at the counter bargaining for supplies. In front of the counter summer visitors stood as usual ten deep mewing pitifully for lemon squash, tinned apricots, washing soda, and other necessities of life, while behind it Mr. Grits, and Will, William, and Willy, his three hired men, strove their best and in the confusion put down two items in the bill for every one they handed over the counter.

At the crucial moment, when William had piled just one more package than she could possibly carry into Sally's arms, a wasp tried to sting her on the neck, so that she exclaimed : " Damned brute ! " meaning the wasp, not William, and dropped everything. George therefore collared the intervening ranks of visitors low, picked up the parcels and escorted Sally outside where their cars stood bonnet by bonnet.

" Did it sting me ? " she asked, offering for his inspection an adorable bare neck and shoulder. Much as George longed for an opportunity to kiss the place and make it well, he could not find the least sign of damage. " Well, then," she went on, " you might chuck those parcels in the back seat and give me a cigarette. I always feel as if I'd been torn limb from limb after a dog-fight in Grits's."

They began that simple exchange of question and answer that the young call conversation.

" Staying here long ? "

" About another three or four weeks. Mummy likes the place because you can do as you like and the riding's cheap."

" So are we. My uncle hates fashionable places, and the golf course suits him. It's all up and down hill, and he loves exercise."

" Exercise ? My God, it's all old people think about ! They're afraid of losing their figures and want to kid themselves they're still young. Look at me f'r instance : Exercises to the gramophone and then ride with Mummy ; then bathe ; then lunch ; then tennis ; then another ride ; then people coming in all the evening, stuffy old goats of thirty and forty, positively senile, and all telling one another how they've got off another pound in weight."

" You too ? " George asked sadly. " Uncle Richard's exactly the same. Now we . . ."

He sketched briefly the arduous day. Sally blew smoke from her distracting nose and shrugged.

" Do you like my car ? What's your name, by the way ? You never told me."

" George—George Atkinson. Yes ; she's a peach. My uncle makes them. I work at the service station, and if ever there's the slightest thing wrong do bring your bus round. I daresay I could wangle you one of our new turbulent cylinder heads. They're hush-hush at present, but they give another five miles an hour."

" She'll do eighty-five as she is," Sally said carelessly, " but thanks awfully, George. I ought to be getting along. I've got to go down to Giles' farm and collect a couple of chickens. We've a dinner party to-night. All the animated skeletons are asked. Isn't life hell ! "

Bribing her to stay with another cigarette, George pleaded : " Can't we ever get away alone together, Sally ? I've such heaps of things I want to talk about. We could go somewhere in my car and picnic and just rest instead of tearing ourselves to pieces all the time."

She climbed into her car from the off-side with a dazzling exhibition of slim bare legs, for no one ever wears stockings at Goldensands and there is no off-side door to the front seats of a sports Greyhound, and curled up limply.

" I loathe these foul open bodies," she complained. " Give me a good fug in a saloon, but of course it's Mummy's car, not mine. All the middle-aged are fresh-air fiends. My dear George, how can I ever get away ? I told you what my day's programme's like. Heaven knows I need rest, but there isn't a hope. I couldn't even manage the local movie. Remember our elders hold the purse-strings so we have to do what they want— not that Mummy isn't perfectly sweet, but I do wish she'd get a lace cap and black silk dress complex."

With a sigh George nodded, comparing mentally Mr. Bolt's twelve thousand a year with his own three hundred. It seemed so silly when a heart-breaking golden-haired girl meant nothing whatever to Mr. Bolt compared with saddle of mutton, McTavish's Very Old Highland Liqueur Cream Whisky, cigars, bridge, and that sort of thing. Then filled with sudden inspiration he said to Sally :

"What time do you go to bed ? Couldn't you get out of your window and come down and sit on the beach with me for an hour ? I'd bring a rug and some chocolates and cigarettes. You see, we've got so much to talk about. You haven't told me the least thing about yourself yet."

Sally reflected a moment and then her highly-coloured lips parted in a smile.

"I don't mind," she said. "Meet me at the end of our road at midnight. Don't forget the rug, because if I sit on the sand I shall get smothered in it and trail it all over the carpets."

She started the engine and was gone, waving a bronzed arm in farewell. George returned to Mr. Grits's, and after a pitched battle lasting a quarter of an hour, bore off six bottles of whisky and a dozen siphons of soda in triumph.

Somehow or other he got through the rest of the day, blistering his poor hands on the shafts of golf clubs and losing as usual to Mr. Bolt. George could never understand why, because strong men had often admired his swing and his drive. But Mr. Bolt brought a devilish efficiency to his approach shots and on the green he was deadly ; and as Bobby Jones used to say, give him the man who can hole his putts in one. So the hour of bridge arrived and George as usual went out across the cornfield to gaze at the lights of "Oh, I Say ! " but in how different a spirit.

"Only another three hours now, my darling," George murmured, adding : "Sally Atkinson " just to hear what it sounded like.

She met him at midnight, a cigarette between her lips and an overcoat shrugged over her wisp of a frock. The moonlight touched her golden mop and George instantly felt weak at the knees, being burdened also like an arctic explorer with rug, chocolates, cigarettes, and a thermos flask of hot coffee.

They followed a path to the cliffs, in these parts about four feet high, and continued down a slope to the beach. The tide had gone out, leaving an expanse of glistening sand. George spread the rug on the sand in the lee of somebody's bathing hut. They sat down, and George said :

"Have some coffee, Sally ? "

"Not now, thanks. What was it you wanted to talk about ? "

"To tell you what a darling you are and how I adore you,"

thought George, " but it's a bit early to start that sort of thing."
He answered instead :

" I wanted to see if we could fix up some way of seeing more
of one another and escaping from this middle-aged tyranny.
You said you were going home in three weeks. Where do you
live ? "

" London."

" Splendid ! So do I."

" I'm thinking of going on the stage. I could do Binnie Hale
parts quite well. I'm very much her build."

" But, darling, you're certain to marry."

" Oh—marriage ! " Sally said contemptuously as though it
were a disease. " I don't know how we can ever see much of
each other down here, George. Your uncle occupies you all
day and Mummy takes all my time. It seems fatal. Of course
I can always meet you at night except when it rains. This hut's
damned hard to lean against. Turn a little my way so that I
can lean against your shoulder."

George obeyed, and all the deliciousness of Sally's golden
head rested against his old Hartonian blazer. She used him as
a prop with no more emotion than if he had been somebody's
bathing hut. He was more comfortable to lean against, and
that was all.

" Your heart's thumping," she said presently.

" Well, can you wonder ? "

" Why should it ? Have you got a weak heart ? "

George slid his arm round her slight shoulders and replied :

" Considering you're the most marvellous girl I ever met
and I'm crazy about you, wouldn't you expect it to thump ? "

" Am I marvellous ? " Sally asked dreamily, merely because
she wanted him to say so again.

Gathering up all his courage George bent his head in the
direction of that divine mouth, but she laid one hand across his
lips and inquired :

" Tell me honestly, George, should I be the first girl you ever
kissed ? "

A wave of regret for his ill-spent life washed over George.
There you were, he thought bitterly. You went racketing about
from this girl to that, and when you met the one you really and
truly loved all the others rose up in judgment between you and her.

" Well, Sally, not exactly——"

The little hand removed itself from his mouth.

" Thank God ! " she exclaimed devoutly. " I simply can't
stand being practised on."

Once as she rested very sweetly in his arms a faint flash of light seemed to illuminate them. He glanced hastily in the direction from which he thought it came and saw nothing. Sally took his chin between her finger and thumb, turned his head and leaned her peach-bloom cheek against his.

" Only summer lightning, darling, or somebody signalling to smugglers out in the bay. Do you love me very much? Why do you love me so much, George? "

" Because——" George answered, and began to explain all over again.

III

Two days later Mr. Bolt, fingering his after-dinner glass of port, looked across at George and said :

" I've got to go up to London to-morrow for a board meeting, George. Higgins will drive me in the car. I shall be back in time for dinner. You won't spend all the day loafing about in idleness for want of some exercise, will you? The great thing in life is to get up a good sweat every day."

" Oh no, Uncle Richard."

" And by the way, I hope you're feeling quite fit, George, but your manner's been most peculiar for the last couple of days. Sometimes you sit looking half-baked, and sometimes you grin all by yourself about nothing, and sometimes when I speak to you you don't appear to hear me. And your golf, my dear boy, is simply rotten. Had I better get Dr. Magsulph to run the rule over you? "

" No thank you, Uncle Richard. I feel very well indeed."

That night on the sands he broke the news to Sally, who clapped her little hands in a fairylike manner and began to croon the latest song hit entitled " There Ain't No Kisses Like Yours." " You see," she explained, " mummy also goes up to town to-morrow, by train. Aunt Millicent is in bed with house-maid's knee or something and she's had a relapse. Darling, do you realize we can spend the day in complete rest? You bring that queer-looking car of yours and I'll collect some food and we'll go miles away and sit in the woods somewhere, and not even speak, and pretend there isn't a tennis racket or a golf club in the world."

" You said a mouthful, Sally. Might there be sausage rolls ? I love sausage rolls. When we're married we'll always have sausage rolls."

" We've got a hope of ever being married, George ! The

young have no chance until they get to be about thirty and then it's too late."

In the morning Mr. Bolt departed for London driven by Higgins, a hard and horrid man of forty, the sort of person who, if the propeller shaft falls off, can effect a temporary repair out of a gentleman's walking stick and a few feet of copper wire. Mr. Bolt and he had a sort of sour respect for one another, partly because, as a rule, Higgins's conversation consisted merely of " Ay ! " or " It is that ! " Nevertheless, when Higgins was held up at Hammersmith Broadway by a policeman and a tradesman's van coming from behind ran into and demolished Higgins's near side rear wing, Higgins's language left little to be desired and that little was supplied by Mr. Bolt.

" You'd better take the car to the works and get a new wing fitted and I'll go down by train to-night," said Mr. Bolt outside the Greyhound offices.

" Ah can take car over and fit wing and bring car back by tea-time," objected Higgins, who came from the north. " 'Tis a quick job 'is job."

" Nobody knows what a clout like that may have done. Get them to examine the chassis thoroughly," Mr. Bolt answered sadly. " Take yourself to the pictures or something and bring the car down to-morrow."

Consequently in the first class Pullman on the 4.39 p.m. from Victoria to Churchminster, where one changes into the local train for Gobbling, Sturton-over-the-Water, Maidengay, and Goldensands, Mr. Bolt found himself seated at a glass-topped table opposite a very charming woman.

Mr. Bolt realized at a glance that she was only a mere child of forty. She had golden hair, cut as far as he could see in some fascinating way, and a little tango-red linen suit with hat and shoes to match and peculiarly expensive stockings. She laid a tango-red bag on the table and began to turn desultorily the pages of an illustrated weekly until the train moved out of Victoria Station. Then she eviscerated the handbag, found a gold cigarette case and opened it with a view to selecting a cigarette.

Alas ! The cigarette case was empty.

Perceiving this, Mr. Bolt considered that he could only do one thing. He produced a large and massive silver case with a gold monogram presented to him by the Society of Motor Manufacturers & Traders on the occasion of a Greyhound's winning the Swiss Grand Prix, and offered it saying : " Excuse me, but will you allow me ? Afraid I only smoke gaspers."

The little girl in front of him stretched out a manicured paw and took a cigarette, remarking : " Thanks awfully. I always smoke gaspers myself. I'm afraid I'm full of bad habits."

Mr. Bolt, lighting her cigarette and his own, chuckled inwardly at the idea of this innocent flapper's having any bad habits. He noticed that she wore a wedding ring. He concluded that she had early divorced an undesirable husband, for the frightful married look was absent from her delicious features. " After all, many a girl makes an initial mistake," reflected Mr. Bolt, " but that is easily remedied nowadays."

Turning on her the shy smile that had often caused agents to order six Greyhounds where they had only meant to order one, he went on :

" Would you allow me to give you tea ? "

The lady looked at him gratefully and answered :

" Thank you. I should love some."

It came. She poured it out for him with a kind of dedicated meekness, and Mr. Bolt, who always went about with his eyes shut as far as people were concerned and was unaware that he had ever seen her before, continued :

" And are you, too, going to Goldensands ? "

A sort of mental telephone exchange in the lady's head clicked out to her : " This is that nice man with the good-looking boy who lives at ' Such Fun ! ' He has an even more recent Greyhound than mine. Obviously rich and looks quite attractive. I've often noticed him on the beach and at the golf club. The good-looking boy put our car right the other day."

She answered :

" Yes, are you ? I'm staying there with my girl. We have a bungalow called ' Oh, I Say ! ' in Mons Road. I think it's an awf'ly good place for young people. They can do as they like as it were, sort of."

" Ah ! My name by the way is Bolt—Richard Bolt."

" Oh yes, Mr. Bolt. My name is Esmée Wright. My husband was killed in an air crash, some years ago."

Mr. Bolt achieved an expression deprecating dumbly all air crashes, more especially the air crash in which the late Mr. Wright had been bumped off. Then he continued :

" Yes. I endeavour to give George, my young nephew, a good time. He's my poor sister Annie's boy. She and her husband were swallowed up in a Japanese earthquake a few years ago. The Japanese are always having earthquakes."

Two very deep grey eyes looked sympathetically at Mr. Bolt, mutely wishing, so to speak, that the Japanese and their earthquakes were in hell.

"But I find it," Mr. Bolt continued, "a bit of a strain."

The grey eyes dilated suddenly and her faintly husky voice asked swiftly : "What do you mean, Mr. Bolt ? "

"I mean, Mrs. Wright, that one has to keep one's end up so with these young people and show them there's life in one's own generation yet, but frankly I get bored to death. We play tennis before breakfast and then we swim and then we golf and then we play more tennis. Must let the boy have a run for his money, but it's a relief to sit down after dinner for a rubber of bridge. George, fortunately, loathes bridge."

Mrs. Wright lay back in her chair and let a cress sandwich slip from her nerveless fingers.

"I understand only too well," she declared gloomily. "I do exactly the same with Sally. First we do our physical jerks, then we ride, and I detest horses. They're so cold and un-emotional. Then we bathe, then we play tennis, then we ride some more. My dear Mr. Bolt, the young people of to-day are nothing but arms and legs and have positively no conversation. God knows what their married lives will be like, if they ever do marry."

"But you—— ? " Mr. Bolt exclaimed. "Surely this isn't so in your case, my dear lady ? You are far too frail and delicate for all this exertion. It doesn't hurt me because I used to swing a sixteen pound sledge-hammer in my youth, but you ought to be careful and not overdo things. Really, I mean it."

Lying back in her chair Esmée Wright savoured the delight of being told by a strong man that she was too frail and delicate for something. She lowered her long lashed eyelids to conceal her enjoyment and answered :

"Oh, I shan't come to any harm. One must keep them amused. They're only young once."

The train roared its way at quite thirty-five miles an hour through the green of England and Mr. Bolt felt himself coming rapidly to a certain conclusion, namely that life might be altogether different with a delightful woman like this constantly about the house, which would echo to her low-pitched laughter and form a background for her charming frocks. Therefore, at last, when they were approaching Goldensands, he gathered courage to ask her to dinner.

"I wish you'd dine with me one evening soon at the Monopol-Metropole, Mrs. Wright. It would give us both a rest from our young people. The Monopol puts up quite a passable dinner. I should be awf'ly—er, pleased if you could."

"Thank you, Mr. Bolt. Now let me see——" She hesitated being perfectly aware that all her evenings for the next week were blank. " I think I could manage the day after to-morrow. Shall we say seven-thirty ? "

In the station yard Sally was waiting with Mrs. Wright's car and Mrs. Wright insisted on dropping Mr. Bolt at " Such Fun ! " Sally gave him a cool stare, banged in her clutch and flew through the gears in a manner which made Mr. Bolt glad that Greyhounds had been bred at Brooklands. They left him at his bungalow full of the most delirious emotions. As he mixed himself a whisky-and-soda before dinner he saw not a glass, a siphon, and a decanter of McTavish's Very Old Liqueur Cream Highland Blend, but a little girl of forty almost unbelievably slender in a tango-red linen suit and peculiarly expensive stockings.

" Esmée ! " murmured Mr. Bolt, lifting his glass, and then rather foolishly : " Esmée Wright. Esmée—Esmée Bolt ! "

IV

AT midnight on the sands, in the lee of somebody's bathing hut, Sally nestled her golden head more comfortably against the old Hartonian blazer and said :

" George darling, shall I tell you something ? "

" Yes. What ? "

" Mummy's clicked with your uncle. They got off together in the train—my dear George, what brazenness ! What are the last generation coming to ?—and she's dining with him at the Monopol—what-is-it to-morrow, at seven-thirty."

" But, Sally, it's not possible. Uncle Richard never looked at a woman in his life."

" Well, you know what the women of our family are like, don't you ? " Sally answered, running her fingers luxuriously through his hair. " You, after all, were perfectly nice till you met me."

" It's——" George proceeded, " it's positively the cat's whiskers."

" It may be the mouse's overcoat, the cockadoodle-doo's umbrella, and the centipede's spats, George, but the fact remains."

" Then, Sally, you must dine with me. It's the chance of a lifetime. Fancy, no stuffy visitors infesting the place. Come round to ' Such Fun ' at a quarter to eight. What would you like to eat, darling ? Our cook adores me. You can have just whatever you like."

G.B.H.

3

Sally sat up and folded her hands meekly in her lap.

" My dear George, sitting opposite you, under your roof, with the whole place whispering to me of you, do you suppose I give a darn what I eat ? I'd like lobster and cutlets and new potatoes and green peas and fruit salad with lashings of cream, please. When I say fruit salad I mean real fruit salad, not the stuff you buy in tins at Grits's. I get enough of that at home."

As George took her in his arms a faint flush of light seemed to illumine them. He glanced hastily in the direction from which he thought it came and saw nothing. Sally leaned her cheek against his.

" Only a Boy Scout calling to its mate, or summer lightning, darling. Do you still love me as much as you did when you told me that you couldn't love me any more if you tried ? "

Mr. Bolt was very glad he had brought his dinner-jacket down to Goldensands, small though the place was, because after all one never knew. He came out of his bedroom on the night of the tryst looking extremely rich and bachelor-like, with a carnation in his buttonhole, and if he had happened to possess the Order of the British Empire (with sash) he would have felt like wearing that too. Nevertheless, it was with some astonishment that he saw George in a very perfect grey flannel suit and a brand-new Old Hartonian tie, and if Mr. Bolt had only known, George was also wearing Old Hartonian braces.

" What are you all dressed up for, George ? " inquired Mr. Bolt. " You generally dine in a pullover and an old pair of flannel bags."

" Oh well, Uncle Richard," George stammered a trifle uncertainly, " I—I rather thought I'd go round to the fair afterwards. You knew there was a fair, didn't you ? The roundabout's topping and there's a sort of lighthouse with a track running round the outside and you slide down it on a mat."

" Personally I should wear my oldest bags for that sort of thing. Hasn't Higgins brought the car round ? Damn the man, can't he ever do what he's told ? "

" The car's been waiting for a quarter of an hour, Uncle Richard."

" Higgins would keep it in the road a quarter of an hour, getting it all dust and filth," Mr. Bolt snorted, and strode majestically down the garden path.

In a quarter of an hour Sally arrived. George saw she had on a little frock of the kind of divine blue that no other girl in this world ever chose and she actually wore stockings in honour of the occasion. George noticed that they were peculiarly expensive stockings, and indeed they belonged rightly to Sally's mother who, unfortunately for her, took the same size in hosiery as her daughter. Sally came in and George led her to the sitting-room. She glanced round it with the eye of an experienced dweller in furnished bungalows.

" I like the wicker furniture," she said. " Ours is all ye olde Britisshe oake. But your pictures are worse than ours, if possible. We've got a Death of Nelson that knocks your Queen of Sheba visiting Solomon into a cocked hat."

A maid announced dinner. They proceeded to the dining-room and were served with lobster, cutlets, and green peas and new potatoes, and fruit salad with lashings of cream, which are the true foods of love. George filled Sally's glass with a soft dry white wine called Château de Blancheforêt 1911 which belonged to Mr. Bolt, but then after all Sally's stockings belonged to Mrs. Wright, so they broke even. And it came to pass that during the stage of cigarettes and coffee, George moved round the table, tilted Sally's chin and kissed that mouth redder than the feet of one who cometh from a forest where he hath slain a lion and seen gilded tigers, until Sally said :

" George, do you know the oddest kind of woman is staring at us from the road outside ? "

As on that historic occasion when old Kaspar's work was done, it was a summer evening, and thanks to the daylight saving regulations, visibility remained excellent. Therefore, when George looked out, he perceived a lady of indefinite age dressed in a tweed skirt that dipped at the back, a pullover, transcontinental brogues, and the sort of felt hat it is more blessed to give than to receive. She carried in her hand a species of ash stick which in rural circles farmers are wont to poke pigs with to find out how they are getting on.

George took his arm from around Sally's neck and said coldly : " She has a face exactly like a sausage."

" Like a sausage and mashed I should think," amended Sally, and they both laughed, for they were young and in love and had not emerged very long from the fourth form. Then the odd woman went away and George demanded for the fifteen-millionth time :

" Sally, darling, swear you'll marry me very soon because I can't bear to live without you."

With that bitter *flair* for the practical which is the curse of all women, Sally answered :

"We can't possibly, George. We have too many responsibilities—I my mother and you your uncle. What are they to do without us? We're all they have. We bring what joy there is into their lives. They've spent money on us and they expect a return. We're the pets of their declining years, like rabbits or guinea pigs or West Highland terriers. Ages hence when you and I are an old man and woman of thirty——"

"Oh Sally!"

"Or even thirty-two, George, and my mother and your uncle are dead, we might be able to marry, but then it'll be too late. All the kick will have gone out of our love and I shall be plain and you'll have a revolting bulge where your tummy oughtn't to be."

Overcome by the pathos of life George kissed her. There seemed no other argument left.

Meanwhile, on the awning-shaded veranda of the Monopol-Metropole, which gives upon smooth green lawns, amid all the *va-et-vient* of the *haut monde* of Goldensands, the *brouhaha* of smart conversation, the *espièglerie*, the *dévergondage*, in fact the entire tra-la-la that make up the hotel life of even the most minor English *plage fleurie*, Mrs. Wright and Mr. Bolt were sipping liqueurs and lingering over that inestimable stage of human companionship when acquaintance is drifting into something higher, wider, nobler, broader, deeper, and fuller. Mr. Bolt thought he had never seen anything more appealing than Esmée in her evening frock, which, if he had only known, was a mere rag she had brought down because anything is good enough for Goldensands, to which she had had to devote ten blasphemous minutes of sewing that evening because it was literally falling to pieces. Her hair, he observed, repeated the exact hue of the burnished brass nuts which attach the inlet manifold of a Greyhound to the cylinder block, and he felt deeply impressed by her beautifully machined arms, which made all the other women's arms look like rough castings.

"She is a lovely job," Mr. Bolt told himself, and in the vocabulary of engineers no higher praise exists. Finally he gazed deep into her grey eyes and she met his gaze with a little permissive smile because she knew exactly what was going to happen and had decided exactly in what manner to give Mr. Bolt the K.O., owing to circumstances over which neither of them, alas, had any control.

"Esmée," Mr. Bolt began at last in the solemn tones of a man who is greatly moved, "I know I am not worthy of you but I love you as I have never loved any woman before. Indeed, women have played little part in my life. I've always been too busy whacking up production at the Works. But if you could possibly bring yourself to look on me in the light of a husband——"

Tenderly she shook her head.

" You're the nicest man I've ever met, Richard, since my husband was killed, but it can't be. I couldn't unload my cross on you, and you've one of your own, anyway. Your active young nephew must be bad enough, but if we married, both he and Sally would have to live with us, and quicksilver is Sally's middle name. The darned girl's never still. Even if you could bear the two of them, I couldn't. No, Richard, we have our responsibilities ; we must sacrifice ourselves to youth. Years hence, perhaps, when you're sixty-five and I'm—well, whatever I shall be then we may creep side by side to some quiet chimney corner and make our plans to totter down to the grave together, but at present it's hopeless."

Feeling worse than he had ever felt in his life, Mr. Bolt glanced up to see an extremely odd woman standing beside him, dressed in a tweed skirt that dipped at the back, a pullover, and carrying an ash stick. She began :

" You, sir, I believe, are the tenant of ' Such Fun ' and you, madam, are the tenant of ' Oh, I Say ! ' I am Miss Emily Paradise, a Resident. I have to inform you, sir, that a young man is luring a young girl to her ruin in what I take to be your dining-room. The girl in question, madam, I have reason to believe is your daughter."

" Poor young man ! " Esmée murmured regretfully. " Do you know, Miss Paradise, that Sally has a backhand drive like the kick of a mule, she can ride almost any horse, she can do a long-arm balance, and also turn cartwheels, and is as hard as nails. There's no one I'd less rather try and lure to ruin against her will."

" I doubt if it is against her will, Mrs.—ah ! Wright I understand your name is," Miss Paradise amplified gloomily. " The association has been going on for some time. They are accustomed to meet at midnight on the sands. I have seen them there."

" And what," inquired Mr. Bolt with the frankest curiosity, " were *you* doing on the sands at midnight, if I may ask the question ? It sounds to me very much like the pot calling the kettle black."

" Being, as I am, a Resident," Miss Paradise answered, " I am interested in the conduct of visitors, Mr.—Bolt, I believe. My experience with the Girl Guides has made me an expert in tracking. Consequently I tracked your unhappy nephew and

Mrs. Wright's unfortunate daughter. By the light of my electric torch I saw——"

Once more Mr. Bolt gazed deep into Esmée's grey eyes.

"It may be," he told her. "The possibility exists. I have always believed in the workings of a merciful providence."

Leaving Miss Paradise, they fled from the Monopol-Metropole, huddled into the car, and bade Higgins speed as he had never sped to "Such Fun." They left the car in the road and tiptoed up the gardens path. They crept through a French window into the sitting-room and beheld the affecting spectacle of Sally seated on George's knee clasped in his arms. Esmée clapped her little hands with an enchanting gesture.

"Oh, my dears, my dears," she faltered, "how I congratulate you! Sally, my darling, I'll give you such a wonderful wedding."

"George, my boy," Mr. Bolt exclaimed, "you've chosen well. Don't let the thought of money distress you. I shall make you distributor for London and the Home Counties at a fat salary. You have picked the most delightful bride!"

The young people sprang to their feet in dismay. Their hearts were touched. Smitten by a sense of guilt they replied in unison:

"Thank you very much, but the sacrifice is too great. We realize you would both be lost without us. We are prepared to forego our happiness. We will be the props of your declining years, your one interest, your ewe lambs. We have so much to look forward to and you have so little."

With that bitter *flair* for the practical which is the curse of all women, Esmée answered:

"As a matter of fact, George, your uncle and I have arranged to get married. There is nothing so romantic as a double wedding, is there? I mean, is there, or is there not?"

That night the bay horse put his head over the partition of his loose box and spoke kindly to the fretful chestnut, who was snuffling at his bedding looking for mice or Bolsheviks, or anything else unpleasant, and spoke soothingly.

"You're all right, Arthur old boy, even if you don't know it," said the bay horse with a smile on his silly face. "It's a wonderful world bang full of oats and bran mashes and it all works out for the best if only you wouldn't be such a temperamental old angel."

" *I am Miss Emily Paradise* "

"BARTIMEUS" (1886–   ) *is the pseudonym of Paymaster Commander L. A. da Costa Ricci, of the " Britannia," Royal Navy. His tales are as varied in mood as the sea of which he writes, but all breathe the spirit of ships and of men who understand them. His first book, " Naval Occasions," published in 1914, gave a vivid account of the Silent Service. " The Leg-Puller " reveals him as an accomplished humorist.*

THE LEG-PULLER

GOVERNMENT DEPARTMENTS have been known in their lighter moments to exchange departmental jests. But the individual is not encouraged to be funny at their expense. It has been attempted from time to time ; but this is a game in which he who laughs last laughs loudest. And the Government department generally laughs last. There is, however, an exception to every rule of life. The exception in the instance I am about to relate was John Octavius Peglar, citizen of the United States of America. For him was reserved the peculiar distinction of having pulled the leg of the British Admiralty—or, anyhow, one of its departments—and he " got away with it."

He did not look a humorist. Few really funny people do. Moreover, he had no intention of being funny at the Admiralty's expense—up to a point. The Admiralty plainly asked for it. The doubt in my mind is the precise point at which John Octavius decided to give them what they asked for.

He was an urbane, clean-shaven little man, wearing rimless pince-nez, precise and business-like in an unobtrusive way, as befitted the head of a big American business firm giving occupation, chiefly in accountancy, to some hundreds of employees, and controlling several millions of dollars.

John Peglar was in London, transacting business on behalf of his firm, when Great Britain declared war on Germany. Apart from business considerations, Mr. Peglar decided this did not call for any active steps on his part. He was perfectly content to let Great Britain and Germany fight while he continued to transact business. But one fine day the *Lusitania* was sunk, and Mr. Peglar awoke to certain vital aspects of the brawl he had not hitherto considered. He gave his own country forty-eight hours and then approached a certain influential Englishman of his acquaintance, with whom he spent a quarter of an hour in private conversation. Emerging from his friend's office, he dispatched two cables—one to his business partner in New York, the other to his wife. He then walked to the Admiralty and sent his card up to an official, with a note from his friend. The official looked up from the note as Mr. Peglar was admitted, and scowled at him.

" Good morning."

" Good morning."

" I understand you are a Canadian ? "

" Er—yes," said Mr. Peglar.

" And you wish to join the British Navy as a Paymaster in the Royal Naval Reserve, having failed for the Army on account of eyesight ? "

" Yes," said Mr. Peglar again.

" Have you any experience of accountancy ? "

" I know the first four rules of arithmetic," was the modest reply from the head of the firm of Peglar and Ziegland.

" So much the better. How would you like to be the Paymaster of an armed boarding steamer ? "

" I could tell you better after I'd been one for a while."

" It's of no consequence. You will be appointed to-night. Please leave your address. Good morning."

" Good morning." In the courtyard outside Mr. Peglar stopped and gazed up at the soot-grimed windows from which King Charles I. had emerged on to the scaffold. A pigeon swooped past, nearly brushing his shoulders with its wings. " Marvellous ! " said Mr. Peglar in an awed voice. Whether he referred to the tameness of the pigeon, or to the historical associations of his surroundings, or his recent interview, I am unable to say.

Once more that day Mr. Peglar gave vent to the same expression of emotion, when some hours after he had visited a Naval outfitter, a cardboard box was delivered at the hotel where he was staying. He bore it up to his room, and in its rococo privacy surveyed himself with an expressionless countenance in front of a long mirror, garbed in the uniform of a British Naval Officer.

" Marvellous ! " repeated Mr. Peglar.

This is not a war story, or one might be tempted to enlarge on some of Mr. Peglar's early experiences, assisting to conduct a blockade of the German coast. Doubtless he found them marvellous, although he did not say so. Nothing, not even seasickness, shook his imperturbable and enigmatical urbanity. But on the subject of the British naval system of accountancy he

permitted himself some comments to the Leading Victualling
Assistant, who composed his Staff. He spent a forenoon examining the ledger, cash, clothing and victualling accounts, the
butt of a cigar between his teeth.

He sighed as he closed the last book. " I stood not long ago
beneath the window out of which King Charles the First stepped
to execution. I was conscious of the associations with the past
which surround Englishmen so closely on all sides. This goes
one better. This links one up with Noah and the Ark. It's a
fine system, but cumbersome."

" Yessir," said the Leading Victualling Assistant without the
least idea what Mr. Peglar was talking about, and bore the books
away.

Mr. Peglar found that the task of feeding, clothing, and paying
a ship's company of fifty souls did not present any very unusual
difficulties. He kept the ledger, checked the Leading Victualling
Assistant's accounts, rendered interminable and apparently pur-
poseless returns to the Admiralty. In leisure moments he per-
used, the inevitable cigar between his teeth, a massive tome that
appeared to afford him inexhaustible interest. It was called
" The King's Regulations and Admiralty Instructions."

Thus two months passed when a cloud rose above the horizon
of Mr. Peglar's serenity. A deputation waited on him from the
Lower Deck with a request for fresh meat. Owing to the service
on which the ship was employed, and the fact that she was not
fitted with a refrigerator, officers and men had been compelled
to subsist chiefly on tinned comestibles.

The ship being still at sea, out of sight of land, Mr. Peglar
thought the request somewhat unreasonable. The British bluejacket was new to him. He temporized with the deputation and
promised them their fill of fresh meat the first time the ship com-
municated with the land. He reported the interview to the
Captain. " They tell me they wouldn't be surprised if scurvy
broke out 'most any time," concluded Mr. Peglar, eyeing his
commanding officer through his glasses with impenetrable gravity.
The Captain, an ex-Merchant Service Skipper holding a Commander's Commission in the Royal Naval Reserve, burst into a
guffaw. " Scurvy, my foot. They've fed like lords ever since
the war started ; I'd like some of 'em to have been at sea with me
when I was a youngster. Windjammers. . . . Scurvy ! Well,
well ! Still, we've got to keep 'em happy, I suppose. We shall
be near an island in the Northern Hebrides by noon to-morrow.
I'll lower a boat and you can go ashore and see what you can
do."

Accordingly the following day the ship hove to, and Mr. Peglar, after a perilous passage which nearly ended in the boat being dashed to pieces on the rocks, landed on a desolate and barren island. He approached the only habitation in sight, a cottage built of turf with a reed thatch. An old deaf woman came to the door, and Mr. Peglar explained his mission. The old woman understood only Gaelic, and was under the impression that the island was being raided by Germans. The subsequent negotiations took some time, but Mr. Peglar succeeded in conveying his requirements and in paying for eight sheep. The old woman waved a wrinkled hand at the bleak hillside, indicating that her visitor might help himself.

Mr. Peglar went back and collected three of the boat's crew. With their aid he succeeded, after two hours and a half of the most violent physical exertions in his experience, in cornering five bleating muttons, and conveyed them, struggling wildly, to the boat. He broke his glasses in the course of the mêlée, and finally arrived on board dishevelled and exhausted, but mildly triumphant ; his flock were collected in an improvised pen, and Mr. Peglar called for a volunteer butcher.

As has been said, he was new to that most baffling of all human enigmas, the processes of the bluejacket's mind. Within five minutes of their arrival on board the sheep had been adopted by the ship's company, christened, ornamented with bows of ribbon, and fed variously upon cigarettes, condensed milk, tinned vegetables, and haricot beans. Mr. Peglar's supplications for their execution fell on shocked and outraged ears. They were the ship's pets, and not a hand would any man raise, except to fondle them.

John Octavius Peglar's jaw took a hard line. It was unfamiliar to his shipmates, but quite a number of men in Wall Street would have recognized it and steered clear. He went down to the First Lieutenant's cabin. " Say, Number One," he said, standing in the doorway and breathing through his nostrils. " Say, can I borrow your automatic revolver ? "

" What's up ? " inquired the startled First Lieutenant.

" Well, these darned sailors asked for fresh meat "—Mr. Peglar slipped the weapon, which the other extended, into his pocket —" and—*and they're going to have it.*"

In due course, the sheep having been consumed, Mr. Peglar rendered his accounts to the Admiralty. They were models of what accounts should be, but in the eyes of Whitehall they lacked one essential detail. Mr. Peglar had omitted to take on charge, and expend by the simple process of throwing overboard, the " arisings " of the sheep.

Now " arisings " are an important item of Naval store accounts. They represent what is left over. For instance, the
" arisings " of a candle is a puddle of wax, which is the property
of the State. The " arisings " of the sheep after they had been
skinned, cut up, and eaten were also, properly speaking, the
property of the State. In this and similar cases the State was
prepared to waive the joys of actual possession, provided it was
made clear that they had not been disposed of in such a way as
to benefit an individual. In other words, provided they were
duly certified as thrown overboard. This Mr. Peglar, with his
New World scorn for non-essentials, had omitted to do.

A few weeks elapsed and the accounts were returned with an
official request that it might be stated by the Accountant Officer
how the " arisings " of sheep, five in number, had been disposed
of. Mr. Peglar was unfamiliar with the term. He summoned
the Leading Victualling Assistant to explain. The Leading
Victualling Assistant explained, in one terse Anglo-Saxon word
that carried complete enlightenment.

" Well ! " said Mr. Peglar. " They can search *me* for them.
Do they think I've eaten them, anyway ? "

" Couldn't say, sir," replied his Staff helpfully.

" I'll write and ask them," said Mr. Peglar, and did so.

The ensuing correspondence need not be repeated in detail.
It reached its climax when Whitehall, having accused Mr. Peglar
of attempting flippancy, was told by that urbane gentleman that
they wouldn't have thought so if they had seen him handling
the First Lieutenant's automatic revolver in the sheep-pen.
Then Whitehall wearied of the jest after the manner of a Great
Government Department who felt that the thing had gone far
enough. In curt official phraseology Mr. Peglar was bidden to
account for the " arisings " or pay for them. Further, he was
informed, in no uncertain terms, that the correspondence on the
subject must cease. Whitehall then, deciding that it had laughed
last, turned its attention to other matters.

Again Mr. Peglar's smooth jaw took on that ominous prominence. " No, sir ! " said the head of the firm of Peglar and
Ziegland. " Not my money. But if it's ' arisings ' you want,
you shall have them."

The ship was then at Dundee, refitting. Mr. Peglar went
ashore and requested a policeman to direct him to the nearest
slaughter-house. Here Mr. Peglar interviewed a gentleman in
ensanguined overalls and explained his mission. " Equivalent
to about five sheep," he concluded. The gentleman indicated
a heap of assorted arisings and invited Mr. Peglar to help himself.

Mr. Peglar filled five sacks and drove them down to the ship in a cab. Here he transferred the contents to a packing-case, nailed it up, and addressed it to the Admiralty Official whose signature ornamented the recent official correspondence. Then feeling in need of refreshment, he repaired to the Wardroom.

The First Lieutenant proffered him an evening newspaper.

" America's entered the war," he said.

Mr. Peglar looked relieved. " Then I guess I'll get along and pack my grip." He rose and moved towards the door. The First Lieutenant looked surprised.

" Why ? Where are you going ? "

Mr. Peglar paused in the doorway.

" America," was the brief reply. " Right now."

The curtain swung to behind him and a dry unfamiliar chuckle.

John Octavius Peglar had laughed last.

J. J. BELL (1871–1934) *in the midst of a Science course at the University took what he described as "the wrong turning" and plunged into literature with no equipment "save pen, ink, paper, some postage stamps, and a little imagination." How much that little imagination was is appreciated by the manifold admirers of Wee MacGregor, who first appeared in Scottish newspapers and later in a book which had a phenomenal success.*

GREEN PAINT

So far Macgregor had spent a delightful evening, although at first he had felt the absence of his devoted chum, Willie Thomson, who, unfortunately, was confined to his home with a swollen face, the result, probably, of a soaking received the previous day while hanging on behind a Corporation watering-cart, which he and Macgregor had too hastily assumed to be empty. But Macgregor had speedily found a companion in Hughie Wilson, a boy whom he had hitherto rather despised, but who on this occasion had proved himself quite worthy of notice, having in his possession a pea-shooter and a fair quantity of appropriate ammunition. Hughie made no objection to sharing his sport with Macgregor, and by the time nearly all the peas were fired away—with more or less painful and irritating effect on pedestrians and owners of windows—or chewed and swallowed by the sharpshooters, the twain were on the best of terms, and all might have been well, had Macgregor only refrained from bragging of and exhibiting his athletic prowess. The competitions, which were begun in a spirit of friendly rivalry, ended in a very different spirit so far as Hughie was concerned, for he had to suffer defeat in everything he attempted, and, while hiding his chargin successfully enough, he was inwardly boiling with mortification and longing to discomfit his victor.

Macgregor, on the other hand, made no effort to conceal his elation.

" I tell't ye I wud bate ye," he said gleefully, as they walked away in the dusk at the end of the series of running and leaping trials.

" I'm no' heedin'," retorted Hughie, slipping a stray pea into his mouth. " Are ye gaun hame noo ? "

" Ay," replied Macgregor, who had promised to be home by

seven (it was now half-past that hour) to study his lessons.
" But ye're no' vera quick on yer feet, Hughie," he continued
pleasantly. " I'll ha'e to gi'e ye a guid stairt the next time we
try a race. Eh ? "

" Och, I'm no' heedin' aboot racin', nor jumpin' either,"
said the other carelessly. " I jist done it to please ye."

" Fine ham ! Ye're jist sayin' that because ye got bate.
D'ye mind thon time when I jamp near twicet as faur as yersel' ?
Eh ? D'ye mind it ? " Macgregor persisted.

" Naw ! " said Hughie shortly.

" Ah, ye mind it fine ! "

They walked several yards in silence, and Hughie said :

" Ye think ye're awfu' clever, but I'll bet ye onything ye like
ye canna sclim a lamp-post."

" Whit's that ye're sayin' ? "

" I'm sayin' ye canna sclim a lamp-post."

" Can I no' ? " Macgregor cried. " I'll shin let ye
see ! "

" Weel, sclim thon yin," said Hughie, pointing to the lamp-
post which they were approaching. " Speel up thon—if ye
can ! "

" I'll speel up it afore ye can whustle ! " exclaimed the valiant
one.

Hughie smiled, it might have been doubtingly.

" D'ye think I canna dae it ? " roared Macgregor, thoroughly
roused, flinging off his cap and jacket, and tossing them into a
convenient entry.

Still smiling, Hughie edged away.

Macgregor spat lightly on his hands. " I'll shin let ye see ! "
he cried, advancing to the post.

At the moment he gripped it with hands and knees Hughie
burst into a jeering laugh and, turning, bolted up the entry.
But, as luck would have it, he tripped over his companion's
jacket, and fell ; and the next instant Macgregor was on the top
of him, kneeling on his back.

" Ye kent the pent wisna dry," Macgregor cried, half choked
with rage. " I'll gi'e ye the best bashin' ye ever——"

" Aw—aw ! Let me alane," howled the other, struggling
desperately, and vainly endeavouring to protect his face and hair
from the sticky, green hands.

" Ye kent it wis wat pent," retorted Macgregor, with a
vicious rub at an exposed patch of cheek.

" I didna ! The—the man maun ha'e ta'en the ticket aff
ower shin. It wis there the day."

" Wis't ?   Aweel, ye *thocht* it wud be wat yet."

" Aw, ma nose ! " yelled the victim, as that organ received a smear.   " I'll tell ma big brither on ye, and he'll——"

" Ye're to get a bashin' first.   Ye'll get it as shin as I clean my haun's on ye.   *There !* . . . an' *there !* . . . an'——"

A door close at hand opened, and a very respectable elderly woman appeared on the scene.

" Mercy me ! " she exclaimed, horrified, " are ye fechtin', ye bad boys ?   Stop it this instant ! "

Hughie redoubled his cries, but Macgregor continued his operations, totally regardless of the intruder.

" Oh, me ! " groaned the old lady.   " I wish ma man wis in the hoose. . . .   Stop fechtin', like guid boys, if ye please," she implored, laying her hand on Macgregor's shoulder.

" Awa' an bile yer heid ! " was his rude command.

" He's killin' me," wailed Hughie.

Driven to desperation, she stooped and captured one of Macgregor's hands, whereupon the victim wriggled himself free, and rose to his feet, exhibiting so fearsome a visage that the would-be peacemaker cried out in horror and let go the victor. Before she realized the condition of her own fingers, and the wrist of one of her sleeves, she was alone, and Macgregor was in hot pursuit of Hughie.   The latter, however, in this instance, won the race, reaching home a woeful and grotesque object.

Having given up the chase at the last moment, Macgregor returned, almost satisfied with his revenge, to the entry for his cap and jacket.   It was not till he had recovered his property, which he did before his breath, that his attention was attracted to the condition of his knickerbockers.   Even in the feeble lamplight the damage looked very, very serious, though it was confined to the cloth on the inner sides of his knees.   The knickerbockers, too, were comparatively new, and he had put them on that afternoon to allow of his mother making some repairs upon his everyday ones.   He remembered that she had warned him to be careful as to what games he played, and the flush of his recent excitement gave way before a chill of remorse and foreboding.

Although his home was just round the corner, it was nearly half-an-hour later ere he knocked at the door and was admitted by his mother.

" Ye've been ower lang ootbye, laddie," she said a little reproachfully, but not crossly.   " Ye sudna furget the time when ye've yer lessons to learn.   Is that pent I smell on ye ? "

" It—it wis on ma haun's, but it's near a' aff," he returned, keeping his knees well together and exhibiting his palms. Fortunately it was not very light in the little lobby.

"Weel, I'm gled ye didna file yer claes, Macgregor. Awa' an' wash yer haun's, an' then get stairtit to yer lessons. Ye'll never be dux if ye gang on like this."

Had her son been in his usual spirits, he would probably have retorted that he did not want to be dux, but on this occasion he followed her into the kitchen in silence.

"Here he comes wi' as mony feet's a hen!" cried his father jovially, looking up from his paper.

Macgregor smiled feebly in response, and with a gait not unlike that of the fowl just mentioned went over to the sink, where he washed long and diligently.

Immediately he had dried his hands he procured his lesson-book and took a chair as far from the fireside as possible.

"Dinna turn in yer taes like that, laddie," said his mother, who, to his relief, was preparing to go out on a domestic errand. "Onybody wud think ye wis deformed."

"Och, dinna fash yersel', Lizzie," put in her husband. "The wean's fine. He'll jist be easin' his legs efter rinnin' aboot. Wha wis ye playin' wi' the nicht, Macgreegor?"

"Hughie Wulson."

"Whit wis ye playin' at?"

"Haud yer tongue, John," interposed Lizzie, "an' let Macgreegor pey attention to his lessons."

"Dod, ay," said John agreeably. "We mauna interfere wi' his lessons. Are ye gaun yer messages noo, Lizzie?"

"Ay. I'll no' be lang. I'm vexed I didna get them done afore ye cam' hame, but I wis gey thrang the day, an' Mrs. M'Ostrich cam' in an' blethered hauf the efternune. She's gaun to ha'e anither pairty, but she's no' askin' Mistress Purdie."

"She's askin' Macgreegor, though."

"Macgreegor'll get, if he's a guid laddie. . . . Weel, I'll awa afore the shopes shut. Luk efter wee Jeannie, if she waukens, an' hear Macgreegor his spellin's, if he's ready afore I come back. . . . Macgreegor, whit wey ha'e ye gotten yer guid breeks a' twistit-like? Pu' them roon' at the knees, an' see an' learn the meanin's furbye the spellin's."

She hurried away, and silence reigned for a little in the kitchen.

John resumed his paper, but ere long he glanced over it at his son. He felt that all was not well with the youngster.

"Are ye wearit, ma mannie?" he asked kindly.

"Naw."

" Are ye no' weel ? "

" I'm fine," replied Macgregor in a voice that belied his words.

Three minutes passed, and John took another glance.

His son was holding the lesson-book to one side, and appeared to be examining with much minuteness the knees of his knicker-bockers.

" Are ye no ' comin' to sit aside me the nicht, Macgreegor ? " John inquired, dropping his paper and stretching out a big inviting hand.

Macgregor hastily resumed his studies.

" Come awa'," his father went on. " I dinna like ye sittin' there as if you an' me had cast oot. . . . Are ye no' comin' ? "

The youngster shook his head ; then gulped slightly.

" John got up and went over to where the penitent sat. " Macgreegor, ye best tell us a' aboot it," he said gently. " Whit's vexin' ye, ma wee man ? "

After a little while Macgregor explained his unhappy plight, easing at the same time his stiffened limbs.

" Puir laddie," said his father sympathetically. " It wis a dirty trick to play on ye," he added indignantly.

" I wiped ma haun's on his heid," Macgregor observed with some satisfaction, " an' I wud ha'e gi'ed him a bashin', if a daft auld wife hadna come oot an'——"

" It's a peety it wisna yer auld breeks," said John reflectively. " I doot yer Maw'll be sair pit aboot. . . . I wonder if we canna get them cleaned afore she comes hame. If I had a wee drap terpentine noo, I wud try it."

" There terpentine in the wee press ablow the jaw-box," said Macgregor eagerly. " She wis cleanin' ma auld breeks wi' some the day."

" The vera thing the doctor ordered ! " his father exclaimed jubilantly, and went to the cupboard indicated.

" It's a black botle, Paw."

Just then wee Jeannie awoke and demanded attention. By the time her father realized that she was determined not to go to sleep again, the clock warned him that his wife might return at any moment.

He wrapped the child in a blanket and sat down with her on his knee by the kitchen fire.

" Here, Macgregor ; bring ower the botle, an' we'll try what we can dae."

" Here the botle, Paw, an' here the wee bit flannen she rubs it in wi'."

"Tak' oot the cork then, an' let's smell to mak' shair it's terpentine,—no' that I'm jist shair o' the smell. . . . Hph ! Ay ; I think that's richt. It's a wee thing like speerits o' wine, but that wudna dae hairm onywey. Weel, we'll ha'e to hurry up, or yer Maw'll catch us. Pit up yer leg, Macgreegor."

Macgregor did as commanded, twisting round the cloth so as to bring into position the splatch of green paint.

"Noo, ma mannie, haud the flannen till I pour a drap o' the terpentine on it—dinna jump like that, Jeannie daurlin'—an' then rub it on the pent. Are ye ready ? "

"Ay, Paw."

"Aweel, here's guid luck to us a' ! " And John with his one free hand cautiously tilted the bottle. "Steady, noo."

"Maw ! " cried wee Jeannie with a bound of delight as a key rattled in the outer door.

Macgregor let out a yell of dismay, while John groaned, "We're done fur noo ! It's the wrang botle ! "

Half-a-pint of lacquer, thickish and intensely black, was running leisurely down Macgregor's leg as Mrs. Robinson, pleasantly smiling, entered the kitchen.

. . . .

Lizzie's little whirlwind of wrath had passed, but her husband's wretchedness was not abated by the awful calm of her displeasure which had followed the outburst, and which now seemed as if it would last for ever.

Macgregor, after having his knickerbockers scraped with the back of a knife, had been sent ignominiously to bed, warned that he would be called to his lessons at half-past six in the morning, and informed that he had forfeited his last chance of getting to Mrs. M'Ostrich's party or to any other entertainment which might occur during the approaching festive season.

"Ye canna gang ony place till ye get new breeks, an' that'll no' be this year, I warrant ye ! " his mother had said. "So ye needna be greetin' like a muckle tawpy, fur it'll no' gar me change ma mind."

"I'm no' greetin'," he had muttered, not without indignation, and had retired to his bed, where he lay miserably awake, swallowing the lump that always came back.

Wee Jeannie, also, had been smartly packed off to her nest, marvelling doubtless at her mother's unwonted sharpness towards her, but fortunately refraining from offering any vocal protest, and falling into placid slumber within five minutes.

By the fireside Mr. Robinson sat silent, a spectacle of profound depression, glancing now and then at his wife, who, having laid her son's spoiled garment on a newspaper methodically spread upon the well-scrubbed deal table, was regarding the green and black stains with eyes from which all earthly hope seemed to have vanished.

" Lizzie," stammered John at last, breaking a wretched silence, " I'm unco vexed, wumman, to gi'e ye a' this bother. I—I done it a' fur the best."

" Aw, it's nae bother ! I've naethin' else to dae, an' ye ken as weel as me that breeks cost naethin'," she returned with cold irony.

" But it wis jist a mishap, Lizzie."

" Deed, ay. I ken that fine. You and Macgreegor never dae onything wrang—it's aye jist a mishap ! Jist that. Hooever, I sud be used to yer mishaps by this time. It's a' ma ain fau't fur gaun oot ma messages an' leavin' ye baith in the hoose. I sud ha'e got Mistress M'Faurlan frae next door to come in an' luk efter ye, the wey she used to dae when I had to leave wee Jeannie in the hoose alane. Oh, I'm no' blamin' you an' Macgreegor, fur it's no' to be expec'it ye can behave when naebody's takin' care o' ye. An' it's fine fun for me ! Ma enjeyment is mair nor I can describe ! " Here she groaned.

" Ye're awfu' severe on a man, Lizzie," sighed her husband, after a short pause, wherein he suppressed a less humble remark.

" I wis speakin' aboot weans."

For a little while Mr. Robinson held his peace. Then he began to plead for his son.

" Ye see, Lizzie, it wis ma fau't. Macgreegor never thocht of the terpentine. *He* wisna fur tryin' to conceal his ain mishap wi' the green pent."

" Wis he no' ? Whit wey wis he turnin' in his taes an' twistin' roon' his breeks ? "

" I wud ha'e done the same masel', Lizzie."

" I've nae doot ye wud."

" Tits, wumman ! " he exclaimed, " whit wud *you* ha'e done ? "

Mrs. Robinson made no answer. She took a shawl from a peg and threw it round her shoulders.

" Ye're no' gaun ootbye again at this time o' nicht ? " said her husband in surprise.

" I'm jist gaun to the druggist. He's open till ten."

" Are ye no' weel, wife ? "

" I'm gaun to see if he's got onything that'll tak' oot yer mess. Maybe benzine'll dae, but I doot it."

" I'll gang fur ye," John said eagerly. " It maybe wudna be

safe to leave me in the hoose, Lizzie," he added with an attempt
at a laugh.

"Maybe ye're richt," she retorted coldly.   "Ye can gang, if ye
like. . . . Tak' the breeks wi' ye. Gang quick, fur it's near ten."

John put on his cap and made for the door. There he halted
for a moment. "Try an' let Macgreegor aff this time," he
whispered.

Lizzie heard the outer door shut quietly, and seated herself
to wait her man's return. It had been an extra hard day, and
she nodded drowsily.

Presently she became aware that her son, barefooted and
mournful of countenance, was standing beside her.

"Whit are ye wantin', Macgreegor ? "

"I—I'm vexed, Maw."

"Muckle need ! . . . Can ye no' sleep ? "

"Naw. . . . It wis me to—to blame, Maw. I—I tell't him
the wrang botle, an'—an' I didna ken the lamp-post wis new
pentit."

"But ye maun try to ha'e some sense, laddie," she said, with
diminishing severity.

"Ay, Maw ; I'll try. . . . But dinna be vexed wi' Paw. . . .
I'm—I'm no' awfu' heedin' aboot Mistress M'Ostrich's pairty, an'
I'll learn ma lessons early in the mornin', an'—an' I'll dae wi'oot
taiblet on Setturday, an' tak' ile, if ye like. But dinna——"

"Whist, dearie ! "

"But——"

Lizzie put her arm round him, and smiled reassuringly, if a
little sadly. "Ye're an awfu' laddie ! " she murmured. "Wull
ye try an' be guid an' wice efter this ?   Eh ? "

"Ay, Maw."

"Weel, gi'e 's a kiss, an' awa' to yer beddy-baw. . . . Come,
an' I'll tuck ye in."

.   .   .   .

Mr. and Mrs. Robinson sat later than usual that evening, and
did not seem to mind the atmosphere being redolent of benzine,
which, after all, was better than having it charged with domestic
electricity.

About eleven o'clock, when they were so comfortable that it
seemed a pity to retire, the door was cautiously opened and
Macgregor peeped in. He saw his parents before they saw him,
and his face lost its anxiety.

"Mercy me ! " cried his mother, " ye're there again ! "

His father smiled as one who has forgotten all his troubles.
" Whit wis ye wantin', ma mannie ? "

" Mercy me ! " cried his mother, *" ye're there again ! "*

Macgregor hesitated.

" Whit is't, dearie ? " asked Lizzie kindly. " Ye sud ha'e
been sleepin' lang syne," she added.

The youngster took heart. " Is the pent aff ma breeks ? " he
inquired.

" Vera near it," replied John. " Yer Maw's the clever yin !
She'll ha'e them as guid as new afore she's done wi' them."

There was a pause. Then—

" Wull I get to Mistress M'Ostrich's pairty ? "

HILAIRE BELLOC (1870–   ), *the son of a French father and an Irish mother, is amongst the most versatile personalities in modern literature. Essays, verse, novels, travels, history, biographies, have all come from his pen. His works in different spheres include a "History of England," "The Path to Rome," "Hills and the Sea," and "Mr. Clutterbuck's Election." "The Joke" is from a collection of his choicest essays.*

THE JOKE

THERE are two kinds of jokes, those jokes that are funny because they are true, and those jokes that would be funny anyhow. Think it out and you will find that that is a great truth. Now the great joke I have here for the delectation of the broken-hearted is of the first sort. It is funny because it is true. It is about a man whom I really saw and really knew and touched and on occasions treated ill. He was. The sunlight played upon his form. Perhaps he may still flounder under the light of the sun, and not yet have gone down into that kingdom whose kings are less happy than the poorest hind upon the upper fields.

It was at College that I knew him and I retained my acquaintance with him—Oh, I retained it in a loving and cherishing manner—until he was grown to young manhood. I would keep it still did Fate permit me so to do, for he was a treasure. I have never met anything so complete for the purposes of laughter, though I am told there are many such in the society which bred his oafish form.

He was noble in his own country, which was somewhere in the pine-forests of the Germanies, and his views of social rank were far, far too simple for the silent subtlety of the English Rich. In his poor turnip of a mind he ordered all men thus :

First, reigning sovereigns and their families.

Secondly, mediatized people.

Third, Princes.

Fourth, Dukes.

Fifth, Nobles.

Then came a little gap, and after that little gap, The Others.

Most of us in our College were The Others. But he, as I have said, was a noble in his distant land.

He had not long been among the young Englishmen when he

discovered that a difficult tangle of titles ran hither and thither
among them like random briars through an undergrowth. There
were Honourables, and there were Lords, and Heaven knows
what, and there were two Sirs, and altogether it puzzled him.

He couldn't understand why a man should be called Mr.
Jinks, and his brother Lord Blefauscu, and then if a man could
be called Lord Blefauscu while his father Lord Brobdignag was
alive, how was it that quite a fresher should be called Sir Howkey
—no—he was Sir John Howkey : and when the Devil did one
put in the Christian name and when didn't one, and why should
one, and what was the order of precedence among all these ?

I think that last point puzzled him more than the rest, for
in his own far distant land in the pine-woods, where peasants
uglier than sin grovelled over the potato crop and called him
" Baron," there were no such devilish contraptions, but black
was black and white was white. Here in this hypocritical
England, to which his father had sent him as an exile, everything
was so wrapped up in deceiving masks ! There was the Captain of the Eleven, or the President of the Boat Club. By the
time he had mastered that there might be great men not only
without the actual title (he had long ago despaired of that), but
without so much as cousinship to one, he would stumble upon a
fellow with nothing whatsoever to distinguish him, not even the
High Jump, and yet " in " with the highest. It tortured him,
I can tell you ! After he had sat upon several Fourth Year men
(he himself a Fresher), from an error as to their rank, after he
had been duly thrown into the water, blackened as to his face
with blacking, sentenced to death in a court-martial and duly
shot with a blank cartridge (an unpleasant thing, by the way,
looking down a barrel) ; after he had had his boots, of which
there were seven pair, packed with earth, and in each one a large
geranium planted ; after all these things had happened to him
in his pursuit of an Anglo-German understanding, he approached
a lanky, pot-bellied youth whom he had discovered with certitude
to be the cousin of a Duke, and begged him secretly to befriend
him in a certain matter, which was this :

The Baron out of the Germanies proposed to give a dinner to
no less than thirty people and he begged the pot-bellied youth in
all secrecy to collect for him an assembly worthy of his rank and
to give him privately not only their names but their actual precedence according to which he would arrange them at the table
upon his right and upon his left.

But what did the pot-bellied youth do ? Why he went out
and finding all his friends one after the other he said :

" You know Sausage ? "

" Yes," said they, for all the University knew Sausage.

" Well, he is going to give a dinner," said the pot-bellied one, who was also slow of speech, " and you have to come, but I'm going to say you are the Duke of Rochester " (or whatever title he might have chosen). And so speaking, and so giving the date and place he would go on to the next. Then, when he had collected not thirty but sixty of all his friends and acquaintances, he sought out the noble Teuton again and told him that he could not possibly ask only thirty men without life-long jealousies and hatreds so sixty were coming, and the Teuton with some hesitation (for he was fond of money) agreed.

Never shall I forget the day when those sixty were ushered solemnly into a large Reception Room in the Hotel, blameless youths of varying aspect, most of them quite sober—since it was but seven o'clock—and presented one by one to the host of the evening, each with his title and style.

To those whom he recognized as equals the Aristocrat spoke with charming simplicity. Those who were somewhat his inferiors (the lords by courtesy and the simple baronets) he put immediately at their ease ; and even the Honourables saw at a glance that he was a man of the world, for he said a few kind words to each. As for a man with no handle to his name, there was not one of the sixty so low, except a Mr. Poopsibah, of whom the gatherer of that feast whispered to the host that he could not but ask him because, though only a second cousin, he was the heir to the Marquis of Quirk—hence his Norman name.

It was a bewilderment to the Baron, for he might have to meet the man later in life as the Marquis of Quirk, whereas for the moment he was only Mr. Poopsibah, but anyhow he was put at the bottom of the table—and that was how the trouble began.

In my time—I am talking of the nineties—young men drank wine : it was before the Bishop of London had noted the Great Change. And Mr. Poopsibah and his neighbour—Lord Henry Job—were quite early in the Feast occupied in a playful contest which ended in Mr. Poopsibah's losing his end seat and going to grass. He rose, not unruffled, with a burst collar, and glared a little uncertainly over the assembled wealth and lineage of the evening. Lord Benin (the son of our Great General Lord Ashantee of Benin—his real name was Mitcham, God Rest His Soul) addressed to the unreal Poopsibah an epithet then fashionable, now almost forgotten, but always unprintable. Mr. Poopsibah forgetting what nobility imposes, immediately hurled at him an as yet half-emptied bottle of Champagne.

Then it was that the bewildered Baron learnt for the last time—and for that matter for the first time—to what the Island Race can rise when it really lets itself go.

I remember (I was a nephew if I remember right) above the din and confusion of lights (for candles also were thrown) loud appeals as in a tone of command, and then as in a tone of supplication, both in the unmistakable accents of the Cousins overseas, and I even remember what I may call the Great Sacrilege of that evening when Lord Gogmagog seizing our host affectionately round the neck, and pressing the back of his head with his large and red left hand, attempted to grind his face into the tablecloth, after a fashion wholly unknown to the haughty lords of the Teufelwald.

During the march homewards—an adventure enlightened with a sharp skirmish and two losses at the hands of the police—I know not what passed through the mind of the youth who had hitherto kept so careful a distinction between blood and blood : whether like Hannibal he swore eternal hatred to the English, or whether in his patient German mind he noted it all down as a piece of historical evidence to be used in his diplomatic career, we shall not be told. I think in the main he was simply bewildered : bewildered to madness.

Of the many other things we made him do before Eights Week I have no space to tell : how he asked us what was the fashionable sport and how we told him Polo and made him buy a Polo pony sixteen hands high, with huge great bones and a broken nose, explaining to him that it was stamina and not appearance that the bluff Englishman loved in a horse. How we made him wear his arms embroidered upon his handkerchief (producing several for a pattern and taking the thing as a commonplace by sly illusion for many preparatory days). How we told him that it was the custom to call every Sunday afternoon for half an hour upon the wife of every married Don of one's College. How we challenged him to the great College feat of throwing himself into the river at midnight. How finally we persuaded him that the ancient custom of the University demanded the presentation to one's Tutor at the end of term of an elaborate thesis one hundred pages long upon some subject of Theology. How he was carefully warned that surprise was the essence of this charming tradition and not a word of it must be breathed to the august recipient of the favour. How he sucked in the knowledge that the more curious and strange the matter the higher would be his place in the schools, and how the poor fool elaborately wasted what God gives such men for brains in

the construction of a damning refutation against the Mono-
physites. How his tutor, a humble little nervous fool, thought
he was having his leg pulled—all these things I have no space to
tell you now.

But he was rich ! Doubtless by the custom of his country
he is now in some great position plotting the ruin of Britannia,
and certainly she deserves it in his case. He was most unmercifully ragged.

ARNOLD BENNETT (1867–1931) *made no secret of the fact that he wrote for money, but this did not prevent him from being always the conscientious and painstaking artist. He was born in one of the Five Towns which form the background of so many of his dispassionate tales of rather grim realities, among the most famous being " The Old Wives' Tale " and the " Clayhanger " series. " The Burglary " well reveals his keen, probing wit.*

THE BURGLARY

LADY DAIN said : " Jee, if that portrait stays there much longer, you'll just have to take me of to Pirehill one of these fine mornings."

Pirehill is the seat of the great local hospital ; but it is also the seat of the great local lunatic asylum ; and when the inhabitants of the Five Towns say merely " Pirehill," they mean the asylum.

" I do declare I can't fancy my food nowadays," said Lady Dain, " and it's all that portrait ! " She stared plaintively up at the immense oil-painting which faced her as she sat at the breakfast-table in her spacious and opulent dining-room.

Sir Jehoshaphat made no remark.

Despite Lady Dain's animadversions upon it, despite the undoubted fact that it was generally disliked in the Five Towns, the portrait had cost a thousand pounds (some said guineas), and though not yet two years old it was probably worth at least fifteen hundred in the picture market. For it was a Cressage ; and not only was it a Cressage—it was one of the finest Cressages in existence.

It marked the summit of Sir Jehoshaphat's career. Sir Jehoshaphat's career was, perhaps, the most successful and brilliant in the entire social history of the Five Towns. This famous man was the principal partner in Dain Brothers. His brother was dead, but two of Sir Jee's sons were in the firm. Dain Brothers were the largest manufacturers of cheap earthenware in the district catering chiefly for the American and Colonial buyer. They had an extremely bad reputation for cutting prices. They were hated by every other firm in the Five Towns, and, to hear rival manufacturers talk, one would gather the impression that Sir Jee had acquired a tremendous fortune by systematically selling goods under cost. They were also hated by between eighteen

95

and nineteen hundred employees. But such hatred, however virulent, had not marred the progress of Sir Jee's career.

He had meant to make a name and he had made it. The Five Towns might laugh at his vulgar snobbishness. The Five Towns might sneer at his calculated philanthropy. But he was, nevertheless, the best known man in the Five Towns, and it was precisely his snobbishness and his philanthropy which had carried him to the top. Moreover, he had been the first public man in the Five Towns to gain a knighthood. The Five Towns could not deny that it was very proud indeed of this knighthood. The means by which he had won this distinction were neither here nor there—he had won it. And was he not the father of his native borough ? Had he not been three times mayor of his native borough ? Was not the whole northern half of the county dotted and spangled by his benefactions, his institutions, his endowments ?

And it could not be denied that he sometimes tickled the Five Towns as the Five Towns likes being tickled. There was, for example, the notorious Sneyd incident. Sneyd Hall, belonging to the Earl of Chell, lies a few miles south of the Five Towns, and from it the pretty Countess of Chell exercises that condescending meddlesomeness which so frequently exasperates the Five Towns. Sir Jee had got his title by the aid of the Countess—" Interfering Iris," as she is locally dubbed. Shortly afterwards he had contrived to quarrel with the Countess ; and the quarrel was conducted by Sir Jee as a quarrel between equals, which delighted the district. Sir Jee's final word in it had been to buy a sizable tract of land near Sneyd village, just off the Sneyd estate, and to erect thereon a mansion quite as imposing as Sneyd Hall, and far more up-to-date, and to call the mansion Sneyd Castle. A mighty stroke ! Iris was furious ; the Earl speechless with fury. But they could do nothing. Naturally the Five Towns was tickled.

It was *à propos* of the house-warming of Sneyd Castle, also of the completion of his third mayoralty, and of the inauguration of the Dain Technical Institute, that the movement had been started (primarily by a few toadies) for tendering to Sir Jee a popular gift worthy to express the profound esteem in which he was officially held in the Five Towns. It having been generally felt that the gift should take the form of a portrait, a local dilettante had suggested Cressage, and when the Five Towns had inquired into Cressage and discovered that that genius from the United States was celebrated throughout the civilized world, and regarded as the equal of Velazquez (whoever Velazquez might

" What's the figure ? " said Smith curtly.

" Figure ? "

" What are you going to give me for the job ? "

" *Give* you for doing the job ? " Sir Jee repeated, his secret and ineradicable meanness aroused. " *Give* you ? Why, I'm giving you the opportunity to honestly steal a picture that's worth over a thousand pounds—I dare say it would be worth two thousand pounds in America—and you want to be paid into the bargain ! Do you know, my man, that people come all the way from Manchester, and even London, to see that portrait ? " He told Smith about the painting.

" Then why are you in such a stew to be rid of it ? " queried the burglar.

" That's my affair," said Sir Jee. " I don't like it. Lady Dain doesn't like it. But it's a presentation portrait, and so I can't—you see, Mr. Smith ? "

" And how am I going to dispose of it when I've got it ? " Smith demanded. " You can't melt a portrait down as if it was silver. By what you say, governor, it's known all over the blessed world. Seems to me I might just as well try to sell the Nelson Column."

" Oh, nonsense ! " said Sir Jee. " Nonsense. You'll sell it in America quite easily. It'll be a fortune for you. Keep it for a year first, and then send it to New York."

William Smith shook his head and drummed his fingers on the table ; and then quite suddenly he brightened and said :

" All right, governor. I'll take it on, just to oblige you."

" When can you do it ? " asked Sir Jee, hardly concealing his joy. " To-night ? "

" No," said Smith mysteriously. " I'm engaged to-night."

" Well, to-morrow night ? "

" Nor to-morrow. I'm engaged to-morrow too."

" You seem to be very much engaged, my man," Sir Jee observed.

" What do you expect ? " Smith retorted. " Business is business. I could do it the night after to-morrow."

" But that's Christmas Eve," Sir Jee protested.

" What if it is Christmas Eve ? " said Smith coldly. " Would you prefer Christmas Day ? I'm engaged on Boxing Day, *and* the day after."

" Not in the Five Towns, I trust ? " Sir Jee remarked.

" No," said Smith shortly. " The Five Towns is about sucked dry."

The affair was arranged for Christmas Eve.

" Now," Sir Jee suggested, " shall I draw you a plan of the castle, so that you can——"

William Smith's face expressed terrific scorn. " Do you suppose," he said, " as I haven't had plans o' your castle ever since it was built ? What do you take me for ? I'm not a blooming excursionist, I'm not. I'm a business man—that's what I am."

Sir Jee was snubbed, and he agreed submissively to all William Smith's arrangements for the innocent burglary. He perceived that in William Smith he had stumbled on a professional of the highest class, and this good fortune pleased him.

" There's only one thing that riles me," said Smith, in parting, " and that is that you'll go and say that after you'd done everything you could for me I went and burgled your castle. And you'll talk about the ingratitude of the lower classes. I know you, governor ! "

III

ON the afternoon of the 24th of December Sir Jehoshaphat drove home to Sneyd Castle from the principal of the three Dain manufactories, and found Lady Dain superintending the work of packing up trunks. He and she were to quit the castle that afternoon in order to spend Christmas on the other side of the Five Towns, under the roof of their eldest son, John, who had a new house, a new wife, and a new baby (male). John was a domineering person, and, being rather proud of his house and all that was his, he had obstinately decided to have his own Christmas at his own hearth. Grandpa and grandmamma, drawn by the irresistible attraction of that novelty, a grandson (though Mrs. John *had* declined to have the little thing named Jehosaphat), had yielded to John's solicitations, and the family gathering, for the first time in history, was not to occur round Sir Jee's mahogany.

Sir Jee, very characteristically, said nothing to Lady Dain immediately. He allowed her to proceed with the packing of the trunks, and then tea was served, and as the time was approaching for the carriage to come round to take them to the station, when at last he suddenly remarked :

" I shan't be able to go with you to John's this afternoon."

" Oh, Jee ! " she exclaimed. " Really, you are tiresome. Why couldn't you tell me before ? "

" I will come over to-morrow morning—perhaps in time for church," he proceeded, ignoring her demand for an explanation.

He always did ignore her demand for an explanation. Indeed, she only asked for explanations in a mechanical and perfunctory manner—she had long since ceased to expect them. Sir Jee had been born like that—devious, mysterious, incalculable. And Lady Dain accepted him as he was. She was somewhat surprised, therefore, when he went on :

" I have some minutes of committee meetings that I really must go carefully through and send off to-night, and you know as well as I do that there'll be no chance of doing that at John's. I've telegraphed to John."

He was obviously nervous and self-conscious.

" There's no food in the house," sighed Lady Dain. " And the servants are all going away except Callear, and he can't cook your dinner to-night. I think I'd better stay myself and look after you."

" You'll do no such thing," said Sir Jee decisively. " As for my dinner, anything will do for that. The servants have been promised their holiday, to start from this evening, and they must have it. I can manage."

Here spoke the philanthropist with his unshakable sense of justice.

So Lady Dain departed, anxious and worried, having previously arranged something cold for Sir Jee in the dining-room, and instructed Callear about boiling the water for Sir Jee's tea on Christmas morning. Callear was the under-coach-man and a useful odd man. He it was who would drive Sir Jee to the station on Christmas morning, and then guard the castle and the stables thereof during the absence of the family and the other servants. Callear slept over the stables.

And after Sir Jee had consumed his cold repast in the dining-room the other servants went, and Sir Jee was alone in the castle, facing the portrait.

He had managed the affair fairly well, he thought. Indeed, he had a talent for chicane, and none knew it better than himself. It would have been dangerous if the servants had been left in the castle. They might have suffered from insomnia, and heard William Smith, and interfered with the operations of William Smith. On the other hand, Sir Jee had no intention whatever of leaving the castle uninhabited to the mercies of William Smith. He felt that he himself must be on the spot to see that everything went right and that nothing went wrong. Thus, the previously arranged scheme for the servants' holiday fitted perfectly into his plans, and all that he had had to do was to refuse to leave the castle till the morrow. It was ideal.

Nevertheless, he was a little afraid of what he had done, and of what he was going to permit William Smith to do. It was certainly dangerous—certainly rather a wild scheme. However, the die was cast. And within twelve hours he would be relieved of the intolerable incubus of the portrait.

And when he thought of the humiliations which that portrait had caused him ; when he remembered the remarks of his sons concerning it, especially John's remarks ; when he recalled phrases about it in London newspapers, he squirmed, and told himself that no scheme for getting rid of it could be too wild and perilous. And, after all, the burglary dodge was the only dodge, absolutely the only conceivable practical method of disposing of the portrait—except burning down the castle. And surely it was preferable to a conflagration, to arson ! Moreover, in case of fire at the castle some blundering fool would be sure to cry : " The portrait ! The portrait must be saved ! " And the portrait would be saved.

He gazed at the repulsive, hateful thing. In the centre of the lower part of the massive gold frame was the legend : " Presented to Sir Jehoshaphat Dain, Knight, as a mark of public esteem and gratitude," etc. He wondered if William Smith would steal the frame. It was to be hoped that he would not steal the frame. In fact, William Smith would find it very difficult to steal that frame unless he had an accomplice or so.

" This is the last time I shall see *you* ! " said Sir Jee to the portrait.

Then he unfastened the catch of one of the windows in the dining-room (as per contract with William Smith), turned out the electric light, and went to bed in the deserted castle.

He went to bed, but not to sleep. It was no part of Sir Jee's programme to sleep. He intended to listen, and he did listen.

And about two o'clock, precisely the hour which William Smith had indicated, he fancied he heard muffled and discreet noises. Then he was sure that he heard them. William Smith had kept his word. Then the noises ceased for a period, and then they recommenced. Sir Jee restrained his curiosity as long as he could, and when he could restrain it no more he rose and silently opened his bedroom window and put his head out into the nipping night air of Christmas. And by good fortune he saw the vast oblong of the picture, carefully enveloped in sheets, being passed by a couple of dark figures through the dining-room window to the garden outside. William Smith had a colleague, then, and he was taking the frame as well as the canvas. Sir Jee

" This is the last time I shall see you ! " said Sir Jee to the portrait

watched the men disappear down the avenue, and they did not reappear. Sir Jee returned to bed.

Yes, he felt himself equal to facing it out with his family and friends. He felt himself equal to pretending that he had no knowledge of the burglary.

Having slept a few hours, he got up early and, half-dressed, descended to the dining-room just to see what sort of a mess William Smith had made.

The canvas of the portrait lay flat on the hearthrug, with the following words written on it in chalk : " This is no use to me." It was the massive gold frame that had gone.

Further, as was later discovered, all the silver had gone. Not a spoon was left in the castle.

GEORGE A. BIRMINGHAM (1865–
), *whose real name is Canon J. O. Hannay,
was for twenty-one years rector of Westport,
County Mayo. He resigned in 1913 and
became rector of Mells in 1924. Humour,
romance, and adventure make his stories fine
entertainment, and notable among his books
are " Spanish Gold " and " Lady Bountiful."*

A LUNATIC AT LARGE*

It was Tuesday, a Tuesday early in October. Dr. Lovaway
finished his breakfast quietly, conscious that he had a long
morning before him and nothing particular to do. Tuesday is
a quiet day in Dunailin ; Wednesday is market day and people
are busy, the doctor as well as everybody else. Young women
who come into town with butter to sell take the opportunity of
having their babies vaccinated on Wednesday. Old women,
with baskets on their arms, find it convenient on that day to ask
the doctor for something to rub into knee-joints where rheumatic
pains are troublesome. Old men, who have ridden into town on
their donkeys, consult the doctor about chronic coughs, and seek
bottles likely to relieve " an impression on the chest."

Fridays, when the Petty Sessions' Court sits, are almost as
busy. Mr. Timothy Flanagan, a magistrate in virtue of the fact
that he is Chairman of the Urban District Council, administers
justice of a rude and uncertain kind in the Court House. While
angry litigants are settling their business there, and repentant
drunkards are paying the moderate fines imposed on them, their
wives ask the doctor for advice about the treatment of whooping-
cough or the best way of treating a child which has incautiously
stepped into a fire. Fair days, which occur once a month, are
the busiest days of all. Every one is in town on fair days, and
every kind of ailment is brought to the doctor. Towards evening
he has to put stitches into one or two cut scalps and sometimes
set a broken limb. On Mondays and Thursdays the doctor sits
in his office for an hour or two to register births and deaths.

But Tuesdays, unless a fair happens to fall on Tuesday, are
quiet days. On this particular Tuesday Dr. Lovaway was
pleasantly aware that he had nothing whatever to do, and might
count on having the whole day to himself. It was raining very

* This short story is taken from *Lady Bountiful*, by George A.
Birmingham, and has no connection with J. Storer Clouston's well-
known novel, *The Lunatic at Large.*

heavily, but the weather did not trouble him at all. He had a plan for the day which rain could not mar.

He sat down at his writing-table, took from a drawer a bundle of foolscap paper, fitted a new nib to his pen, and filled his ink bottle. He began to write.

"A study of the Remarkable Increase of Lunacy in Rural Connaught."

The title looked well. It would, he felt, certainly attract the attention of the editor of *The British Medical Journal*.

But Dr. Lovaway did not like it. It was not for the editor of *The British Medical Journal*, or, indeed, for a scientific public that he wanted to write. He started fresh on a new sheet of paper.

"Lunacy in the West of Ireland : Its Cause and Cure."

That struck him as the kind of title which would appeal to the philanthropist out to effect a social reform of some kind. But Dr. Lovaway was not satisfied with it. He respected reformers and was convinced of the value of their work, but his real wish was to write something of a literary kind. With prodigal extravagance he tore up another sheet of foolscap and began again.

"The Passing of the Gael. Ireland's Crowded Madhouses."

He purred a little over that title and then began the article itself. What he wanted to say was clear in his mind. He had been weeks in Dunailin, and he had spent more time over lunatics than anything else. Almost every day he found himself called upon by Sergeant Rahilly to "certify" a lunatic, to commit some unfortunate person with diseased intellect to an asylum. Sometimes he signed the required document. Often he hesitated, although he was always supplied by the sergeant and his constables with a wealth of lurid detail about the dangerous and homicidal tendencies of the patient. Dr. Lovaway was profoundly impressed.

He gave his whole mind to the consideration of the problem which pressed on him. He balanced theories. He blamed tea, inter-marriage, potatoes, bad whisky, religious enthusiasm, and did not find any of them nor all of them together satisfactory as explanations of the awful facts. He fell back finally on a theory of race decadence. Already fine phrases were forming themselves in his mind : "The inexpressible beauty of autumnal decay." "The exquisiteness of the decadent efflorescence of a passing race."

He covered a sheet of foolscap with a bare—he called it detached—statement of the facts about Irish lunacy. He had just begun to recount his own experience when there was a knock at the door. The housekeeper, a legacy from Dr. Farelly, came in to tell him that Constable Malone wished to speak to him. Dr. Lovaway left his MS. with a sigh. He found Constable Malone, a tall man of magnificent physique, standing in the hall, the raindrops dripping from the cape he wore.

" The sergeant is after sending me round to you, sir," said Constable Malone, " to know would it be convenient for you to attend at Ballygran any time this afternoon to certify a lunatic ? "

" Surely not another ! " said Dr. Lovaway.

" It was myself found him, sir," said the constable, with an air of pride in his achievement. " The sergeant bid me say that he'd have Patsy Doolan's car engaged for you, and that him and me would go with you so that you wouldn't have any trouble more than the trouble of going to Ballygran, which is an out-of-the-way place sure enough, and it's a terrible day."

" Is the man violent ? " asked Dr. Lovaway.

By way of reply Constable Malone gave a short account of the man's position in life.

" He's some kind of a nephew of Mrs. Finnegan," he said, " and they call him Jimmy Finnegan, though Finnegan might not be his proper name. He does be helping Finnegan himself about the farm, and they say he's middling useful. But, of course, now the harvest's gathered, Finnegan will be able to do well enough without him till the spring."

This did not seem to Dr. Lovaway a sufficient reason for incarcerating Jimmy in an asylum.

" But is he violent ? " he repeated. " Is he dangerous to himself or others ? "

" He never was the same as other boys," said the constable, " and the way of it with fellows like that is what you wouldn't know. He might be quiet enough to-day and be slaughtering all before him to-morrow. And what Mrs. Finnegan says is that she'd be glad if you'd see the poor boy to-day, because she's in dread of what he might do to-morrow night."

" To-morrow night ! Why to-morrow night ? "

" There's a change in the moon to-morrow," said the constable, " and they do say that the moon has terrible power over fellows that's took that way."

Dr. Lovaway, who was young and trained in scientific methods, was at first inclined to argue with Constable Malone about the effect of the moon on the human mind. He refrained, reflecting that it is an impious thing to destroy an innocent superstition. One of the great beauties of Celtic Ireland is that it still clings to faiths forsaken by the rest of the world.

At two o'clock that afternoon Dr. Lovaway took his seat on Patsy Doolan's car. It was still raining heavily. Dr. Lovaway wore an overcoat of his own, a garment which had offered excellent protection against rainy days in Manchester. In Dunailin, for a drive to Ballygran, the coat was plainly insufficient. Mr. Flanagan hurried from his shop with a large oilskin cape taken from a peg in his men's outfitting department. Constable Malone, under orders from the sergeant, went to the priest's house and borrowed a waterproof rug. Johnny Conerney the butcher appeared at the last moment with a sou'wester which he put on the doctor's head and tied under his chin. It would not be the fault of the people of Dunailin if Lovaway, with his weak lungs, " died on them."

Patsy Doolan did not contribute anything to the doctor's outfit, but displayed a care for his safety.

" Take a good grip now, doctor," he said. " Take a hold of the little rail there beside you. The mare might be a bit wild on account of the rain, and her only clipped yesterday, and the road to Ballygran is jolty in parts."

Sergeant Rahilly and Constable Malone sat on one side of the car, Dr. Lovaway was on the other. Patsy Doolan sat on the driver's seat. Even with that weight behind her the mare proved herself to be " a bit wild." She went through the village in a series of bounds, shied at everything she saw in the road, and did not settle down until the car turned into a rough track which led up through the mountains to Ballygran. Dr. Lovaway held on tight with both hands. Patsy Doolan, looking back over his left shoulder, spoke words of encouragement.

" It'll be a bit strange to you at first, so it will," he said. " But by the time you're six months in Dunailin we'll have you taught to sit a car, the same as it might be an arm-chair you were on."

Dr. Lovaway, clinging on for his life while the car bumped over the boulders, did not believe that a car would ever become to him as an arm-chair.

Ballygran is a remote place, very difficult of access. At the bottom of the steep hill, a stream, which seemed a raging torrent to Dr. Lovaway, flowed across the road. The mare objected very strongly to wading through it. Farther on the track along which they drove became precipitous and more stony than ever. Another stream, scorning its properly appointed course, flowed down the road, rolling large stones with it. Patsy Doolan was obliged to get down and lead the mare. After persuading her to advance twenty yards or so he called for the help of the police.

Sergeant Rahilly took the other side of the mare's head. Constable Malone pushed at the back of the car. Dr. Lovaway, uncomfortable and rather nervous, wanted to get down and wade too. But the sergeant would not hear of this.

"Let you sit still," he said. "The water's over the tops of my boots, so it is, and where's the use of you getting a wetting that might be the death of you ? "

"Is it much farther ? " asked Lovaway.

The sergeant considered the matter.

"It might be a mile and a bit," he said, "from where we are this minute."

The mile was certainly an Irish mile, and Dr. Lovaway began to think that there were some things in England, miles for instance, which are better managed than they are in Ireland. "The bit" which followed the mile belonged to a system of measurement even more generous than Irish miles and acres.

"I suppose now," said the sergeant, "that the country you come from is a lot different from this."

He had taken up his seat again on the car after leading the mare up the river. He spoke in a cheery, conversational tone. Dr. Lovaway thought of Manchester and the surrounding district, thought of trams, trains, and paved streets.

"It is different," he said, "very different indeed."

Ballygran appeared at last, dimly visible through the driving rain. It was a miserable-looking hovel, roofed with sodden thatch, surrounded by a sea of mud. A bare-footed woman stood in the doorway. She wore a tattered skirt and a bodice fastened across her breast with a brass safety-pin. Behind her stood a tall man in a soiled flannel jacket and a pair of trousers which hung in a ragged fringe round his ankles.

"Come in," said Mrs. Finnegan, "come in the whole of yez. It's a terrible day, Sergeant, and I wonder at you bringing the doctor out in the weather that does be it in. Michael "—she turned to her husband who stood behind her—"let Patsy Doolan be putting the mare into the shed, and let you be helping him. Come in now, Doctor, and take an air of the fire. I'll wet a cup of tea for you, so I will."

Dr. Lovaway passed through a low door into the cottage. His eyes gradually became accustomed to the gloom inside and to the turf smoke which filled the room. In a corner, seated on a low stool, he saw a young man crouching over the fire.

"That's him," said Mrs. Finnegan. "That's the poor boy, Doctor. The sergeant will have been telling you about him."

The boy rose from his stool at the sound of her voice.

"Speak to the gentleman now," said Mrs. Finnegan. "Speak to the doctor, Jimmy alannah, and tell him the way you are."

"Your honour's welcome," said Jimmy, in a thin, cracked voice. "Your honour's welcome surely, though I don't mind that ever I set eyes on you before."

"Whisht now, Jimmy," said the sergeant. "It's the doctor that's come to see you, and it's for your own good he's come."

"I know that," said Jimmy, "and I know he'll be wanting to have me put away. Well, what must be, must be, if it's the will of God, and if it's before me it may as well be now as any other time."

"You see the way he is," said the sergeant. "And I have the papers here ready to be signed."

Dr. Lovaway saw, or believed he saw, exactly how things were. The boy was evidently of weak mind. There was little sign of actual lunacy, no sign at all of violence about him. Mrs. Finnegan added a voluble description of the case.

"It might be a whole day," she said, "and he wouldn't be speaking a word, nor he wouldn't seem to hear if you speak to him, and he'd just sit there by the fire the way you seen him without he'd be doing little turns about the place, feeding the pig, or mending a gap in the wall or the like. I will say for Jimmy, the poor boy's always willing to do the best he can."

"Don't be troubling the doctor now, Mrs. Finnegan," said the sergeant. "He knows the way it is with the boy without your telling him. Just let the doctor sign what has to be signed and get done with it. Aren't we wet enough as it is without standing here talking half the day?"

The mention of the wet condition of the party roused Mrs. Finnegan to action. She hung a kettle from a blackened hook in the chimney and piled up turf on the fire. Jimmy was evidently quite intelligent enough to know how to boil water. He took the bellows, went down on his knees, and blew the fire diligently. Mrs. Finnegan spread a somewhat dirty tablecloth on a still dirtier table and laid our cups and saucers on it.

Dr. Lovaway was puzzled. The boy at the fire might be, probably was, mentally deficient. He was not a case for an asylum. He was certainly not likely to become violent or to do any harm either to himself or any one else. It was not clear why Mrs. Finnegan, who seemed a kindly woman, should wish to have him shut up. It was very difficult to imagine any reason for the action of the police in the matter. Constable Malone had discovered the existence of the boy in this remote place. Sergeant

Rahilly had taken a great deal of trouble in preparing papers for his committal to the asylum, and had driven out to Ballygran on a most inclement day. Dr. Lovaway wished he understood what was happening.

Finnegan, having left Patsy Doolan's mare, and apparently Patsy Doolan himself in the shed, came into the house.

Dr. Lovaway appealed to him.

"It doesn't seem to me," he said, "that this boy ought to be sent to an asylum. I shall be glad to hear anything you have to tell me about him."

"Well now," said Mr. Finnegan, "he's a good, quiet kind of a boy, and if he hasn't too much sense there's many another has less."

"That's what I think," said Dr. Lovaway.

Jimmy stopped blowing the fire and looked round suddenly.

"Sure, I know well you're wanting to put me away," he said.

"It's for your own good," said the sergeant.

"It'll do him no harm anyway," said Finnegan, "if so be he's not kept there."

"Kept !" said the sergeant. "Is it likely now that they'd keep a boy like Jimmy ? He'll be out again as soon as ever he's in. I'd say now a fortnight is the longest he'll be there."

"I wouldn't like," said Finnegan, "that he'd be kept too long. I'll be wanting him for spring work, but I'm willing to spare him from this till Christmas if you like."

Dr. Lovaway, though a young man and constitutionally timid, was capable of occasional firmness.

"I'm certainly not going to certify that boy as a lunatic," he said.

"Come now, Doctor," said the sergeant persuasively, "after coming so far and the wet day and all. What have you to do only to put your name at the bottom of a piece of paper ? And Jimmy's willing to go. Aren't you, Jimmy ? "

"I'll go if I'm wanted to go," said Jimmy.

The water boiled. Mrs. Finnegan was spreading butter on long slices cut from a home-baked loaf. It was Jimmy who took the kettle from the hook and filled the teapot.

"Mrs. Finnegan," said Dr. Lovaway, "why do you want the boy put into an asylum ? "

"Is it me wanting him put away ? " she said. "I want no such thing. The notion never entered my head, nor Michael's either, who's been like a father to the boy. Only when Constable Malone came to me, and when it was a matter of pleasing him and the sergeant, I didn't want to be disobliging, for the sergeant is always a good friend of mine, and Constable Malone is a young man I've a liking for. But as for wanting to get rid of Jimmy ! Why would I ? Nobody'd grudge the bit the creature would eat, and there's many a little turn he'd be doing for me about the house."

Mr. Finnegan was hovering in the background, half hidden in the smoke which filled the house. He felt that he ought to support his wife.

"What I said to the sergeant," he said, "no longer ago than last Friday when I happened to be in town about a case I had on in the Petty Sessions' Court—what I said to the sergeant was this : ' So long as the boy isn't kept there too long, and so long as he's willing to go——' "

Jimmy, seated again on his low stool before the fire, looked up.

"Amn't I ready to go wherever I'm wanted ? " he said.

"There you are now, Doctor," said the sergeant. "You'll not refuse the poor boy when he wants to go ? "

"Sergeant," said Dr. Lovaway, " I can't, I really can't certify that boy as a lunatic. I don't understand why you ask me to. It seems to me——"

Poor Lovaway was much agitated. It seemed to him that he had been drawn into an infamous conspiracy against the liberty of a particularly helpless human being.

"I don't think you ought to have asked me to come here," he said. "I don't think you should have suggested—— It seems to me, Sergeant, that your conduct has been most reprehensible. I'm inclined to think I ought to report the matter to—to——" Dr. Lovaway was not quite sure about the proper place to which to send a report about the conduct of a sergeant of the Irish Police. "To the proper authorities," he concluded feebly.

"There, there," said the sergeant soothingly, "we'll say no more about the matter. I wouldn't like you to be vexed, Doctor."

But Dr. Lovaway, having once begun to speak his mind, was not inclined to stop.

"This isn't the first time this sort of thing has happened," he said. "You've asked me to certify lunacy in some very doubtful cases. I don't understand your motives, but——"

"Well, well," said the sergeant, " there's no harm done anyway."

Mrs. Finnegan, like all good women, was anxious to keep the peace among the men under her roof.

"Is the tea to your liking, Doctor," she said, "or will I give you a taste more sugar in it ? I'm a great one for sugar myself, but they tell me there's them that drinks tea with ne'er a grain of sugar in it at all. They must be queer people that do that."

She held a spoon, heaped up with sugar, over the doctor's cup as she spoke. He was obliged to stop lecturing the sergeant in order to convince her that his tea was already quite sweet enough. It was, indeed, far too sweet for his taste, for he was one of those queer people whose tastes Mrs. Finnegan could not understand.

The drive home ought to have been in every way pleasanter than the drive out to Ballygran. Patsy Doolan's mare was subdued in temper ; so docile, indeed, that she allowed Jimmy to put her between the shafts. She made no attempt to stand on her hind legs, and did not shy even at a young pig which bolted across the road in front of her. Dr. Lovaway could sit on his side of the car without holding on. The rain had ceased, and great wisps of mist were sweeping clear of the hilltops, leaving fine views of grey rock and heather-clad slopes. But Dr. Lovaway did not enjoy himself. Being an Englishman he had a strong sense of duty, and was afflicted as no Irishman ever is by a civic conscience. He felt that he ought to bring home somehow to Sergeant Rahilly a sense of the iniquity of trying to shut up sane, or almost sane, people in lunatic asylums. Being of a gentle and friendly nature, he hated making himself unpleasant to any one, especially to a man like Sergeant Rahilly, who had been very kind to him.

The path of duty was not made any easier to him by the behaviour of the sergeant. Instead of being overwhelmed by a sense of discovered guilt, the police, both Rahilly and Constable Malone, were pleasantly chatty, and evidently bent on making the drive home as agreeable as possible for the doctor. They told him the names of the hills and the more distant mountains. They showed the exact bank at the side of the road from behind which certain murderous men had fired at a land agent in 1885. They explained the route of a light railway which a forgotten Chief Secretary had planned but had never built owing to change of Government and his loss of office. Not one word was said about Jimmy, or lunatics, or asylums. It was with great difficulty that Dr. Lovaway succeeded at last in breaking in on the smooth flow of chatty reminiscences. But when he did speak he spoke strongly. As with most gentle and timid men, his language was almost violent when he had screwed himself up to the point of speaking at all.

The two policemen listened to all he said with the utmost good humour. Indeed, the sergeant supported him.

" You hear what the doctor's saying to you, Constable Malone," he said.

" I do, surely," said the constable.

" Well, I hope you'll attend to it," said the sergeant, " and let there be no more of the sort of work that the doctor's complaining of."

" But I mean you too, Sergeant," said Dr. Lovaway. " You're just as much to blame as the constable. Indeed more, for you're his superior officer."

" I know that," said the sergeant ; " I know that well. And what's more, I'm thankful to you, Doctor, for speaking out what's in your mind. Many a one wouldn't do it. And I know that every word you've been saying is for my good and for the good of Constable Malone, who's a young man yet and might improve if handled right. That's why I'm thanking you, Doctor, for what you've said."

When Solomon said that a soft answer turneth away wrath, he understated a great truth. A soft answer, if soft enough, will deflect the stroke of the sword of justice. Dr. Lovaway, though his conscience was still uneasy, could say no more. He felt that it was totally impossible to report Sergeant Rahilly's way of dealing with lunatics to the higher authorities.

That night Sergeant Rahilly called on Mr. Flanagan, going into the house by the back door, for the hour was late. He chose porter rather than whisky, feeling perhaps that his nerves needed soothing and that a stronger stimulant might be a little too much for him. After finishing a second bottle and opening a third, he spoke.

" I'm troubled in my mind," he said, " over this new doctor. Here am I doing the best I can for him ever since he came to the town, according to what I promised Dr. Farelly."

" No man," said Flanagan, " could do more than what you've done. Every one knows that."

" I've set the police scouring the country," said the sergeant, " searching high and low and in and out for any one, man or woman, that was the least bit queer in the head. They've worked hard, so they have, and I've worked hard myself."

" No man harder," said Flanagan.

" And every one we found," said the sergeant, " was a guinea into the doctor's pocket. A guinea, mind you ; that's the fee for certifying a lunatic, and devil a penny either I or the constables get out of it."

"Nor you wouldn't be looking for it, Sergeant. I know that."

"I would not. And I'm not complaining of getting nothing. But it's damned hard when the doctor won't take what's offered to him, when we've had to work early and late to get it for him. Would you believe it now, Mr. Flanagan, he's refused to certify half of the ones we've found for him?"

"Do you tell me that?" said Flanagan.

"Throwing good money away," said the sergeant ; "and to-day, when I took him to see that boy that does be living in Finnegan's, which would have been two guineas into his pocket, on account of being outside his own district, instead of saying 'Thank you' like any ordinary man would, nothing would do him only to be cursing and swearing. 'It's a crime,' says he, 'and a scandal,' says he, 'and it's swearing away the liberty of a poor man,' says he ; and more to that. Now I ask you, Mr. Flanagan, where's the crime and where's the scandal?"

"There's none," said Flanagan. "What harm would it have done the lad to be put away for a bit?"

"That's what I said to the doctor. What more, they'd have let the boy out in a fortnight, as soon as they knew what way it was with him. I told the doctor that, but 'crime,' says he, and 'scandal,' says he, and 'conspiracy,' says he. Be damn, but to hear him talk you'd think I was trying to take two guineas out of his pocket, instead of trying to put it in, and there's the thanks I get for going out of my way to do the best I could for him so as he'd rest content in this place and let Dr. Farelly stay where he is to be cutting the legs off the Germans."

"It's hard, so it is," said Flanagan, "and I'm sorry for you, Sergeant. But that's the way things is. As I was saying to you once before and maybe oftener, the English is queer people, and the more you'd be trying to please them, the less they like it. It's not easy to deal with them, and that's a fact."

ERNEST BRAMAH *is best known for the books about Max Carrados, the blind detective, and his other stories centring round that subtle, amusing Chinaman, Kai Lung. It is from a collection of the latter anecdotes, entitled " The Wallet of Kai-Lung, that the tale below is taken. These are written in imitation of the Oriental manner, but the reader will perceive that the humour and characterization are essentially Western.*

THE PROBATION OF SEN HENG

RELATED BY KAI LUNG, AT WU-WHEI, AS A REBUKE TO WANG YU AND CERTAIN OTHERS WHO HAD QUESTIONED THE PRACTICAL VALUE OF HIS STORIES

" IT is an undoubted fact that this person has not realized the direct remunerative advantage which he confidently anticipated," remarked the idle and discontented pipe-maker, Wang Yu, as, with a few other persons of similar inclination, he sat in the shade of the great mulberry-tree at Wu-whei, waiting for the evil influence of certain very mysterious sounds, which had lately been heard, to pass away before he resumed his occupation. " When the seemingly proficient and trustworthy Kai Lung first made it his practice to journey to Wu-whei and narrate to us the doings of persons of all classes of life," he continued, " it seemed to this one that by closely following the recital of how mandarins obtained their high position, and exceptionally rich persons their wealth, he must, in the end, inevitably be rendered competent to follow in their illustrious footsteps. Yet in how entirely contrary a direction has the whole course of events tended ! In spite of the honourable intention which involved a frequent absence from his place of commerce, those who journeyed thither with the set purpose of possessing one of his justly famed opium pipes so perversely regarded the matter that, after two or three fruitless visits, they deliberately turned their footsteps towards the workshop of the inelegant Ming-yo, whose pipes are confessedly greatly inferior to those produced by the person who is now speaking. Nevertheless, the rapacious Kai Lung, to whose influence the falling off in custom was thus directly attributable, persistently declined to bear any share whatever in the loss which his profession

caused, and, indeed, regarded the circumstances from so grasping
and narrow-minded a point of observation that he would not
even go to the length of suffering this much-persecuted one to
join the circle of his hearers without on every occasion making
the customary offering.   In this manner a well-intentioned
pursuit of riches has insidiously led this person within measurable
distance of the bolted dungeon for those who do not meet their
just debts, while the only distinction likely to result from his
assiduous study of the customs and methods of those high in
power is that of being publicly bow-strung as a warning to
others.   Manifestly the pointed finger of the unreliable Kai Lung
is a very treacherous guide."

"It is related," said a dispassionate voice behind them,
"that a person of limited intelligence, on being assured that he
would certainly one day enjoy an adequate competence if he
closely followed the industrious habits of the thrifty bee, spent
the greater part of his life in anointing his thighs with the yellow
powder which he laboriously collected from the flowers of the
field.   It is not so recorded ; but doubtless the nameless one in
question was by profession a maker of opium pipes, for this
person has observed from time to time how that occupation,
above all others, tends to degrade the mental faculties, and to
debase its followers to a lower position than that of the beasts
of labour.   Learn therefrom, O superficial Wang Yu, that wisdom
lies in an intelligent perception of great principles, and not in
a slavish imitation of details which are, for the most part,
beyond your simple and insufficient understanding."

"Such may, indeed, be the case, Kai Lung," replied Wang
Yu sullenly—for it was the story-teller in question who had
approached unperceived, and who now stood before them—
"but it is none the less a fact that, on the last occasion when
this misguided person joined the attending circle at your up-
lifted voice, a mandarin of the third degree chanced to pass
through Wu-whei, and halted at the doorstep of ' The Fountain
of Beauty,' fully intending to entrust this one with the designing
and fashioning of a pipe of exceptional elaborateness.   This
matter, by his absence, has now passed from him, and to-day,
through listening to the narrative of how the accomplished
Yuiu-Pel doubled his fortune, he is the poorer by many
taels."

"Yet to-morrow, when the name of the Mandarin of the
third degree appears in the list of persons who have transferred
their entire property to those who are nearly related to them
in order to avoid it being seized to satisfy the just claims made

against them," replied Kai Lung, " you will be able to regard yourself the richer by so many taels."

At these words, which recalled to the minds of all who were present the not uncommon manner of behaving observed by those of exalted rank, who freely engaged persons to supply them with costly articles without in any way regarding the price to be paid, Wang Yu was silent.

" Nevertheless," exclaimed a thin voice from the edge of the group which surrounded Kai Lung, " it in nowise follows that the stories are in themselves excellent, or of such a nature that the hearing of their recital will profit a person. Wang Yu may be satisfied with empty words, but there are others present who were studying deep matters when Wang Yu was learning the art of walking. If Kai Lung's stories are of such remunerative benefit as the person in question claims, how does it chance that Kai Lung himself, who is assuredly the best acquainted with them, stands before us in mean apparel, and on all occasions confessing an unassumed poverty ? "

" It is Yan-hi Pung," went from mouth to mouth among the bystanders—" Yan-hi Pung, who traces on paper the words of chants and historical tales, and sells them to such as can afford to buy. And although his motive in exposing the emptiness of Kai Lung's stories may not be Heaven-sent—inasmuch as Kai Lung provides us with such matter as he himself purveys, only at a much more moderate price—yet his words are well considered, and must, therefore, be regarded."

" O Yan-hi Pung," replied Kai Lung, hearing the name from those who stood about him, and moving towards the aged person, who stood meanwhile leaning upon his staff, and looking from side to side with quickly moving eyelids in a manner very offensive towards the story-teller, " your just remark shows you to be a person of exceptional wisdom, even as your well-bowed legs prove you to be one of great bodily strength ; for justice is ever obvious and wisdom hidden, and they who build structures for endurance discard the straight and upright and insist upon such an arch as you so symmetrically exemplify."

Speaking in his conciliatory manner, Kai Lung came up to Yan-hi Pung, and taking between his fingers a disc of thick polished crystal, which the aged and short-sighted chant-writer used for the purpose of magnifying and bringing nearer the letters upon which he was engaged, and which hung around his neck by an embroidered cord, the story-teller held it aloft, crying aloud :

" Observe closely, and presently it will be revealed and made

clear how the apparently very conflicting words of the wise
Yan-hi Pung, and those of this unassuming but nevertheless
conscientious person who is now addressing you, are, in reality,
as one great truth."

With this assurance Kai Lung moved the crystal somewhat,
so that it engaged the sun's rays, and concentrated them upon
the uncovered crown of the unsuspecting and still objectionably
engaged person before him. Without a moment's pause, Yan-hi
Pung leapt high into the air, repeatedly pressing his hand to
the spot thus selected, and crying aloud :

"Evil dragons and thunderbolts ! but the touch was as hot
as a scar left by the uncut nail of the sublime Buddha ! "

"Yet the crystal——" remarked Kai Lung composedly,
passing it into the hands of those who stood near.

"Is as cool as the innermost leaves of the riverside syca-
more," they declared.

Kai Lung said nothing further, but raised both his hands
above his head, as if demanding their judgment. Thereupon
a loud shout went up on his behalf, for the greater part of them
loved to see the manner in which he brushed aside those who
would oppose him ; and the sight of the aged person Yan-hi
Pung leaping far into the air had caused them to become exceptionally amused, and, in consequence, very amiably disposed
towards the one who had afforded them the entertainment.

"The story of Sen Heng," began Kai Lung, when the discussion had terminated in the manner already recorded, " concerns itself with one who possessed an unsuspecting and ingenuous nature, which ill-fitted him to take an ordinary part
in the everyday affairs of life, no matter how engaging such a
character rendered him among his friends and relations. Having
at an early age been entrusted with a burden of rice and other
produce from his father's fields to dispose of in the best possible
manner at a neighbouring mart, and having completed the
transaction in a manner extremely advantageous to those with
whom he trafficked, but very intolerable to the one who had
sent him, it at once became apparent that some other means
of gaining a livelihood must be discovered for him.

"'Beyond all doubt,' said his father, after considering the
matter for a period, ' it is a case in which one should be governed
by the wise advice and example of the Mandarin Poo-chow.'

"'Illustrious sire,' exclaimed Sen Heng, who chanced to
be present, ' the illiterate person who stands before you is entirely unacquainted with the one to whom you have referred ;
nevertheless, he will, as you suggest, at once set forth, and

journeying with all speed to the abode of the estimable Poo-chow, solicit his experience and advice.'

" ' Unless a more serious loss should be occasioned,' replied the father coldly, ' there is no necessity to adopt so extreme a course. The benevolent Mandarin in question existed at a remote period of the Thang dynasty, and the incident to which an illusion has been made arose in the following way : To the public court of the enlightened Poo-chow there came one day a youth of very inferior appearance and hesitating manner, who besought his explicit advice, saying : " The degraded and un-prepossessing being before you, O select and venerable Mandarin, is by nature and attainments a person of the utmost timidity and fearfulness. From this cause life itself has become a detestable observance in his eyes, for those who should be his companions of both sexes hold him in undisguised contempt, making various unendurable allusions to the colour and nature of his internal organs whenever he would endeavour to join them. Instruct him, therefore, the manner in which this cowardice may be removed, and no service in return will be esteemed too great." " There is a remedy," replied the benevolent Mandarin, without any hesitation whatever, " which if properly carried out is efficacious beyond the possibility of failure. Certain component parts of your body are lacking, and before the desired result can be obtained these must be supplied from without. Of all courageous things the tiger is the most fearless, and in consequence it combines all those ingredients which you require ; furthermore, as the teeth of the tiger are the instruments with which it accomplishes its vengeful purpose, there reside the essential principles of its inimitable courage. Let the person who seeks instruction in the matter, therefore, do as follows : Taking the teeth of a full-grown tiger as soon as it is slain, and before the essences have time to return into the body, he shall grind them to a powder, and, mixing the powder with a portion of rice, consume it. After seven days he must repeat the observance, and yet again a third time, after another similar lapse. Let him, then, return for further guidance ; for the present the matter interests this person no further."

" ' At these words the youth departed, filled with a new and inspired hope ; for the wisdom of the sagacious Poo-chow was a matter which did not admit of any doubt whatever, and he had spoken with well-defined certainty of the success of the experiment. Nevertheless, after several days industriously spent in endeavouring to obtain by purchase the teeth of a newly-slain tiger, the details of the undertaking began to assume a new and entirely unforeseen aspect; for those whom he approached as being the most likely to possess what he required either became very immoderately and disagreeably amused at the nature of the request, or regarded it as a new and ill-judged form of ridicule, which they prepared to avenge by blows and by base remarks of the most personal variety. At length it became unavoidably obvious to the youth that if he was to obtain the articles in question it would first be necessary that he should become adept in the art of slaying tigers, for in no other way were the required conditions likely to be present. Although the prospect was one which did not greatly tend to allure him, yet he did not regard it with the utterly incapable emotions which would have been present on an earlier occasion ; for the habit of continually guarding himself from the onslaughts of those who received his inquiry in an attitude of narrow-minded distrust had inspired him with a new-found valour, while his amiable and unrestrained manner of life increased his bodily vigour in every degree. First perfecting himself in the use of the bow and arrow, therefore, he betook himself to a wild and very extensive forest, and there concealed himself among the upper foliage of a tall tree standing by the side of a pool of water.

" ' On the second night of his watch the youth perceived a large but somewhat ill-conditioned tiger approaching the pool for the purpose of quenching its thirst, whereupon he tremblingly fitted an arrow to his bow-string, and, profiting by the instruction he had received, succeeded in piercing the creature to the heart. After fulfilling the observance laid upon him by the discriminating Poo-chow, the youth determined to remain in the forest, and sustain himself upon such food as fell to his weapons, until the time arrived when he should carry out the rite for the last time. At the end of seven days, so subtle had he become in all kinds of hunting, and so strengthened by the meat and herbs upon which he existed, that he disdained to avail himself of the shelter of the tree, but standing openly by the side of the water, he engaged the attention of the first tiger which came to drink, and discharged arrow after arrow into its body with unfailing power and precision. So entrancing, indeed, had the pursuit become that the next seven days lengthened out into the apparent period of as many moons, in such a leisurely manner did they rise and fall.

" ' On the appointed day, without waiting for the evening to arrive, the youth set out with the first appearance of light, and penetrated into the most inaccessible jungles, crying aloud words of taunt-laden challenge to all the beasts therein, and accusing the ancestors of their race of every imaginable variety of evil behaviour. Yet so great had become the renown of the one who stood forth, and so widely had the warning voice been passed from tree to tree, preparing all who dwelt in the forest against his anger, that not even the fiercest replied openly, though low growls and mutterings proceeded from every cave within a bowshot's distance around. Wearying quickly of such feeble and timorous demonstrations, the youth rushed into the cave from which the loudest murmurs proceeded, and there discovered a tiger of unnatural size, surrounded by the bones of innumerable ones whom it had devoured ; for from time to time its ravages became so great and unbearable that armies were raised in the neighbouring villages and sent to destroy it, but more than a few stragglers never returned. Plainly recognizing that a just and inevitable vengeance had overtaken it, the tiger made only a very inferior exhibition of resistance, and the youth, having first stunned it with a blow of his closed hand, seized it by the middle, and repeatedly dashed its head against the rocky sides of its retreat. He then performed for the third time the ceremony enjoined by the Mandarin, and having cast upon the cringing and despicable forms concealed in the surrounding woods and caves a look of dignified and ineffable contempt, set out upon his homeward journey, and in the space of three days' time reached the town of the versatile Poo-chow.'

" "" Behold," exclaimed that person when, lifting up his eyes, he saw the youth approaching laden with the skins of the tigers and other spoils, " now at least the youths and maidens of your native village will no longer withdraw themselves from the company of so undoubtedly heroic a person." " Illustrious Mandarin," replied the other, casting both his weapons and his trophies before his inspired adviser's feet, " what has this person to do with the little ones of either sex ? Give him rather the foremost place in your ever-victorious company of bowmen, so that he may repay in part the undoubted debt under which he henceforth exists." This proposal found favour with the pure-minded Poo-chow, so that in course of time the unassuming youth who had come supplicating his advice became the valiant commander of his army, and the one eventually chosen to present plighting gifts to his only daughter.'

" When the father had completed the narrative of how the faint-hearted youth became in the end a courageous and resourceful leader of bowmen, Sen looked up, and not in any degree understanding the purpose of the story, or why it had been set forth before him, exclaimed :

" ' Undoubtedly the counsel of the graceful and intelligent Mandarin Poo-chow was of inestimable service in the case recorded, and this person would gladly adopt it as his guide for the future, on the chance of it leading to a similar honourable career ; but alas ! there are no tigers to be found throughout this Province.'

" ' It is a loss which those who are engaged in commerce in the city of Hankow strive to supply adequately,' replied his father, who had an assured feeling that it would be of no avail to endeavour to show Sen that the story which he had just related was one setting forth a definite precept rather than fixing an exact manner of behaviour. ' For that reason,' he continued, ' this person has concluded an arrangement by which you will journey to that place, and there enter into the house of commerce of an expert and conscientious vendor of moving contrivances. Among so rapacious and keen-witted a class of persons as they of Hankow, it is exceedingly unlikely that your amiable disposition will involve any individual one in an unavoidable serious loss, and even should such an unforeseen event come to pass, there will, at least, be the undeniable satisfaction of the thought that the unfortunate occurrence will in no way affect the prosperity of those to whom you are bound by the natural ties of affection.'

" ' Benevolent and virtuous-minded father,' replied Sen gently, but speaking with an inspired conviction ; ' from his earliest infancy this unassuming one has been instructed in an inviolable regard for the Five General Principles of Fidelity to the Emperor, Respect for Parents, Harmony between Husband and Wife, Agreement among Brothers, and Constancy in Friendship. It will be entirely unnecessary to inform so pious-minded a person as the one now being addressed that no evil can attend the footsteps of an individual who courteously observes these enactments.'

" ' Without doubt it is so arranged by the protecting Deities,' replied the father ; ' yet it is an exceedingly desirable thing for those who are responsible in the matter that the footsteps to which reference has been made should not linger in the neighbourhood of this village, but should, with all possible speed, turn in the direction of Hankow.'

" In this manner it came to pass that Sen Heng set forth on the following day, and coming without delay to the great and powerful city of Hankow, sought out the house of commerce known as ' The Pure Gilt Dragon of Exceptional Symmetry,' where the versatile King-y-Yang engaged in the entrancing occupation of contriving moving figures, and other devices of an ingenious and mirth-provoking character, which he entrusted into the hands of numerous persons to sell throughout the Province. From this cause, although enjoying a very agreeable recompense from the sale of the objects, the greatly perturbed King-y-Yang suffered continual internal misgivings ; for the habit of behaving of those whom he appointed to go forth in the manner described was such that he could not entirely dismiss from his mind an assured conviction that the details were not invariably as they were represented to be. Frequently would one return in a very deficient and unpresentable condition of garment, asserting that on his return, while passing through a lonely and unprotected district, he had been assailed by an armed band of robbers, and despoiled of all he possessed. Another would claim to have been made the sport of evil spirits, who led him astray by means of false signs in the forest, and finally destroyed his entire burden of commodities, accompanying the unworthy act by loud cries of triumph, and remarks of an insulting nature concerning King-y-Yang ; for the honourable character and charitable actions of the person in question had made him very objectionable to that class of beings. Others continually accounted for the absence of the required number of taels by declaring that at a certain point of their journey they were made the object of marks of amiable condescension on the part of a high and dignified public official, who, on learning in whose service they were, immediately professed an intimate personal friendship with the estimable King-y-Yang, and, out of a feeling of gratified respect for him, took away all such contrivances as remained undisposed of, promising to arrange the payment with the refined King-y-Yang himself when they should next meet. For these reasons King-y-Yang was especially desirous of obtaining one whose spoken word could be received, upon all points, as an assured fact, and it was, therefore, with an emotion of internal lightness that he confidently heard from those who were acquainted with the person that Sen Heng was, by nature and endowments, utterly incapable of representing matters of even the most insignificant degree to be otherwise than what they really were.

" Filled with an acute anxiety to discover what amount of success would be accorded to his latest contrivance, King-y-Yang led Sen Heng to a secluded chamber, and there instructed him in the method of selling certain apparently very ingeniously constructed ducks, which would have the appearance of swimming about on the surface of an open vessel of water, at the same time uttering loud and ever-increasing cries, after the manner of their kind. With ill-restrained admiration at the skilful nature of the deception, King-y-Yang pointed out that the ducks which were to be disposed of, and upon which a seemingly very low price was fixed, did not, in reality, possess any of these accomplishments, but would, on the contrary, if placed in water, at once sink to the bottom in a most incapable manner ; it being part of Sen's duty to exhibit only a specially prepared creature which was restrained upon the surface by means of hidden cords, and, while bending over it, to simulate the cries as agreed upon. After satisfying himself that Sen could perform these movements competently, King-y-Yang sent him forth, particularly charging him that he should not return without a sum of money which fully represented the entire number of ducks entrusted to him, or an adequate number of unsold ducks to compensate for the deficiency.

" At the end of seven days Sen returned to King-y-Yang, and although entirely without money, even to the extent of being unable to provide himself with the merest necessities of a frugal existence, he honourably returned the full number of ducks with which he had set out. It then became evident that although Sen had diligently perfected himself in the sounds and movements which King-y-Yang had contrived, he had not fully understood that they were to be executed stealthily, but had, in consequence, manifested the accomplishment openly, not unreasonably supposing that such an exhibition would be an additional inducement to those who appeared to be well-disposed towards the purchase. From this cause it came about that although large crowds were attracted by Sen's manner of conducting the enterprise, none actually engaged to purchase even the least expensively valued of the ducks, although several publicly complimented Sen on his exceptional proficiency, and repeatedly urged him to louder and more frequent cries, suggesting that by such means possible buyers might be attracted to the spot from remote and inaccessible villages in the neighbourhood.

" When King-y-Yang learned how the venture had been carried out, he became most intolerably self-opinionated in his expressions towards Sen's mental attainments and the manner of his bringing up. It was entirely in vain that the one referred to pointed out in a tone of persuasive and courteous restraint that he had not, down to the most minute particulars, transgressed either the general or the specific obligations of the Five General Principles, and that, therefore, he was blameless, and

even worthy of commendation for the manner in which he had
acted. With an inelegant absence of all refined feeling, King-y-
Yang most incapably declined to discuss the various aspects of
the controversy in an amiable manner, asserting, indeed, that
for the consideration of as many brass cash as Sen had mentioned
principles he would cause him to be thrown into prison as a
person of unnatural ineptitude. Then, without rewarding Sen
for the time spent in his service, or even inviting him to partake
of food and wine, the insufferable deviser of very indifferent
animated contrivances again sent him out, this time into the
streets of Hankow with a number of delicately inlaid boxes,
remarking in a tone of voice which plainly indicated an exactly
contrary desire that he would be filled with an overwhelming
satisfaction if Sen could discover any excuse for returning a
second time without disposing of anything. This remark Sen's
ingenuous nature led him to regard as a definite fact, so that
when a passer-by, who tarried to examine the boxes, chanced
to remark that the colours might have been arranged to greater
advantage, in which case he would certainly have purchased
at least one of the articles, Sen hastened back, although in a
distant part of the city, to inform King-y-Yang of the suggestion,
adding that he himself had been favourably impressed with the
improvement which would be effected by such an alteration.

" The nature of King-y-Yang's emotion when Sen again
presented himself before him—and when by repeatedly applied
tests on various parts of his body he understood that he was
neither the victim of malicious demons, nor wandering in an
insensible condition in the Middle Air, but that the cause of
the return was such as had been plainly stated—was of so mixed
and benumbing a variety that for a considerable space of time
he was quite unable to express himself in any way, either by
words or by signs. By the time these attributes returned there
had formed itself within King-y-Yang's mind a design of most
contemptible malignity, which seemed to present to his enfeebled
intellect a scheme by which Sen would be adequately punished,
and finally disposed of without causing him any further trouble
in the matter. For this purpose he concealed the real condition
of his sentiments towards Sen, and warmly expressed himself in
terms of delicate flattery regarding that one's sumptuous and
unfailing taste in the matter of the blending of the colours.
Without doubt, he continued, such an alteration as the one
proposed would greatly increase the attractiveness of the inlaid
boxes, and the matter should be engaged upon without delay.
In the meantime, however, not to waste the immediate services

of so discriminating and persevering a servant, he would entrust
Sen with a mission of exceptional importance, which would
certainly tend greatly to his remunerative benefit.   In the
district of Yun, in the north-western part of the Province, said
the crafty and treacherous King-y-Yang, a particular kind of
insect was greatly esteemed on account of the beneficent influence
which it exercised over the rice plants, causing them to mature
earlier, and to attain a greater size than ever happened in its
absence.   In recent years this creature had rarely been seen in
the neighbourhood of Yun, and, in consequence, the earth-
tillers throughout that country had been brought into a most
disconcerting state of poverty, and would, inevitably, be prepared to exchange whatever they still possessed for even a few
of the insects, in order that they might liberate them to increase,
and so entirely reverse the objectionable state of things.   Speaking
in this manner, King-y-Yang entrusted to Sen a carefully prepared box containing a score of the insects, obtained at a great
cost from a country beyond the Bitter Water, and after giving
him further directions concerning the journey, and enjoining the
utmost secrecy about the valuable contents of the box, he sent
him forth.

"The discreet and sagacious will already have understood
the nature of King-y-Yang's intolerable artifice,; but, for the
benefit of the amiable and unsuspecting, it is necessary to make
it clear that the words which he had spoken bore no sort of
resemblance to affairs as they really existed.   The district around
Yun was indeed involved in a most unprepossessing destitution,
but this had been caused, not by the absence of any rare and
auspicious insect, but by the presence of vast hordes of locusts,
which had overwhelmed and devoured the entire face of the
country.   It so chanced that among the recently constructed
devices at ' The Pure Gilt Dragon of Exceptional Symmetry '
were a number of elegant representations of rice fields and fruit
gardens so skilfully fashioned that they deceived even the
creatures, and attracted, among other living things, all the
locusts in Hankow into that place of commerce.   It was a number
of these insects that King-y-Yang vindictively placed in the
box which he instructed Sen to carry to Yun, well knowing that
the reception which would be accorded to anyone who appeared
there on such a mission would be of so fatally destructive a kind
that the consideration of his return need not engage a single
conjecture.

"Entirely tranquil in intellect—for the possibility of King-
y-Yang's intention being in any way other than what he had

represented it to be did not arise within Sen's ingenuous mind—
the person in question cheerfully set forth on his long but unavoidable march towards the region of Yun. As he journeyed
along the way, the nature of his meditation brought before him
the events which had taken place since his arrival at Hankow ;
and, for the first time, it was brought within his understanding
that the story of the youth and the three tigers, which his father
had related to him, was in the likeness to a proverb, by which
counsel and warning is conveyed in a graceful and inoffensive
manner. Readily applying the fable to his own condition, he
could not doubt but that the first two animals to be overthrown
were represented by the two undertakings which he had already
conscientiously performed in the matter of the mechanical ducks
and the inlaid boxes, and the conviction that he was even then
engaged on the third and last trial filled him with an intelligent
gladness so unobtrusive and refined that he could express his
entrancing emotions in no other way than by lifting up his voice
and uttering the far-reaching cries which he had used on the
first of the occasions just referred to.

" In this manner the first part of the journey passed away
with engaging celerity. Anxious as Sen undoubtedly was to
complete the third task, and approach the details which, in his
own case, would correspond with the command of the bowmen
and the marriage with the Mandarin's daughter of the person
in the story, the noontide heat compelled him to rest in the shade
by the wayside for a lengthy period each day. During one of
these pauses it occurred to his versatile mind that the time which
was otherwise uselessly expended might be well disposed of in
endeavouring to increase the value and condition of the creatures
under his care by instructing them in the performance of some
simple accomplishments, such as might not be too laborious for
their feeble and immature understanding. In this he was more
successful than he had imagined could possibly have been the
case, for the discriminating insects, from the first, had every
appearance of recognizing that Sen was inspired by a sincere
regard for their ultimate benefit, and was not merely using them
for his own advancement. So assiduously did they devote themselves to their allotted tasks, that in a very short space of time
there was no detail in connection with their own simple domestic
arrangements that was not understood and daily carried out by
an appointed band. Entranced at this intelligent manner of
conducting themselves, Sen industriously applied his time to the
more congenial task of instructing them in the refined arts, and
presently he had the enchanting satisfaction of witnessing a

number of the most cultivated faultlessly and unhesitatingly
perform a portion of the well-known gravity-removing play
entitled ' The Benevolent Omen of White Dragon Tea Garden ;
or, Three Times a Mandarin.' Not even content with this
elevating display, Sen ingeniously contrived, from various objects
which he discovered at different points by the wayside, an
effective and lifelike representation of a war-junk, for which he
trained a crew, who, at an agreed signal, would take up their
appointed places and go through the required movements, both
of sailing and of discharging the guns, in reliable and efficient
manner.

   " As Sen was one day educating the least competent of the
insects, in the simpler parts of banner-carriers, gong-bearers,
and the like, to their more graceful and versatile companions,
he lifted up his eyes and beheld, standing by his side, a person
of very elaborately embroidered apparel and commanding
personality, who had all the appearance of one who had been
observing his movements for some space of time. Calling up
within his remembrance the warning which he had received
from King-y-Yang, Sen was preparing to restore the creatures
to their closed box, when the stranger, in a loud and dignified
voice, commanded him to refrain, adding :

   " ' There is, resting at a spot within the immediate neighbourhood, a person of illustrious name and ancestry, who would
doubtless be gratified to witness the diverting actions of which
this one has recently been a spectator. As the reward of a tael
cannot be unwelcome to a person of your inferior appearance
and unpresentable garments, take up your box without delay,
and follow the one who is now before you.'

   " With these words the richly clad stranger led the way
through a narrow woodland path, closely followed by Sen, to
whom the attraction of the promised reward—a larger sum,
indeed, than he had ever possessed—was sufficiently alluring to
make him determined that the other should not, for the briefest
possible moment, pass beyond his sight.

   " Not to withhold that which Sen was entirely ignorant of
until a later period, it is now revealed that the person in question
was the official Provider of Diversions and Pleasurable Occupations to the sacred and illimitable Emperor, who was then
engaged in making an unusually extensive march through the
eight Provinces surrounding his Capital—for the acute and well-
educated will not need to be reminded that Nankin occupied
that position at the time now engaged with. Until his provi-
dential discovery of Sen, the distinguished Provider had been

immersed in a most unenviable condition of despair, for his enlightened but exceedingly perverse-minded master had, of late, declined to be in any way amused, or even interested, by the simple and unpretentious entertainment which could be obtained in so inaccessible a region. The well-intentioned efforts of the followers of the Court, who engagingly endeavoured to divert the Imperial mind by performing certain feats which they remembered to have witnessed on previous occasions, but which, until the necessity arose, they had never essayed, were entirely without result of a beneficial order. Even the accomplished Provider's one attainment—that of striking together both the hands and the feet thrice simultaneously while leaping into the air, and at the same time producing a sound not unlike that emitted by a large and vigorous bee when held captive in the fold of a robe, an action which never failed to throw the illustrious Emperor into a most uncontrollable state of amusement when performed within the Imperial Palace—now only drew from him the unsympathetic, if not actually offensive, remark that the attitude and the noise bore a marked resemblance to those produced by a person when being bowstrung, adding, with unprepossessing significance, that of the two entertainments he had an unevadable conviction that the bowstringing would be the more acceptable and gravity-removing.

" When Sen beheld the size and the silk-hung magnificence of the camp into which his guide led him, he was filled with astonishment, and at the same time recognized that he had acted in an injudicious and hasty manner by so readily accepting the offer of a tael ; whereas, if he had been in possession of the true facts of the case as they now appeared, he would certainly have endeavoured to obtain double that amount before consenting. As he was hesitating in a most uncongenial state of uncertainty, and debating within himself whether the matter might not even yet be arranged in a more advantageous manner, he was suddenly led forward into the most striking and ornamental of the tents, and commanded to engage the attention of the one in whose presence he found himself, without delay.

" From the first moment when the inimitable creatures began, at Sen's spoken word, to go through the ordinary details of their domestic affairs, there was no sort of doubt as to the nature of the success with which their well-trained exertions would be received. The dark shadows instantly forsook the enraptured Emperor's select brow, and from time to time he expressed himself in words of most unrestrained and intimate encouragement. So exuberant became the overjoyed Provider's

emotion at having at length succeeded in obtaining the services
of one who was able to recall his Imperial master's unclouded
countenance, that he came forward in a most unpresentable
state of haste, and rose into the air uncommanded, for the display
of his usually not unwelcome acquirement. This he would
doubtless have executed competently had not Sen, who stood
immediately behind him, suddenly and unexpectedly raised his
voice in a very vigorous and proficient duck cry, thereby causing
the one before him to endeavour to turn round in alarm while
yet in the air—an intermingled state of movements of both the
body and the mind that caused him to abandon his original
intention in a manner which removed the gravity of the Emperor
to an even more pronounced degree than had been effected by
the diverting attitudes of the insects.

"When the gratified Emperor had beheld every portion of
the tasks which Sen had instilled into the minds of the insects,
down even to the minutest detail, he called the well-satisfied
Provider before him, and, addressing him in a voice which might
be designed to betray either sternness or an amiable indulgence,
said :

" ' You, O Shan-se, are reported to be a person of no particular intellect or discernment, and, for this reason, these ones
who are speaking have a desire to know how the matter will
present itself in your eyes. Which is it the more commendable
and honourable for a person to train to a condition of unfailing
excellence, human beings of confessed intelligence or insects of
a low and degraded standard ? '

" To this remark the discriminating Shan-se made no reply,
being, indeed, undecided in his mind whether such a course
was expected of him. On several previous occasions the somewhat introspective Emperor had addressed himself to persons in
what they judged to be the form of a question, as one might say,
' How blue is the unapproachable air canopy, and how delicately
imagined the colour of the clouds ! ' yet when they had expressed
their deliberate opinion on the subjects referred to, stating the
exact degree of blueness, and the like, the nature of their reception ever afterwards was such that, for the future, persons
endeavoured to determine exactly the intention of the Emperor's
mind before declaring themselves in words. Being exceedingly
doubtful on this occasion, therefore, the very cautious Shan-se
adopted the more prudent and uncompromising attitude, and
smiling acquiescently, he raised both his hands with a self-
deprecatory movement.

" ' Alas ! ' exclaimed the Emperor, in a tone which plainly

Sen suddenly and unexpectedly raised his voice in a very vigorous and proficient duck cry

indicated that the evasive Shan-se had adopted a course which did not commend itself, ' how unendurable a condition of affairs is it for a person of acute mental perception to be annoyed by the inopportune behaviour of one who is only fit to mix on terms of equality with beggars and low-caste street cleaners——'

" ' Such a condition of affairs is indeed most offensively unbearable, illustrious Being,' remarked Shan-se, who clearly perceived that his former silence had not been productive of a delicate state of feeling towards himself.

" ' It has frequently been said,' continued the courteous and pure-minded Emperor, only signifying his refined displeasure at Shan-se's really ill-considered observation by so arranging his position that the person in question no longer enjoyed the sublime distinction of gazing upon his beneficent face, ' that titles and offices have been accorded, from time to time, without any regard for the fitting qualifications of those to whom they were presented. The truth that such a state of things does occasionally exist has been brought before our eyes during the past few days by the abandoned and inefficient behaviour of one who will henceforth be a marked official ; yet it has always been our endeavour to reward expert and unassuming merit, whenever it is discovered. As we were setting forth, when we were interrupted in a most obstinate and superfluous manner, the one who can guide and cultivate the minds of unthinking, and not infrequently obstinate and rapacious, insects would certainly enjoy an even greater measure of success if entrusted with the discriminating intellects of human beings. For this reason it appears that no more fitting person could be found to occupy the important and well-rewarded position of Chief Arranger of the Competitive Examinations than the one before us—provided his opinions and manner of expressing himself are such as commend themselves to us. To satisfy us on this point let Sen Heng now stand forth and declare his beliefs.'

" On this invitation Sen advanced the requisite number of paces, and not in any degree understanding what was required of him, determined that the occasion was one when he might fittingly declare the Five General Principles, which were ever present in his mind. ' Unquestioning Fidelity to the Sacred Emperor—' he began, when the person in question signified that the trial was over.

" ' After so competent and inspired an expression as that which has just been uttered, which, if rightly considered, includes all lesser things, it is unnecessary to say more,' he declared affably. ' The appointment which has already been specified is now declared to be legally conferred. The evening will be devoted to a repetition of the entrancing manœuvres performed by the insects, to be followed by a feast and music in honour of the recognized worth and position of the accomplished Sen Heng. There is really no necessity for the apparently over-fatigued Shan-se to attend the festival.'

" In such a manner was the foundation of Sen's ultimate prosperity established, by which he came in the process of time to occupy a very high place in public esteem. Yet, being a person of honourable-minded conscientiousness, he did not hesitate, when questioned by those who made pilgrimages to him for the purpose of learning by what means he had risen to so remunerative a position, to ascribe his success, not entirely to his own intelligent perception of persons and events, but, in part also, to a never-failing regard for the dictates of the Five General Principles, and a discriminating subservience to the inspired wisdom of the venerable Poo-chow, as conveyed to him in the story of the faint-hearted youth and the three tigers. This story Sen furthermore caused to be inscribed in letters of gold, and displayed in a prominent position in his native village, where it has since doubtless been the means of instructing and advancing countless observant ones who have not been too insufferable to be guided by the experience of those who have gone before."

G. K. CHESTERTON (1874–   ) *has found essays, criticism, novels, and short stories all successful mediums for tilting against the accepted idea. His provocative wit most often expresses itself in startling paradox, from which equally startling truths emerge. This amusing and fantastic story of a queer adventure is not without a hint to erring humanity.*

THE ECCENTRIC SECLUSION OF THE OLD LADY

THE conversation of Rupert Grant had two great elements of interest—first, the long fantasias of detective deduction in which he was engaged, and, second, his genuine romantic interest in the life of London. His brother Basil said of him : " His reasoning is particularly cold and clear, and invariably leads him wrong. But his poetry comes in abruptly and leads him right." Whether this was true of Rupert as a whole, or no, it was certainly curiously supported by one story about him which I think worth telling.

We were walking along a lonely terrace in Brompton together. The street was full of that bright blue twilight which comes about half-past eight in summer, and which seems for the moment to be not so much a coming of darkness as the turning on of a new azure illuminator, as if the earth were lit suddenly by a sapphire sun. In the cool blue the lemon tint of the lamps had already begun to flame, and as Rupert and I passed them, Rupert talking excitedly, one after another the pale sparks sprang out of the dusk. Rupert was talking excitedly because he was trying to prove to me the nine hundred and ninety-ninth of his amateur detective theories. He would go about London, with this mad logic in his brain, seeing a conspiracy in a cab accident, and a special providence in a falling fusee. His suspicions at the moment were fixed upon an unhappy milkman who walked in front of us. So arresting were the incidents which afterwards overtook us that I am really afraid that I have forgotten what were the main outlines of the milkman's crime. I think it had something to do with the fact that he had only one small can of milk to carry, and that of that he had left the lid loose and walked so quickly that he spilled milk on the pavement. This showed that he was not thinking of his small burden, and this again showed that he anticipated some other than lacteal business at the end of his walk, and this (taken in conjunction with something about muddy boots) showed something else that I have entirely forgotten. I am afraid that I derided this detailed revelation unmercifully ; and I am afraid that Rupert Grant, who, though the best of fellows, had a good deal of the sensitiveness of the artistic temperament, slightly resented my derision. He endeavoured to take a whiff of his cigar with the placidity which he associated with his profession, but the cigar, I think, was nearly bitten through.

" My dear fellow," he said acidly, " I'll bet you half a crown that wherever that milkman comes to a real stop I'll find out something curious."

" My resources are equal to that risk," I said, laughing. "˳ Done."

We walked on for about a quarter of an hour in silence in the trail of the mysterious milkman. He walked quicker and quicker, and we had some ado to keep up with him ; and every now and then he left a splash of milk, silver in the lamplight. Suddenly, almost before we could note it, he disappeared down the area steps of a house. I believe Rupert really believed that the milkman was a fairy ; for a second he seemed to accept him as having vanished. Then calling something to me which somehow took no hold on my mind, he darted after the mystic milkman, and disappeared himself into the area.

I waited for at least five minutes, leaning against a lamp-post in the lonely street. Then the milkman came swinging up the steps without his can and hurried off clattering down the road. Two or three minutes more elapsed and then Rupert came bounding up also, his face pale but yet laughing ; a not uncommon contradiction in him, denoting excitement.

" My friend," he said, rubbing his hands, " so much for all your scepticism. So much for your philistine ignorance of the possibilities of a romantic city. Two and sixpence, my boy, is the form in which your prosaic good nature will have to express itself."

" What ? " I said incredulously, " do you mean to say that you really did find anything the matter with the poor milkman ? "

His face fell.

" Oh, the milkman," he said, with a miserable affectation at having misunderstood me. " No, I—I—didn't exactly bring anything home to the milkman himself, I——"

" What did the milkman say and do ? " I said, with inexorable sternness.

" Well, to tell the truth," said Rupert, shifting restlessly from one foot to another, " the milkman himself, as far as merely physical appearances went, just said, ' Milk, Miss,' and handed in the can. That is not to say, of course, that he did not make some secret sign or some——"

I broke into a violent laugh. " You idiot," I said, " why don't you own yourself wrong and have done with it ? Why should he have made a secret sign any more than any one else ? You own he said nothing and did nothing worth mentioning. You own that, don't you ? "

His face grew grave.

" Well since you ask me, I must admit that I do. It is possible that the milkman did not betray himself. It is even possible that I was wrong about him."

" Then come along with you," I said, with a certain amicable anger, " and remember that you owe me half a crown."

" As to that, I differ from you," said Rupert coolly. " The milkman's remarks may have been quite innocent. Even the milkman may have been. But I do not owe you half a crown. For the terms of the bet were, I think, as follows, as I propounded them, that wherever that milkman came to a real stop I should find out something curious."

" Well ? " I said.

" Well," he answered, " I jolly well have. You just come with me," and before I could speak he had turned tail once more and whisked through the blue dark into the moat or basement of the house. I followed almost before I made any decision.

When we got down into the area I felt indescribably foolish— literally, as the saying is, in a hole. There was nothing but a closed door, shuttered windows, the steps down which we had come, the ridiculous well in which I found myself, and the ridiculous man who had brought me there, and who stood there with dancing eyes. I was just about to turn back when Rupert caught me by the elbow.

" Just listen to that," he said, and keeping my coat gripped in his right hand, he rapped with the knuckles of his left on the shutters of the basement window. His air was so definite that I paused and even inclined my head for a moment towards it. From inside was coming the murmur of an unmistakable human voice.

" Have you been talking to somebody inside ? " I asked suddenly, turning to Rupert.

" No, I haven't," he replied, with a grim smile, " but I should very much like to. Do you know what somebody is saying in there ? "

" No, of course not," I replied.

" Then I recommend you to listen," said Rupert sharply.

In the dead silence of the aristocratic street at evening, I stood a moment and listened. From behind the wooden partition, in which there was a long lean crack, was coming a continuous and moaning sound which took the form of the words : " When shall I get out ? When shall I get out ? Will they ever let me out ? " or words to that effect.

" Do you know anything about this ? " I said, turning upon Rupert very abruptly.

" Perhaps you think I am the criminal, he said sardonically, " instead of being in some small sense the detective. I came into this area two or three minutes ago, having told you that I knew there was something funny going on, and this woman behind the shutters (for it evidently is a woman) was moaning like mad. No, my dear friend, beyond that I do not know anything about her. She is not, startling as it may seem, my disinherited daughter, or a member of my secret seraglio. But when I hear a human being wailing that she can't get out, and talking to herself like a mad woman and beating on the shutters with her fists, as she was doing two or three minutes ago, I think it worth mentioning, that is all."

" My dear fellow," I said, " I apologise ; this is no time for arguing. What is to be done ? "

Rupert Grant had a long clasp-knife naked and brilliant in his hand.

" First of all," he said, " house-breaking." And he forced the blade into the crevice of the wood and broke away a huge splinter, leaving a gap and glimpse of the dark window-pane inside. The room within was entirely unlighted, so that for the first few seconds the window seemed a dead and opaque surface, as dark as a strip of slate. Then came a realization which, though in a sense gradual, made us step back and catch our breath. Two large dim human eyes were so close to us that the window itself seemed suddenly to be a mask. A pale human face was pressed against the glass within, and with increased distinctness, with the increase of the opening came the words :

" When shall I get out ? "

" What can all this be ? " I said.

Rupert made no answer, but lifting his walking-stick and pointing the ferrule like a fencing sword at the glass, punched a hole in it, smaller and more accurate than I should have supposed possible. The moment he had done so the voice spouted out of the hole, so to speak, piercing and querulous and clear, making the same demand for liberty.

"Can't you get out, madam?" I said, drawing near the hole in some perturbation.

"Get out. Of course I can't," moaned the unknown female bitterly. "They won't let me. I told them I would be let out. I told them I'd call the police. But it's no good. Nobody knows, nobody comes. They could keep me as long as they liked only——"

I was in the very act of breaking the window finally with my stick, incensed with this very sinister mystery, when Rupert held my arm hard, held it with a curious, still, and secret rigidity as if he desired to stop me, but did not desire to be observed to do so. I paused a moment, and in the act swung slightly round, so that I was facing the supporting wall of the front door steps. The act froze me into a sudden stillness like that of Rupert, for a figure almost as motionless as the pillars of the portico, but unmistakably human, had put his head out from between the door-posts and was gazing down into the area. One of the lighted lamps of the street was just behind his head, throwing it into abrupt darkness. Consequently, nothing whatever could be seen of his face beyond one fact, that he was unquestionably staring at us. I must say I thought Rupert's calmness magnificent. He rang the area bell quite idly, and went on talking to me with the easy end of a conversation which had never had any beginning. The black glaring figure in the portico did not stir. I almost thought it was really a statue. In another moment the grey area was golden with gaslight as the basement door was opened suddenly and a small and decorous housemaid stood in it.

"Pray excuse me," said Rupert, in a voice which he contrived to make somehow or other at once affable and underbred, "but we thought perhaps that you might do something for the Waifs and Strays. We don't expect——"

"Not here," said the small servant, with the incomparable severity of the menial of the non-philanthropic, and slammed the door in our faces.

"Very sad, very sad—the indifference of these people," said the philanthropist, with gravity as we went together up the steps. As we did so the motionless figure in the portico suddenly disappeared.

"Well, what do you make of that?" asked Rupert, slapping his gloves together when we got into the street.

I do not mind admitting that I was seriously upset. Under such conditions I had but one thought.

"Don't you think," I said a trifle timidly, "that we had better tell your brother?"

"Oh, if you like," said Rupert, in a lordly way. "He is quite near, as I promised to meet him at Gloucester Road Station. Shall we take a cab? Perhaps, as you say, it might amuse him."

Gloucester Road Station had, as if by accident, a somewhat deserted look. After a little looking about we discovered Basil Grant with his great head and his great white hat blocking the ticket-office window. I thought at first that he was taking a ticket for somewhere and being an astonishingly long time about it. As a matter of fact, he was discussing religion with the booking-office clerk, and had almost got his head through the hole in his excitement. When we dragged him away it was some time before he would talk of anything but the growth of an Oriental fatalism in modern thought, which had been well typified by some of the official's ingenious but perverse fallacies. At last we managed to get him to understand that we had made an astounding discovery. When he did listen, he listened attentively, walking between us up and down the lamp-lit street, while we told him in a rather feverish duet of the great house in South Kensington, of the equivocal milkman, of the lady imprisoned in the basement, and the man staring from the porch. At length he said:

"If you're thinking of going back to look the thing up, you must be careful what you do. It's no good you two going there. To go twice on the same pretext would look dubious. To go on a different pretext would look worse. You may be quite certain that the inquisitive gentleman who looked at you looked thoroughly, and will wear, so to speak, your portraits next his heart. If you want to find out if there is anything in this without a police raid I fancy you had better wait outside. I'll go in and see them."

His slow and reflective walk brought us at length within sight of the house. It stood up ponderous and purple against the last pallor of twilight. It looked like an ogre's castle. And so apparently it was.

"Do you think it's safe, Basil," said his brother, pausing, a little pale, under the lamp, "to go into that place alone? Of course we shall be near enough to hear if you yell, but these devils might do something—something sudden—or odd. I can't feel it's safe."

"I know of nothing that is safe," said Basil composedly,

" except, possibly—death," and he went up the steps and rang at the bell. When the massive respectable door opened for an instant, cutting a square of gaslight in the gathering dark, and then closed with a bang, burying our friend inside, we could not repress a shudder. It had been like the heavy gaping and closing of the dim lips of some evil leviathan. A freshening night breeze began to blow up the street, and we turned up the collars of our coats. At the end of twenty minutes, in which we had scarcely moved or spoken, we were as cold as icebergs, but more, I think, from apprehension than the atmosphere. Suddenly Rupert made an abrupt movement towards the house.

" I can't stand this," he began, but almost as he spoke sprang back into the shadow, for the panel of gold was again cut out of the black house front, and the burly figure of Basil was silhouetted against it coming out. He was roaring with laughter and talking so loudly that you could have heard every syllable across the street. Another voice, or, possibly, two voices, were laughing and talking back at him from within.

" No, no, no," Basil was calling out, with a sort of hilarious hostility. " That's quite wrong. That's the most ghastly heresy of all. It's the soul, my dear chap, the soul that's the arbiter of cosmic forces. When you see a cosmic force you don't like, trick it, my boy. But I must really be off."

" Come and pitch into us again," came the laughing voice from out of the house. " We still have some bones unbroken."

" Thanks, very much, I will—good-night," shouted Grant, who had by this time reached the street.

" Good-night," came the friendly call in reply, before the door closed.

" Basil," said Rupert Grant, in a hoarse whisper, " what are we to do ? "

The elder brother looked thoughtfully from one of us to the other.

" What is to be done, Basil ? " I repeated in uncontrollable excitement.

" I'm not sure," said Basil doubtfully. " What do you say to getting some dinner somewhere and going to the Court Theatre to-night ? I tried to get those fellows to come, but they couldn't."

We stared blankly.

" Go to the Court Theatre ? " repeated Rupert. " What would be the good of that ? "

" Good ? What do you mean ? " answered Basil, staring also. " Have you turned Puritan or Passive Resister, or something ? For fun, of course."

"But, great God in heaven ! What are we going to do, I mean ! " cried Rupert. "What about the poor woman locked up in that house ? Shall I go for the police ? "

Basil's face cleared with immediate comprehension, and he laughed.

"Oh, that," he said. "I'd forgotten that. That's all right. Some mistake, possibly. Or some quite trifling private affair. But I'm sorry those fellows couldn't come with us. Shall we take one of these green omnibuses ? There is a restaurant in Sloane Square."

"I sometimes think you play the fool to frighten us," I said irritably. "How can we leave that woman locked up ? How can it be a mere private affair ? How can crime and kidnapping and murder, for all I know, be private affairs ? If you found a corpse in a man's drawing-room, would you think it bad taste to talk about it just as if it was a confounded dado or an infernal etching ? "

Basil laughed heartily.

"That's very forcible," he said. "As a matter of fact, though, I know it's all right in this case. And there comes the green omnibus."

"How do you know it's all right in this case ? " persisted his brother angrily.

"My dear chap, the thing's obvious," answered Basil, holding a return ticket between his teeth while he fumbled in his waist-coat pocket. "Those two fellows never committed a crime in their lives. They're not the kind. Have either of you chaps got a halfpenny ? I want to get a paper before the omnibus comes."

"Oh, curse the paper ! " cried Rupert, in a fury. "Do you mean to tell me, Basil Grant, that you are going to leave a fellow-creature in pitch darkness in a private dungeon, because you've had ten minutes' talk with the keepers of it and thought them rather good men ? "

"Good men do commit crimes sometimes," said Basil, taking the ticket out of his mouth. "But this kind of good man doesn't commit that kind of crime. Well, shall we get on this omnibus ? "

The great green vehicle was indeed plunging and lumbering along the dim wide street towards us. Basil had stepped from the curb, and for an instant it was touch and go whether we should all have leaped on to it and been borne away to the restaurant and the theatre.

"Basil," I said, taking him firmly by the shoulder. "I simply won't leave this street and this house."

"Nor will I," said Rupert, glaring at it and biting his fingers. "There's some black work going on there. If I left it I should never sleep again."

Basil Grant looked at us both seriously.

"Of course if you feel like that," he said, "we'll investigate further. You'll find it's all right, though. They're only two young Oxford fellows. Extremely nice, too, though rather infected with this pseudo-Darwinian business. Ethics of evolution and all that."

"I think," said Rupert darkly, ringing the bell, "that we shall enlighten you further about their ethics."

"And may I ask," said Basil gloomily, "what it is that you propose to do?"

"I propose, first of all," said Rupert, "to get into this house; secondly, to have a look at these nice young Oxford men; thirdly, to knock them down, bind them, gag them, and search the house."

Basil stared indignantly for a few minutes. Then he was shaken for an instant with one of his sudden laughs.

"Poor little boys," he said. "But it almost serves them right for holding such silly views, after all," and he quaked again with amusement; "there's something confoundedly Darwinian about it."

"I suppose you mean to help us?" said Rupert.

"Oh yes, I'll be in it," answered Basil, "if it's only to prevent your doing the poor chaps any harm."

He was standing in the rear of our little procession, looking indifferent and sometimes even sulky, but somehow the instant the door opened he stepped first into the hall, glowing with urbanity.

"So sorry to haunt you like this," he said. "I met two friends outside who very much want to know you. May I bring them in?"

"Delighted, of course," said a young voice, the unmistakable voice of the Isis, and I realized that the door had been opened, not by the decorous little servant girl, but by one of our hosts in person. He was a short, but shapely young gentleman, with curly dark hair and a square, snub-nosed face. He wore slippers and a sort of blazer of some incredible college purple.

"This way," he said; "mind the steps by the staircase. This house is more crooked and old-fashioned than you would think from its snobbish exterior. There are quite a lot of odd corners in the place really."

"That," said Rupert, with a savage smile, "I can quite believe."

We were by this time in the study or back parlour, used by the young inhabitants as a sitting-room, an apartment littered with magazines and books ranging from Dante to detective stories. The other youth, who stood with his back to the fire smoking a corn-cob, was big and burly, with dead brown hair brushed forward and a Norfolk jacket. He was that particular type of man whose every feature and action is heavy and clumsy, and yet who is, you would say, rather exceptionally a gentleman.

"Any more arguments?" he said, when introductions had been effected. "I must say, Mr. Grant, you were rather severe upon eminent men of science such as we. I've half a mind to chuck my D.Sc. and turn minor poet."

"Bosh," answered Grant. "I never said a word against eminent men of science. What I complain of is a vague popular philosophy which supposes itself to be scientific when it is really nothing but a sort of new religion and an uncommonly nasty one. When people talked about the fall of man they knew they were talking about a mystery, a thing they didn't understand. Now that they talk about the survival of the fittest they think they do understand it, whereas they have not merely no notion, they have an elaborately false notion of what the words mean. The Darwinian movement has made no difference to mankind, except that, instead of talking unphilosophically about philosophy, they now talk unscientifically about science."

"That is all very well," said the big young man, whose name appeared to be Burrows. "Of course, in a sense, science, like mathematics or the violin, can only be perfectly understood by specialists. Still, the rudiments may be of public use. Greenwood here," indicating the little man in the blazer, "doesn't know one note of music from another. Still, he knows something. He knows enough to take off his hat when they play 'God save the King.' He doesn't take it off by mistake when they play 'Oh, dem Golden Slippers.' Just in the same way science——"

Here Mr. Burrows stopped abruptly. He was interrupted by an argument uncommon in philosophical controversy and perhaps not wholly legitimate. Rupert Grant had bounded on him from behind, flung an arm round his throat, and bent the giant backwards.

"Knock the other fellow down, Swinburne," he called out, and before I knew where I was I was locked in a grapple with the man in the purple blazer. He was a wiry fighter, who bent and sprang like whalebone, but I was heavier and had taken him utterly by surprise. I twitched one of his feet from under him; he swung for a moment on the single foot, and then we fell with a crash amid the litter of newspapers, myself on top.

My attention for a moment released by victory, I could hear Basil's voice finishing some long sentence of which I had not heard the beginning.

". . . wholly, I must confess, unintelligible to me, my dear sir, and I need not say unpleasant. Still one must side with one's old friends against the most fascinating new ones. Permit me, therefore, in tying you up in this antimacassar, to make it as commodious as handcuffs can reasonably be while . . ."

I had staggered to my feet. The gigantic Burrows was toiling in the garrotte of Rupert, while Basil was striving to master his mighty hands. Rupert and Basil were both particularly strong, but so was Mr. Burrows ; how strong, we knew a second afterwards. His head was held back by Rupert's arm, but a convulsive heave went over his whole frame. An instant after his head plunged forward like a bull's, and Rupert Grant was slung head over heels, a catherine wheel of legs, on the floor in front of him. Simultaneously the bull's head butted Basil in the chest, bringing him also to the ground with a crash, and the monster, with a Berserker roar, leaped at me and knocked me into the corner of the room, smashing the waste-paper basket. The bewildered Greenwood sprang furiously to his feet. Basil did the same. But they had the best of it now.

Greenwood dashed to the bell and pulled it violently, sending peals through the great house. Before I could get panting to my feet, and before Rupert, who had been literally stunned for a few moments, could even lift his head from the floor, two footmen were in the room. Defeated even when we were in a majority, we were now outnumbered. Greenwood and one of the footmen flung themselves upon me, crushing me back into the corner upon the wreck of the paper basket. The other two flew at Basil, and pinned him against the wall. Rupert lifted himself on his elbow, but he was still dazed.

In the strained silence of our helplessness I heard the voice of Basil come with a loud incongruous cheerfulness.

" Now this," he said, " is what I call enjoying oneself."

I caught a glimpse of his face, flushed and forced against the bookcase, from between the swaying limbs of my captors and his. To my astonishment his eyes were really brilliant with pleasure, like those of a child heated by a favourite game.

I made several apoplectic efforts to rise, but the servant was on top of me so heavily that Greenwood could afford to leave me to him. He turned quickly to come to reinforce the two who were mastering Basil. The latter's head was already sinking lower and lower, like a leaning ship, as his enemies pressed him

down.   He flung up one hand just as I thought him falling and
hung on to a huge tome in the bookcase, a volume, I afterwards
discovered, of St. Chrysostom's theology.   Just as Greenwood
bounded across the room towards the group, Basil plucked the
ponderous tome bodily out of the shelf, swung it, and sent it
spinning through the air, so that it struck Greenwood flat in the
face and knocked him over like a rolling ninepin.   At the same
instant Basil's stiffness broke, and he sank, his enemies closing
over him.

Rupert's head was clear, but his body shaken ; he was hanging
as best he could on to the half-prostrate Greenwood.   They were
rolling over each other on the floor, both somewhat enfeebled
by their falls, but Rupert certainly the more so.   I was still
successfully held down.   The floor was a sea of torn and trampled
papers and magazines, like an immense waste-paper basket.
Burrows and his companion were almost up to the knees in them,
as in a drift of dead leaves.   And Greenwood had his leg struck
right through a sheet of the *Pall Mall Gazette*, which clung to it
ludicrously, like some fantastic trouser frill.

Basil, shut from me in a human prison, a prison of powerful
bodies, might be dead for all I knew.   I fancied, however, that
the broad back of Mr. Burrows, which was turned towards me,
had a certain bend of effort in it as if my friend still needed some
holding down.   Suddenly that broad back swayed hither and
thither.   It was swaying on one leg ; Basil, somehow, had hold
of the other.   Burrows' huge fist and those of the footmen were
battering Basil's sunken head like an anvil, but nothing could get
the giant's ankle out of his sudden and savage grip.   While his
own head was forced slowly down in darkness and great pain,
the right leg of his captor was being forced in the air.   Burrows
swung to and fro with a purple face.   Then suddenly the floor
and the walls and the ceiling shook together, as the colossus fell,
all his length seeming to fill the floor.   Basil sprang up with
dancing eyes, and with three blows like battering-rams knocked
the footman into a cocked hat.   Then he sprang on top of
Burrows, with one antimacassar in his hand and another in his
teeth, and bound him hand and foot almost before he knew
clearly that his head had struck the floor.   Then Basil sprang at
Greenwood, whom Rupert was struggling to hold down, and
between them they secured him easily.   The man who had hold
of me let go and turned to his rescue, but I leaped up like a spring
released, and, to my infinite satisfaction, knocked the fellow down.
The other footman, bleeding at the mouth and quite demoralized,
was stumbling out of the room.   My late captor, without a word,

slunk after him, seeing that the battle was won. Rupert was sitting astride the pinioned Mr. Greenwood, Basil astride the pinioned Mr. Burrows.

To my surprise the latter gentleman, lying bound on his back, spoke in a perfectly calm voice to the man who sat on top of him.

" And now, gentlemen," he said, " since you have got your own way, perhaps you wouldn't mind telling us what the deuce all this is ? "

" This," said Basil, with a radiant face, looking down at his captive, " this is what we call the survival of the fittest."

Rupert, who had been steadily collecting himself throughout the later phases of the fight, was intellectually altogether himself again at the end of it. Springing up from the prostrate Greenwood, and knotting a handkerchief round his left hand, which was bleeding from a blow, he sang out quite coolly :

" Basil, will you mount guard over the captive of your bow and spear and antimacassar ? Swinburne and I will clear out the prison downstairs."

" All right," said Basil, rising also and seating himself in a leisured way in an armchair. " Don't hurry for us," he said, glancing round at the litter of the room, " we have all the illustrated papers."

Rupert lurched thoughtfully out of the room, and I followed him even more slowly ; in fact, I lingered long enough to hear, as I passed through the room, the passages and the kitchen stairs, Basil's voice continuing conversationally :

" And now, Mr. Burrows," he said, settling himself sociably in the chair, " there's no reason why we shouldn't go on with that amusing argument. I'm sorry that you have to express yourself lying on your back on the floor, and, as I told you before, I've no more notion why you are there than the man in the moon. A conversationalist like yourself, however, can scarcely be seriously handicapped by any bodily posture. You were saying, if I remember right, when this incidental fracas occurred, that the rudiments of science might with advantage be made public."

" Precisely," said the large man on the floor in an easy tone. " I hold that nothing more than a rough sketch of the universe as seen by science can be . . ."

And here the voices died away as we descended into the basement. I noticed that Mr. Greenwood did not join in the amicable controversy. Strange as it may appear, I think he looked back upon our proceedings with a slight degree of resentment. Mr. Burrows, however, was all philosophy and chattiness. We left them, as I say, together, and sank deeper and deeper into the underworld of that mysterious house, which perhaps appeared to us somewhat more Tartarian than it really was, owing to our knowledge of its semi-criminal mystery and of the human secret locked below.

The basement floor had several doors, as is usual in such a house ; doors that would naturally lead to the kitchen, the scullery, the pantry, the servants' hall, and so on. Rupert flung open all the doors with indescribable rapidity. Four out of the five opened on entirely empty apartments. The fifth was locked. Rupert broke the door in like a bandbox, and we fell into the sudden blackness of the sealed, unlighted room.

Rupert stood on the threshold, and called out like a man calling into an abyss :

" Whoever you are, come out. You are free. The people who held you captive are captives themselves. We heard you crying and we came to deliver you. We have bound your enemies upstairs hand and foot. You are free."

For some seconds after he had spoken into the darkness there was a dead silence in it. Then there came a kind of muttering and moaning. We might easily have taken it for the wind or rats if we had not happened to have heard it before. It was unmistakably the voice of the imprisoned woman, drearily demanding liberty, just as we had heard her demand it.

" Has anybody got a match ? " said Rupert grimly. " I fancy we have come pretty near the end of this business."

I struck a match and held it up. It revealed a large, bare yellow-papered apartment with a dark-clad figure at the other end of it near the window. An instant after it burned my fingers and dropped, leaving darkness. It had, however, revealed something more practical—an iron gas bracket just above my head. I struck another match and lit the gas. And we found ourselves suddenly and seriously in the presence of the captive.

At a sort of workbox in the window of this subterranean breakfast-room sat an elderly lady with a singularly high colour and almost startling silver hair. She had, as if designedly to relieve these effects, a pair of Mephistophelean black eyebrows and a very neat black dress. The glare of the gas lit up her piquant hair and face perfectly against the brown background of the shutters. The background was blue and not brown in one place ; at the place where Rupert's knife had torn a great opening in the wood about an hour before.

" Madam," said he, advancing with a gesture of the hat, " permit me to have the pleasure of announcing to you that you are free. Your complaints happened to strike our ears as we passed down the street, and we have therefore ventured to come to your rescue."

The old lady with the red face and the black eyebrows looked at us for a moment with something of the apoplectic stare of a parrot. Then she said, with a sudden gust or breathing of relief :

" Rescue ? Where is Mr. Greenwood ? Where is Mr. Burrows ? Did you say you had rescued me ? "

" Yes, madam," said Rupert, with a beaming condescension. " We have very satisfactorily dealt with Mr. Greenwood and Mr. Burrows. We have settled affairs with them very satisfactorily."

The old lady rose from her chair and came very quickly towards us.

" What did you say to them ? How did you persuade them ? " she cried.

" We persuaded them, my dear madam," said Rupert, laughing, " by knocking them down and tying them up. But what is the matter ? "

To the surprise of every one the old lady walked slowly back to her seat by the window.

" Do I understand," she said, with the air of a person about to begin knitting, " that you have knocked down Mr. Burrows and tied him up ? "

" We have," said Rupert proudly ; " we have resisted their oppression and conquered it."

" Oh, thanks," answered the old lady, and sat down by the window.

A considerable pause followed.

" The road is quite clear for you, madam," said Rupert pleasantly.

The old lady rose, cocking her black eyebrows and her silver crest at us for an instant.

" But what about Greenwood and Burrows ? " she said. " What did I understand you to say had become of them ? "

" They are lying on the floor upstairs," said Rupert, chuckling. " Tied hand and foot."

" Well, that settles it," said the old lady, coming with a kind of bang into her seat again, " I must stop where I am."

Rupert looked bewildered.

" Stop where you are ? " he said. " Why should you stop any longer where you are ? What power can force you now to stop in this miserable cell ? "

" The question rather is," said the old lady, with composure, " what power can force me to go anywhere else ? "

We both stared wildly at her and she stared tranquilly at us both.

At last I said, "Do you really mean to say that we are to leave you here?"

"I suppose you don't intend to tie me up," she said, "and carry me off? I certainly shall not go otherwise."

"But, my dear madam," cried out Rupert, in a radiant exasperation, "we heard you with our own ears crying because you could not get out."

"Eavesdroppers often hear rather misleading things," replied the captive grimly. "I suppose I did break down a bit and lose my temper and talk to myself. But I have some sense of honour for all that."

"Some sense of honour?" repeated Rupert, and the last light of intelligence died out of his face, leaving it the face of an idiot with rolling eyes.

He moved vaguely towards the door and I followed. But I turned yet once more in the toils of my conscience and curiosity. "Can we do nothing for you, madam?" I said forlornly.

"Why," said the lady, "if you are particularly anxious to do me a little favour you might untie the gentlemen upstairs."

Rupert plunged heavily up the kitchen staircase, shaking it with his vague violence. With mouth open to speak he stumbled to the door of the sitting-room and scene of battle.

"Theoretically speaking, that is no doubt true," Mr. Burrows was saying, lying on his back and arguing easily with Basil; "but we must consider the matter as it appears to our senses. The origin of morality . . ."

"Basil," cried Rupert, gasping, "she won't come out."

"Who won't come out?" asked Basil, a little cross at being interrupted in an argument.

"The lady downstairs," replied Rupert. "The lady who was locked up. She won't come out. And she says that all she wants is for us to let these fellows loose."

"And a jolly sensible suggestion," cried Basil, and with a bound he was on top of the prostrate Burrows once more and was unknotting his bonds with hands and teeth.

"A brilliant idea. Swinburne, just undo Mr. Greenwood."

In a dazed and automatic way I released the little gentleman in the purple jacket, who did not seem to regard any of the proceedings as particularly sensible or brilliant. The gigantic Burrows, on the other hand, was heaving with herculean laughter.

"Well," said Basil, in his cheeriest way, "I think we must be getting away. We've so much enjoyed our evening. Far too much regard for you to stand on ceremony. If I may so express myself, we've made ourselves at home. Good-night. Thanks so much. Come along, Rupert."

"Basil," said Rupert desperately, "for God's sake come and see what you can make of the woman downstairs. I can't get the discomfort out of my mind. I admit that things look as if we had made a mistake. But these gentlemen won't mind perhaps . . ."

"No, no," cried Burrows, with a sort of Rabelaisian uproariousness. "No, no, look in the pantry, gentlemen. Examine the coal-hole. Make a tour of the chimneys. There are corpses all over the house, I assure you."

This adventure of ours was destined to differ in one respect from others which I have narrated. I had been through many wild days with Basil Grant, days for the first half of which the sun and the moon seemed to have gone mad. But it had almost invariably happened that towards the end of the day and its adventure things had cleared themselves like the sky after rain, and a luminous and quiet meaning had gradually dawned upon me. But this day's work was destined to end in confusion worse confounded. Before we left that house, ten minutes afterwards, one half-witted touch was added which rolled all our minds in cloud. If Rupert's head had suddenly fallen off on the floor, if wings had begun to sprout out of Greenwood's shoulders, we could scarcely have been more suddenly stricken. And yet of this we had no explanation. We had to go to bed that night with the prodigy and get up next morning with it and let it stand in our memories for weeks and months. As will be seen, it was not until months afterwards that by another accident and in another way it was explained. For the present I only state what happened.

When all five of us went down the kitchen stairs again, Rupert leading, the two hosts bringing up the rear, we found the door of the prison again closed. Throwing it open we found the place again as black as pitch. The old lady, if she was still there, had turned out the gas ; she seemed to have a weird preference for sitting in the dark.

Without another word Rupert lit the gas again. The little old lady turned her bird-like head as we all stumbled forward in the strong gaslight. Then, with a quickness that almost made me jump, she sprang up and swept a sort of old-fashioned curtsey or reverence. I looked quickly at Greenwood and Burrows, to whom it was natural to suppose this subservience had been offered. I felt irritated at what was implied in this subservience, and desired to see the faces of the tyrants as they received it. To my surprise they did not seem to have seen it at all ; Burrows was paring his nails with a small penknife. Greenwood was at the back of the group and had hardly entered the room. And then an amazing fact became apparent. It was Basil Grant who stood foremost of the group, the golden gaslight lighting up his strong face and figure. His face wore an expression indescribably conscious, with the suspicion of a very grave smile. His head was slightly bent with a restrained bow. It was he who had acknowledged the lady's obeisance. And it was he, beyond any shadow of reasonable doubt, to whom it had really been directed.

" So I hear," he said, in a kindly yet somehow formal voice, " I hear, madam, that my friends have been trying to rescue you. But without success."

" No one, naturally, knows my faults better than you," answered the lady with a high colour. " But you have not found me guilty of treachery."

" I willingly attest it, madam," replied Basil, in the same level tones, " and the fact is that I am so much gratified with your exhibition of loyalty that I permit myself the pleasure of exercising some very large discretionary powers. You would not leave this room at the request of these gentlemen. But you know that you can safely leave it at mine."

The captive made another reverence. " I have never complained of your injustice," she said. " I need scarcely say what I think of your generosity."

And before our staring eyes could blink she had passed out of the room, Basil holding the door open for her.

He turned to Greenwood with a relapse into joviality. " This will be a relief to you," he said.

" Yes, it will," replied that immovable young gentleman with a face like a sphinx.

We found ourselves outside in the dark blue night, shaken and dazed as if we had fallen into it from some high tower.

" Basil," said Rupert at last, in a weak voice. " I always thought you were my brother. But are you a man ? I mean— are you only a man ? "

" At present," replied Basil, " my mere humanity is proved by one of the most unmistakable symbols—hunger. We are too late for the theatre in Sloane Square. But we are not too late for the restaurant. Here comes the green omnibus ! " and he had leaped on it before we could speak.

.   .   .   .

As I said, it was months after that Rupert Grant suddenly

entered my room, swinging a satchel in his hand and with a general air of having jumped over the garden wall, and implored me to go with him upon the latest and wildest of his expeditions. He proposed to himself no less a thing than the discovery of the actual origin, whereabouts, and headquarters of the source of all our joys and sorrows—the Club of Queer Trades. I should expand this story for ever if I explained how ultimately we ran this strange entity to its lair. The process meant a hundred interesting things. The tracking of a member, the bribing of a cabman, the fighting of roughs, the lifting of a paving stone, the finding of a cellar, the finding of a cellar below the cellar, the finding of the subterranean passage, the finding of the Club of Queer Trades.

I have had many strange experiences in my life, but never a stranger one than that I felt when I came out of those rambling, sightless, and seemingly hopeless passages into the sudden splendour of a sumptuous and hospitable dining-room, surrounded upon almost every side by faces that I knew. There was Mr. Montmorency, the Arboreal House-Agent, seated between the two brisk young men who were occasionally vicars, and always Professional Detainers. There was P. G. Northover, founder of the Adventure and Romance Agency. There was Professor Chadd, who invented the Dancing Language.

As we entered all the members seemed to sink suddenly into their chairs, and with the very action the vacancy of the presidential seat gaped at us like a missing tooth.

" The president's not here," said Mr. P. G. Northover, turning suddenly to Professor Chadd.

" N—no," said that philosopher, with more than his ordinary vagueness. " I can't imagine where he is."

" Good heavens," said Mr. Montmorency, jumping up, " I really feel a little nervous. I'll go and see." And he ran out of the room.

An instant after he ran back again, twittering with a timid ecstasy.

" He's there, gentlemen—he's there all right—he's coming in now," he cried, and sat down. Rupert and I could hardly help feeling the beginnings of a sort of wonder as to who this person might be who was the first member of this insane brotherhood. Who, we thought indistinctly, could be maddest in this world of madmen ; what fantastic was it whose shadow filled all these fantastics with so loyal an expectation ?

Suddenly we were answered. The door flew open and the room was filled and shaken with a shout, in the midst of which

Basil Grant, smiling and in evening dress, took his seat at the head of the table.

How we ate that dinner I have no idea. In the common way I am a person particularly prone to enjoy the long luxuriance of the club dinner. But on this occasion it seemed a hopeless and endless string of courses. *Hors-d'œuvres* sardines seemed as big as herrings, soup seemed a sort of ocean, larks were ducks, ducks were ostriches until that dinner was over. The cheese course was maddening. I had often heard of the moon being made of green cheese. That night I thought the green cheese was made of the moon. And all the time Basil Grant went on laughing and eating and drinking, and never threw one glance at us to tell us why he was there, the king of these capering idiots.

At last came the moment which I knew must in some way enlighten us, the time of the club speeches and the club toasts. Basil Grant rose to his feet amid a surge of song and cheers.

" Gentlemen," he said, " it is a custom in this society that the president for the year opens the proceedings not by any general toast or sentiment, but by calling upon each member to give a brief account of his trade. We then drink to that calling and to all who follow it. It is my business, as the senior member, to open by stating my claim to membership of this club. Years ago, gentlemen, I was a judge ; I did my best in that capacity to do justice and to administer the law. But it gradually dawned on me that in my work, as it was, I was not touching even the fringe of justice. I was seated in the seat of the mighty, I was robed in scarlet and ermine ; nevertheless, I held a small and lowly and futile post. I had to go by a mean rule as much as a postman, and my red and gold was worth no more than his. Daily there passed before me taut and passionate problems, the stringency of which I had to pretend to relieve by silly imprisonments or silly damages, while I knew all the time, by the light of my living common sense, that they would have been far better relieved by a kiss or a thrashing, or a few words of explanation, or a duel, or a tour in the West Highlands. Then, as this grew on me, there grew on me continuously the sense of a mountainous frivolity. Every word said in the court, a whisper or an oath, seemed more connected with life than the words I had to say. Then came the time when I publicly blasphemed the whole bosh, was classed as a madman and melted from public life."

Something in the atmosphere told me that it was not only Rupert and I who were listening with intensity to this statement.

" Well, I discovered that I could be of real use. I offered myself privately as a purely moral judge to settle purely moral differences. Before very long these unofficial courts of honour (kept strictly secret) had spread over the whole of society. People were tried before me not for the practical trifles for which nobody cares, such as committing a murder, of keeping a dog without a licence. My criminals were tried for the faults which really make social life impossible. They were tried before me for selfishness, or for an impossible vanity, or for scandal-mongering, or for stinginess to guests or dependents. Of course these courts had no sort of real coercive powers. The fulfilment of their punishments rested entirely on the honour of the ladies and gentlemen involved, including the honour of the culprits. But you would be amazed to know how completely our orders were always obeyed. Only lately I had a most pleasing example. A maiden lady in South Kensington whom I had condemned to solitary confinement for being the means of breaking off an engagement through backbiting, absolutely refused to leave her prison, although some well-meaning persons had been inopportune enough to rescue her."

Rupert Grant was staring at his brother, his mouth fallen agape. So, for the matter of that, I expect, was I. This, then, was the explanation of the old lady's strange discontent and her still stranger content with her lot. She was one of the culprits of his Voluntary Criminal Court. She was one of the clients of his Queer Trade.

We were still dazed when we drank, amid a crash f glasses, the health of Basil's new judiciary. We had only a confused sense of everything having been put right, the sense men will have when they come into the presence of God. We dimly heard Basil say :

"Mr. P. G. Northover will now explain the Adventure and Romance Agency."

And we heard equally dimly Northover beginning the statement he had made long ago to Major Brown. Thus our epic ended where it had begun, like a true cycle.

AGATHA CHRISTIE *displays not only
an amazing originality, and at times sheer inspiration, in the weaving of detective tales (such
as " The Murder of Roger Ackroyd" and other
of her brilliant stories abundantly prove), but
also a very keen sense of fun, which adds to
the delight with which her mysteries are read.
The amusing tale of " The Rajah's Emerald"
demonstrates her skill as a short story writer.*

THE RAJAH'S EMERALD

WITH a serious effort James Bond bent his attention once
more on the little yellow book in his hand. On its outside
the book bore the simple but pleasing legend, " Do you
want your salary increased by £300 per annum ? " Its price was
one shilling. James had just finished reading two pages of crisp
paragraphs instructing him to look his boss in the face, to cultivate
a dynamic personality, and to radiate an atmosphere of efficiency.
He had now arrived at subtler matter, " There is a time for
frankness, there is a time for discretion," the little yellow book
informed him. " A strong man does not always blurt out *all* he
knows." James let the little book close, and raising his head,
gazed out over a blue expanse of ocean. A horrible suspicion
assailed him that he was *not* a strong man. A strong man would
have been in command of the present situation, not a victim to
it. For the sixtieth time that morning James rehearsed his wrongs.

This was his holiday. His holiday ! Ha, ha ! Sardonic
laughter. Who had persuaded him to come to that fashionable
seaside resort, Kimpton-on-Sea ? Grace. Who had urged him
into an expenditure of more than he could afford ? Grace.
And he had fallen in with the plan eagerly. She had got him
here, and what was the result ? Whilst he was staying in an
obscure boarding-house about a mile and a half from the sea-
front, Grace who should have been in a similar boarding-house
(not the same one—the proprieties of James's circle were very
strict) had fragrantly deserted him, and was staying at no less
than the Esplanade Hotel upon the sea-front.

It seemed that she had friends there. Friends ! Again
James laughed sardonically. His mind went back over the last
three years of his leisurely courtship of Grace. Extremely
pleased she had been when he first singled her out for notice.

That was before she had risen to heights of glory in the millinery salons at Messrs. Bartles in the High Street. In those early days it had been James who gave himself airs, now alas! the boot was on the other leg. Grace was what is technically known as " earning good money." It had made her uppish. Yes, that was it, thoroughly uppish. A confused fragment out of a poetry book came back to James's mind, something about " thanking heaven fasting, for a good man's love." But there was nothing of that kind of thing observable about Grace. Well fed on an Esplanade Hotel breakfast, she was ignoring the good man's love utterly. She was indeed accepting the attentions of a poisonous idiot called Claud Sopworth, a man, James felt convinced, of no moral worth whatsoever.

James ground a heel into the earth, and scowled darkly at the horizon. Kimpton-on-Sea. What had possessed him to come to such a place? It was pre-eminently a resort of the rich and fashionable, it possessed two large hotels, and several miles of picturesque bungalows belonging to fashionable actresses, rich Jews, and those members of the English aristocracy who had married wealthy wives. The rent, furnished, of the smallest bungalow was twenty-five guineas a week. Imagination boggled at what the rent of the large ones might amount to. There was one of these palaces immediately behind James's seat. It belonged to that famous sportsman Lord Edward Campion, and there were staying there at the moment a houseful of distinguished guests including the Rajah of Maraputna, whose wealth was fabulous. James had read all about him in the local weekly newspaper that morning ; the extent of his Indian possessions, his palaces, his wonderful collection of jewels, with a special mention of one famous emerald which the papers declared enthusiastically was the size of a pigeon's egg. James, being town bred, was somewhat hazy about the size of a pigeon's egg, but the impression left on his mind was good.

" If I had an emerald like that," said James, scowling at the horizon again, " I'd show Grace."

The sentiment was vague, but the enunciation of it made James feel better. Laughing voices hailed him from behind, and he turned abruptly to confront Grace. With her was Clara Sopworth, Alice Sopworth, Dorothy Sopworth, and—alas ! Claud Sopworth. The girls were arm in arm and giggling.

" Why, you are quite a stranger," cried Grace archly.

" Yes," said James.

He could, he felt, have found a more telling retort. You cannot convey the impression of a dynamic personality by the use of the one word " yes." He looked with intense loathing at Claud Sopworth. Claud Sopworth was almost as beautifully dressed as the hero of a musical comedy. James longed passionately for the moment when an enthusiastic beach dog should plant wet, sandy forefeet on the unsullied whiteness of Claud's flannel trousers. He himself wore a serviceable pair of dark grey flannel trousers which had seen better days.

" Isn't the air beau-tiful ? " said Clara, sniffing it appreciatively. " Quite sets you up, doesn't it ? "

She giggled.

" It's ozone," said Alice Sopworth. " It's as good as a tonic, you know." And she giggled also.

James thought :

" I should like to knock their silly heads together. What is the sense of laughing all the time ? They are not saying anything funny."

The immaculate Claud murmured languidly :

" Shall we have a bathe, or is it too much of a fag ? "

The idea of bathing was accepted shrilly. James fell into line with them. He even managed, with a certain amount of cunning, to draw Grace a little behind the others.

" Look here ! " he complained. " I am hardly seeing anything of you."

Well, I am sure we are all together now," said Grace, " and you can come and lunch with us at the hotel, at least——"

She looked dubiously at James's legs.

" What is the matter ? " demanded James ferociously. " Not smart enough for you, I suppose ? "

" I do think, dear, you might take a little more pains," said Grace. " Every one is so fearfully smart here. Look at Claud Sopworth ! "

" I have looked at him," said James grimly. " I have never seen a man who looked a more complete ass than he does."

Grace drew herself up.

" There is no need to criticize my friends, James, it's not manners. He's dressed just like any other gentleman at the hotel is dressed."

" Bah ! " said James. " Do you know what I read the other day in ' Society Snippets ' ? Why, that the Duke of—the Duke of, I can't remember, but one Duke, anyway, was the worst dressed man in England, there ! "

" I dare say," said Grace, " but then, you see, he is a duke."

" Well ? " demanded James. " What is wrong with my being a duke some day ? At least, well, not perhaps a duke, but a peer."

He slapped the yellow book in his pocket, and recited to her a long list of peers of the realm who had started life much more obscurely than James Bond. Grace merely giggled.

"Don't be so soft, James," she said. "Fancy you Earl of Kimpton-on-Sea ! "

James gazed at her in mingled rage and despair. The air of Kimpton-on-Sea had certainly gone to Grace's head.

The beach at Kimpton is a long, straight stretch of sand. A row of bathing-huts and boxes stretches evenly along it for about a mile and a half. The party had just stopped before a row of six huts all labelled imposingly, " For visitors to the Esplanade Hotel only."

" Here we are," said Grace brightly ; " but I'm afraid you can't come in with us, James, you'll have to go along to the public tents over there, we'll meet you in the sea. So long ! "

" So long ! " said James, and he strode off in the direction indicated.

Twelve dilapidated tents stood solemnly confronting the ocean. An aged mariner guarded them, a roll of blue paper in his hand. He accepted a coin of the realm from James, tore him off a blue ticket from his roll, threw him over a towel, and jerked one thumb over his shoulder.

" Take your turn," he said huskily.

It was then that James awoke to the fact of competition. Others besides himself had conceived the idea of entering the sea. Not only was each tent occupied, but outside each tent was a determined looking crowd of people glaring at each other. James attached himself to the smallest group and waited. The strings of the tent parted, and a beautiful young woman, sparsely clad, emerged on the scene settling her bathing-cap with the air of one who had the whole morning to waste. She strolled down to the water's edge, and sat down dreamily on the sands.

" That's no good," said James to himself, and attached himself forthwith to another group.

After waiting five minutes, sounds of activity were apparent in the second tent. With heavings and strainings, the flaps parted asunder and four children and a father and mother emerged. The tent being so small, it had something of the appearance of a conjuring trick. On the instant two women sprang forward, each grasping one flap of the tent.

" Excuse me," said the first young woman, panting a little.

" Excuse *me*," said the other young woman, glaring,.

" I would have you know I was here quite ten minutes before you were," said the first young woman rapidly.

" I have been here a good quarter of an hour, as any one will tell you," said the second young woman defiantly.

" Now then, now then," said the aged mariner, drawing near.

Both young women spoke to him shrilly. When they had finished, he jerked his thumb at the second young woman, and said briefly :

" It's yours."

Then he departed, deaf to remonstrances. He neither knew nor cared which had been there first; but his decision, as they say in newspaper competitions, was final. The despairing James caught at his arm.

" Look here ! I say ! "

" Well, mister ? "

" How long is it going to be before I get a tent ? "

The aged mariner threw a dispassionate glance over the waiting throng.

" Might be an hour, might be an hour and a half, I can't say."

At that moment James espied Grace and the Sopworth girls running lightly down the sands towards the sea.

" Damn ! " said James to himself.   " Oh, damn ! "

He plucked once more at the aged mariner.

" Can't I get a tent anywhere else ?   What about one of these huts along here ?   They all seem empty."

" The huts," said the ancient mariner with dignity, " are PRIVATE."

Having uttered this rebuke, he passed on. With a bitter feeling of having been tricked, James detached himself from the waiting groups, and strode savagely down the beach.   It was the limit !   It was the absolute, complete limit !   He gazed savagely at the trim bathing-boxes he passed.   In that moment from being an Independent Liberal, he became a red-hot Socialist.   Why should the rich have bathing-boxes and be able to bathe any minute they chose without waiting in a crowd ?   " This system of ours," said James vaguely, " is all *wrong*."

From the sea came the coquettish screams of the splashed. Grace's voice !   And above her squeaks, the inane " Ha, ha, ha ! " of Claud Sopworth.

." Damn ! " said James, grinding his teeth, a thing which he had never before attempted, only read about in works of fiction.

He came to a stop, twirling his stick savagely, and turning his back firmly on the sea.   Instead, he gazed with concentrated hatred upon Eagle's Nest, Buena Vista, and Mon Desir.   It was the custom of the inhabitants of Kimpton-on-Sea to label their bathing-huts with fancy names.   Eagle's Nest merely struck

James as being silly, and Buena Vista was beyond his linguistic accomplishments. But his knowledge of French was sufficient to make him realize the appositeness of the third name.

" Mong Desire," said James. " I should jolly well think it was."

And on that moment he saw that while the doors of the other bathing-huts were tightly closed, that of Mon Desir was ajar. James looked thoughtfully up and down the beach: this particular spot was mainly occupied by mothers of large families, busily engaged in superintending their offspring. It was only ten o'clock, too early as yet for the aristocracy of Kimpton-on-Sea to have come down to bathe.

" Eating quails and mushrooms in their beds as likely as not, brought to them on trays by powdered footmen, pah ! Not one of them will be down here before twelve o'clock," thought James.

He looked again towards the sea. With the obedience of a well-trained " leit motif," the shrill scream of Grace rose upon the air. It was followed by the " Ha, ha, ha! " of Claud Sopworth.

" I will," said James between his teeth.

He pushed open the door of Mon Desir and entered. For the moment he had a fright, as he caught sight of sundry garments hanging from pegs, but he was quickly reassured. The hut was partitioned into two, on the right-hand side a girl's yellow sweater, a battered panama hat, and a pair of beach shoes were depending from a peg. On the left-hand side an old pair of grey flannel trousers, a pullover, and a sou'wester proclaimed the fact that the sexes were segregated. James hastily transferred himself to the gentlemen's part of the hut, and undressed rapidly. Three minutes later he was in the sea puffing and snorting importantly, doing extremely short bursts of professional-looking swimming—head under the water, arms lashing the sea—that style.

" Oh, there you are ! " cried Grace. " I was afraid you wouldn't be in for ages with all that crowd of people waiting there."

" Really ? " said James.

He thought with affectionate loyalty of the yellow book. " The strong man can on occasions be discreet." For the moment his temper was quite restored. He was able to say pleasantly but firmly to Claud Sopworth, who was teaching Grace the overarm stroke :

" No, no, old man, you have got it all wrong. *I'll* show her."

And such was the assurance of his tone that Claud withdrew discomfited. The only pity of it was that his triumph was short-lived. The temperature of our English waters is not such as to induce bathers to remain in them for any length of time. Grace and the Sopworth girls were already displaying blue chins and chattering teeth. They raced up the beach, and James pursued his solitary way back to Mon Desir. As he towelled himself vigorously and slipped his shirt over his head, he was pleased with himself. He had, he felt, displayed a dynamic personality.

And then suddenly he stood still, frozen with terror. Girlish voices sounded from outside, and voices quite different from those of Grace and her friends. A moment later he had realized the truth, the rightful owners of Mon Desir were arriving. It is possible that if James had been fully dressed, he would have waited their advent in a dignified manner, and attempted an explanation. As it was he acted on panic. The windows of Mon Desir were modestly screened by dark green curtains. James flung himself on the door and held the knob in a desperate clutch. Hands tried ineffectually to turn it from outside.

" It's locked after all," said a girl's voice. " I thought Pug said it was open."

" No, Woggle said so."

" Woggle is the limit," said the other girl. " How perfectly foul, we shall have to go back for the key."

James heard their footsteps retreating. He drew a long, deep breath. In desperate haste he huddled on the rest of his garments. Two minutes later saw him strolling negligently down the beach with an almost aggressive air of innocence. Grace and the Sopworth girls joined him on the beach a quarter of an hour later. The rest of the morning passed agreeably in stone throwing, writing in the sand, and light badinage. Then Claud glanced at his watch.

" Lunch-time," he observed. " We'd better be strolling back."

" I'm terribly hungry," said Alice Sopworth.

All the other girls said that they were terribly hungry too.

" Are you coming, James ? " asked Grace.

Doubtless James was unduly touchy. He chose to take offence at her tone.

" Not if my clothes are not good enough for you," he said bitterly. "Perhaps, as you are so particular, I'd better not come."

That was Grace's cue for murmured protestations, but the seaside air had affected Grace unfavourably. She merely replied :

" Very well. Just as you like, see you this afternoon then."

James was left dumbfounded.

" Well ! " he said, staring after the retreating group. " Well, of all the——"

He strolled moodily into the town. There are two cafés in Kimpton-on-Sea, they are both hot, noisy, and overcrowded. It was the affair of the bathing-huts once more, James had to wait his turn. He had to wait longer than his turn, an unscrupulous matron who had just arrived forestalling him when a vacant seat did present itself. At last he was seated at a small table. Close to his left ear three raggedly bobbed maidens were making a determined hash of Italian opera. Fortunately James was not musical. He studied the bill of fare dispassionately, his hands thrust deep into his pockets. He thought to himself :

"Whatever I ask for it's sure to be ' off.' That's the kind of fellow I am."

His right hand, groping in the recesses of his pocket, touched an unfamiliar object. It felt like a pebble, a large round pebble.

"What on earth did I want to put a stone in my pocket for ? " thought James.

His fingers closed round it. A waitress drifted up to him.

"Fried plaice and chipped potatoes, please," said James.

"Fried plaice is ' off,' murmured the waitress, her eyes fixed dreamily on the ceiling.

"Then I'll have curried beef," said James.

"Curried beef is ' off.' "

"Is there anything on this beastly menu that isn't ' off ' ? " demanded James.

The waitress looked pained, and placed a pale-grey forefinger against haricot mutton. James resigned himself to the inevitable and ordered haricot mutton. His mind still seething with resentment against the ways of cafés, he drew his hand out of his pocket, the stone still in it. Unclosing his fingers, he looked absent-mindedly at the object in his palm. Then with a shock all lesser matters passed from his mind, and he stared with all his eyes. The thing he held was not a pebble, it was—he could hardly doubt it—an emerald, an enormous green emerald. James stared at it horror-stricken. No, it couldn't be an emerald, it must be coloured glass. There couldn't be an emerald of that size, unless—printed words danced before James's eyes, " The Rajah of Maraputna—famous emerald the size of a pigeon's egg." Was it—could it be—*that* emerald at which he was looking now ? The waitress returned with the haricot mutton, and James closed his fingers spasmodically. Hot and cold shivers chased themselves up and down his spine. He had the sense of being caught in a terrible dilemma. If this was the emerald—but was it ? Could it be ? He unclosed his fingers and peeped anxiously. James was no expert on precious stones, but the depth and the glow of the jewel convinced him this was the real thing. He put both elbows on the table and leaned forward staring with unseeing eyes at the haricot mutton slowly congealing on the dish in front of him. He had got to think this out. If this was the Rajah's emerald, what was he going to do about it? The word " police " flashed into his mind. If you found anything of value you took it to the police station. Upon this axiom had James been brought up.

Yes, but—how on earth had the emerald got into his trousers pocket? That was doubtless the question the police would ask. It was an awkward question, and it was moreover a question to which he had at the moment no answer. How had the emerald got into his trousers pocket? He looked despairingly down at his legs, and as he did so a misgiving shot through him. He looked more closely. One pair of old grey flannel trousers is very much like another pair of old grey flannel trousers, but all the same, James had an instinctive feeling that these were not his trousers after all. He sat back in his chair stunned with the force of the discovery. He saw now what had happened, in the hurry of getting out of the bathing-hut, he had taken the wrong trousers. He had hung his own, he remembered, on an adjacent peg to the old pair hanging there. Yes, that explained matters so far, he had taken the wrong trousers. But all the same, what on earth was an emerald worth hundreds and thousands of pounds doing there? The more he thought about it, the more curious it seemed. He could, of course, explain to the police——

It was awkward, no doubt about it, it was decidedly awkward. One would have to mention the fact that one had deliberately entered some one else's bathing-hut. It was not, of course, a serious offence, but it started him off wrong.

" Can I bring you anything else, sir? "

It was the waitress again. She was looking pointedly at the untouched haricot mutton. James hastily dumped some of it on his plate and asked for his bill. Having obtained it, he paid and went out. As he stood undecidedly in the street, a poster opposite caught his eye. The adjacent town of Harchester possessed an evening paper, and it was the contents bill of this paper that James was looking at. It announced a simple, sensational fact : " THE RAJAH'S EMERALD STOLEN." " My God," said James faintly, and leaned against a pillar. Pulling himself together he fished out a penny and purchased a copy of the paper. He was not long in finding what he sought. Sensational items of local news were few and far between. Large headlines adorned the front page. " Sensational Burglary at

" Fried plaice is ' off ' "

Lord Edward Campion's. Theft of Famous Historical Emerald. Rajah of Maraputna's Terrible Loss." The facts were few and simple. Lord Edward Campion had entertained several friends the evening before. Wishing to show the stone to one of the ladies present, the Rajah had gone to fetch it and had found it missing. The police had been called in. So far no clue had been obtained. James let the paper fall to the ground. It was still not clear to him how the emerald had come to be reposing in the pocket of an old pair of flannel trousers in a bathing-hut, but it was borne in upon him every minute that the police would certainly regard his own story as suspicious. What on earth was he to do ? Here he was, standing in the principal street of Kimpton-on-Sea with stolen booty worth a king's ransom reposing idly in his pocket, whilst the entire police force of the district were busily searching for just that same booty. There were two courses open to him. Course number one, to go straight to the police station and tell his story—but it must be admitted that James funked that course badly. Course number two, somehow or other to get rid of the emerald. It occurred to him to do it up in a neat little parcel and post it back to the Rajah. Then he shook his head, he had read too many detective stories for that sort of thing. He knew how your super-sleuth could get busy with a magnifying glass and every kind of patent device. Any detective worth his salt would get busy on James's parcel and would in half an hour or so have discovered the sender's profession, age, habits, and personal appearance. After that it would be a mere matter of hours before he was tracked down.

It was then that a scheme of dazzling simplicity suggested itself to James. It was the luncheon hour, the beach would be comparatively deserted, he would return to Mon Desir, hang up the trousers where he had found them, and regain his own garments. He started briskly towards the beach.

Nevertheless, his conscience pricked him slightly. The emerald *ought* to be returned to the Rajah. He conceived the idea that he might perhaps do a little detective work—once, that is, that he had regained his own trousers and replaced the others. In pursuance of this idea, he directed his steps towards the ancient mariner, whom he rightly regarded as being an inexhaustible source of Kimpton information.

"Excuse me ! " said James politely ; " but I believe a friend of mine has a hut on this beach, Mr. Charles Lampton. It is called Mon Desir, I fancy ? "

The aged mariner was sitting very squarely in a chair, a pipe

in his mouth, gazing out to sea.   He shifted his pipe a little, and
replied without removing his gaze from the horizon :

" Mon Desir belongs to his lordship, Lord Edward Campion ;
every one knows that.   I never heard of Mr. Charles Lampton,
he must be a newcomer."

" Thank you," said James, and withdrew.

The information staggered him.   Surely the Rajah could not
himself have slipped the stone into the pocket and forgotten it.
James shook his head, the theory did not satisfy him, but evidently
some member of the house-party must be the thief.   The situation
reminded James of some of his favourite works of fiction.

Nevertheless, his own purpose remained unaltered.   All fell
out easily enough.   The beach was, as he hoped it would be,
practically deserted.   More fortunate still, the door of Mon
Desir remained ajar.   To slip in was the work of a moment.
Edward was just lifting his own trousers from the hook, when a
voice behind him made him spin round suddenly.

" So I have caught you, my man ! " said the voice.

James stared open-mouthed.   In the doorway of Mon Desir
stood a stranger ; a well-dressed man of about forty years of age,
his face keen and hawk-like.

" So I have caught you ! " the stranger repeated.

" Who—who are you ? "stammered James.

" Detective-Inspector Merrilees from the Yard," said the
other crisply.   "And I will trouble you to hand over that
emerald."

" The—the emerald ? "

James was seeking to gain time.

" That's what I said, didn't I ? " said Inspector Merrilees.

He had a crisp, business-like enunciation.   James tried to pull
himself together.

" I don't know what you are talking about," he said with an
assumption of dignity.

" Oh yes, my lad, I think you do."

" The whole thing," said James, " is a mistake.   I can explain it quite easily——" He paused.

A look of weariness had settled on the face of the other.

" They always say that," murmured the Scotland Yard man
dryly.   " I suppose you picked it up as you were strolling along
the beach, eh ?   That is the sort of explanation."

It did indeed bear a resemblance to it, James recognized the
fact, but still he tried to gain time.

" How do I know you are what you say you are ? " he demanded weakly.

Merrilees flapped back his coat for a moment, showing a badge. James stared at him with eyes that popped out of his head.

" And now," said the other almost genially, " you see what you are up against ! You are a novice—I can tell that. Your first job, isn't it ? "

James nodded.

" I thought as much. Now, my boy, are you going to hand over that emerald, or have I got to search you ? "

James found his voice.

" I—I haven't got it on me," he declared.

He was thinking desperately.

" Left it at your lodgings ? " queried Merrilees.

James nodded.

" Very well, then," said the detective, " we will go there together."

He slipped his arm through James's.

" I am taking no chances of your getting away from me," he said gently. " We will go to your lodgings, and you will hand that stone over to me."

James spoke unsteadily,

" If I do, will you let me go ? " he asked tremulously.

Merrilees appeared embarrassed.

" We know just how that stone was taken," he explained, " and about the lady involved, and, of course, as far as that goes —well, the Rajah wants it hushed up. You know what these native rulers are ? "

James who knew nothing whatsoever about native rulers, except for one *cause célèbre*, nodded his head with an appearance of eager comprehension.

" It will be most irregular, of course," said the detective ; but you *may* get off scot-free."

Again James nodded. They had walked the length of the Esplanade, and were now turning into the town. James intimated the direction, but the other man never relinquished his sharp grip on James's arm.

Suddenly James hesitated and half-spoke. Merrilees looked up sharply, and then laughed. They were just passing the police station, and he noticed James's agonized glances at it.

" I am giving you a chance first," he said good-humouredly.

It was at that moment that things began to happen. A loud bellow broke from James, he clutched the other's arm, and yelled at the top of his voice :

" Help ! thief ! Help ! thief ! "

A crowd surrounded them in less than a minute. Merrilees was trying to wrench his arm from James's grasp.

" I charge this man," cried James. " I charge this man, he picked my pocket."

" What are you talking about, you fool ? " cried the other.

A constable took charge of matters. Mr. Merrilees and James were escorted into the police station. James reiterated his complaint.

" This man has just picked my pocket," he declared excitedly. " He has got my note-case in his right-hand pocket, there ! "

" The man is mad," grumbled the other. " You can look for yourself, inspector, and see if he is telling the truth."

At a sign from the inspector, the constable slipped his hand deferentially into Merrilees's pocket. He drew something up and held it out with a gasp of astonishment.

" My God ! " said the inspector, startled out of professional decorum. " It must be the Rajah's emerald."

Merrilees looked more incredulous than any one else.

" This is monstrous," he spluttered ; " monstrous. The man must have put it into my pocket himself as we were walking along together. It's a plant."

The forceful personality of Merrilees caused the inspector to waver. His suspicions swung round to James. He whispered something to the constable, and the latter went out.

" Now then, gentlemen," said the inspector, " let me have your statements please, one at a time."

" Certainly," said James. " I was walking along the beach, when I met this gentleman, and he pretended he was acquainted with me. I could not remember having met him before, but I was too polite to say so. We walked along together. I had my suspicions of him, and just when we got opposite the police station, I found his hand in my pocket, I held on to him and shouted for help."

The inspector transferred his glance to Merrilees.

" And now you, sir."

Merrilees seemed a little embarrassed.

" The story is very nearly right," he said slowly ; " but not quite. It was not I who scraped acquaintance with him, but he who scraped acquaintance with me. Doubtless he was trying to get rid of the emerald, and slipped it into my pocket while we were talking."

The inspector stopped writing.

" Ah ! " he said impartially. " Well, there will be a gentleman here in a minute who will help us to get to the bottom of the case."

Merrilees frowned.

"It is really impossible for me to wait," he murmured, pulling out his watch. "I have an appointment. Surely, inspector, you can't be so ridiculous as to suppose I'd steal the emerald and walk along with it in my pocket?"

"It is not likely, sir, I agree," the inspector replied. "But you will have to wait just a matter of five or ten minutes till we get this thing cleared up. Ah! here is his lordship."

A tall man of forty strode into the room. He was wearing a pair of dilapidated trousers and an old sweater.

"Now then, inspector, what is all this?" he said. "You have got hold of the emerald, you say? That's splendid, very smart work. Who are these people you have got here?

His eye ranged over James and came to rest on Merrilees. The forceful personality of the latter seemed to dwindle and shrink.

"Why—Jones!" exclaimed Lord Edward Campion.

"You recognize this man, Lord Edward?" asked the inspector sharply.

"Certainly I do," said Lord Edward dryly. "He is my valet, came to me a month ago. The fellow they sent down from London was on to him at once, but there was not a trace of the emerald anywhere among his belongings."

"He was carrying it in his coat pocket," the inspector declared. "This gentleman put us on to him." He indicated James.

In another minute James was being warmly congratulated and shaken by the hand.

"My dear fellow," said Lord Edward Campion. "So you suspected him all along, you say?"

"Yes," said James. "I had to trump up the story about my pocket being picked to get him into the police station."

"Well, it is splendid," said Lord Edward, "absolutely splendid. You must come back and lunch with us, that is, if you haven't lunched? It is late, I know, getting on for two o'clock."

"No," said James; "I haven't lunched—but——"

"Not a word, not a word," said Lord Edward. "The Rajah, you know, will want to thank you for getting back his emerald for him. Not that I have quite got the hang of the story yet."

They were out of the police station by now, standing on the steps.

" As a matter of fact," said James, " I think I should like to tell you the true story."

He did so. His lordship was very much entertained.

" Best thing I ever heard in my life," he declared. " I see it all now. Jones must have hurried down to the bathing-hut as soon as he had pinched the thing, knowing that the police would make a thorough search of the house. That old pair of trousers I sometimes put on for going out fishing, nobody was likely to touch them, and he could recover the jewel at his leisure. Must have been a shock to him when he came to-day to find it gone. As soon as you appeared, he realized that you were the person who had removed the stone. I still don't quite see how you managed to see through that detective pose of his, though ! "

" A strong man," thought James to himself, " knows when to be frank and when to be discreet."

He smiled deprecatingly whilst his fingers passed gently over the inside of his coat lapel feeling the small silver badge of that little-known club, the Merton Park Super Cycling Club. An astonishing coincidence that the man Jones should also be a member, but there it was !

" Hallo, James ! "

He turned. Grace and the Sopworth girls were calling to him from the other side of the road. He turned to Lord Edward.

" Excuse me a moment ? "

He crossed the road to them.

" We are going to the pictures," said Grace. " Thought you might like to come."

" I am sorry," said James, " I am just going back to lunch with Lord Edward Campion. Yes, that man over there in the comfortable old clothes. He wants me to meet the Rajah of Maraputna."

He raised his hat politely and rejoined Lord Edward.

WALTER DE LA MARE (1893–   )
*has a charm of style and sincerity of touch
which characterize both his prose and his
poetry. He has written some of the most
delightful of childhood studies, of which " The
Mistletoe Child " is perhaps the finest example,
and many novels, volumes of short stories, and
mystic poems. In " The Orgy " we have humour which bears the mark of a fastidious artist.*

THE ORGY

IT was a Wednesday morning, and May Day, and London,
its West End too, crisp, brisk, scintillating. Even the horses
had come out in their Sunday best. With their nosegays and
ribbons and rosettes they might have been on their way to a
wedding—the nuptials of Labour and Capital, perhaps. As for
people, the wide pavements of the great street were packed with
them. Not so many busy idlers of the one sex as of the other,
of course, at this early hour—a top-hat here, a pearl-grey
Homburg there ; but of the feminine a host as eager and varie-
gated as the butterflies in an Alpine valley in midsummer ; some
stepping daintily down from their landaulettes like " Painted
Ladies " out of the chrysalis, and thousands of others, blues and
browns and speckleds and sables and tawnies and high-fliers and
maiden's blushes, from all parts of the world and from most of
the suburbs, edging and eddying along, this way, that way, their
eyes goggling, their tongues clacking, but most of them, their
backs to the highway, gazing, as though mesmerized, in and in
through the beautiful plate-glass windows at the motley merchan-
dise on the other side. And much of that on the limbs and trunks
of beatific images almost as lifelike but a good deal less active
than themselves.

The very heavens, so far as they could manage to peep under
the blinds, seemed to be smiling at this plenty. Nor had they
any need for care concerning the future, for nursemaids pushing
their baby-carriages before them also paraded the pavements,
their infant charges laid in dimpled sleep beneath silken awning
and coverlet, while here and there a tiny tot chattered up into
the air like a starling.

A clock, probably a church clock, and only just audible,
struck eleven. The sun from its heights far up above the roof-

177

tops blazed down upon the polished asphalt and walls with such an explosion of splendour that it looked as if everything had been repainted overnight with a thin coat of crystalline varnish and then sprinkled with frozen sea-water. And every human creature within sight seemed to be as heart-free and gay as this beautiful weather promised to be brief. With one exception only—poor Philip Pim.

And why not? He was young—so young in looks, indeed, that if Adonis had been stepping along at his side they might have been taken for cousins. He was charmingly attired, too, from his little, round, hard felt hat—not unlike Mercury's usual wear, but without the wings—to his neat brogue shoes; and he was so blonde, with his pink cheeks and flaxen hair, that at first you could scarcely distinguish his silken eyebrows and eyelashes, though they made up for it on a second glance. Care seemed never to have sat on those young temples. Philip looked as harmless as he was unharmed.

Alas! this without of his had no resemblance whatever to his within. He eyed vacantly a buzzing hive-like abandonment he could not share; first, because though he had the whole long day to himself he had no notion of what to do with it; and next, because only the previous afternoon the manager of the bank in which until then he had had a stool specially reserved for him every morning had shaken him by the hand and had wished him well—for ever. He had said how deeply he regretted Philip's services could not be indulged in by the bank any longer. He would miss him. Oh yes, very much indeed—but missed Philip must be.

The fact was, that Philip had never been able to add up pounds, shillings, and pence so that he could be certain the total was correct. His 9's, too, often looked like 7's, his 5's like 3's. And as "simple addition" was all but his sole duty in the bank, he would not have adorned its premises for a week if his uncle, Colonel Crompton Pim, had not been acquainted with one of its most stylish directors, and was not in the habit of keeping a large part of his ample fortune in its charge. He had asked Mr. Bumbleton to give Philip a chance. But chances—some as rapidly as Manx cats—come to an end. And Philip's had.

Now, if Colonel Pim had sent his nephew when he was a small boy to a nice public school, he might have been able by this time to do simple sums very well indeed. Philip might have become an accurate adder-up. It is well to look on the bright side of things. Unfortunately, when Philip was an infant, his health had not been very satisfactory—at least to his widowed mother—and he had been sent instead to a private academy.

There a Mr. Browne was the mathematical master—a Mr. Browne so much attached to algebra and to reading *The Times* in school hours that he had not much patience with the rudiments of arithmetic. "Just add it up," he would say, "and look up the answer. And if it isn't right, do it again."

It was imprudent of him, but in these early years poor Philip had never so much as dreamed that some day he was going to be a clerk on a stool. If he had, he might not perhaps have been so eager to look up the answers. But then, his uncle was fabulously rich and yet apparently unmarriageable, and Philip was his only nephew. Why, then, should he ever have paid any attention to banks, apart from the variety on which the wild thyme grows?

Term succeeded term, and still, though "a promising boy," he remained backward—particularly in the last of the three R's. And his holidays, so called, would be peppered with such problems as (*a*) if a herring and a half cost three half-pence, how many would you get for a shilling? (*b*) If a brick weighs a pound and half a brick, how much does it weigh? (*c*) If Moses was the son of Pharaoh's daughter, etc. ; and (*d*) Uncles and brothers have I none, and so on. And since, after successive mornings with a sheet of foolscap and a stub of pencil, Philip's answers would almost invariably reappear as (*a*) 18, (*b*) $1\frac{1}{2}$ lb., (*c*) his sister, and (*d*) himself, Colonel Pim grew more and more impatient, and Nature had long ago given him a good start.

He had a way, too, when carpeting poor Philip, of flicking his shepherd-plaid trouser-leg with his handkerchief, which seemed useless to every one concerned. And at last, instead of transferring his nephew from Mr. Browne to Christ Church, Oxford, or to Trinity College, Cambridge, or to some less delectable resort at an outlying university, he first (before setting out in pursuit of big game all around the world) consigned him to a tutor, who thanked his lucky stars the expedition would take the Colonel a long time ; and, on his return, gave them both a prolonged vacation.

And *then* had fallen the bolt from the blue. On the morning of his twenty-first birthday, which had promised to be so cool, so calm, so bright, Philip received a letter from his uncle. He opened it with joy ; he read it with consternation. It was in terms as curt as they looked illegible, and it was merely to tell him that what the Colonel called a post (but which was, in fact, a high stool) had been secured for his nephew, and that unless Philip managed to keep his seat on it for twelve consecutive months he would be cut off with a shilling.

Of these drear months about two and a half had somehow managed to melt away, and now not only was the stool rapidly following them into the limbo of the past, but at this very moment the Colonel was doubtless engaged, and with his usual zest, in keeping his promise. What wonder, then, Philip was not exactly a happy young man as he wandered this sunny populous May morning aimlessly on his way. There was nothing—apart from Everything around him—to make him so, except only one minute stroke of luck that had befallen him before breakfast.

When he had risen from his tumbled bed in his London lodgings, the sight of his striped bank trousers and his black bank coat and waistcoat had filled him with disgust. Opening the grained cupboard which did duty for a wardrobe—and in the indulgence of his tailor it was pretty full—he took down from a peg the festive suit he was now wearing, but which otherwise he had left unheeded since Easter. He found himself faintly whistling as he buttoned it on ; but his delight can be imagined when, putting his anger and thumb into an upper waistcoat pocket, he discovered—a sovereign. And an excellent specimen of one, with St. George in his mantle and the dragon on the one side of it, and King Edward VII.'s head—cut off at the neck as if he had sat to its designer in his bath—on the other. This, with four others very much like it, had been bestowed on Philip many months ago by his Uncle Charles—a maternal uncle, who had since perished in Paris. As the rest of Philip's pockets contained only 7½d. in all, this coin—how forgotten, he simply could not conjecture—was treasure trove indeed.

Now, poor Philip had never really cared for money. Perhaps he had always associated it with herrings and half-bricks. Perhaps he had never needed it quite enough. Since, moreover, immediately opposite his perch at the Bank there hung a framed antique picture of this commodity in process of being shovelled out of receptacles closely resembling coal-scuttles into great vulgar heaps upon a polished counter, and there weighed in brass scales like so much lard or glucose, he had come to like it less and less. On the other hand, he dearly enjoyed spending it. As with Adam and the happy birds in the Garden of Eden—linnet and kestrel and wren—he enjoyed seeing it fly. In this he was the precise antithesis of his uncle.

Colonel Crompton Pim loved money. He exulted in it (not vocally, of course) *en masse*, as the Pharaohs exulted in pyramids. And he abhorred spending it. For this (and for many another) reason he had little affection for mere objects —apart, that is, from *such* objects as golf clubs, shooting boots, or hippopotamus-hoof ink-stands, and he had not the smallest pleasure in buying anything for mere buying's sake.

His immense dormitory near Cheltenham, it is true, was full of furniture, but it was furniture, acquired in the 'sixties or thereabouts, for use and not for joy. Prodigious chairs with pigskin seats ; tables of a solidity that defied time and of a wood that laughed at the worm ; bedsteads of the Gog order ; wardrobes resembling Assyrian sarcophagi ; and ottomans which would seat with comfort and dignity a complete royal family. As for its " ornaments," they came chiefly from Benares.

And simply because poor Philip delighted in spending money and hated impedimenta such as these with the contempt a humming-bird feels for the corpse of a rhinoceros, he had never been able to take to his uncle—not even for the sake of what he owned. And it was impossible—as he fondly supposed—for any human being to take to him for any other reason. No, there was nothing in common between them, except a few branches of the family tree. And these the Colonel might already have converted into firewood.

Now, as poor Philip meandered listlessly along the street, fingering his Uncle Charles's golden sovereign in his pocket, he came on one of those gigantic edifices wherein you can purchase anything in the world—from a white elephant to a performing flea, from a cargo of coco-nuts to a tin-tack. This was the " store " at which his uncle " dealt." And by sheer force of habit, Philip mounted the welcoming flight of steps, crossed a large, flat, rubber mat, and went inside.

Having thus got safely in, he at once began to ponder how he was to get safely out—with any fraction, that is, of his golden sovereign still in his pocket. And he had realized in the recent small hours that with so little on earth now left to spend, except an indefinite amount of leisure, he must strive to spend that little with extreme deliberation.

So first, having breakfasted on a mere glance at the charred remnant of a kipper which his landlady had served up with his chicory, he entered a large gilded lift, or elevator, as the directors preferred to call it, *en route* to the restaurant. There he seated himself at a vacant table and asked the waitress to be so kind as to bring him a glass of milk and a bun. He nibbled, he sipped, and he watched the people—if people they really were, and not, as seemed more probable, automata intended to advertise the Ecclesiastical, the Sports, the Provincial, the Curio, the Export and the Cast-Iron Departments.

With this first sip of milk he all but made up his mind to buy

a little parting present for his uncle. It would be at least a
gentle gesture. With his second he decided that the Colonel
would be even less pleased to receive a letter *and*, say, a velvet
smoking-cap, or a pair of mother-of-pearl cuff-links, than just a
letter. By the time he had finished his bun he had decided to
buy a little something for himself. But try as he might, he could
think of nothing (for less than a guinea) that would be worthy of
the shade of his beloved Uncle Charles. So having pushed
seven-fifteenths of all he else possessed under his plate for his
freckled waitress, with the remaining fourpence he settled his bill
and went steadily downstairs. Nineteen minutes past ten—he
would have a good look about him before he came to a decision.

Hunger, it has been said, sharpens the senses, but it is apt
also to have an edgy effect upon the nerves. If, then, Philip's
breakfast had been less exacting, or his lunch had made up for
it, he might have spent the next few hours of this pleasant May
morning as a young man should—in the open air. Or he might
have visited the British Museum, or the National Gallery, or
Westminster Abbey. He might never, at any rate, in one brief
morning of his mortal existence have all but died again and again
of terror, abandon, shame, rapture, and incredulity. He might
never—but all in good time.

He was at a loose end, and it is then that habits are apt to
prevail. And of all his habits, Philip's favourite was that of
ordering " goods " on behalf of his uncle. The Colonel in his
fantastic handwriting would post him two weekly lists—one consisting of the " wanted," the other of complaints about the
previous week's " supplied." Armed with these, Philip would
set out for the building he was now actually in. The first list,
though not a thing of beauty, was a joy as long as it lasted. The
second, for he had always flatly refused to repeat his uncle's
sulphurous comments to any underling, he reserved for his old
enemy, the secretary of the establishment, Sir Leopold Bull.
And though in these weekly interviews Sir Leopold might boil
with rage and chagrin, he never boiled over. For the name of
Pim was a name of power in the secretary's office. The name of
Pim was that of a heavy shareholder ; and what the Colonel
wanted he invariably in the long-run got. A chest, say, of
Ceylon tea, " rich, fruity, bright infusion " ; a shooting-stick
(extra heavy, Brugglesdon tube pattern) ; a quart size tantalus,
for a wedding present, with a double spring sterling silver
Brahmin lock ; a hundredweight of sago ; a stymie, perhaps, or
a click—something of that sort.

These " order days " had been the balm of Philip's late

existence. His eyes fixed on his ledger and his fancy on, say, " Saddlery " or " Sports," he looked forward to his Wednesdays like a thirsty Arab in the desert to an oasis of palms and a well of water. Indeed, his chief regret at the bank, apart from little difficulties with his 9's and 3's, had been that his uncle's stores were closed on Saturday afternoons. And on Sundays. His hobby had, therefore, frequently given him indigestion, since he could indulge it only between 1 and 2 p.m. It was a pity, of course, that Colonel Pim was a man of wants so few, and those of so narrow a range. Possibly the suns of India had burned the rest out of him. But for Philip, any kind of vicarious purchase had been better than none. And now these delights, too, were for ever over. His fountain had run dry ; Sir Leopold had triumphed.

At this moment he found himself straying into the Portmanteau and Bag Department. There is nothing like leather, and here there was nothing *but* leather, and all of it made up into articles ranging in size from trunks that would hold the remains of a Daniel Lambert to card-cases that would hold practically nothing at all. And all of a sudden Philip fancied he would like to buy a cigarette-case. He would have preferred one of enamel or gold or morocco or tortoise-shell or lizard or shagreen ; or even of silver or suede. But preferences are expensive. And as he sauntered on, his dreamy eye ranging the counters in search merely of a cigarette-case he could *buy*, his glance alighted on a " gent's dressing-case."

It was of pigskin, and it lay, unlike the central figure in Rembrandt's " Lesson in Anatomy," so that the whole of its interior was in full view, thus revealing a modest row of silver-topped bottles, similar receptacles for soap, tooth-brushes, hair-oil, and eau-de-Cologne ; a shoe-horn, a boot hook, an ivory paper-knife and hair brushes, " all complete." Philip mused on it for a moment or two, perplexed by a peculiar effervescence that was going on in his vitals. He then approached the counter and asked its price.

" The price, sir ? " echoed the assistant, squinnying at the tiny oblong of pasteboard attached by a thread to the ring of the handle ; " the price of that article is seventeen, seventeen, six."

He was a tubby little man with boot-button eyes, and his " pounds," Philip thought, was a trifle unctuous.

" Ah," he said, putting a bold face on the matter, " it looks a sound work-a-day bag. A little mediocre perhaps. Have you anything—less ordinary ? "

" Something more expensive, sir ? Why, yes, indeed. This

is only a stock line—the "Archdeacon" or "County Solicitor" model. We have prices to suit all purses. Now if you were thinking of something which you might call resshersy, sir "— and Philip now was—" there's a dressing-case under the window over there was specially made to the order of Haitch Haitch the Maharaja of Jolhopolloluli. Unfortunately, sir, the gentleman deceased suddenly a week or two ago ; climate, I understand. His funeral obliquies were in the newspaper, you may remember. The consequence being, his ladies not, as you might say, con-curring, the dressing-case in a manner of speaking is on our hands—and at a considerable reduction. Only six hundred and seventy-five guineas, sir ; or rupees to match."

"May I look at it ? " said Philip. "Colonel Crompton Pim."

" By all means, sir," cried the little man as if until that moment he had failed to notice that Philip was a long-lost son ; " Colonel Crompton Pim ; of course. Here is the article, sir, a very handsome case, and quite unique, one of the finest, in fact, I have ever had the privilege of handling since I was trans-ferred to this Department—from the Sports, sir."

He pressed a tiny knob, the hinges yawned and Philip's mouth began to water. It was in sober sooth a handsome dress-ing-case, and the shaft of sunlight that slanted in on it from the dusky window seemed pleased to be exploring it. It was a dressing-case of tooled red Levant morocco, with gold locks and clasps and a lining of vermilion watered silk, gilded with a chaste design of lotus flowers, peacocks, and houris, the " fittings " being of gold and tortoise-shell, and studded with so many minute brilliants and seed pearls that its contents, even in that rather dingy sunbeam, appeared to be delicately on fire.

Philip's light blue eyes under their silken lashes continued to dwell on its charms in so spellbound a silence that for a moment the assistant thought the young man was about to swoon.

" Thank you very much," said Philip at last, turning away with infinite reluctance and with a movement as graceful as that of a fawn, or a *première danseuse* about to rest ; " I will keep it in mind. You are sure the management can afford the reduction ? "

Having made this rather airy comment, it seemed to Philip impolite, if not impossible, to ask the price of a " job line " of mock goatskin cigarette-cases that were piled up in dreary dis-order on a tray near at hand. So he passed out into the next de-partment, which happened to be that devoted to goods described as " fancy," though, so far as he could see, not very aptly.

Still he glanced around him as he hurried on, his heart bleeding for the unfortunates, old and helpless, or young and defenceless, doomed some day to welcome these exacerbating barbarous jocosities as gifts. But at sight of an obscure, puffy, maroon object demonstratively labelled " Pochette : Art Nouveau," his very skin contracted, and he was all but about to inquire of a large, veiled old lady with an ebony walking-stick who was manfully pushing her way through his *mélange*, possibly in search of a *prie-dieu*, how such dreadful phenomena were " begot, how nourishèd," and was himself preparing to join in the chorus, when a little beyond it his glance alighted on a minute writing-case, so fraily finished, so useless, so delicious to look at, handle, and smell, that even Titania herself might have paused to admire it. Philip eyed it with unconcealed gusto. His features had melted into the smile that so often used to visit them when as a little boy he had confided in his Uncle Charles that he preferred éclairs to doughnuts. Its price, he thought, was ridiculously moderate : only £67,10s.

" It's the décor, sir—Parisian, of course—that makes it a trifle costly," the assistant was explaining. " But it's practical as well as sheek and would add distinction to *any* young lady's boudoir, bedchamber, or lap. The ink, as you see, sir, cannot possibly leak from the bottle, if the case, that is, is held the right way up—so. The pencil, the ' *Sans Merci*,' as you observe, is of solid gold ; and the pen, though we cannot guarantee the nib, is set with life-size turquoises. The flaps will hold at least six sheets of small-size notepaper, and envelopes to—or not to— match. And *here* is a little something, a sort of calendar, sir, by which you can tell the day of the week of any day of the month in any year in any century from one A.D. to nine hundred and ninety-nine thousand, nine hundred and ninety-nine. It could then be renewed."

" M'm, very ingenious," Philip murmured, " and even Leap Year, I see. Is it unique, and so on ? "

" No doubt of it, sir. As a matter of fact a lady from Philadelphia—the United States of America, sir—ordered fifty facsillimies, platinum mounts, of this very article—only yesterday afternoon ; they get married a good deal over there, sir ; wedding presents."

" Quite, thank you, no," said Philip, firmly but pleasantly. " They say there is safety in numbers, but there seems to be precious little else. Have you anything less reproducible ? "

" Reproducible, sir ? Why, naturally, sir. You see this is only a counter article. While catering for the many, sir, we

are bound to keep an eye upon the few. For that very reason,
the management prefer to have the costlier specimens under
cover."

"Again, thank you," said Philip hurriedly. "What evils
are done in thy name, O Philadelphia! I may return
later."

He emerged from the Fancy Goods Department, feeling at
the same moment crestfallen and curiously elated. His mind,
in fact, at this moment resembled a volcano the instant before its
gloom is fated to burst into a blazing eruption. Though very
hazily, he even recognized the danger he was in. So in hope to
compose himself he sat down for a minute or two on a Madeira
wicker chair intended perhaps by the management for this very
purpose, and found himself gazing at a large black Chinese cat,
in the glossiest of glazed earthenware, and as lifelike as Oriental
artifice could make it. It was seated in a corner under a high
potted palm, and it wore a grin upon its features that may have
come from Cheshire, but which showed no symptom whatever of
vanishing away. At sight of it—for Philip was not only partial
to cats but knew the virtues of the black variety—a secret fibre
seemed to have snapped in his head. "Good luck!" the
creature smirked at him. And Philip smirked back. A flame
of anguished defiance and desire had leapt up in his body. He
would show his uncle what was what. He would learn him to
cut nephews off with shillings. He would dare and do and die!

He rose, refreshed and renewed. It was as if he had tossed
off a bumper of "Veuve Clicquot" of 1066. He must himself
have come over with the Conqueror. A shop-walker lurking near
was interrupted in the middle of an enormous gape by the
spectacle of this Apollonian young figure now entering his department—Pianofortes and American Organs. There was something in the leopard-like look of him, something so princely and
predatory in his tread, that this Mr. Jackson would have been
almost ready to confess that he was moved. Frenchily dark and
Frenchily sleek, he bowed himself almost double.

"Yes, sir?" he remarked out loud.

"I want, I think, a pianoforte," said Philip. "A Grand."

"Thank you, sir; this way, please. Grand pianofortes,
Mr. Smithers."

"I want a Grand piano," repeated Philip to Mr. Smithers,
an assistant with a slight cast in his left eye and an ample
gingerish moustache. But in spite of these little handicaps
Philip liked him much better than Mr. Jackson. A far-away
glimpse of Mrs. Smithers and of all the little Smitherses seated

round their Sunday leg of mutton at Hackney or at Brondesbury, maybe, had flashed into his mind.

"Grands, sir," cried Mr. Smithers, moving his moustache up and down with a curious rotary constriction of the lips ; "this way, please."

The young man was conducted along serried ranks of Grands. They stood on their three legs, their jaws tight shut, as mute as troops on parade. Philip paced on and on, feeling very much like the late Duke of Cambridge reviewing a regiment of his Guards. He paused at length in front of a "Style 8 ; 7 ft. 9 in., square-legged, blackwood, mahogany-trimmed Bismarck."

"It *looks* spacious," he smiled amiably. "But the finish ! And why overhung ? "

"Overstrung, sir ? " said Mr. Smithers. "That's merely a manner of speaking, sir, relating solely to its inside. But this, of course, is not what we specificate as a *grand* Grand. For tone and timber and resonance and pedal work and solidity and *wear* —there isn't a better on the market. I mean on the rest of the market. And if you were having in mind an everlasting instrument for the nursery or for a practice room—and we supply the new padded partitioning—this would be precisely the instrument, sir, you were having in mind. The young are sometimes a little hard on pianofortes, sir. They mean well, but they are but children after all ; and——"

"Now let—me—think," Philip interposed. "To be quite candid, I wasn't having anything of that sort in mind. My sentiments are England for the English ; and Bismarck, you know, though in girth and so on a remarkable man, was in other respects, a little—well, miscellaneous. It is said that he mixed his champagne with stout—or was it cocoa ? On the other hand, I have no wish to be insular, and I *may* order one of these constructions later. For a lady, the niece, as a matter of fact, of a governess of my uncle Colonel Crompton Pim's when he was young—as young at least as it was possible for him to be—who is, I believe, thinking of taking—of taking in—pupils. But we will see to that later. Have you anything that I could really look at ? "

Mr. Smithers's moustaches twirled like a weathercock. "Why, yes, sir. Just now we are up to our eyes in pianos— flooded ; and if I may venture to say so, sir, Bismarck was never no friend of *mine*. All this," and he swept his thumb in the direction of the avenue of instruments that stretched behind them, "they may be Grands, but they're most of them foreign, and if you want a little something as nice to listen to as it is natty to look at, and *not* a mere menadjery fit only for an 'awl,

there is a little what they call a harpsichord over yonder, sir.
It's a bijou model, de Pompadour case, hand-painted throughout—cupids and scallops and what-not, all English gut, wire,
metal, and jacks, and I defy any dealer in London to approximate it, sir, in what you might call pure form.   No noise and all
music, sir, and that *mellow* you scarcely know where to look.   A
lady's instrument—a titled lady's.   And only seven hundred and
seventy-seven guineas, sir, all told."

" Is it unique ? " Philip inquired.

" Unique, sir ?   There's not another like it in Europe."

Philip smiled at Mr. Smithers very kindly out of his blue
eyes.   " But what about America ? " he said.

The assistant curved what seemed an almost unnecessarily
large hand round his lips.   " Between you and me, sir, if by
America," he murmured, " you're meaning the United States,
why, Messrs. Montferas *&* de Beauguyou refuse to ship in that
direction.   It ruins their tone.   In fact, sir, they are what's
called *difficult*.   They make for nobody and nowhere but as a
favour ;   and that instrument over there was built for——"

He whispered the sesame so low that water rustling on a
pebbled beach would have conveyed to Philip tidings more intelligible.   But by the look in Mr. Smithers's eyes Philip guessed
that the lady in question moved in a lofty, though possibly a
narrow, circle.

" Ah ! " he said ;   " then that settles it.   A home away from
home.   Charity begins there.   I shall want it to-morrow.   I shall
want them both to-morrow.   I mean the pianos.   And perhaps
a more democratic instrument for the servants' hall.   But I will
leave that to you."

Mr. Smithers pretended not to goggle.   " Why, yes, sir, that
can be easily arranged.   In London, I *ho*—conjecture ? "

" In London," said Philip, " Grosvenor Square."   For at
that very instant, as if at the summons of a jinnee, there had
wafted itself into his memory the image of a vacant and " highly
desirable residence," which his casual eye had glanced upon
only the afternoon before, and which had proclaimed itself " to
be let."

" Grosvenor Square, sir ;   oh yes, sir ? "   Mr. Smithers was
ejaculating, order-book in hand.   " I will arrange for their
removal at once.   The three of them—quite a nice little set, sir."

" Pim, Crompton, Colonel," chanted Philip.   " R-*O*-M ;
deferred account ;   *thank* you.   4-4-4, yes, four hundred and forty-
four, Grosvenor Square.   I am—that is, *we* are furnishing
there."

But his gentle emphasis on the " we " was so courtly in effect that it sounded more like an afterthought than a piece of information. Nevertheless it misled Mr. Smithers. Intense fellow-feeling beamed from under his slightly overhung forehead. " And I am sure, sir, if I may make so bold, I wish you both every happiness. I am myself of a matrimonial turn. And regret it, sir ? *never !* I always say if every——"

" That's very kind indeed of you," said Philip, averting his young cheek, which having flushed had now turned a little pale. " And, if *I* may be so bold, I am perfectly certain Mrs. Smithers is of the same way of thinking. Which is the best way to the Best Man's Department, if I take in Portmanteaux and the Fancies on my way ? "

Mr. Smithers eyed him with the sublimest admiration. " Straight through, sir, on the left behind them Chappels. On the same floor, but right out on the farther side of the building. As far as you can go."

" That is exactly what I was beginning to wonder—precisely how far I can go. This little venture of mine is a rather novel experience, and at the moment I am uncertain of its issue. But tell me, why is it our enterprising American friends have not yet invented a *lateral* lift ? "

" Now that's passing strange, too, sir ; for I've often fancied it myself," said Mr. Smithers. " But you see in a department like this there's not much time for quiet thought, sir, with so much what you might call hidden din about. As a matter of fact, when I was younger, sir—and that happens to us all—I did invent a harmonium key-stifler—rubber, and pith and wool— *so*—and a small steel spring, quite neat and entirely unnoticeable. But the manufacturers wouldn't look at it ; not they ! "

" I don't believe," said Philip, folding up his bill, " they ever look at anything. Not closely, you know. But if ever I do buy a harmonium," he put his head a little on one side and again smiled at Mr. Smithers, " I shall insist on the stifler. I suppose," he added reflectively, " you haven't by any chance a nice pedigree Amati or Stradivarius in stock ? I have a little weakness for fiddles."

Mr. Smithers, leaning heavily on the counter on both his thumbs, smiled, but at the same time almost imperceptibly shook his head.

" I fancied it was unlikely," said Philip. " What's that over there ; in the glass case, I mean ? "

" That, sir," said Mr. Smithers, twinkling up, " in that glass case there ? That's a harp, sir. And a lovely little piece

that is. Child's size, sir. What they call minnychoore, and well
over a century old, but still as sweet as a canary. It was made,
so they say, for Mozart, the composer, sir, as you might be
aware, in 1781, and up in the top corner is scratched the letters
A. W. No doubt of it, sir—A. W. I've seen a picture of the
mite himself playing like an angel in his nightcap, and not a day
over seven ; you'd hardly believe it, and his parents coming in
at the door. Surprising. Then Schumann, *he* had it, sir—I
mean the harp ; and Schumann, though I don't know how he
could dissuade himself to part with it, *he* passed it on to Brahms,
another composer—and very much thought of even though a bit
nearer *our* day. But you'll find it all neatly set out on the brass
label at the foot. It's all there, sir. There's many a custo——"

"Indeed ! " said Philip ; "Brahms, Schumann, Mozart,
what scenes we are recalling ! And here it rests at last. The
knacker's yard. How very, very sad. Why, of course, Mr.
Smithers, we must have that sent on too—and packed very, very
carefully. Is the glass case extra ? "

Mr. Smithers gulped. "I am exceedingly sorry, sir," he said,
" exceedingly sorry, but it's not for sale ; I mean—*except* the case."

"Not for sale," retorted Philip impulsively. "But what
is the use, Mr. Smithers, of a mercenary institution like this
unless everything in it is for sale ? You cannot mean for raw
advertisement ? "

Mr. Smithers was covered with confusion. " I am sure,
sir," he said, " that the directors would do their utmost to consider your wishes. They would be very happy to do so. But if
you will excuse my mentioning it, I should myself very much miss
that harp. I have been in this department thirteen years now.
. . . My little boy. . . . It is the only thing . . ."

It was Philip's turn to be all in confusion. " Good gracious
me, I quite understand," he said ; " not another word, Mr.
Smithers. I wouldn't *think* of pressing the point. None the
less I can assure you that even if it had been for sale I should
always have welcomed you whenever you care to come to
Grosvenor Square and take another look at it. And, of course,
your little boy too—*all* your little boys."

Mr. Smithers appeared to be lost in gratitude. " If only,"
he began, a light that never was on sea or land in his eye—but
words failed him.

At the other end of the " Chappels " Philip again encountered the walker, Mr. Jackson, still looking as much like a self-
possessed bridegroom as it is possible for a high collar and a
barber to achieve.

" I see," said Philip, " you exhibit specimens of the tuber-phone (and, by the way, I would suggest *a* instead of ' er '), the tubaphone, the clogbox, and the Bombaboo, iniquities at the same time negroid and old-fashioned, but though in a recent visit to Budapest I found even the charming little linden-shaded shops—along the Uffel-gang, you know, not, of course, a fashion-able part of the city—crammed with models of the ' Haba-Stein,' a microtonic instrument with five keyboards and Hindu effects, intended, of course, for the polytonal decompositions of the ' Nothing-but-Music ' school—*most* interesting ; I see *no* trace of it here. I am not a neoteromaniac, but still, we must keep abreast, we must keep abreast ! "

He waved a not unfriendly glove over his head, smiled, and went on.

Mr. Smithers had also watched the slim, grey, young figure until it had turned the corner and was out of sight. He then had a word with his floor chief.

" Pim, eh, Crompton," said Mr. Jackson, squinting morosely at his underling's open order-book. " ' Setting up house ? ' Then I suppose the old gent must have sent in his checks. Not that I'm surprised this nephew of his hasn't bought his black yet. Close-fisted, purple-nosed, peppery old —— ! There won't be many to cry their eyes out over *his* arums and gardenias."

Mr. Smithers, being a family man, felt obliged to seem to enjoy as much as possible his immediate chief's society.

" All I can say *is*," he ventured, " that young feller, and he's a gentleman if ever there was one, is making it fly."

He *was*. At this moment Philip was assuring Assistant No. 6 in the Portmanteau Department that unless the Maharaja of Jolhopolloluli's dressing-case could be dispatched next day to reach No. 444 Grosvenor Square by tea-time he need not trouble. " A few other little things," he explained, " are being sent at the same time." No. 6 at once hastened to the house tele-phone and asked for the secretary's office. The line was engaged.

But he need not have hesitated, for when a young man with a Pim for an uncle and of so much suavity and resource makes his wishes known, this world is amiability itself. Philip was warming up. However bland in outward appearance, he was by this time at a very enlivening temperature. He had tasted blood, as the saying goes ; and he was beginning to see the need of setting a good example. Customers, like the coneys, are usually a feeble folk. His little sortie was turning into a crusade.

By this time he had all but finished disporting himself in the Furniture Department. " Three large reception rooms, one of them extensive," had run his rather naked catalogue, " a ballroom, a dining-room, a breakfast-room, and a little pretty dumpy all-kinds of angles morning-room with a Cherubini ceiling and a Venetian chimney-piece, eighteenth century, in lapis lazuli and glass. Bedrooms, let me see, say, twenty-two— just to go on with (but not in), eleven of them for personal use, and the rest, staff. That, I think, will do for the present. We face east or west as the case may be ; and nothing, please, of the 'decorative,' the quaint, or the latest thing out. Nothing shoddy, shapeless, or sham. I dislike the stuffy and the fussy and mere trimmings ; and let the beds be *beds*. Moreover, I confess to being sadly disappointed in the old, the 'antique,' furniture you have shown me. The choice is restricted, naïve, and incongruous, and I have looked in vain for anything that could not be easily rivalled in the richer museums. However, let there be as many so-called antique pieces as possible, and those as antique as you can manage. Period, origin, design, harmony —please bear these in mind."

The assistants clustering round him, bowed.

" If I have time I will look through the department again on my way down. Seven hundred guineas for the cheaper of the Chippendale four-posters seems a little exorbitant ; and three hundred and fifty for the William and Mary wall-glass—I fear it's been resilvered and patched. Still, I agree you can but do your best—I say you can all of you but do your best—and I must put up with that. What I *must* insist on, however, is that everything I have mentioned—everything—must be in its place to-morrow afternoon—carpets and so on will, of course, precede them—by four o'clock. And let there be no trace left of that indescribable odour of straw and wrappings—from Delhi, I should think—which accompanies removals. 444 Grosvenor Square. Pim — Crompton — Colonel : R-*O*-M. Thank you. To the left ? *Thank* you."

This " floor-chief" hastened on in front of his visitor as if he were a Gehazi in attendance on a Naaman, and the young man presently found himself in a scene overwhelmingly rich with the colours, if not the perfumes, of the Orient. Here a complete quarter of an hour slid blissfully by. Mere wooden furniture, even when adorned with gilt, lacquer, ivory, or alabaster, can be disposed of with moderate ease ; and especially if the stock of the tolerable is quickly exhausted. But Persian, Chinese, if not Turkey, carpets are another matter.

Philip sat erect on a gimcrack gilded chair, his cane and hat in his left hand, his gloves in his right, while no less than three sturdy attendants in baize aprons at one and the same moment strewed their matchless offerings at his feet, and an infuriated and rapidly multiplying group of would-be customers in search of floorcloth, lino, and coco-nut matting stood fuming beyond. But first come first served is a good old maxim, and even apart from it Philip was unaware of their company. He lifted not so much as an eyebrow in their direction.

In the meantime, however, the cash balance in his uncle's bank, and much else besides, had long since as rapidly vanished as the vapour from a locomotive on a hot summer's day. From the Carpet Department, vexed that time allowed him only one of London's chief treasuries to ransack—such are the glories of Bokhara and Ispahan—he hastened down to the wine counters. Here, childishly confident in the cellarage of No. 444, Philip indulged a pretty palate *not* inherited from his uncle : claret, Burgundy, hock, sherry, cherry brandy, green Chartreuse, and similar delicate aids to good talk and reflection. He was ingenuous but enthusiastic. Port he ignored.

From " Wines " he made his way through the galleries exhibiting curtains and " hangings " (he shuddered), and china and glass—" most discouraging." His spirits revived a little when yet another defunct and barbaric prince, this time from Abyssinia, supplied him in the Car Department with a vehicle whose only adequate use, to judge from the modesty of its dashboard, the simplicity of its engine, and its price, would be a journey from this world into the next. Nevertheless his Highness had left it behind.

Fleeting visits to counters bristling with ironmongery, turnery, kitchen utensils, and provisions, and from motives of principle he omitted all mention of mulligatawny paste, chutney, West India pickles, and similar fierce and barbarous comestibles, vanished out of memory like the patterns of a kaleidoscope. The rather noisy annexe reserved for live stock Philip left unvisited. After deserts of dead stock it sounded inviting, but Philip's was a dainty nose and he was sorry for orang-outangs.

So, too, with books. He had clear convictions of what a gentleman's library should be without, but decided that it would take more leisure than he could spare this morning to expound them. Even the sight of a Work of Reference, however, is an excellent sedative ; he ordered the choicest of who's-whos, dictionaries, atlases, encyclopædias, bird, flower, and cookery books—with a copy of " Bradshaw "—and retired.

As for pictures and statuary, one anguished glance into the dreadful chambers devoted to the fine arts had sent him

scurrying on like a March hare. Nor, as he rather sadly
realized, had he any cause to linger at the portals of the
Monumental-Masonry Department, and he now suddenly
found himself in the midst of a coruscating blaze of the
precious metals and the still more precious stones. He had
strayed into " Jewellery "—a feast for Aladdin. Gold in particular—goblets and bowls and tankards, plates, platters, and
dishes of it; clocks, chronometers, watches—from massive
turnips, memorial of the Georges, to midgets like a threepenny-
piece in crystal and enamel, many of them buzzing like bees,
and all of them intent on the kind of time which is *not* wild or
always nectarous, but of which Philip had always supposed there
was an inexhaustible supply. But not, alas, for all purposes.
Indeed, these officious reminders of the actual hour had for the
first time a little scared him.

In the peculiar atmosphere that hangs over any abundant
array of sago, cooked meats, candles, biscuits, coffee, tea, ginger,
and similar wares, he had been merely a young bachelor on the
brink of an establishment. But at sight of this otiose display of
gew-gaws in the lamplit mansion in which he now found himself,
his fancy had suddenly provided him with a bride. She was of a
fairness incomparably fair. The first faint hint of this eventu-
ality had almost unnerved him. He lost his head and—his
heart being inconcerned—his taste also. In tones as languid as
the breezes of Arabia he had at once ordered her rings, bracelets,
necklaces, pendants, brooches, ear-rings, not to speak of be-
diamonded plumes and tiaras, that would daunt the dreams even
of the complete bevy of musical comedy young ladies on the
British stage—not to mention those of Buenos Aires. And then,
oddly enough, he had come to himself, and paused.

At the very moment of opening his mouth in repetition of a
solo with which he was now entirely familiar—" R-*O*-M," and
so on—he sat instead, gaping at the tall, calm, bald, venerable
old gentleman on the other side of the counter. He had flushed.

" Have you," he inquired almost timidly at last, his eyes fixed
on a chastely printed list of cutlery and silverware that lay on the
glass case at his elbow, " have you just one really simple, lovely,
rare, precious, and, well, unique little trinket suitable for a lady ?
Young, you know ? An *un*-birthday present ? "

The old gentleman looked up, looked at, looked *in*, smiled
fondly, reminiscently, and, selecting a minute key on a ring
which he had drawn out of his pocket, opened a safe not half a
dozen yards away. " We have this," he said.

" This," at first, was a little fat morocco leather case. He pressed the spring. Its lid flew open. And for an instant Philip went gravel blind. But it was not so much the suppressed lustre of the jewels within that had dazed his imagination as the delicate marvel of their setting. They lay like lambent dewdrops on the petals of a flower. The old gentleman gazed too.

" The meaning of the word ' simple,' " he suggested ruminatively, " is one of many degrees. This, sir, is a Benvenuto Cellini piece." He had almost whispered the last few syllables as if what in workmanship were past all rivalry was also beyond any mortal pocket ; as if, in fact, he were telling secrets of the unattainable. The tone piqued Philip a little.

" It is charming," he said. " But have you nothing, then, of Jacques de la Tocqueville's, or of Rudolph von Himmeldommer's, nothing of—dear me, the name escapes me—the earlier Florentine, you will remember, no doubt referred to in *Sordello*, who designed the chryselephantine bowl for the Botticelli weddingfeast ? But never mind. Nothing Greek ? Nothing Etruscan— *poudre d'or ?* Are you suggesting that the Winter Palace was thrice looted in vain ? "

The old gentleman was accustomed to the airs and graces of fastidious clients and merely smiled. He had not been listening very intently. " You will appreciate the difficulty, sir, of keeping anything but our more trifling pieces actually within reach of the nearest burglar with a stick of gun-cotton or an acetylene lamp. This "—he stirred the little leather case with his finger as lightly as a cat the relics of a mouse, and its contents seemed softly to sizzle in subdued flames of rose and amber and blue—" this," he said, " happens not to be our property. It is merely in our keeping. And though to an article of such a nature it is absurd to put a price, we have been asked to dispose of it ; and by—well, a client for whom we have the profoundest respect."

" I see." Philip pondered coldly on the bauble, though his heart was a whirlpool of desire and admiration. He swallowed. The remote tiny piping of a bird that was neither nightingale nor skylark, and yet might be either or both, had called to him as from the shores of some paradisal isle hidden in the mists of the future. He glanced up at the old gentleman, but his bald, long, grey countenance was as impassive as ever.

" I'll take it," Philip said, and for a while could say no more. When speech was restored to him, he asked that it should be delivered not " with the other things," and not to any butler or major-domo or other crustacean that might appear in answer to a knock at No. 444, but by special messenger into his own personal private hands.

" Precisely at half-past four, if you please." The old gentleman bowed. As there was not enough room in the money column
of his order-book for the noughts, he had written in the price in
longhand, and was engaged in printing the figures 444 in the
place reserved for the customer's address, when a small but
clearly actual little voice at Philip's elbow suddenly shrilled up
into his ear—

" Mr. Philip Pim, sir ? " Philip stood stock-still, stiffened,
his heart in his ears. " The sekkertary, sir," the piping voice
piped on, " asks me to say he'd be much obliged if you would be
so kind as to step along into his office on your way *hout*, sir."

The tone of this invitation, though a little Cockney in effect,
was innocence and courtesy itself ; yet at sound of it every
drop of blood in Philip's body—though he was by no means a
bloated creature—had instantly congealed. This was the end,
then. His orgy was over. His morning of mornings was done.
The afflatus that had wafted him on from floor to floor had
wisped out of his mind like the smoke of a snuffed-out candle.
Yet *still* the bright thought shook him : he had had a Run for his
money. No—better than that : he had had a Run *gratis*.

He must collect his wits : they had gone wool-gathering.
At last he managed to turn his head and look down at the small,
apple-cheeked, maroon-tunicked page-boy at his side—apple-
cheeked, alas, only because he had but that week entered the
sekkertary's service and his parents were of country stock.

" Tell Sir Leopold Bull "—Philip smiled at the infant—
" that I will endeavour to be with him in the course of the afternoon. Thank you. That," he added for the ear of his friend
on the other side of the counter, " that will be all."

But Philip was reluctant to leave him. These four syllables,
as he had heard himself uttering them, sounded on in his ear with
the finality of a knell. He was extremely dubious of what would
happen if he let go of the counter. His knees shook under him.
A dizzy vacancy enveloped him in. With a faint wan smile at
the old gentleman, who was too busily engaged in returning his
treasures to the safe to notice it, he managed to edge away at last.

Every mortal thing around him, gilded ceiling to grandfather clock, was at this moment swaying and rotating, as will the
ocean in the eyes of a sea-sick traveller gloating down upon it
from an upper deck. He felt ill with foreboding.

But breeding tells. And courage is a mistress that has never
been known to jilt a faithful heart. Philip was reminded of this
as he suddenly caught sight of a sort of enormous purple beef-
eater, resembling in stature a Prussian dragoon, and in appearance

a Javanese Jimjam. This figure stood on duty in the doorway, and appeared to be examining him as closely as if he were the heir to the English throne (or the most nefarious crook from Chicago). As Philip drew near he looked this monster full in his fish-like eye, since he was unable to do anything else. But try as he might, he could not pass him in silence.

" Ask Sir Leopold Bull, please," he said, " to send an official to show me the way to his office. He will find me somewhere in the building."

" I can take you there meself," replied the giant hoarsely. He could indeed—bodily.

" Thank you," replied Philip. " I have no doubt of it. But I should be much obliged if you would at once deliver my message."

He then groped his way to yet another wicker chair not many yards along a corridor festooned with knick-knacks from Japan and the Near East, and clearly intended for speedy disposal. He eyed them with immense distaste and sat down.

" Nothing, whatever, thank you," he murmured to a waitress who had approached him with a card containing a list of soft drinks. Never in his life had he so signally realized the joys of self-restraint. And though at the same moment he thrust finger and thumb into his waistcoat pocket in search of his Uncle Charles's last sovereign, it was with a view not to material but to moral support. Years before he had often tried the same device when as a small boy deadly afraid of the dark he had managed at last to thrust his fevered head up and out from under his bed-clothes, and to emit a dreadful simulacrum of a croupy cough. He had never known it to fail of effect, and it was always nice to know his mother was *there*.

So, too, with his Uncle Charles's sovereign. It was nice to know it was there, though it was not the dark Philip was now afraid of, but the light. Resting the ivory handle of his walking-stick on his lower lip, he began to think. What would his sentence be ? A first offender, but not exactly a novice. Not, at any rate, he hoped, in taste and judgment. Months or years ? Hard labour or penal servitude ? So swift is the imagination that in a few seconds Philip found himself not only—his sentence served, the smiling governor bidding farewell—*out* and a free man again, but fuming with rage that he had not managed to retain a single specimen of his spoils. The Jobbli dressing-bag, for instance, or that tiny, that utterly and inimitable " unique " little Sheraton Sheridan writing-desk.

He came back a little stronger from this expedition into the future. For reassurance, like hope, springs eternal in the human breast. His one regret was not so much that he had been found out (that might come later), but that he had been found out so soon. How much bolder, less humiliating, nobler, to have actually bearded that old " curmudgen " of an uncle of his, swapp or bogie in hand, in his den !

That in any event he would have been " found out " on the morrow, as soon, that is, as the first van arrived at No. 444, he had realized long ago. He certainly would not have been found " in " ! But even one brief night in May seems, in prospect, a long interval between being a Crœsus and a felon in Holloway Jail.

He was recalled from these reflections by a young man whose sleek black hair was parted as neatly in front and in the middle as his morning coat was parted behind. A few paces distant, like a mass of gilded pudding-stone, stood the giant from the Jewellery Department. Were they in collusion ? Philip could not decide.

" If you would step this way, sir, to the secretary's office," said the young man, " Sir Leopold Bull would be very much obliged."

Philip mounted to his feet and, though he flatly refused to step *that* way, followed him—to his doom. That, however, was not to be instantaneous, for on his arrival Sir Leopold Bull, rising from his roll-top desk with a brief but thrilling smile, first proffered a plump white hand to his visitor and then a chair. It seemed to be a needlessly polite preamble to the interview that was to follow. Philip ignored the hand but took the chair.

" Thank you," he said. " I do hope you will some day take my advice, Sir Leopold, to *sim*plify the arrangement of this building. It is a perfect labyrinth, and I always miss my way." With a sigh he sank down into the cushions. He was tired.

" My uncle, Colonel Crompton Pim," he continued, " is unable to spare a moment to see you this morning. I regret to say he strongly disapproved of the Bombay ducks, or was it the Clam Chowder, you sent him on Friday. They were beneath contempt."

Sir Leopold smiled once more, but even more placatingly. " I had the privilege of seeing Colonel Crompton Pim only yesterday afternoon," he replied. " He then expressed his satisfaction, for the time being, at the golf balls—the new *Excelsior* brand—with one of which we had the pleasure of supplying him *gratis* a week or two ago. The Bombay ducks shall be withdrawn immediately. I must apologize for not seeking you out in person, Mr. Pim, but what I have to say is somewhat of a private nature, and——"

" Yes," said Philip, realizing how thin was the edge of the

wedge which Sir Leopold was at this moment insinuating into the matter in hand. "Yes, quite." And he opened his innocent blue eyes as wide as he could, to prevent them from blinking. He kept them fixed, too, on the close-shaven face, its octopus-like mouth and prominent eyes, with ill-suppressed repulsion. To be a fly that had fallen a victim to such a spider as this !

" It would please me better," he went on, "if you would arrive as rapidly as possible at the matter you wish to discuss with me. I am free for five minutes, but I must beg you not to waste our time. And please tell your porter over there to go away. Scenes are distasteful to me."

The face of the porter, who seemed to have been created solely for his bulk, turned as crimson as a specimen of *sang-du-bœuf*. He appeared to be hurt at having been described as a " scene." But wages are of more importance than feelings, and he withdrew.

" You have had a busy morning, Mr. Pim," said the secretary. " No less than seven of my assistants who have had the privilege of waiting upon you have been monopolizing me for some time with telephone messages. I hope I am not being too intrusive if I venture to congratulate you, sir, on what I suppose to be Colonel Crompton Pim's approaching——"

" Candidly, Sir Leopold," said Philip firmly, " that *would* be venturing too far. Much too far. Let us say no more about it. What precise charge are you intending to bring against me ? "

There was a pause while the world continued to rotate.

" For which article ? " breathed Sir Leopold.

Philip gazed steadily at the full, bland, secretive countenance. It was as if once again he had heard that seraphic bird-like voice sounding in the remote blue sky above the storm-clouds that now hung so heavily over his beating heart.

" Oh, I mean for delivery," he said. " Mine was—was a large order."

" But, my dear sir, we shouldn't dream of making *any* such charge. *Any* service to Colonel Pim . . ." The faint sob in his voice would have done credit to Caruso.

Philip stooped to hide the cataract of relief that had swept over his face, then raised his head again. How could he be sure that this was anything more than play-acting—the torture of suspense ? " Ah, well," he said, " that is no matter now. I gather there was some other point you had in mind—in *view*, I should say."

" Oh, only," said Sir Leopold, " to ask if Colonel Pim would be so kind as to subscribe as usual to our Fund for the Ameliora-

tion of the Conditions of the Offspring of Superannuated Shop
Assistants. Mainly orphans, Mr. Pim. We must all die, Mr.
Pim, and some of us have to die earlier in life than others. Still,
our average here is little worse than that of any other large London
establishment. In Petrograd, or was it Los Angeles, I am given
to understand, a shop assistant at two-and-thirty is a shop assistant with at least one foot in the grave. It is the little orphans,
the fatherless ones, who, from no apparent fault of their own,
have to be left to the tender mercies of a busy world ? It would
grieve you, sir, which Heaven forbid, if I told you how many of
these wee small things there are now on our hands. Chubby,
joysome, rosebud little creatures, as happy as the day is long.
Nevertheless it is a little thoughtless to marry, Mr. Pim, when
it is only orphans one can leave behind one. On the other hand,
there is a silver lining to *every* cloud. Without these infants we
should be deprived of a good cause. An excellent cause. And
it's causes that keep us going. Last year I think Colonel Pim
very kindly contributed half a guinea."

" In cash ? " Philip inquired sharply.

" We debited his account," said Sir Leopold.

" Well, then," said Philip, " please understand that my uncle
regrets that little laxity. He has hardened. He now entirely
disapproves of orphans and orphanages. The shop assistant,
he was saying to me only the other day, is a person who should
be grateful to Providence that *he* has no justification for dabbling
in matrimony. The more celibate they are, in his opinion, the
better. But recollect, Sir Leopold, that until we arrive at the
higher and fewer salaried officials in your establishment, I feel
myself in no way bound to *share* my uncle's views. Your staff is
as courteous and considerate as it appears to be unappreciated.
A man's a man for a' that. And a' that. Let us talk of brighter
things."

Sir Leopold did his utmost to conceal the wound to his vanity.
" I am sorry to seem to be persistent," he assured his client, " but
Colonel Pim only yesterday was so kind as to say he would *con-
sider* my appeal. I take it, then, that he has changed his mind ? "

" My uncle," retorted Philip tartly, " has a mind that is the
better for being changed." For an instant he saw the face before
him as it would appear in due course in the witness-box ; and
his very soul revolted. That pitiless Machine called Society
might have its merits, but not *this* cog in its wheel ! " I myself
implored my uncle," he added bitterly, " to give the orphans the
cold shoulder. What in the chronic sirocco of his next world
would be the use to him of a mere half-guinea's worth of cooling

breezes? Scarcely a sop in the pan. Indeed, only a passion for the conventional prevented him from asking for his previous donations to be returned."

Sir Leopold appeared to be engaged in rapidly bolting something—possibly his pride. It was at any rate not part of his secretarial duties to detect insanity in the family of any solvent shareholder.

" There is only one other little point," he went on rather hollowly. " Colonel Pim asked me to send him a detailed account of his purchases during the last month. We met by happy chance as he was yesterday alighting from a taxi-cab at the entrance to his bank. After to-day's purchases that will perhaps take an hour or two. But it shall reach him to-morrow morning—without fail."

Philip had risen. It is better to stand when one is at bay. While with a gentle absent smile he stood drawing on his gloves he was faced with the wildest effort of his life—to make sure of what lay in hiding behind these last remarks. Anything *might*.

" Oh, he did—did he," he remarked very softly. " I fancy " —and at last he lifted his gentle eyes to meet his adversary's— " I *believe* there's an empty whisky jar that has not yet been credited to him. Perhaps that was on his mind."

" Well, Mr. Pim," said Sir Leopold, " turning " at last, " if *that's* his only jar it's soon adjusted."

Philip took a deep breath. He playfully wagged a finger.

" Now *that*, Sir Leopold," he said, " was blank verse. I hope you dont't intend to put my little purchases of this morning into *rhyme*. The effort, I assure you, would be wasted on my uncle."

He wheeled lightly and turned towards the door. Sir Leopold, his face now at liberty to resume its office of expressing his feelings, accompanied him. Indeed he continued to accompany him to the very entrance of his gigantic abode. And there Philip almost fainted. A deluge, compared with which that of Noah and his family was nothing but an April shower, was descending on the street.

" A taxi," roared Sir Leopold at a group of his satellites in the porch, caparisoned in shiny waterproofs and armed with gigantic *parapluies*.

But though at least nineteen of these vehicles were instantly battling their way towards this goal, Philip with incredible agility had eluded their attention. Before Sir Leopold had had time even to arrange his face to smile a farewell, our young friend had gone leaping up the staircase behind him and had without a moment's pause vanished into the Tropical Department.

One fugitive glance at its pith and pucka contents, and at the dusky assistants in attendance, had only accelerated his retreat. In less than half a minute he found himself confronting a young woman seated in the midst of a stockade of umbrellas.

The coincidence was too extreme to be ignored. He would at least carry off *some* little souvenir of his morning's outing. What better value could he get for hard cash than an implement that would be at the same time a refuge from the elements—for other he would soon presently have none—and a really formidable weapon at hand for his next interview with Sir Leopold?

He had but just enough breath left to express himself. He pointed.

" I *want* one, please," he cried at the young woman. " Cash."

" One, two, three, four, *five* guineas ? " she murmured, looking as if she were less in need of her stock than of her lunch. " Partridge, malacca, horn, ivory, rhinoceros, natural, *gold* ? Union, gloria, glacé, taffeta, cotton, mixture, or *twill* ? "

" Not a toy ; an umbrella," Philip expostulated. " To keep off rain. A nephew returning to school—ten years' wear. Gingham, alpaca, calico, cast-iron—*anything* ; so long as it is hefty, solid, endurable, awful, and *cheap*."

" We have here what is *called* an umbrella," replied the assistant a trifle coldly. " The ' Miss and Master Brand.' Lignum-vitæ stick, whalebone ribs, blunted ferrule, non-poisonous handle, guaranteed not to break, fray, fade, or scale. Nine elevenpence complete."

" Bill ; in haste ; cash ; just as it is ; thanks," cried Philip, and seized the dreadful object. With a groan he laid his Uncle Charles's sovereign in the narrow brass trough of the pay-desk. The obese young person in the wooden box seemed about to lift it to her lips, glanced at him again, put it aside, smiled, and gave him his change.

" The way to the back exit, I think, is over here," Philip murmured, waving his gloves due west.

The young person smiled again, and he withdrew. He withdrew down the back steps and into the deluge : there to face a watery world, the possessor of ten shillings and a penny (in his pocket), a wardrobe of old suits, about a hundred and fifty books, three of them unmerited prizes for good conduct, a juvenile collection of postage stamps, a hypothetical legacy of a shilling, and an uncle who, if he faced his liabilities as an English gentleman should, had to all intents and purposes overdrawn his bank account that afternoon by, say roughly, a couple of hundred thousand pounds.

CHARLES DICKENS (1812–1870), *the greatest of caricaturists, portrayed the little vanities and self-delusions of his fellows with as sure a pen as he did their deepest and most insurgent emotions. In "Horatio Sparkins" we find him pointing an ironical finger at a type of character with whom we are not unfamiliar to-day—the family who have "got on" and would fain forget how they arrived.*

HORATIO SPARKINS

"INDEED, my love, he paid Teresa very great attention on the last assembly night," said Mrs. Malderton, addressing her spouse, who, after the fatigues of the day in the City, was sitting with a silk handkerchief over his head, and his feet on the fender, drinking his port ; "very great attention ; and I say again, every possible encouragement ought to be given him. He positively must be asked down here to dine."

"Who must ? " inquired Mr. Malderton.

"Why, you know whom I mean, my dear—the young man with the black whiskers and the white cravat, who has just come out at our assembly, and whom all the girls are talking about. Young—— Dear me ! what's his name ?—Marianne, what *is* his name ? " continued Mrs. Malderton, addressing her youngest daughter, who was engaged in netting a purse and looking sentimental.

"Mr. Horatio Sparkins, ma," replied Miss Marianne with a sigh.

"Oh, yes, to be sure ! Horatio Sparkins," said Mrs. Malderton. "Decidedly the most gentleman-like young man I ever saw. I am sure, in the beautifully made coat he wore the other night, he looked like—like——"

"Like Prince Leopold, ma—so noble, so full of sentiment ! " suggested Marianne, in a tone of enthusiastic admiration.

"You should recollect, my dear," resumed Mrs. Malderton, "that Teresa is now eight-and-twenty ; and that it really is very important that something should be done."

Miss Teresa Malderton was a very little girl, rather fat, with vermilion cheeks, but good humoured, and still disengaged, although, to do her justice, the misfortune arose from no lack of perseverance on her part. In vain had she flirted for ten years ;

in vain had Mr. and Mrs. Malderton assiduously kept up an extensive acquaintance among the young eligible bachelors of Camberwell, and even of Wandsworth and Brixton ; to say nothing of those who " dropped in " from town. Miss Malderton was as well known as the lion on the top of Northumberland House, and had an equal chance of " going off."

" I am quite sure you'd like him," continued Mrs. Malderton ; " he is so gentlemanly ! "

" So clever ! " said Miss Marianne.

" And has such a flow of language ! " added Miss Teresa.

" He has a great respect for you, my dear," said Mrs. Malderton to her husband. Mr. Malderton coughed, and looked at the fire.

" Yes, I'm sure he's very much attached to pa's society," said Miss Marianne.

" No doubt of it," echoed Miss Teresa.

" Indeed, he said as much to me in confidence," observed Mrs. Malderton.

" Well, well," returned Mr. Malderton, somewhat flattered ; " if I see him at the assembly to-morrow perhaps I'll ask him down. I hope he knows we live at Oak Lodge, Camberwell, my dear ? "

" Of course—and that you keep a one-horse carriage."

" I'll see about it," said Mr. Malderton, composing himself for a nap ; " I'll see about it."

Mr. Malderton was a man whose whole scope of ideas was limited to Lloyd's, the Exchange, the India House, and the Bank. A few successful speculations had raised him from a situation of obscurity and comparative poverty to a state of affluence. As frequently happens in such cases, the ideas of himself and his family became elevated to an extraordinary pitch as their means increased ; they affected fashion, taste, and many other fooleries, in imitation of their betters, and had a very decided and becoming horror of anything which could, by possibility, be considered *low*. He was hospitable from ostentation, illiberal from ignorance, and prejudiced from conceit. Egotism and the love of display induced him to keep an excellent table ; convenience, and the love of the good things of this life, insured him plenty of guests. He liked to have clever men, or what he considered such, at his table, because it was a great thing to talk about ; but he never could endure what he called " sharp fellows." Probably he cherished this feeling out of compliment to his two sons, who gave their respected parent no uneasiness in that particular. The family were ambitious of forming acquaintances and connections in some sphere of society superior to that in which they themselves moved ; and one of the necessary consequences of this desire, added to their utter ignorance of the world beyond their own small circle was, that any one who could lay claim to an acquaintance with people of rank and title had a sure passport to the table at Oak Lodge, Camberwell.

The appearance of Mr. Horatio Sparkins at the assembly had excited no small degree of surprise and curiosity among its regular frequenters. Who could he be ? He was evidently reserved, and apparently melancholy. Was he a clergyman ?— He danced too well. A barrister ?—He said he was not called. He used very fine words, and talked a great deal. Could he be a distinguished foreigner, come to England for the purpose of describing the country, its manners and customs, and frequenting public balls and public dinners with the view of becoming acquainted with high life, polished etiquette, and English refinement ?—No, he had not a foreign accent. Was he a surgeon, a contributor to the magazines, a writer of fashionable novels, or an artist ?—No ; to each and all of these surmises there existed some valid objection—" Then," said everybody, " he must be *somebody*."—" I should think he must be," reasoned Mr. Malderton within himself, " because he perceives our superiority, and pays us so much attention."

The night succeeding the conversation we have just recorded was " assembly " night. The double fly was ordered to be at the door of Oak Lodge at nine o'clock precisely. The Miss Maldertons were dressed in sky-blue satin trimmed with artificial flowers ; and Mrs. M. (who was a little fat woman), in ditto ditto, looked like her eldest daughter multiplied by two. Mr. Frederick Malderton, the eldest son, in full dress costume, was the very *beau ideal* of a smart waiter ; and Mr. Thomas Malderton, the youngest, with his white dress-stock, blue coat, bright buttons, and red watch-ribbon, strongly resembled the portrait of that interesting, but rash young gentleman, George Barnwell. Every member of the party had made up his or her mind to cultivate the acquaintance of Mr. Horatio Sparkins. Miss Teresa, of course, was to be as amiable and interesting as ladies of eight-and-twenty on the look-out for a husband usually are. Mrs. Malderton would be all smiles and graces. Miss Marianne would request the favour of some verses for her album. Mr. Malderton would patronize the great unknown by asking him to dinner. Tom intended to ascertain the extent of his information on the interesting topics of snuff and cigars. Even Mr. Firederick Malderton himself, the family authority on all points of taste, dress, and fashionable arrangement ; who had lodgings of his own in town ; who had a free admission to Covent Garden Theatre ; who always dressed according to the fashions of the months ; who went up the water twice a week in the season ; and who actually had an intimate friend who once knew a gentleman who formerly lived in the Albany—even he had determined that Mr. Horatio Sparkins must be a devilish good fellow, and that he would do him the honour of challenging him to a game at billiards.

The first object that met the anxious eyes of the expedient family, on their entrance into the ball-room, was the interesting Horatio, with his hair brushed off his forehead, and his eyes fixed on the ceiling, reclining in a contemplative attitude on one of the seats.

" There he is, my dear," whispered Mrs. Malderton to Mr. Malderton.

" How like Lord Byron ! " murmured Miss Teresa.

" Or Montgomery ! " whispered Miss Marianne.

" Or the portraits of Captain Cook ! " suggested Tom.

" Tom, don't be an ass ! " said his father, who checked him on all occasions, probably with a view to prevent his becoming " sharp "—which was very unnecessary.

The elegant Sparkins attitudinized with admirable effect, until the family had crossed the room. He then started up with the most natural appearance of surprise and delight ; accosted Mrs. Malderton with the utmost cordiality ; saluted the young ladies in the most enchanting manner ; bowed to, and shook hands with Mr. Malderton, with a degree of respect amounting almost to veneration ; and returned the greetings of the two young men in a half-gratified, half-patronizing manner, which fully convinced them that he must be an important, and, at the same time, condescending personage.

" Miss Malderton," said Horatio after the ordinary salutations, and bowing very low, " may I be permitted to presume to hope that you will allow me to have the pleasure——"

" I don't *think* I am engaged," said Miss Teresa, with a dreadful affectation of indifference—" but really—so—many——"

Horatio looked handsomely miserable.

" I shall be most happy," simpered the interesting Teresa at last. Horatio's countenance brightened up, like an old hat in a shower of rain.

" A very genteel young man, certainly ! " said the gratified Mr. Malderton, as the obsequious Sparkins and his partner joined the quadrille which was just forming.

" He has a remarkably good address," said Mr. Frederick.

" Yes, he is a prime fellow," interposed Tom, who always managed to put his foot in it—" he talks just like an auctioneer."

" Tom ! " said his father solemnly, " I think I desired you before not to be a fool." Tom looked as happy as a cock on a drizzly morning.

" How delightful ! " said the interesting Horatio to his partner, as they promenaded the room at the conclusion of the set—" how delightful, how refreshing it is, to retire from the cloudy storms, the vicissitudes, and the troubles of life, even if it be but for a few short fleeting moments ; and to spend those moments, fading and evanescent though they be, in the delightful, the blessed society of one individual—whose frowns would be death, whose coldness would be madness, whose falsehood would be ruin, whose constancy would be bliss ; the possession of whose affection would be the brightest and best reward that heaven could bestow on man ! "

" What feeling ! what sentiment ! " thought Miss Teresa, as she leaned more heavily on her companion's arm.

" But enough—enough ! " resumed the elegant Sparkins, with a theatrical air. " What have I said ? what have I—I—to do with sentiments like these ? Miss Malderton "—here he stopped short—" may I hope to be permitted to offer the humble tribute of——"

" Really, Mr. Sparkins," returned the enraptured Teresa, blushing in the sweetest confusion, " I must refer you to papa. I never can, without his consent, venture to——"

" Surely he cannot object——"

" Oh, yes ! Indeed, indeed, you know him not ! " interrupted Miss Teresa, well knowing there was nothing to fear, but wishing to make the interview resemble a scene in some romantic novel.

" He cannot object to my offering you a glass of negus," returned the adorable Sparkins, with some surprise.

" Is that all ? " thought the disappointed Teresa. " What a fuss about nothing ! "

" It will give me the greatest pleasure, sir, to see you to dinner at Oak Lodge, Camberwell, on Sunday next at five o'clock, if you have no better engagement," said Mr. Malderton, at the conclusion of the evening, as he and his sons were standing in conversation with Mr. Horatio Sparkins.

Horatio bowed his acknowledgments, and accepted the flattering invitation.

" I must confess," continued the father, offering his snuff-box to his new acquaintance, " that I don't enjoy these assemblies half so much as the comfort—I had almost said the luxury—of Oak Lodge. They have no great charms for an elderly man."

"And, after all, sir, what is man?" said the metaphysical Sparkins. "I say, what is man?"

"Ah! very true," said Mr. Malderton; "very true."

"We know that we live and breathe," continued Horatio, " that we have wants and wishes, desires and appetites——"

"Certainly," said Mr. Frederick Malderton, looking profound.

"I say, we know that we exist," repeated Horatio, raising his voice, " but there we stop; there is an end to our knowledge; there, is the summit of our attainments; there, is the termination of our ends. What more do we know?"

"Nothing," replied Mr. Frederick—than whom no one was more capable of answering for himself in that particular. Tom was about to hazard something, but, fortunately for his reputation, he caught his father's angry eye, and slunk off like a puppy convicted of petty larceny.

"Upon my word," said Mr. Malderton the elder, as they were returning home in the fly, " that Mr. Sparkins is a wonderful young man. Such surprising knowledge! such extraordinary information! and such a splendid mode of expressing himself!"

"I think he must be somebody in disguise," said Miss Marianne. "How charmingly romantic!"

"He talks very loud and nicely," timidly observed Tom, " but I don't exactly understand what he means."

"I almost begin to despair of *your* understanding anything, Tom," said his father, who, of course, had been much enlightened by Mr. Horatio Sparkins's conversation.

"It strikes me, Tom," said Miss Teresa, " that you have made yourself very ridiculous this evening."

"No doubt of it," cried everybody—and the unfortunate Tom reduced himself into the least possible space. That night Mr. and Mrs. Malderton had a long conversation respecting their daughter's prospects and future arrangements. Miss Teresa went to bed, considering whether, in the event of her marrying a title, she could conscientiously encourage the visits of her present associates; and dreamed all night of disguised noblemen, large routs, ostrich plumes, bridal favours, and Horatio Sparkins.

Various surmises were hazarded on the Sunday morning as to the mode of conveyance which the anxiously expected Horatio would adopt. Did he keep a gig?—was it possible he could come on horseback ?—or would he patronize the stage ? These, and various other conjectures of equal importance, engrossed the attention of Mrs. Malderton and her daughters during the whole morning after church.

" Upon my word, my dear, it's a most annoying thing that that vulgar brother of yours should have invited himself to dine here to-day," said Mr. Malderton to his wife. " On account of Mr. Sparkins's coming down, I puposely abstained from asking any one but Flamwell. And then to think of your brother —a tradesman—it's insufferable ! I declare I wouldn't have him mention his shop before our new guest—no, not for a thousand pounds ! I wouldn't care if he had the good sense to conceal the disgrace he is to the family ; but he's so fond of his horrible business, that he *will* let people know what he is."

Mr. Jacob Barton, the individual alluded to, was a large grocer ; so vulgar, and so lost to all sense of feeling, that he actually never scrupled to avow that he wasn't above his business ; " he'd made his money by it, and he didn't care who knowed it."

" Ah ! Flamwell, my dear fellow, how d'ye do ? " said Mr. Malderton, as a little spoffish man, with green spectacles, entered the room. " You got my note ? "

" Yes, I did ; and here I am in consequence."

" You don't happen to know this Mr. Sparkins by name ? You know everybody."

Mr. Flamwell was one of those gentlemen of remarkably extensive information whom one occasionally meets in society, who pretend to know everybody, but in reality know nobody. At Malderton's, where any stories about great people were received with a greedy ear, he was an especial favourite ; and, knowing the kind of people he had to deal with, he carried his passion of claiming acquaintance with everybody to the most immoderate length. He had rather a singular way of telling his greatest lies in a parenthesis, and with an air of self-denial, as if he feared being thought egotistical.

" Why, no, I don't know him by that name," returned Flamwell, in a low tone, and with an air of immense importance. " I have no doubt I know him, though. Is he tall ? "

" Middle-sized," said Miss Teresa.

" With black hair ? " inquired Flamwell, hazarding a bold guess.

" Yes," returned Miss Teresa eagerly.

" Rather a snub nose ? "

" No," said the disappointed Teresa, " he has a Roman nose."

"I said a Roman nose, didn't I?" inquired Flamwell.
"He's an elegant young man?"

"Oh, certainly!"

"With remarkably prepossessing manners?"

"Oh, yes!" said all the family together. "You must know him."

"Yes, I thought you knew him, if he was anybody," triumphantly exclaimed Mr. Malderton. "Who d'ye think he is?"

"Why, from your description," said Flamwell, ruminating, and sinking his voice almost to a whisper, "he bears a strong resemblance to the Honourable Augustus Fitz-Edward Fitz-John Fitz-Osborne. He's a very talented young man, and rather eccentric. It's extremely probable he may have changed his name for some temporary purpose."

Teresa's heart beat high. Could he be the Honourable Augustus Fitz-Edward Fitz-John Fitz-Osborne? What a name to be elegantly engraved upon two glazed cards, tied together with a piece of white satin ribbon! "The Honourable Mrs. Augustus Fitz-Edward Fitz-John Fitz-Osborne!" The thought was transport.

"It's five minutes to five," said Mr. Malderton, looking at his watch; "I hope he's not going to disappoint us."

"There he is!" exclaimed Miss Teresa, as a loud double knock was heard at the door. Everybody endeavoured to look —as people when they particularly expect a visitor always do— as if they were perfectly unsuspicious of the approach of anybody.

The room door opened. "Mr. Barton!" said the servant.

"Confound the man!" murmured Malderton. "Ah! my dear sir, how d'ye do? Any news?"

"Why, no," returned the grocer, in his usual bluff manner. "No, none partickler. None that I am much aware of. How d'ye do, gals and boys? Mr. Flamwell, sir—glad to see you."

"Here's Mr. Sparkins!" said Tom, who had been looking out at the window, "on *such* a black horse!" There was Horatio, sure enough, on a large black horse, curveting and prancing along, like an Astley's supernumerary. After a great deal of reining in, and pulling up, with the accompaniments of snorting, rearing, and kicking, the animal consented to stop at about a hundred yards from the gate, where Mr. Sparkins dismounted, and confided him to the care of Mr. Malderton's groom. The ceremony of introduction was gone through in all due form. Mr. Flamwell looked from behind his green spectacles at Horatio with an air of mysterious importance; and the gallant Horatio looked unutterable things at Teresa.

" Is he the Honourable Mr. Augustus What's-his-name ? "
whispered Mrs. Malderton to Flamwell, as he was escorting her
to the dining-room.

" Why, no—at least not exactly," returned that great
authority—" not exactly."

" Who *is* he, then ? "

" Hush ! " said Flamwell, nodding his head with a grave air,
importing that he knew very well ; but was prevented, by some
grave reasons of state, from disclosing the important secret.
It might be one of the ministers making himself acquainted with
the views of the people.

" Mr. Sparkins," said the delighted Mrs. Malderton, " pray
divide the ladies. John, put a chair for the gentleman between
Miss Teresa and Miss Marianne." This was addressed to a man
who, on ordinary occasions, acted as half groom, half gardener ;
but who, as it was important to make an impression on Mr.
Sparkins, had been forced into a white neckerchief and shoes,
and touched up and brushed, to look like a second footman.

The dinner was excellent ; Horatio was most attentive to
Miss Teresa, and every one felt in high spirits, except Mr.
Malderton, who, knowing the propensity of his brother-in-law,
Mr. Barton, endured that sort of agony which the newspapers
inform us is experienced by the surrounding neighbourhood
when a potboy hangs himself in a hayloft, and which is " much
easier to be imagined than described."

" Have you seen your friend, Sir Thomas Noland, lately, Flamwell?" inquired Mr. Malderton, casting a sidelong look at Horatio,
to see what effect the mention of so great a man had upon him.

" Why, no—not very lately. I saw Lord Gubbleton the day
before yesterday."

" Ah ! I hope his lordship is very well ? " said Malderton,
in a tone of the greatest interest. It is scarcely necessary to
say that, until that moment, he had been quite innocent of the
existence of such a person.

" Why, yes ; he was very well—very well indeed. He's a
devilish good fellow. I met him in the City, and had a long
chat with him. Indeed, I'm rather intimate with him. I couldn't
stop to talk to him as long as I could wish, though, because I
was on my way to a banker's, a very rich man, and a Member
of Parliament, with whom I am also rather, indeed I may say
very intimate."

" I know whom you mean," returned the host consequentially
—in reality knowing as much about the matter as Flamwell
himself. " He has a capital business."

This was touching on a dangerous topic.

"Talking of business," interposed Mr. Barton from the centre of the table, "a gentleman whom you knew very well, Malderton, before you made that first lucky spec of yours, called at our shop the other day, and——"

"Barton, may I trouble you for a potato?" interrupted the wretched master of the house, hoping to nip the story in the bud.

"Certainly," returned the grocer, quite insensible of his brother-in-law's object—"and he said in a very plain manner——"

"*Floury*, if you please," interrupted Malderton, again; dreading the termination of the anecdote, and fearing a repetition of the word "shop."

"He said, says he," continued the culprit, after despatching the potato; "says he, How goes on your business? So I said jokingly—you know my way—says I, I'm never above my business, and I hope my business will never be above me. Ha, ha!"

"Mr. Sparkins," said the host, vainly endeavouring to conceal his dismay, "a glass of wine?"

"With the utmost pleasure, sir."

"Happy to see you."

"Thank you."

"We were talking the other evening," resumed the host, addressing Horatio, partly with the view of displaying the conversational powers of his new acquaintance, and partly in the hope of drowning the grocer's stories—"we were talking the other night about the nature of man. Your argument struck me very forcibly."

"And me," said Mr. Frederick. Horatio made a graceful inclination of the head.

"Pray, what is your opinion of woman, Mr. Sparkins?" inquired Mrs. Malderton. The young ladies simpered.

"Man," replied Horatio—"man, whether he ranged the bright, gay, flowery plains of a second Eden, or the more sterile, barren, and I may say commonplace, regions to which we are compelled to accustom ourselves, in times such as these; man, under any circumstance, or in any place—whether he were bending beneath the withering blasts of the frigid zone, or scorching under the rays of a vertical sun—man, without woman, would be—alone."

"I am very happy to find you entertain such honourable opinions, Mr. Sparkins," said Mrs. Malderton.

"And I," added Miss Teresa. Horatio looked his delight, and the young lady blushed.

" Now, it's my opinion——" said Mr. Barton.

" I know what you're going to say," interposed Malderton, determined not to give his relation another opportunity, " and I don't agree with you."

" What ? " inquired the astonished grocer.

" I am sorry to differ from you, Barton," said the host, in as positive a manner as if he really were contradicting a position which the other had laid down, " but I cannot give my assent to what I consider a very monstrous proposition."

" But I meant to say——"

" You never can convince me," said Malderton, with an air of obstinate determination. . " Never."

" And I," said Mr. Frederick, following up his father's attack, " cannot entirely agree in Mr. Sparkins's argument."

" What ! " said Horatio, who became more metaphysical, and more argumentative, as he saw the female part of the family listening in wondering delight—" what ! Is effect the consequence of cause ? Is cause the precursor of effect ? "

" That's the point," said Flamwell.

" To be sure," said Mr. Malderton.

" Because, if effect is the consequence of cause, and if cause does precede effect, I apprehend you are wrong," added Horatio.

" Decidedly," said the toad-eating Flamwell.

" At least, I apprehend that to be the just and logical deduction ? " said Sparkins, in a tone of interrogation.

" No doubt of it," chimed in Flamwell again. " It settles the point."

" Well, perhaps it does," said Mr. Frederick ; " I didn't see it before."

" I don't exactly see it now," thought the grocer ; " but I suppose it's all right."

" How wonderfully clever he is ! " whispered Mrs. Malderton to her daughters as they retired to the drawing-room.

" Oh, he's quite a love ! " said both the young ladies together ; " he talks like an oracle. He must have seen a great deal of life ! "

The gentlemen being left to themselves, a pause ensued, during which everybody looked very grave, as if they were quite overcome by the profound nature of the previous discussion. Flamwell, who had made up his mind to find out who and what Mr. Horatio Sparkins really was, first broke silence.

" Excuse me, sir," said that distinguished personage, " I presume you have studied for the bar ? I thought of entering once, myself—indeed, I'm rather intimate with some of the highest ornaments of that distinguished profession."

"N—no!" said Horatio, with a little hesitation; "not exactly."

"But you have been among the silk gowns, or I mistake?" inquired Flamwell deferentially.

"Nearly all my life," returned Sparkins.

The question was thus pretty well settled in the mind of Mr. Flamwell. He was a young gentleman "about to be called."

"I shouldn't like to be a barrister," said Tom, speaking for the first time, and looking round the table to find somebody who would notice the remark.

No one made any reply.

"I shouldn't like to wear a wig," said Tom, hazarding another observation.

"Tom, I beg you will not make yourself ridiculous," said his father. "Pray listen and improve yourself by the conversation you hear, and don't be constantly making these absurd remarks."

"Very well, father," replied the unfortunate Tom, who had not spoken a word since he had asked for another slice of beef at a quarter-past five o'clock P.M., and it was then eight.

"Well, Tom," observed his good-natured uncle, "never mind! *I* think with you. *I* shouldn't like to wear a wig. I'd rather wear an apron."

Mr. Malderton coughed violently. Mr. Barton resumed— "For if a man's above his business——"

The cough returned with tenfold violence, and did not cease until the unfortunate cause of it, in his alarm, had quite forgotten what he intended to say.

"Mr. Sparkins," said Flamwell, returning to the charge, "do you happen to know Mr. Delafontaine, of Bedford Square?"

"I have exchanged cards with him; since which, indeed, I have had an opportunity of serving him considerably," replied Horatio, slightly colouring; no doubt, at having been betrayed into making the acknowledgment.

"You are very lucky if you have had an opportunity of obliging that great man," observed Flamwell, with an air of profound respect.

"I don't know who he is," he whispered to Mr. Malderton confidentially, as they followed Horatio up to the drawing-room. "It's quite clear, however, that he belongs to the law, and that he is somebody of great importance, and very highly connected."

"No doubt, no doubt," returned his companion.

The remainder of the evening passed away most delightfully. Mr. Malderton, relieved from his apprehensions by the circum-

stance of Mr. Barton's falling into a profound sleep, was as affable
and gracious as possible. Miss Teresa played the "Fall of Paris,"
as Mr. Sparkins declared, in a most masterly manner, and both
of them, assisted by Mr. Frederick, tried over glees and trios
without number ; they having made the pleasing discovery that
their voices harmonized beautifully. To be sure, they all sang
the first part ; and Horatio, in addition to the slight drawback
of having no ear, was perfectly innocent of knowing a note of
music ; still they passed the time very agreeably ; and it was
past twelve o'clock before Mr. Sparkins ordered the mourning-
coach-looking steed to be brought out—an order which was only
complied with on the distinct understanding that he was to repeat
his visit on the following Sunday.

"But perhaps Mr. Sparkins will form one of our party
to-morrow evening ? " suggested Mrs. M. "Mr. Malderton
intends taking the girls to see the pantomime." Mr. Sparkins
bowed, and promised to join the party in box 48, in the course
of the evening.

"We will not tax you for the morning," said Miss Teresa
bewitchingly ; "for ma is going to take us to all sorts of places,
shopping. I know that gentlemen have a great horror of that
employment." Mr. Sparkins bowed again, and declared that
he should be delighted, but business of importance occupied him
in the morning. Flamwell looked at Malderton significantly—
"It's term time ! " he whispered.

At twelve o'clock on the following morning the " fly " was at
the door of Oak Lodge, to convey Mrs. Malderton and her
daughters on their expedition for the day. They were to dine
and dress for the play at a friend's house. First, driving thither
with their band-boxes, they departed on their first errand to
make some purchases at Messrs. Jones, Spruggins, and Smith's,
of Tottenham Court Road ; after which, they were to go to
Redmayne's, in Bond Street ; thence to innumerable places that
no one ever heard of. The young ladies beguiled the tediousness
of the ride by eulogizing Mr. Horatio Sparkins, scolding their
mamma for taking them so far to save a shilling, and wondering
whether they should ever reach their destination. At length,
the vehicle stopped before a dirty-looking ticketed linen-draper's
shop, with goods of all kinds, and labels of all sorts and sizes, in
the window. There were dropsical figures of seven with a little
three-farthings in the corner, " perfectly invisible to the naked
eye " ; three hundred and fifty thousand ladies boas *from* one
shilling and a penny halfpenny ; real French kid shoes, at
two and ninepence per pair ; green parasols, at an equally cheap

rate ; and " every description of goods," as the proprietors said—
and they must know best—" fifty per cent. under cost price."

"Lor, ma, what a place you have brought us to ! " said Miss
Teresa. "What *would* Mr. Sparkins say if he could see us ? "

"Ah ! what, indeed ! " said Miss Marianne, horrified at the
idea.

"Pray be seated, ladies. What is the first article ? " inquired
the obsequious master of the ceremonies of the establishment,
who, in his large white neckcloth and formal tie, looked like a
bad " portrait of a gentleman " in the Somerset House exhibition.

"I want to see some silks," answered Mrs. Malderton.

"Directly, ma'am—Mr. Smith ! Where *is* Mr. Smith ? "

"Here, sir ! " cried a voice at the back of the shop.

"Pray make haste, Mr. Smith," said the M.C. "You never
are to be found when you're wanted, sir."

Mr. Smith, thus enjoined to use all possible despatch, leaped
over the counter with great agility, and placed himself before the
newly-arrived customers. Mrs. Malderton uttered a faint scream.
Miss Teresa, who had been stooping down to talk to her sister,
raised her head, and beheld—Horatio Sparkins !

"We will draw a veil," as novel-writers say, over the scene
that ensued. The mysterious, philosophical, romantic, metaphysical Sparkins—he who, to the interesting Teresa, seemed like
the embodied idea of the young dukes and poetical exquisites in
blue silk dressing-gowns, and ditto ditto slippers, of whom she
had read and dreamed, but had never expected to behold, was
suddenly converted into Mr. Samuel Smith, the assistant at a
" cheap shop " ; the junior partner in a slippery firm of some
three weeks' existence. The dignified evanishment of the hero
of Oak Lodge, on this unexpected recognition, could only be
equalled by that of a furtive dog with a considerable kettle at
his tail. All the hopes of the Maldertons were destined at once
to melt away, like the lemon ices at a Company's dinner ;
Almacks was still to them as distant as the North Pole ; and
Miss Teresa had as much chance of a husband as Captain Ross
had of the north-west passage.

Years have elapsed since the occurrence of this dreadful
morning. The daisies have thrice bloomed on Camberwell
Green ; the sparrows have thrice repeated their vernal chirps in
Camberwell Grove ; but the Miss Maldertons are still unmated.
Miss Teresa's case is more desperate than ever ; but Flamwell
is yet in the zenith of his reputation ; and the family have the
same predilection for aristocratic personages, with an increased
aversion to anything *low*.

JEFFERY FARNOL (1878–) *who made his name with " Chronicles of the Imp," written whilst scene-painting in America, has done some of his best work in " period " novels, such as the story of that dashing character " The Amateur Gentleman," which made such a fine film. In " The Divine Phyllidia " he directs his raillery at four charming lovers of a later, but perhaps not less romantic, age.*

THE DIVINE PHYLLIDIA

I HAVE more than once been called a cynic, yet if there is any truth in the statement I am not totally devoid of the human milk of kindness—as the case of the " Cherub " shows.

He drifted dejectedly into my chambers one evening, with a woebegone expression on his usually placid face, and, sinking into the most comfortable arm-chair, sat staring moodily at the empty fireplace.

" Liver ? " I inquired at last, breaking in upon a long-drawn-out sigh.

" Don't you think you might be a little less objectionable," he said reproachfully. " You see," he continued after a pause, " when a fellow wants to—to screw himself up to the point, you know, how the dickens can he, when the girl as good as tells him she hates him like—er—like the very——"

" Exactly ! " I put in, " it's not to be done, my dear chap."

" No, I was afraid not," said the Cherub, " that's why I came to ask your advice."

" Certainly," I said encouragingly, " suppose you begin at the right end and tell me all about it ! "

Forthwith he plunged into a rambling account of his hopes and fears, and her cruelty, etc.

As becomes a true cynic I sniggered. He rebuked me with a look.

" I thought perhaps you might give me a ' leg up ' with the affair," he said gloomily.

The Cherub in love was something new, so that I examined him through the blue wreaths of my pipe with an awakened interest.

" My good chap," I said, " this sort of thing doesn't suit

you ; give it up. Love," I continued, warming to my theme, " love is a disease, and should be treated as such. What you want is change of air ; go down to your country place, and you'll come back cured in a month."

The Cherub shook his head moodily.

" It's easy enough for you to sit there and talk lightly of the matter, just because you never happen to have been ' hit,' but I call it beastly low," and he ran his fingers through his curls with an air of such utter dejection that even my cynicism was not proof against it. I reached down a favourite pipe, filled it, and handed it to him.

" Now," I began, when it was well alight, " how long have you been in this state ? "

" Oh, about a month now," he replied in a tone of dreary pleasure.

We smoked for a while in silence.

" Tried flowers ? " I inquired at length.

" Flowers ! " he repeated.

" Yes," I said, " they're the right and usual medium to start with, I believe."

" Well," he hesitated, " I gave her a rose once."

" Good ! But did you stick it in her hair ? "

The Cherub gasped. " Oh no ! " he exclaimed.

" Ah ! you should have done so—in an off-hand, matter-of-fact, brotherly sort of way, of course, but with a suggestion of hidden passion, you know, just to let her see you meant it."

The Cherub's speechless admiration flattered me.

" Gad ! you seem pretty well up to all the moves considering your pose as a——"

" My dear Cherub," I broke in, " I look on these things from a purely philosophical standpoint."

" Look here, Gip," he said earnestly, " you must tackle her for me—sort of lay the groundwork, talk me up to her, and all that—you understand ; I fancy I could manage if you would. It would be quite easy," he went on, " they are staying with the mater at Fernleigh—she and her cousin, I mean ; you and I might run down for a day or two."

" House-parties are an abomination ! " I said.

The Cherub assented, and reached down a time-table. " There's a train leaving Paddington in an hour," he suggested.

" Well ? "

" If we catch that we shall be there in time for dinner."

Now it is one thing to sit in one's own chambers and describe the right and proper way to carry so delicate a matter to a successful issue—but quite another thing to face the haughty *she* one's self, defenceless and alone. My mind was made up in an instant.

" Such an idea is not to be thought of," I said decidedly.

The Cherub's smile was anything but cherubic.

" Meaning," he said, " that theory is one thing and practice another ! "

" My dear Cherub, don't be a fool," I said. " Of course I'll stand by you in the affair, but a—a—unfortunately I've promised to go fishing with Pattison this week."

" Put him off," he cried. " Pat won't mind—urgent business, called out of town, etc., you know the style." he beamed, thrusting a sheet of notepaper before me.

I groaned inwardly and took up the pen. I am not a weak man as a rule, but what could one do in the face of such determination ?

Thus, while I lied to Pattison the Cherub busied himself with throwing things into my portmanteau ; as I sealed the note he was in the act of ramming in a dress coat.

" Hurry up ! " he panted, " or we shall lose that train."

" Toothbrush in ? " I inquired.

" It can't go in here," he cried excitedly, " no room," and with a mighty effort he closed the portmanteau and wiped his brow.

" But, my dear chap," I remonstrated.

" All right, I'll make a parcel of the rest," he said, buckling the straps feverishly.

Thus exactly fifty-eight minutes later we were facing each other, somewhat out of breath, in the express bound for Fernleigh.

" By the way, you're not much of a dab at parcels, are you ? " I said, glancing up at the bulging, misshapen object in the rack.

" Oh, it'll be all right," he said easily, and leaning back he puffed at his pipe with a dreamy expression that warned me of what was coming.

Presently he sighed. " She's wonderful, old chap ! " he exclaimed.

" Since I'm in for it, you might tell me her name and have done with it," I said.

" Well, I call her ' The Divine Phyllidia.' "

" Look here, Cherub, do you expect me to lie about you to a girl with a name like that ? "

He looked a trifle uncomfortable.

" Well—er, you needn't go it very much, Gip ; and then I'll back you up, you know."

After this we travelled some time in silence ; the Cherub seemed to be turning the matter over in his mind.

" Yes," he said suddenly, " she's wonderful—with eyes——"

" Extraordinary ! " said I.

" Black, my boy, as a moonless night, that flash at you, man, beneath low brows crowned with misty hair."

I hid a smile, but he seemed rather pleased with himself than otherwise and repeated the sentence slowly, dwelling upon it with marked appreciation.

When we reached Fernleigh, of course there was no conveyance to be had for miles round, and the Cherub, taking the paper parcel gingerly under his arm—I had secured the portmanteau—elected to show me a short cut.

" By the way," I said, " looks a trifle unwell—that parcel. Somewhat feeble—what ? "

" Oh, it will hang together all right until we get there ; it isn't far, you know—this way."

So saying, he led me down a narrow, leafy by-lane, climbed a bank, and we found ourselves in a tiny coppice.

Here the Cherub suddenly stood still and swore—the parcel had gone wrong.

"Just what I expected," I said, " and, by the way, what *did* you do with my toothbrush ? "

" Toothbrush be hanged ! " he cried, struggling with the riot which had been a parcel. " Come and help me with the confounded thing."

But instead of complying—fancying I heard voices, I stole towards a clump of bushes and peered round stealthily. Within a few inches of mine was a face so close that I might almost have kissed it—a piquant face it was, and just now full of the witchery of laughter and mischief, and warm with the rich colouring of scarlet mouth and raven hair. I started back.

" I beg your pardon," I began, and lifted my hat, but as I did so something leapt thence to the grass—it was my errant toothbrush. I trod upon it immediately—but too late ! for I heard a half-suppressed laugh behind me, and, turning, I saw another face peeping at me over a furze bush—but this time the hair was red gold and the laughing eyes wonderfully blue. I was standing there with my foot upon my toothbrush, looking from one to the other helplessly when the Cherub appeared. I fancy he must have had a bad time with that parcel, for it was torn in several places, from one of which dangled a white flannel trouser leg.

" Phyllidia ! " he gasped, and, dropping the parcel, stood staring.

In a moment Phyllidia was on her knees busy setting it to rights.

" This is outrageously packed, and just look, Kate, tied with two bootlaces ! "

The Cherub looked apologetic.

" You see," he began, but meeting the cousin's blue eyes, stopped.

" We were in rather a hurry packing, and the Cherub has no idea of a parcel," I said.

" And pray, is it your custom to carry toothbrushes in your hat ? " inquired Phyllidia, flashing a laughing glance up at me, the while with a few dexterous touches she transformed the Cherub's haggard bundle to serene package.

" As a matter of fact," I said, as we strolled after the cousin and the Cherub towards the house, " I have always found a toothbrush a source of worry and anxiety ; I never travel anywhere but I begin to try and recollect if I packed it, and if so, where, and after turning my things over I generally end by finding it in my waistcoat pocket or tobacco pouch."

Phyllidia laughed, and just then the others joined us. He seemed rather taken with the cousin, I thought, and no wonder.

" So that," I said to myself as I followed him upstairs later, " is the girl I have come to win—for the Cherub." Somehow the idea seemed singularly repulsive, and I felt unreasonably angry with him.

" Well," he asked, as I dressed for dinner, " what do you think of her, eh ? "

" She is——"

" Magnificent," he broke in, " and her eyes——"

" ' Black as a moonless night,' " I repeated, " ' that flash at you, man, from under low brows crowned with misty hair.' "

The Cherub glanced at me guiltily and changed the subject.
" Cousin's rather nice ? "

" Very," I said, arranging my tie. " Prepare yourself, Cherub," I continued, " I shall commence operations for you at dinner to-night," and somehow I found myself sighing heavily.

But I did not, for sitting with her voice in my ears, and an occasional glance into her black-fringed eyes, I forgot the Cherub's very existence.

Thus as the days passed, my promise became a grisly phantom

haunting me in all places; my sleep was broken, and when I met the Cherub's eye by accident I felt a traitor, and though I argued that he was unworthy of her, that such a mind as hers would be wasted on him, my conscience refused to be quieted. True, he had ceased to worry me lately concerning the progress I had made, but that served only to add coals of fire.

I determined, therefore, to have it over once and for all at the next opportunity.

That evening, sitting in a quiet corner of the drawing-room, chance favoured me.

" Why do you call Mr. Fancourt ' Cherub ' ? " she inquired, glancing to where he and the cousin were turning over some music at the piano.

" Oh, he got that at Cambridge," I began, " all the men were fond of the Cherub, you know."

" And what did they call you ? "

It was always the same ; if ever I managed to get started, she always pulled me up. I sighed. " They called me—Gip."

" Gip ? " she repeated, and her eyes belied her solemn mouth. " I have a dog named ' Gip '—the dearest old fellow."

I suggested that *that* was common to the name.

" I believe," she continued, unheeding my remark, " that he loves me more than anybody else in the world."

" After all," I said, " there's a strange affinity between men and some animals ; especially dogs, for instance now——" I really believe in another moment I should have said more than I ought ; an expectant look had crept into her eyes, and my fingers itched to clasp the hand lying so near mine, but at that instant Kate, the cousin, began playing, and I pulled myself up in time.

" Well," she said, under cover of the music.

" For instance, if I were a dog, I believe I could get to—to love even the—Cherub—in time," I ended lamely.

Her lips quivered, and I felt she was laughing at me.

" You see," I continued hurriedly, " he's such a—a splendid fellow—er—not bad-looking, I mean—any woman might——"

" Love him," she said softly, without looking up.

I felt annoyed. " Though some people object to fair men, I understand—think them unstable and all that—but, of course, the Cherub——"

" Is perfection," she said, opening and shutting her fan.

The cousin, Kate, was playing a soft, dreamy air, and as I sat watching Phyllidia's half-averted face a bitter feeling took

possession of me. Why should I do this thing? I asked myself.
What right had the Cherub——?

My hand closed suddenly over hers. I felt her start, and
for a moment I glanced into her eyes, and read there—what?

Her lashes dropped, her fingers slipped from mine; and I
had a sense of sudden shame.

"I once saw a fire," I began desperately, "such a fire as
few have witnessed. Standing in the pale-faced crowd I watched
the fruitless endeavours of the fire-engines. Suddenly, high up
at one of the windows, I saw something that turned me faint
and sick; it was a child. I closed my eyes. When I looked
again an escape had been run up, and a fireman was trying to
fight his way to that blazing window, but without success. A
great murmuring sigh went up to the blood-red heavens for
that little helpless child. Suddenly a tall, golden-haired figure,
conspicuous in the fire-glow, began to ascend, climbing with
strong, firm steps. And now a great silence fell upon all, broken
only by the roar of the flames. Nearer he got and nearer; once
I saw his sleeve puff out in flame, but still he climbed; men
held their breath. I could have screamed aloud. Then came
a wild roar of exultation about me. He had reached the window,
snatched the trembling child, and as I watched, a hundred arms
were outstretched to welcome him, safe and unharmed, save for
his hands—and," I ended, turning to my companion, who had
listened with bent head, " the marks are there to this day—it
was the Cherub."

Why I told her all this—Heaven knows! No one could have
been more surprised than myself. Perhaps the music inspired
it; perhaps the sense of wrong I had so nearly done him. The
music stopped, and seeing him approach I rose, and slipping
out upon the terrace I leaned there, staring up at the moon,
with a sense of duty nobly done.

And it had been a near thing—the touch of her fingers
thrilled me yet.

Despite my philosophy, my heart was strangely heavy as I
shut myself into my room that night. Anyhow, I had kept my
word, I told myself; but at what a cost! Looking at the matter
in a colder light, I began to wish I had not made the Cherub
appear quite so heroic. True, it was cheap melodrama; but,
then, women liked that sort of thing, I told myself, with a cynical
laugh. Of course, he was not worthy of her, but—I shrugged my
shoulders—she might think so, and how could it affect me?

So I went to bed, but not to sleep, and dawn found me
tossing restlessly. I heard the first sleepy notes of a blackbird

under my window, and presently up came the sun, and with it a determination that I would not stop to see their happiness ; I would go. I rose, and having packed my portmanteau, slipped from my room and, opening a side door, stepped out into the morning.

At the edge of the coppice a tree had fallen, and sitting down, I lit my pipe, and listened to the merry carol of the birds about me. And as the smoke rose in the still air I seemed to see the face of Phyllidia peeping at me through the blue wreaths, full of laughter and mischief, as I had seen it first.

I sighed deeply, and as I did so a bush rustled behind me, and, glancing up, I saw—no dream-face this time—but Phyllidia herself, fresh as the morning, coming towards me. She carried her hat in her hand, and her black hair was braided low on her temples.

She walked slowly, with eyes drooped ; but as I rose she glanced up quickly. I saw the colour burning in her cheeks, and she stopped.

" Phyllidia ! " I said, using her name unconsciously.

She greeted me with a studied ease.

" You are down very early," I said, wondering why she did not always dress her hair so,

" Oh, I'm fond of the early morning," she answered ; " and you ? "

" Well, you see, I'm going back to town by the early train."

She evinced no surprise. " Then I'm glad I saw you, because I want to ask you why you told me all that about Mr. Fancourt last night, about the fire, and the little child ; you must have known it was totally untrue."

" Untrue ! " I repeated, trying to look hurt, " you surely don't think——"

" His hands are quite unmarked, except for one small scar, and that he told me he did with a ginger-beer bottle years and years ago, and he told me besides he had never seen a big fire in his life."

I could joyfully have kicked the Cherub at that moment.

" Let me explain," I began. Phyllidia sat down.

" Well," she said, seeing I hesitated.

" Well, you see, I came down to help the Cherub with the —ah—with the—the affair," I stammered.

" The affair ? " she said, with raised brows, " what affair ? "

" Oh, _the_ affair—to propose, you know."

" To propose ? " she echoed.

" Yes—you see—fact is—he's got no idea how to manage

these things and so—so he got me to promise to—to lend him a hand, you know."

" And, of course, you succeeded ? "

" I'm afraid so," I said bitterly, " that's why I'm going—I can't stop to see your happiness."

She glanced swiftly up. " My happiness ! " she exclaimed.

" Yours and his," I added. " I couldn't bear it—just at present—so I'm going."

For a moment she looked at me as if scarcely comprehending, then turned suddenly away, and I saw her shoulders heave. " After all," I thought, " my going away does affect her then, and it is something to have such a woman shed tears over one."

" You'll think of me sometimes, Phyllidia—in my loneliness —when—when you are happy ? " I said, leaning above her bowed head. I was surprised to notice my voice quivered strangely ; on the whole, it pleased me.

She did not answer.

I leaned nearer until I could see her face and—Phyllidia was laughing. Yes, there was no doubt—she was actually laughing, and seeing she was discovered she cast aside all dissimulation.

" And that," she cried, dabbing her eyes with a tiny lace handkerchief, " was why you told me that wonderful story of the fire ! Oh ! it's too funny," and she went off into another peal of laughter.

I felt distinctly hurt and annoyed. " I am glad you see it in that light," I said stiffly, " but to me it is a—a tragedy."

She seemed somewhat ashamed, I thought, at least she kept her face hidden. Mechanically I took out my pipe and began filling it.

" As it is," I said, with an effort, " you have my sincerest wishes for your happiness—though, of course, the Cherub can never appreciate you as—as——" I stopped suddenly.

" As Gip does," she ended, peeping at me over her hand-kerchief.

The pipe dropped from my fingers, and I seized her hands, handkerchief and all.

" Phyllidia ! "

" I did not say which Gip," she said, and the droop of her lashes was divine. Then I bent forward and kissed her.

Some one approached whistling " Chin, Chin, Chinaman," with astonishing power and volume.

" Now what the dickens is he doing at this time of day ? " I exclaimed. " Confound him."

Phyllidia smiled. " Kate told me he was to show her over the farm," she said naïvely.

" Kate," I cried, with a sense of sudden awakening. " The cousin—why then—good heavens ! "

" Exactly ! " said Phyllidia, " and now do let me go—please. I wouldn't let him see me just now—for worlds—please," she pleaded.

" On condition," I began, but she eluded my arm dexterously and disappeared into the coppice.

I turned to meet the Cherub with a sense of offended virtue at his perfidy and the thought of what I had endured on his account. On seeing me he dodged behind a bush.

With pitiless irony I demanded to know if he had taken to bird's-nesting. He came forth, looking a trifle uncomfortable, I fancied.

" You're down awfully early," he began, but I brushed this aside.

" I've spoken to Phyllidia," I said, regarding him sternly.

" Oh, really—awfully topping of you—but, as a matter of fact, I—I fancy I made a mistake."

" A mistake ! " I repeated, with lifted brows.

" Yes—you see, fact is," he stammered, avoiding my eye— " what I mean is—I thought—that is, I fancy I was a trifle premature."

" You begged me to speak—and I've done so," I said, with a sensation of virtue beaming in the very buttons of my coat.

The Cherub appeared utterly unabashed.

" Oh Lord ! " he groaned, " what an infernal mess. I meant to tell you—but you've dodged me lately, you know, and—and —it's Kate, you know."

I shrugged my shoulders. " I promised to do it, and I've done it," I repeated.

" What did she say ? " he asked in a dreary, hopeless sort of fashion.

I took out my pipe and carefully lit it ere I answered.

" She gave me to understand she would marry me," I said.

The Cherub sprang forward and grasped my hand.

" Thank Heaven ! " he cried. " Good old Gip—I congratulate——"

But I broke away from him, and found " The Divine Phyllidia " in the coppice.

J. S. FLETCHER (1863–1935) *is best known as a fluent and skilful writer of detective stories, although his talents as a historian and antiquarian were considerable. In " The Provisions of Partnership " we find this versatile Yorkshireman in the rôle of humorist, and revealing himself just as capable in handling the short story as the full-length novel.*

PROVISIONS OF PARTNERSHIP

" THIS," dismally observed Mr. George Plumb, as he emerged from the small office in which Mr. Mappaway, grocer and Italian warehouseman, of Paradise Street, Edgware Road, kept his books of account, wrote his letters, and interviewed commercial travellers—" this is a nice go ! "

Mr. Thomas Filcher, principal assistant to Mr. Mappaway, absent-mindedly engaged in tidying up for the night, turned, in an abstracted fashion, to his fellow-worker.

" What's a nice go ? " he inquired.

Mr. Plumb glanced at the door which he had just closed, and made a face expressive of deep disgust.

" Guv'nor says I've got to stop and help him with those blessed books ! " he growled. " Picks out this very night of all nights ! And me intending to take the girl to the second house at the Met. ! Cruel hard luck, I call it ! "

" Make it another night," suggested Mr. Filcher.

" Got the blooming tickets given for to-night ! " answered Mr. Plumb. " Chap as I know what works there give me two stalls. Special occasion, too. It's Dolly D'Arcy's benefit."

Mr. Filcher restored certain goods to their appointed places on the shelves.

" There is things in this world, George, what's got to be done," he remarked sententiously. " Likewise endured. Got to be done and endured, whether you like it or not."

Mr. Plumb made a sound expressive of still deeper resentment.

" I ain't a philosopher, Thomas," he remarked. " And what I'm thinking of is—what will the girl say ? "

" She'll say what I've just said," replied Mr. Filcher. " What can't be cured must be endured. At least," he added, with a touch of reflective caution, " she will say so if she's got any sense."

227

" Plenty of sense," said Mr. Plumb shortly. " More than most folks. But this is where it is. The guv'nor wants me at once, sharp, and I ain't time to slip up the road and tell her. Weren't to meet till nine-ten, and I shall be hard at it with him then."

" Oh ! " said Mr. Filcher.

Mr. Plumb bestowed a side-glance at the principal assistant.

" I suppose you ain't doing nothing particular to-night, Thomas ? " he inquired.

" Wha' for ? " asked Mr. Filcher with sudden suspicion.

" I was thinking," replied Mr. Plumb, still watching his friend thoughtfully. " I was thinking that if you wasn't, and as it 'ud be a great pity to waste these here tickets, p'r'aps you'd go instead of me."

" Ain't got nobody to go with," said Mr. Filcher.

" I meant with her," said Mr. Plumb.

Mr. Filcher sniffed.

" I was thinking of going round to the Young Men's," he observed. " We've started a new gymnasium class on the Swedish principles, and I'm considering about joining it—this here physical culture, you know, George. Besides, I don't know the young lady."

" That," said Mr. Plumb, " is one of them matters as can be settled easy, Thomas. Middleish in height, fair, wear—will be wearing, I mean, blue serge tailor-made, with hat to match. She'll be opposite the Tube Station at nine-ten punctual."

" What I meant," said Mr. Filcher, taking off his apron— " What I meant, George, was that I've not been introduced to her. Situations like them, George, is what they call delicate."

" Oh, it's all right ! " said Mr. Plumb. " She isn't one to stand on ceremony, isn't Euphemia. You tell her what I say, and it'll be all right. Here's the tickets, Thomas. I'd do the same for you if—if a similar occasion was to arise."

Mr. Plumb laid the tickets on the counter, and Mr. Filcher looked at them as if they were a long way off.

" What—what might the young lady's other name be, George ? " he asked casually.

" Dobbs," replied Mr. Plumb promptly. " Miss Euphemia Dobbs. I'm much obliged to you. Now, if old Map only lets me get away, I'll meet you outside when the show's over. But you know him. It was nearer one o'clock than twelve last time when we'd finished. So if you don't see me when you come out, Thomas, perhaps you'd see Euphemia home. 'Tain't far, only up Sutherland Avenue way."

"Anything to oblige you, George," replied Mr. Filcher. "I'll see to it."

Then, in order that he might put on a clean collar and his best necktie, Mr. Filcher hurried away to his lodgings ; and Mr. Plumb, having turned out the errand-boy and the girl who took the cash, made a wry face, and entered the office wherein Mr. Mappaway was already surrounded with ledgers and account books.

II

THERE was no George Plumb to be seen when Mr. Filcher and Miss Dobbs emerged from the Metropolitan Music Hall at half-past eleven, and, after waiting about a little at the corner of the Harrow Road, they concluded that Mr. Mappaway was clearing up his arrears of bookkeeping in thorough style, and that Mr. Plumb was not to be waited for. Accordingly, they turned over Paddington Green in the direction of Sutherland Avenue, and Mr. Filcher realized that he must now make conversation of a more serious and lasting nature than had been necessary in the stalls wherein he and Miss Dobbs had sedately spent the later hours of the evening.

"Hard luck on old George ! " he observed. "Up to his eyes in figures he'll be, no doubt. He's a regular slave-driver is Mappaway, when he's that way inclined. Leaves his books to the last, and then wants 'em done all in a minute, as it were."

Miss Dobbs coughed.

"I look forward," she observed—"I look forward, Mr. Filcher, to George occupying a very much better position. I often say to him : 'What you need, George,' I say, 'is ambition.'"

"Push ! " said Mr. Filcher.

"Ambition and push," agreed Miss Dobbs. "They are both useful qualities in young business gentlemen, don't you think, Mr. Filcher ? "

It was Mr. Filcher's way never to agree in direct fashion with anybody. He remarked that chance was the finest thing in the world, and Miss Dobbs coughed once more.

"I often say to George," she remarked. "'George,' I say, ' why don't you get into one of the grocery departments of some of the really big establishments ? ' I say. 'With your talents, George, you ought to be at the Army and Navy or the Civil Service,' I say, ' not at a poky little place like Mappaway's,' I say. Which, of course, doesn't cast any reflection on you, Mr. Filcher, You're the manager, of course."

"Well, of course my position is different to poor old George's," condescendingly remarked Mr. Filcher. "Of course, I get more money than what George gets, and, being careful, I've saved. Between you and me and the post, as the saying is, I don't intend to stop long at Mappaway's. I'm thinking of setting up. Besides, I've expectations—rich uncle. Getting on, too, he is, and it would surprise me if he sees this year out ; it would, indeed ! Eighty, and failing very fast last time I saw him."

"I hope it will turn out well, Mr. Filcher," said Miss Dobbs.

"Ought to," replied Mr. Filcher. "Always promised me, he has. 'Thomas, my lad,' is what he's always said, 'Thomas, my lad,' he's said more times than I could count, 'keep steady and sober, and save all you can,' he's said. 'And when my time comes there'll be something for you that'll make you thankful you took your uncle's advice,' he's said. And, as I remarked just now, eighty, and failing very fast."

"Well, I'm sure that's pleasant news to hear," said Miss Dobbs. "I always like to hear of good fortune coming to friends. I wish George had expectations."

"Ah," remarked Mr. Filcher, "there's not much to be made in our line, unless you've got expectations or ready capital. It's a poor game, being a grocer's assistant. Of course, I always knew that I should set up for myself ; we've money in our family, both sides. But to stop as a mere assistant until you're approaching middle age—no, not for me ! 'Tain't good enough. I've my eye on a snug little business at this moment."

"Have you, really ? " said Miss Dobbs. "How interesting, Mr. Filcher ! I like young gentlemen to be ambitious. Perhaps you'll go on till you've quite a big place like—like Whiteley's or some of the others.

Mr. Filcher replied with dark significance that he was not the sort to let grass grow under his feet, and that he knew a thing or two.

"I'm sure you do," said Miss Dobbs admiringly. "I thought so as soon as I saw you."

Then, having reached the particular part of Sutherland Avenue in which Miss Dobbs resided, they said farewell and pressed each other's hands ; and Mr. Filcher raised his hat with a graceful sweep of his elbow and went away, humming very thoughtfully the refrain of the popular air with which Miss Dolly D'Arcy had bewitched the house that night. As for Miss Dobbs, she retired to her room to look at herself in the square foot of mirror above her dressing-table, and subsequently to summon up mental portraits of Mr. Plumb and Mr. Filcher.

Mr. Plumb was shortish, inclined, young as he was, to stoutness. He had a snub nose, fox-coloured hair, and a multitude of freckles. Mr. Filcher was tall, slender, dark, and wore a silky moustache and an expression which Miss Dobbs set down as sweetly poetic. She went to bed genuinely interested in the state of Mr. Filcher's rich uncle's health.

III

IT may have been about a month later than the event just recorded that Mr. Filcher, who had displayed a certain amount of absent-mindedness one evening during the tidying-up and closing-the-shop process, joined Mr. Plumb, when they were outside Mappaway's, and announced his intention of walking part of the way home with him. Mr. Plumb, suspecting nothing, agreed gladly, making, however, a proviso to the effect that he should be allowed to escape at the end of Harrow Road, as he wished to go Sutherland Avenue way.

" Just so," agreed Mr. Filcher. " Er—the fact is, George, I wished to have a little private conversation with you."

" Oh ! " said Mr. Plumb, a little surprised. " Indeed, Thomas ? "

" Yes," replied Mr. Filcher. " Yes, George. In fact, at the request of Miss Dobbs—of Euphemia."

" Of Miss Dobbs—of Euphemia ? " said Mr. Plumb. " Oh, indeed, Thomas—oh ! "

" Let's turn aside into this street," said Mr. Filcher, steering Mr. Plumb into one of the side streets which lead towards Sussex Square. " It's more retired. Yes—h'm—I think there was never any proper or formal engagement between you and Miss Dobbs, George ? You never gave her a ring, I believe ? "

Mr. Plumb stopped and regarded his friend with widening eyes. His jaw began to drop.

" What," he began—" what——"

" Take it easy, George," said Mr. Filcher. " It's the only way. Be a man, George ! The fact of the matter is, Miss Dobbs and yours truly have conceived a mutual affection for each other."

" A mutual affection for each other ! " gasped Mr. Plumb.

" And have become engaged to be married," continued Mr. Filcher, gaining confidence. " I gave her a ring last night, George. A very handsome article it is ; cost me as much as twenty-seven and sixpence—pearls and diamonds. And, as I say, be a man ! "

Mr. Plumb gasped a few times, looked all round him wildly, and clenched his fists, which he had already plunged into the pockets of his trousers. He tried to speak.

" I—I," he stammered. " I——"

" Now, George, be calm," said Mr. Filcher. " You'll always find me fair and honourable, George. It wasn't my fault, George, that out of good nature I obliged you by giving the pleasure of my company to Miss Dobbs—Euphemia—at the music-hall. It wasn't my fault that Miss Dobbs—Euphemia—conceived an ardent affection for me there and then. These things, George, is above all of us. Marriages, you know, are made in heaven, as the saying goes. This is what I called inevitable. Be a man ! "

Mr. Plumb collected himself.

" Strikes me," he observed, " strikes me as how it doesn't much matter to you whether I'm a man or a mouse. Done it behind my back, you have, and——"

" Now, George," said Mr. Filcher admonishingly—" now, George, don't sully that fair flower of friendship with unworthy suspicions. There hasn't been nothing done behind your back. You wasn't engaged to the young lady. Love, George, is a thing that won't be trammelled in a cage—it must be free as—as the air, George. Miss Dobbs, when she met me, loved for the first time. It was a gone case, George. Now, I've broke it to you as gentle as I could, us being old friends, and I'm sure you'll be a man and recognize the—the fitness of things. She never could have been yours, you know, George ; you're not affinities. As you'll see, George, if you read this letter which Miss Dobbs—Euphemia—asked me to give you."

Here Mr. Filcher produced an envelope, and handed it over to Mr. Plumb with another exhortation to manliness. And Mr. Plumb drew out a typewritten document, to which was appended a scrawling signature. He was not surprised to see the formal-looking lines of violet ink. Miss Dobbs was a typist in a warehouse, and she had no doubt snatched a few moments from her work in order to communicate with him. He held the paper up, and read.

" DEAR GEORGE "—wrote Miss Dobbs—" Having deeply searched my heart, I have arrived at the conclusion that you and me are not quite suited to each other, and that friendship is the only possible state between us. I find a great affinity of feeling with Mr. Filcher, who corresponds to the ideal I have long cherished in secret, and I have become engaged to him.

So regretting I shall be unable to meet you at the pillar-box
to-night.

> "I am, dear George,
>> "Your true well-wisher,
>>> "Euphemia Dobbs."

Mr. Plumb smacked his lips.

"And this," he said—" this is the girl I took to the pictures—
front seats, too, only last half-closing day ! "

Mr. Filcher lifted a forefinger, and wagged it.

"The—the event hadn't happened then, George," he said.
"And, if it comes to that, me and Euphemia—Miss Dobbs—was
at the Hippodrome—dress circle, George—since then. Be a
man ! "

Mr. Plumb muttered something, and abruptly turned away.
Mr. Filcher stepped hurriedly and anxiously after him.

"You—you won't go over to Sutherland Avenue, George,"
he said.

Mr. Plumb glared over his shoulder.

"I shall go to hell, if I like ! " he snarled.   " Yah ! "

Then, crushing the typewritten document in his hand, he
walked away with bent head and rounded shoulders ; and Mr.
Filcher, having smoothed his dark, silky moustache, hemmed
twice or thrice, and went off in the direction which he had
requested his friend not to take.

IV

Mr. plumb lodged in one of the small streets which lie between
St. Mary's Mansions and the bend of the Harrow Road ; he
occupied a room at the extreme top of the house, and in it he
kept, as Lares and Penates, a few family portraits, a collection
of picture postcards, a chiming clock which he had won in a race
at the swimming baths, and a piccolo flute, on which, in inspired
moments, he discoursed music that afflicted his fellow lodgers to
tears, if they were women, and to smothered curses if they were
men.   He went home after leaving Mr. Filcher, read Miss Dobbs's
leave-taking note once more, put it in his pocket, laughed loudly
and wildly, smote his fox-coloured hair, and then, picking up
his flute, seated himself on the edge of his bed, and began to
play, "When other lips and other hearts their tales of love shall
tell," with variations of his own devising suited to the emotion
of the moment.   And he had just arrived at a really tender
rendering of the line, " Then you'll remember me," when his

eye, a little suffused, caught sight of a letter which lay neglected
on his dressing-table.

The reception of a letter was such an uncommon event in
the drab monotony of Mr. Plumb's life, that his lips immediately
withdrew themselves from his instrument.   He laid the flute
down, and picked the letter up.   As most people do who receive
letters in unknown handwriting, he turned it over before opening
it, and saw that it bore an embossed lozenge-shaped stamp on
the flap.   Mr. Plumb read what was on that stamp with amazed
interest.

"Billiter & Bagworthy, Solicitors, St. Mary Axe," he
muttered to himself.   "What do they want with me?   I don't
owe nobody nothing."

Then it occurred to him to open the letter, and presently
he found himself gazing at another typewritten communication—
and, as it proved, one of a very different nature to that with
which Mr. Filcher had presented to him earlier in the
evening.

"Dear Sir "—ran the letter—" We have great pleasure in
informing you that, in accordance with the terms of the will of
the late Mr. Abraham Plumb, lime and cement merchant, of
Greyborough, Yorks, who died on April 21 last, you are entitled
to a legacy of £1500, which sum the executor of the deceased's
will are prepared to pay over to you at any time.   We shall
esteem it a favour if you would call at these offices as soon as it
may be convenient to yourself.

"Yours truly,
"Billiter & Bagworthy."

Mr. Plumb laid this epistle down on the bed, and stared at it
for a full minute and a half.   Then he took up the piccolo flute
and played another line of " When other lips " quite steadily,
and with simple variations.   Then he laid down the flute, and
took up the letter and read every word of it once more.   And that
done, he placed the letter in his breast pocket, unscrewed his
flute, and put it away, and unlocking his one trunk, felt for, and
found, a wallet.   He carefully abstracted a pound note, clapped
on his hat, and went out.

Ten minutes later he walked into an oyster-bar in Praed
Street, demanded a dozen of the very best, a plate of brown
bread-and-butter, with a lemon, and, sending the errand-boy for
a large bottle of stout, swelled out into a condition of lordly
magnificence.   And, as oyster followed oyster, Mr. Plumb

chuckled, and began to feel somewhat consoled for the cruel wrong which Fortune had done him an hour previously.

He thought cynically of life, and took a first step into the realms of philosophy by informing himself that that was just where it was—you were down one minute and up sky-high the next. Anyhow, fifteen hundred of the best was a fact of indubitable strength, and he wasn't going to forget it.

Next morning Mr. Filcher, the girl at the cash-desk, and the youth who made himself generally useful, were all astonished to find that Mr. Plumb did not turn up at the usual time for opening the shop. He was the most punctual of the four, and when half-past eight came, and he was still absent, Mr. Filcher grew seriously alarmed, and began to fear that Mr. Plumb had committed suicide by drowning himself in the waters of the canal which transects Maida Vale—it was convenient, opined Mr. Filcher, for despairing lovers. And he was wondering if he and Euphemia would be called at the inquest, when Mr. Mappaway, who was a very self-satisfied and highly important gentleman, strutted in, and took a general survey of the premises. His alert eye noticed the absence of Mr. Plumb from the cheese and bacon counter behind which George usually appeared.

" Where's Mr. Plumb ? " he inquired sharply.

" Not come yet, sir," replied Mr. Filcher. " I'm afraid he must be ill, sir ; he was looking out of sorts last night, and——"

But at that moment George appeared, attired in his best clothes, and looking in such remarkably good spirits that every freckle in his face shone. He ignored Mr. Filcher, and went straight up to Mr. Mappaway.

" Could I have a word with you, sir ? " he said. " Something important, sir."

Five minutes later, Mr. Plumb walked out of the private office, and, with a cool " Good-morning, Thomas," passed through the shop and disappeared. Mr. Mappaway, tying on his apron, came counterwards, smiling.

" Nice stroke of fortune for young Plumb there, Mr. Filcher," he remarked. " Told you, I expect, eh ? "

" No, sir," answered Mr. Filcher wonderingly. " Fortune, I think you said, sir ? "

" Quite a nice little fortune," said Mr. Mappaway. " Legacy from uncle that he hadn't heard of for some years. Tidy amount, too. Fifteen hundred pounds. Just stepped down to the lawyers to see about it. Has the fresh consignment of Irish roll come in, Mr. Filcher ? "

V

IN spite of his fifteen hundred pounds, Mr. Plumb was lonely. The piccolo flute failed—at times—to console him, and he took to wandering along the north bank of the canal, beneath the dwarf plane-trees. This had been a favourite walk with him and Euphemia on moonlighted nights ; in spite of the fact that he had never given her a ring, they had been very loverlike, and Mr. Plumb felt a painful pleasure in recalling their tender moments. There was a particular spot along that canal-side where they had exchanged their first kiss ; George took a mournful interest in it. And there one night, soon after he had become a wealthy man, he met Euphemia—by sheer accident.

In the glare of the neighbouring gas-lamp he saw, or fancied he saw, Euphemia grow pale. Her left hand instinctively went to her heart. Mr. Plumb pulled himself up.

" If my presence is unpleasant, Euphemia," he said, in a deep voice—" if it's inconvenient, I will remove it. The wonder is that I haven't deposited it before now in these waters ! "

Miss Dobbs uttered a faint scream. She made a show of appealing to the railings of the towing-path for physical support, and Mr. Plumb stretched out a hand, and somehow found it in the neighbourhood of her waist. His gloomy notions, and his assumed dignity melted like wax.

" You treated me cruel, Euphemia ! " he said chokingly. " What's this here fortune that's come to me compared to you ? I can't do nothing with it for thinking of you. There it lies untouched, eating its head off, as the saying is. If you'd ha' stuck to me, I'd ha' bought a partnership, and we'd ha' been married and—and all for the sake of a chap like Tom Filcher, what hasn't a soul above currants and raisins ! "

Miss Dobbs, who appeared to shrink more confidingly into Mr. Plumb's trembling arm with every moment, began to sob.

" He—he fascinated me, George ! " she murmured. " He— he'd such a way with him—soft and poetic, you know. P'r'aps it was all put on, George. If it had only been you that had come that night to the Met, George, this wouldn't have happened ! "

" Euphemia," said Mr. Plumb sternly. " It's never too late to turn back, even if you're on the very brink of a precipice, Euphemia. It's my nature, Euphemia, to let bygones be bygones. Now, Euphemia——"

The result of this conversation was that Mr. Plumb accompanied Miss Dobbs homewards, and waited outside the house in

Sutherland Avenue, wherein the young lady lodged with a distant relative, while she penned a letter to Mr. Thomas Filcher, in which she announced—somewhat curtly, in accordance with Mr. Plumb's instructions—that she found she had been mistaken in her feelings, and claimed a lady's right of changing her mind. Within the letter she enclosed the engagement ring of pearls and diamonds which had cost twenty-seven-and-sixpence.

Mr. Plumb presented this missive to Mr. Filcher next morning, choosing a convenient moment when Mr. Mappaway had stepped out to the back.

The recipient changed colours several times when he saw the ring, and gasped when he read the letter ; but when he emerged from behind the pile of tinned lobster to which he had retired for privacy, his countenance had assumed an expression which was cynical and sardonic. He laughed, just as Mr. Plumb had heard the gentlemanly stage villain laugh when he was foiled or circumvented. That laugh made Mr. Plumb shiver.

" Oh, it's a laughing matter, is it ? " he said uneasily. " Well, I don't see nothing to laugh at myself."

Mr. Filcher began to weigh up quarter-pounds of tea.

" I dare say not, George," he replied. " I dare say not, and you ain't remarkable for your powers of observation, you know. Ah, I pity you, George, I do, indeed. It's a terrible thing to be married for one's money."

" Who's going to be married for money ? " demanded Mr. Plumb. " Who ? "

" You, George," retorted Mr. Filcher, shaking his head. " Ah, I see through it all ! If you hadn't come into a fortune, George, she wouldn't have looked at the side of the street you were on after knowing me. No ! "

" That's a lie !" vociferated Mr. Plumb. " And you're a liar !"

" No language, I beg, George," protested Mr. Filcher. " No language. Remember where we are. Ah, well, I'm sorry for you, George, but I'm thankful that I'm delivered. A lady that marries a gentleman because he happens to have had a fortune left him is—well, I won't say any more, George. All the same, I pity you from the bottom of my heart."

Customers entered the shop at that moment, and Mr. Plumb concentrated his mental abilities upon them. But at intervals during the day he thought much on what Mr. Filcher had insinuated, and he grew more and more miserable. Whenever he approached his fellow-assistant he was received with a deep sigh and a shake of the head ; it was quite evident that Mr. Filcher regarded him as an object of compassion. He went home uneasy, and gained no comfort from a short performance on the piccolo flute.

Over his supper-tea Mr. Plumb evolved a dark scheme. It appeared to him to be Machiavellian in its wickedness, but he remembered that all is fair in love. And when he met Miss Dobbs at the pillar-box half an hour later, he assumed an anxious and a gloomy air.

" Euphemia," he said, as they walked away arm-in-arm, " don't you build too much on that legacy. There's a doubt cropped up." Miss Dobbs showed genuine concern. " Can't talk about it now," continued Mr. Plumb. " Tell you more to-morrow night. But don't build, Euphemia, don't build."

Miss Dobbs sighed deeply.

" Oh, George ! " she exclaimed. " What a dreadful thing if you lose it ! "

" I should still have you," said Mr. Plumb.

Miss Dobbs made no reply to that. She was very thoughtful during the rest of the evening, and her last words were an admonition to Mr. Plumb to do his best to discover the truth.

" For the suspense, George," she added, " must be most trying to you—it'll affect your health."

Mr. Plumb sighed deeply.

" If the worst comes to the worst, Euphemia," he said, " I shall still have you, as I remarked previous."

" All the same," remarked Miss Dobbs—" all the same, George, to have the cup of happiness raised to one's lips and then dashed away is not at all pleasant."

Mr. Plumb repaired to the rendezvous next evening with a still gloomier air. He shook his head when Miss Dobbs approached him.

" It's all UP, Euphemia," he said dolefully. " There was a mistake. I'm just the same George Plumb. But," he added, in a would-be sprightly fashion, " I still have you."

Miss Dobbs backed a little away from the insidious approach of Mr. Plumb's arm.

" Well, I don't know, George Plumb," she replied. " I must say that I consider it a very strange thing for a young gentleman to approach an engaged young lady—with a pearl and diamond ring too !—and strive to lead her away from her—her allegiance by a cock-and-bull tale of a fortune. I consider that I've been deceived—shamefully."

" Now, Euphemia," exclaimed Mr. Plumb, with a world of tender reproach and entreaty in his voice—" Euphemia, what about—about love, Euphemia ? Love, you know ? "

But Miss Dobbs remained cold. She made further remarks upon the subject of the pearl and diamond ring, and said that she had been obliged to tell her fellow-typist at the warehouse that she had taken it to get a stone reset, and she added comments on the wickedness of deceitful men, and she and Mr. Plumb parted on terms which he did not quite understand. But he understood things better next morning, for the first post brought him a letter from Miss Dobbs in which she declined his further attentions. And in the epistle she did not express any wish to be even a friend to him.

Mr. Plumb went to business, and found Mr. Filcher smiling more sardonically than ever.

" I've had a letter, George," said Mr. Filcher. " From her."

" So have I," said Mr. Plumb.

" Says you've deceived her cruel, and wants the pearl and diamond ring back," said Mr. Filcher.

Then Mr. Plumb confessed to Mr. Filcher ; and Mr. Filcher, having heard everything, shook his head, and said, solemnly, that he didn't like it. He had heard, he said, of young ladies that were—he couldn't think of the word just then, but he believed it was a Latin word which meant that they had a keen nose for money, and he was afraid, very much afraid, that Euphemia was one of them.

" We shall have to put our heads together, George," he said. " This is a serious matter. It's one of those matters that need consideration."

The result of the consideration was that Mr. Filcher met Miss Dobbs that evening, and placidly accepted whatever she said to him. He excused himself for not having brought the twenty-seven-and-sixpenny ring. He had been so much upset, he said, by the return of it that he had sent it by registered post to his sister in Canada, as a belated wedding present.

" But you shall have a better one when the old uncle dies, and I come into my money, Euphemia," he said consolingly. " I might run to as much as two pound this time."

" How is your uncle, Thomas ? " asked Miss Dobbs.

" I went to see him last Sunday," answered Mr. Filcher. " The old chap's recovered from his illness, and looks quite hearty. I shouldn't wonder if he lives another ten or twelve years ; ours is a long-lived family on both sides. But what is ten years to you and me, Euphemia ? We can wait, so long as we have each other."

" Yes," said Miss Dobbs, a little faintly. " Likely to last all that time, is he ? "

" He is," replied Mr. Filcher cheerily. " Oh, yes ! And,

talking about uncles, that's a funny affair about poor old George and his uncle—very funny ! "

" What's that ? " inquired Miss Dobbs.

" Why, the other day poor old George got the idea that there'd been a mistake, and that he wasn't going to have any legacy at all," answered Mr. Filcher. " Now it turns out that there wasn't any mistake, and that instead of its being only fifteen hundred, it was more—more ! "

" So he'll get it after all ? " said Miss Dobbs, even more faintly.

" Get it ! " exclaimed Mr. Filcher. " He's got it ! Paid over to him this very afternoon, it was. He did the handsome, did George, I must say. Took me and old Mappaway out, and stood a bottle of sham and the best cigars—real sixpenny ones— and gave the cash-girl and the errand-boy a bob each. Oh, yes, he's touched it, has poor old George, right enough ! "

Next evening, in accordance with the deeply laid conspiracy which he and Mr. Filcher had hatched, Mr. Plumb wandered, apparently disconsolate, by the side of the canal, and before him suddenly appeared Miss Dobbs, tearful and contrite, stretching out an appealing hand.

" Oh, George," she exclaimed, " can you ever forgive me for treating you so unkindly the other night ? I didn't mean it, George ; I didn't, indeed, and I've never slept a wink since ! Oh, George——"

But Mr. Plumb lifted hands of horror, uttered a deep groan, and, turning, fled in the direction of the lights of Maida Vale.

VI

IT was a much disillusioned George Plumb who walked into Mappaway's next morning. He knew now that Euphemia was meretricious ; she had loved his money and not him. He lifted soured and disappointed eyes as he entered, and was surprised to see Mr. Filcher's countenance wreathed in ecstatic smiles.

" Now what's up ? " he growled. " Ain't no need to grin like a Cheshire cat at this time of the morning, as I know of ! "

Mr. Filcher pulled Mr. Plumb inside the counter, and produced a slip of pink paper from an ancient pocket-book. He spread it out upon the counter, and revealed a cheque for fifteen hundred pounds.

" Good God ! " exclaimed Mr. Plumb.

" Ah, my boy ! " said Mr. Filcher. " I thought that would surprise you. Last night, George, the old uncle what I've told you of asked all his nephews and nieces to supper—roast chickens and sherry wine, George, and all up to the mark, I tell you ! and made us a speech. Said he was damned if he was going to pay these here death duties, and so, as he'd got plenty more that 'ud last him his time, he'd share out at present what he meant to leave the six of us that was there ; and wound up, George, by handing us each one of these here cheques."

"Good business," said Mr. Plumb. "Then you'll stand treat ? "

"I'll stand treat to you and Mappaway, George, with pleasure," replied Mr. Filcher, "and I won't forget the boy and girl, neither. And I'll tell you what, George ; you and me'll go into partnership. We'll buy that business I told you of down at Stonybeach. There's my fifteen hundred and there's your fifteen hundred, and——"

"Mine's fifteen hundred and sixty odd," said Mr. Plumb.

"You can have a spree on the sixty, and then we shall start fair," said Mr. Filcher. "But, mind you, George, there'll be provisions of partnership—strict provisions ! "

"Such as—what ? " demanded Mr. Plumb.

Mr. Filcher's countenance grew dark and determined.

"No love matters," he said determinedly. "No woman. Our motto will be ' business and nothing but business.' "

Mr. Plumb sighed. Then he thought of the meretricious Euphemia, and he, too, frowned.

"I'm on ! " he said.

VII

THE solicitor who drew up the deed of partnership between Thomas Filcher and George Plumb was greatly astonished when he was strictly commanded to insert (1) a clause which provided that neither of the partners should enter into an engagement to marry without the other's consent—if either did so, he should pay to the other a forfeit of five hundred pounds ; and (2) a further clause providing that if either partner married within a term of ten years from the signing of the deed, he should retire from the business and should pay a sum of one thousand pounds to the other. These conditions struck the man of law as being as harsh as they were remarkable, and he said so ; but Mr. Filcher, assuming an expression full of sinister meaning, replied that he and Mr. Plumb knew what they were after, and the clauses went in.

Stonybeach was at that time a rapidly growing seaside resort and the establishment of Messrs. Filcher & Plumb prospered.

The two partners worked hard, kept their eyes opened, and studied modern methods. They were considered to be models of industry ; to the outside world they seemed to do nothing but work. They lived in rooms over the shop ; they made no friends. In their scanty hours of relaxation they played a game or two of draughts, and talked of Euphemia. For now that they had escaped from her presence, they cherished memories of her which were rapidly becoming mellowed and tender. Sometimes, when they took their one glass of weak whisky and water before going to bed, they grew very confidential.

" With all her faults—and we all have 'em—she was a very nice girl, Thomas ! " observed Mr. Plumb one night, when the partnership had been in existence some two years. " A very nice girl ! "

" She was, George," said Mr. Filcher fervently, " And a very handsome girl ! "

" It wouldn't surprise me," said Mr. Plumb, sipping his mixture thoughtfully, " it wouldn't surprise me, Thomas, if the truth was that Euphemia was in love with both of us. Poor girl ! "

" Ah, p'r'aps so," said Mr. Filcher, " p'r'aps so ! I quite expect, George, that Euphemia has remained single for our sakes. She wouldn't easily forget either of us."

" No," said Mr. Plumb sorrowfully ; " I'm sure she wouldn't. She was tender-hearted at times, was Euphemia, as no doubt you're aware, Thomas."

" Ah ! " answered Mr. Filcher, sighing. " You're right ! "

They went to bed that night thinking very affectionately of certain memories of Euphemia, and condoling with her on the single-blessedness to which they felt sure she had resigned herself. And they may have been still thinking of her next morning when, as both stood together at the counter looking over some letters that had just arrived, there sailed into the shop a glowing young matron, dressed in the height of Maida Vale fashion, who was attended by a white-clad nurse, carrying a remarkably fine infant in arms. The lady stared at the proprietors ; the proprietors stared at her. All three gasped and blushed.

" Euphemia ! " murmured Mr. Filcher.

" Herself ! " whispered Mr. Plumb.

The customer smiled widely.

" Well, I never did ! " she exclaimed. " Filcher & Plumb, of course. And me never noticing the name ! Mrs. Mosenstein now, if you please, gentlemen ; married this eighteen months to a highly respected member of the Stock Exchange. This is our

first. Take his veil off, Johnston, and let the gentlemen see him.
Yes ; Mr. Mosenstein's taken one of those beautiful houses on
the esplanade for the summer, and I'm sure I shall be delighted
to give you our custom, gentlemen ! Now, what's the very
best Dorsetshire butter a pound, Mr. Plumb ? "

That night, when Mr. Filcher handed his partner the usual
allowance of whisky, he did so with a meaning look.

" George," he said, " to-morrow we will revise that deed of
partnership. Human nature is human nature, George, and if
some folks marry—well, all the more reason why others should
follow their example ! "

THOMAS HARDY (1840–1928), *the son of a builder, worked in a London office by day and wrote novels at night. "Far from the Madding Crowd" brought him acknowledgment, and eventually he was able to devote himself to those powerful, intense studies of rural life in his beloved Wessex. His sense of humour is revealed in the creation of such pleasant rustics as people the pages of "The Greenwood Tree" and the story below.*

TONY KYTES,
THE ARCH-DECEIVER

I SHALL never forget Tony's face. 'Twas a little, round, firm, tight face, with a seam here and there left by the smallpox, but not enough to hurt his looks in a woman's eye, though he'd had it badish when he was a boy. So very serious looking and unsmiling 'a was, that young man, that it really seemed as if he couldn't laugh at all without great pain to his conscience. He looked very hard at a small speck in your eye when talking to 'ee. And there was no more sign of a whisker or beard on Tony Kytes's face than on the palm of my hand. He used to sing "The Tailor's Breeches" with a religious manner, as if it were a hymn :

"*O the petticoats went off, and the breeches they went on!*"

and all the rest of the scandalous stuff. He was quite the women's favourite, and in return for their likings he loved 'em in shoals.

But in course of time Tony got fixed down to one in particular, Milly Richards, a nice, light, small, tender little thing ; and it was soon said that they were engaged to be married. One Saturday he had been to market to do business for his father, and was driving home the wagon in the afternoon. When he reached the foot of the very hill we shall be going over in ten minutes, who should he see waiting for him at the top but Unity Sallet, a handsome girl, one of the young women he'd been very tender towards before he'd got engaged to Milly.

As soon as Tony came up to her she said, " My dear Tony, will you give me a lift home ? "

" That I will, darling," said Tony. " You don't suppose I could refuse 'ee ? "

244

She smiled a smile, and up she hopped, and on drove Tony.

"Tony," she says, in a sort of tender chide, "why did ye desert me for that other one? In what is she better than I? I should have made 'ee a finer wife, and a more loving one, too. 'Tisn't girls that are so easily won at first that are the best. Think how long we've known each other—ever since we were children almost—now haven't we, Tony?"

"Yes, that we have," says Tony, a-struck with the truth o't.

"And you've never seen anything in me to complain of, have ye, Tony? Now tell the truth to me!"

"I never have, upon my life," says Tony.

"And—can you say I'm not pretty, Tony? Now look at me!"

He let his eyes light upon her for a long while. "I really can't," says he. "In fact, I never knowed you was so pretty before!"

"Prettier than she?"

What Tony would have said to that nobody knows, for before he could speak, what should he see ahead, over the hedge past the turning, but a feather he knew well—the feather in Milly's hat—she to whom he had been thinking of putting the question as to giving out the banns that very week.

"Unity," says he, as mild as he could, "here's Milly coming. Now I shall catch it mightily if she sees 'ee riding here with me; and if you get down she'll be turning the corner in a moment, and, seeing 'ee in the road, she'll know we've been coming on together. Now, dearest Unity, will ye, to avoid all unpleasantness, which I know ye can't bear any more than I, will ye lie down in the back part of the wagon, and let me cover you over with the tarpaulin till Milly has passed? It will all be done in a minute. Do!—and I'll think over what we've said, and perhaps I shall put a loving question to you after all, instead of to Milly. 'Tisn't true that it is all settled between her and me."

Well, Unity Sallet agreed, and lay down at the back end of the wagon, and Tony covered her over, so that the wagon seemed to be empty but for the loose tarpaulin; and then he drove on to meet Milly.

"My dear Tony," cries Milly, looking up with a little pout at him as he came near. "How long you've been coming home! Just as if I didn't live at Upper Longpuddle at all! And I've come to meet you as you asked me to do, and to ride back with you, and talk over our future home—since you asked me, and I promised. But I shouldn't have come else, Mr. Tony!"

"Ay, my dear, I did ask 'ee—to be sure I did, now I think of it—but I had quite forgot it. To ride back with me, did you say, dear Milly?"

"Well, of course! What can I do else? Surely you don't want me to walk, now I've come all this way?"

"O no, no! I was thinking you might be going on to town to meet your mother. I saw her there—and she looked as if she might be expecting 'ee."

"O no; she's just home. She came across the fields, and so got back before you."

"Ah! I didn't know that," says Tony. And there was no help for it but to take her up beside him.

They talked on very pleasantly, and looked at the trees, and beasts, and birds, and insects, and at the ploughmen at work in the fields, till presently who should they see looking out of the upper window of a house that stood beside the road they were following, but Hannah Jolliver, another young beauty of the place at that time, and the very first woman that Tony had fallen in love with—before Milly, and before Unity, in fact— the one that he had almost arranged to marry instead of Milly. She was a much more dashing girl than Milly Richards, though he'd not thought much of her of late. The house Hannah was looking from was her aunt's.

"My dear Milly—my coming wife, as I may call 'ee," says Tony in his modest way, and not so loud that Unity could overhear, "I see a young woman a-looking out of window, who I think may accost me. The fact is, Milly, she had a notion that I was wishing to marry her, and since she's discovered I've promised another, and a prettier than she, I'm rather afeard of her temper if she sees us together. Now, Milly, would you do me a favour—my coming wife, as I may say?"

"Certainly, dearest Tony," says she.

"Then would ye creep under the empty sacks just here in the front of the wagon, and hide there out of sight till we've passed the house? She hasn't seen us yet. You see, we ought to live in peace and goodwill since 'tis almost Christmas, and 'twill prevent angry passions rising, which we always should do."

"I don't mind, to oblige you, Tony," Milly said; and though she didn't care much about doing it, she crept under, and crouched down just behind the seat, Unity being snug at the other end. So they drove on till they got near the road-side cottage. Hannah had soon seen him coming, and waited at the window, looking down upon him. She tossed her head a little disdainful and smiled off-hand.

"Well, aren't you going to be civil enough to ask me to ride home with you?" she says, seeing that he was for driving past with a nod and a smile.

"Ah, to be sure! What was I thinking of?" said Tony, in a flutter. "But you seem as if you was staying at your aunt's?"

"No, I am not," she said. "Don't you see I have my bonnet and jacket on? I have only called to see her on my way home. How can you be so stupid, Tony?"

"In that case—ah—of course you must come along wi' me," says Tony, feeling a dim sort of sweat rising up inside his clothes. And he reined in the horse, and waited till she'd come downstairs, and then helped her up beside him, her feet outside. He drove on again, his face as long as a face that was a round one by nature well could be.

Hannah looked round sideways into his eyes. "This is nice, isn't it, Tony?" she says. "I like riding with you."

Tony looked back into her eyes. "And I with you," he said after a while. In short, having considered her, he warmed up, and the more he looked at her the more he liked her, till he couldn't for the life of him think why he had ever said a word about marriage to Milly or Unity while Hannah Jolliver was in question. So they sat a little closer and closer, their feet upon the foot-board and their shoulders touching, and Tony thought over and over again how handsome Hannah was. He spoke tenderer and tenderer, and called her "dear Hannah" in a whisper at last.

"You've settled it with Milly by this time, I suppose?" said she.

"N—no, not exactly."

"What? How low you talk, Tony."

"Yes—I've a kind of hoarseness. I said, not exactly."

"I suppose you mean to?"

"Well, as to that——" His eyes rested on her face, and hers on his. He wondered how he could have been such a fool as not to follow up Hannah. "My sweet Hannah!" he bursts out, taking her hand, not being really able to help it, and forgetting Milly and Unity, and all the world besides. "Settled it? I don't think I have!"

"Hark!" says Hannah.

"What?" says Tony, letting go her hand.

"Surely I heard a sort of little screaming squeak under those sacks? Why, you've been carrying corn, and there's mice in this wagon, I declare!" She began to haul up the tails of her gown.

"O no, 'tis the axle," said Tony in an assuring way. "It do go like that sometimes in dry weather."

"Perhaps it was. . . . Well, now, to be quite honest, dear Tony, do you like her better than me? Because—because, although I've held off so independent, I'll own at last that I do like 'ee, Tony, to tell the truth; and I wouldn't say no if you asked me—you know what."

Tony was so won over by this pretty offering mood of a girl who had been quite the reverse (Hannah had a backward way with her at times, if you can mind) that he just glanced behind, and then whispered very soft, "I haven't quite promised her, and I think I can get out of it, and ask you that question you speak of."

"Throw over Milly?—all to marry me! How delightful!" broke out Hannah, quite loud, clapping her hands.

At this there was a real squeak—an angry, spiteful squeak, and afterward a long moan, as if something had broke its heart, and a movement of the empty sacks.

"Something's there!" said Hannah, starting up.

"It's nothing, really," says Tony in a soothing voice, and praying inwardly for a way out of this. "I wouldn't tell 'ee at first, because I wouldn't frighten 'ee. But, Hannah, I've really a couple of ferrets in a bag under there, for rabbiting, and they quarrel sometimes. I don't wish it knowed, as 'twould be called poaching. Oh, they can't get out, bless 'ee—you are quite safe! And—and—what a fine day it is, isn't it, Hannah, for this time of year? Be you going to market next Saturday? How is your aunt now?" And so on, says Tony, to keep her from talking any more about love in Milly's hearing.

But he found his work cut out for him, and wondering again how he should get out of this ticklish business, he looked about for a chance. Nearing home he saw his father in a field not far off, holding up his hand as if he wished to speak to Tony.

"Would you mind taking the reins a moment, Hannah," he said, much relieved, "while I go and find out what father wants?"

She consented, and away he hastened into the field, only too glad to get breathing time. He found that his father was looking at him with rather a stern eye.

"Come, come, Tony," says old Mr. Kytes, as soon as his son was alongside him, "this won't do, you know."

"What?" says Tony.

"Why, if you mean to marry Milly Richards, do it, and there's an end o't. But don't go driving about the country with

Jolliver's daughter and making a scandal. I won't have such things done."

" I only asked her—that is, she asked me, to ride home."

" She ? Why, now, if it had been Milly, 'twould have been quite proper ; but you and Hannah Jolliver going about by yourselves——"

" Milly's there, too, father."

" Milly ? Where ? "

" Under the corn-sacks ! Yes, the truth is, father, I've got rather into a nunnywatch, I'm afeard ! Unity Sallet is there, too—yes, at the other end, under the tarpaulin. All three are in that wagon, and what to do with 'em I know no more than the dead ! The best plan is, as I'm thinking, to speak out loud and plain to one of 'em before the rest, and that will settle it ; not but what 'twill cause 'em to kick up a bit of a miff, for certain. Now which would you marry, father, if you was in my place ? "

" Whichever of 'em did *not* ask to ride with thee."

" That was Milly, I'm bound to say, as she only mounted by my invitation. But Milly——"

" Then stick to Milly, she's the best. . . . But look at that ! "

His father pointed toward the wagon. " She can't hold that horse in. You shouldn't have left the reins in her hands. Run on and take the horse's head, or there'll be some accident to them maids ! "

Tony's horse, in fact, in spite of Hannah's tugging at the reins, had started on his way at a brisk walking pace, being very anxious to get back to the stable, for he had had a long day out. Without another word Tony rushed away from his father to overtake the horse.

Now, of all things that could have happened to wean him from Milly there was nothing so powerful as his father's recommending her. No ; it could not be Milly, after all. Hannah must be the one, since he could not marry all three as he longed to do. This he thought while running after the wagon. But queer things were happening inside it.

It was, of course, Milly who had screamed under the sack-bags, being obliged to let off her bitter rage and shame in that way at what Tony was saying, and never daring to show, for very pride and dread o' being laughed at, that she was in hiding. She became more and more restless, and in twisting herself about, what did she see but another woman's foot and white stocking close to her head. It quite frightened her, not knowing that Unity Sallet was in the wagon likewise. But after the fright was over she determined to get to the bottom of all this, and she crept and crept along the bed of the wagon, under the tarpaulin, like a snake, when lo and behold she came face to face with Unity.

" Well, if this isn't disgraceful ! " says Milly in a raging whisper to Unity.

" 'Tis," says Unity, " to see you hiding in a young man's wagon like this, and no great character belonging to either of ye ! "

" Mind what you are saying ! " replied Milly, getting louder. " I am engaged to be married to him, and haven't I a right to be here ? What right have you, I should like to know ? What has he been promising you ? A pretty lot of nonsense, I expect ! But what Tony says to other women is all mere wind, and no concern to me ! "

" Don't you be too sure ! " says Unity. " He's going to have Hannah, and not you, nor me either ; I could hear that."

Now at these strange voices sounding from under the cloth Hannah was thunderstruck a'most into a swound ; and it was just at this time that the horse moved on. Hannah tugged away wildly, not knowing what she was doing ; and as the quarrel rose louder and louder Hannah got so horrified that she let go the reins altogether. The horse went on at his own pace, and coming to the corner where we turn round to drop down the hill to Lower Longpuddle he turned too quick, the off wheels went up the bank, the wagon rose sideways till it was quite on edge upon the near axles, and out rolled the three maidens into the road in a heap. The horse looked round and stood still.

When Tony came up, frightened and breathless, he was relieved enough to see that neither of his darlings was hurt, beyond a few scratches from the brambles of the hedge. But he was rather alarmed when he heard how they were going on at one another.

" Don't ye quarrel, my dears—don't ye ! " says he, taking off his hat out of respect to 'em. And then he would have kissed them all round, as fair and square as a man could, but they were in too much of a taking to let him, and screeched and sobbed till they was quite spent.

" Now I'll speak out honest, because I ought to," says Tony, as soon as he could get heard. " And this is the truth," says he. " I've asked Hannah to be mine, and she is willing, and we are going to put up the banns next——"

Tony had not noticed that Hannah's father was coming up behind, nor had he noticed that Hannah's face was beginning

Out rolled the three maidens into the road

to bleed from the scratch of a bramble. Hannah had seen her father, and had run to him, crying worse than ever.

" My daughter is *not* willing, sir ! " says Mr. Jolliver hot and strong. " Be you willing, Hannah ? I ask ye to have spirit enough to refuse him, if yer virtue is left to 'ee and you run no risk ? "

" She's as sound as a bell for me, that I'll swear ! " says Tony, flaring up. " And so's the others, come to that, though you may think it an onusual thing in me ! "

" I have spirit, and I do refuse him ! " says Hannah, partly because her father was there, and partly, too, in a tantrum because of the discovery, and the scar that might be left on her face. " Little did I think when I was so soft with him just now that I was talking to such a false deceiver ! "

" What, you won't have me, Hannah ? " says Tony, his jaw hanging down like a dead man's.

" Never—I would sooner marry no—nobody at all ! " she gasped out, though with her heart in her throat, for she would not have refused Tony if he had asked her quietly, and her father had not been there, and her face had not been scratched by the bramble. And having said that, away she walked upon her father's arm, thinking and hoping he would ask her again.

Tony didn't know what to say next. Milly was sobbing her heart out ; but as his father had strongly recommended her he couldn't feel inclined that way. So he turned to Unity.

" Well, will you, Unity dear, be mine ? " he says.

" Take her leavings ? Not I ! " says Unity. " I'd scorn it ! " And away walks Unity Sallet likewise, though she looked back when she'd gone some way, to see if he was following her.

So there at last were left Milly and Tony by themselves, she crying in watery streams, and Tony looking like a tree struck by lightning.

" Well, Milly," he says at last, going up to her, " it do seem as if fate had ordained that it should be you and I, or nobody. And what must be must be, I suppose. Hey, Milly ? "

" If you like, Tony. You didn't really mean what you said to them ? "

" Not a word of it ! " declares Tony, bringing down his fist upon his palm.

And then he kissed her, and put the wagon to rights, and they mounted together ; and their banns were put up the very next Sunday. I was not able to go to their wedding, but it was a rare party they had, by all account.

FRANCIS BRET HARTE (1839-1902) *went to California at the age of fifteen, and became gold-miner, schoolmaster, and editor successively. Absorbing the atmosphere of the rough-and-tumble mining camp, he pictured with deft and sympathetic touches the play of human emotions against this rugged background. "Miggles" is a good example of the humorously tender style which made his stories famous.*

MIGGLES

WE were eight, including the driver. We had not spoken during the passage of the last six miles, since the jolting of the heavy vehicle over the roughening road had spoiled the Judge's last poetical quotation. The tall man beside the Judge was asleep, his arm passed through the swaying strap and his head resting upon it—altogether a limp, helpless-looking object, as if he had hanged himself and been cut down too late. The French lady on the back seat was asleep too, yet in a half-conscious propriety of attitude, shown even in the disposition of the handkerchief which she held to her forehead, and which partly veiled her face. The lady from Virginia City, travelling with her husband, had long since lost all individuality in a wild confusion of ribbons, veils, furs, and shawls. There was no sound but the rattling of wheels and the dash of rain upon the roof. Suddenly the stage stopped, and we became dimly aware of voices. The driver was evidently in the midst of an exciting colloquy with some one in the road—a colloquy of which such fragments as " bridge gone," " twenty feet of water," " can't pass," were occasionally distinguishable above the storm. Then came a lull, and a mysterious voice from the road shouted the parting adjuration :

" Try Miggles's."

We caught a glimpse of our leaders, as the vehicle slowly turned, of a horseman vanishing through the rain, and we were evidently on our way to Miggles's.

Who and where was Miggles ? The Judge, our authority, did not remember the name, and he knew the country thoroughly. The Washoe traveller thought Miggles must keep an hotel. We only knew that we were stopped by high water in front and rear, and that Miggles was our rock of refuge. A ten-minutes' splashing through a tangle by-road, scarcely wide enough for the stage, and we drew up before a barred and boarded gate in a wide stone wall or fence about eight feet high. Evidently Miggles's, and evidently Miggles did not keep an hotel.

The driver got down and tried the gate. It was securely locked.

" Miggles ! Oh Miggles ? "

No answer.

" Migg-ells ! You Miggles ! " continued the driver, with rising wrath.

"Migglesy ! " joined in the expressman, persuasively. " Oh Miggy ! Mig ! "

But no reply came from the apparently insensate Miggles. The Judge, who had finally got the window down, put his head out, and propounded a series of questions, which, if answered categorically, would have undoubtedly elucidated the whole mystery, but which the driver evaded by replying that " if we didn't want to sit in the coach all night, we had better rise up and sing out for Miggles."

So we rose up and called on Miggles in chorus ; then separately. And when we had finished, a Hibernian fellow-passenger from the roof called for " Maygells ! " whereat we all laughed. While we were laughing the driver cried " Shoo ! "

We listened. To our infinite amazement the chorus of " Miggles " was repeated from the other side of the wall, even to the final and supplemental " Maygells."

" Extraordinary echo," said the Judge.

" Extraordinary d——d skunk ! " roared the driver, contemptuously. " Come out of that, Miggles, and show yourself ! Be a man, Miggles ! Don't hide in the dark ; I wouldn't if I were you, Miggles," continued Yuba Bill, now dancing about in an excess of fury.

" Miggles ! " continued the voice, " Oh Miggles ! "

" My good man ! Mr. Myghail ! " said the Judge, softening the asperities of the name as much as possible. " Consider the inhospitality of refusing shelter from the inclemency of the weather to helpless females. Really, my dear sir——" But a succession of " Miggles," ending in a burst of laughter, drowned his voice.

Yuba Bill hesitated no longer. Taking a heavy stone from the road he battered down the gate, and, with the expressman, entered the enclosure. We followed. Nobody was to be seen. In the gathering darkness all that we could distinguish was that we were in a garden—from the rose-bushes that scattered over us a minute spray from their dripping leaves—and before a long, rambling wooden building.

"Do you know this Miggles?" asked the Judge of Yuba Bill.

"No; nor don't want to," said Bill shortly, who felt the Pioneer Stage Company insulted in his person by the contumacious Miggles.

"But, my dear sir," expostulated the Judge, as he thought of the barred gate.

"Lookee here," said Yuba Bill, with fine irony, "hadn't you better go back and sit in the coach till yer introduced? I'm going in"; and he pushed open the door of the building.

A long room, lighted only by the embers of a fire that was dying on the large hearth at its farther extremity; the walls curiously papered, and the flickering firelight bringing out its grotesque pattern; somebody sitting in a large arm-chair by the fireplace. All this we saw as we crowded together into the room, after the driver and expressman.

"Hello, be you Miggles?" said Yuba Bill to the solitary occupant.

The figure neither spoke nor stirred. Yuba Bill walked wrathfully towards it, and turned the eye of his coach-lantern upon its face. It was a man's face, prematurely old and wrinkled, with very large eyes, in which there was that expression of perfectly gratuitous solemnity which I had sometimes seen in an owl's. The large eyes wandered from Bill's face to the lantern, and finally fixed their gaze on that luminous object, without further recognition.

Bill restrained himself with an effort.

"Miggles! Be you deaf? You ain't dumb, anyhow, you know"; and Yuba Bill shook the insensate figure by the shoulder.

To our great dismay, as Bill removed his hand, the venerable stranger apparently collapsed, sinking into half his size and an undistinguishable heap of clothing.

"Well, dern my skin," said Bill, looking appealingly at us, and hopelessly retiring from the contest.

The Judge now stepped forward, and we lifted the mysterious invertebrate back into his original position. Bill was dismissed with the lantern to reconnoitre outside, for it was evident that from the helplessness of this solitary man there must be attendants near at hand, and we all drew around the fire. The Judge, who had regained his authority, and had never lost his conversational amiability—standing before us with his back to the hearth—charged us, as an imaginary jury, as follows:

"It is evident that either our distinguished friend here has reached that condition described by Shakespeare as 'the sere and yellow leaf,' or has suffered some premature abatement of his mental and physical faculties. Whether he is really the Miggles——"

Here he was interrupted by "Miggles! Oh Miggles! Migglesy! Mig!" and, in fact, the whole chorus of Miggles, in very much the same key as it had once before been delivered unto us.

We gazed at each other for a moment in some alarm. The Judge, in particular, vacated his position quickly, as the voice seemed to come directly over his shoulder. The cause, however, was soon discovered in a large magpie who was perched upon a shelf over the fireplace, and who immediately relapsed into a sepulchral silence, which contrasted singularly with his previous volubility. It was, undoubtedly, his voice which we had heard in the road, and our friend in the chair was not responsible for the discourtesy. Yuba Bill, who re-entered the room after an unsuccessful search, was loth to accept the explanation, and still eyed the helpless sitter with suspicion. He had found a shed in which he had put up his horses, but he came back dripping and sceptical. "Thar ain't nobody but him within ten miles of the shanty, and that 'ar d——d old skeesicks knows it."

But the faith of the majority proved to be securely based. Bill had scarcely ceased growling before we heard a quick step upon the porch, the trailing of a wet skirt, the door was flung open, and with a flash of white teeth, a sparkle of dark eyes, and an utter absence of ceremony or diffidence, a young woman entered, shut the door, and, panting, leaned back against it.

"Oh, if you please, I'm Miggles!"

And this was Miggles! This bright-eyed, full-throated young woman, whose wet gown of coarse blue stuff could not hide the beauty of the feminine curves to which it clung; from the chestnut crown of whose head, topped by a man's oilskin sou'wester, to the little feet and ankles, hidden somewhere in the recesses of her boy's brogans, all was grace—this was Miggles, laughing at us, too, in the most airy, frank, off-hand manner imaginable.

"You see, boys," said she, quite out of breath, and holding one little hand against her side, quite unheeding the speechless discomfiture of our party, or the complete demoralization of Yuba Bill, whose features had relaxed into an expression of gratuitous and imbecile cheerfulness—"you see, boys, I was mor'n two miles away when you passed down the road. I thought you might pull up here, and so I ran the whole way, knowing nobody was home but Jim—and—and—I'm out of breath—and—that lets me out."

And here Miggles caught her dripping oilskin hat from her head, with a mischievous swirl that scattered a shower of rain-drops over us ; attempted to put back her hair ; dropped two hair-pins in the attempt ; laughed and sat down beside Yuba Bill, with her hands crossed lightly on her lap. The Judge recovered himself first, and essayed an extravagant compliment.

" I'll trouble you for that thar hair-pin," said Miggles, gravely. Half-a-dozen hands were eagerly stretched forward ; the missing hair-pin was restored to its fair owner ; and Miggles, crossing the room, looked keenly in the face of the invalid. The solemn eyes looked back at hers with an expression we had never seen before. Life and intelligence seemed to struggle back into the rugged face. Miggles laughed again—it was a singularly eloquent laugh—and turned her black eyes and white teeth once more towards us.

" This afflicted person is——" hesitated the Judge.

" Jim," said Miggles.

" Your father ? "

" No."

" Brother ? "

" No."

" Husband ? "   Miggles darted a quick, half-defiant glance at the two lady passengers who I had noticed did not participate in the general masculine admiration of Miggles, and said, gravely, " No : it's Jim."

There was an awkward pause. The lady passengers moved closer to each other ; the Washoe husband looked abstractedly at the fire ; and the tall man apparently turned his eyes inward for self-support at this emergency. But Miggles's laugh, which was very infectious, broke the silence.   " Come," she said briskly, " you must be hungry.   Who'll bear a hand to help me get tea ? "

She had no lack of volunteers.   In a few moments Yuba Bill was engaged like Caliban in bearing logs for this Miranda ; the expressman was grinding coffee on the veranda ; to myself, the arduous duty of slicing bacon was assigned ; and the Judge lent each man his good-humoured and voluble counsel.   And when Miggles, assisted by the Judge and our Hibernian " deck passenger," set the table with all the available crockery, we had become quite joyous in spite of the rain that beat against windows, the wind that whirled down the chimney, the two ladies who whispered together in the corner, or the magpie who uttered a satirical and croaking commentary on their conversation from his perch above.   In the now bright, blazing fire we could see that the walls were papered with illustrated journals, arranged with feminine taste and discrimination. The furniture was extemporized and adapted from candle-boxes and packing-cases, and covered with gay calico, or the skin of some animal. The arm-chair of the helpless Jim was an ingenious variation of a flour-barrel. There was neatness, and even a taste for the picturesque, to be seen in the few details of the long, low room.

The meal was a culinary success. But more, it was a social triumph—chiefly, I think, owing to the rare tact of Miggles in guiding the conversation, asking all the questions herself, yet bearing throughout a frankness that rejected the idea of any concealment on her own part, so that we talked of ourselves, of our prospects, of the journey, of the weather, of each other—of everything but our host and hostess. It must be confessed that Miggles's conversation was never elegant, rarely grammatical, and that at times she employed expletives, the use of which had generally been yielded to our sex. But they were delivered with such a lighting up of teeth and eyes, and were usually followed by a laugh—a laugh peculiar to Miggles—so frank and honest that it seemed to clear the moral atmosphere.

Once during the meal we heard a noise like the rubbing of a heavy body against the outer walls of the house. This was shortly followed by a scratching and sniffing at the door. "That's Joaquin," said Miggles, in reply to our questioning glances; "would you like to see him?" Before we could answer she had opened the door and disclosed a half-grown grizzly, who instantly raised himself on his haunches, with his forepaws hanging down in the popular attitude of mendicancy, and looked admiringly at Miggles, with a very singular resemblance in his manner to Yuba Bill. "That's my watch-dog," said Miggles in explanation. "Oh, he don't bite," she added, as the two lady passengers fluttered into a corner. "Does he, old Tuppy?" (the latter remark being addressed directly to the sagacious Joaquin). "I tell you what, boys," continued Miggles, after she had fed and closed the door on *Ursa Minor*, "you were in big luck that Joaquin wasn't hanging round when you dropped in to-night."

"Where was he?" asked the Judge.

"With me," said Miggles.

"Lord love you! he trots round with me nights like as if he was a man."

We were silent for a few moments, and listened to the wind. Perhaps we all had the same picture before us—of Miggles walking through the rainy woods with her savage guardian at her side. The Judge, I remember, said something about Una and her lion ; but Miggles received it, as she did other compliments, with quiet gravity. Whether she was altogether unconscious of the admiration she excited—she could hardly have been oblivious of Yuba Bill's adoration—I know not, but her very frankness suggested a perfect sexual equality that was cruelly humiliating to the younger members of our party.

The incident of the bear did not add anything in Miggles's favour to the opinions of those of her own sex who were present. In fact, the repast over, a chilliness radiated from the two lady passengers that no pine-boughs brought in by Yuba Bill and cast as a sacrifice upon the hearth could wholly overcome. Miggles felt it ; and, suddenly declaring that it was time " to turn in," offered to show the ladies to their beds in an adjoining room. " You, boys, will have to camp out here by the fire as well as you can," she added, " for thar ain't but the one room."

Our sex—by which, my dear sir, I allude of course to the stronger portion of humanity—has been generally relieved from the imputation of curiosity or a fondness for gossip. Yet I am constrained to say, that hardly had the door closed on Miggles than we crowded together, whispering, snickering, smiling, and exchanging suspicions, surmises, and a thousand speculations in regard to our pretty hostess and her singular companion. I fear that we even hustled that imbecile paralytic who sat like a voiceless Memnon in our midst, gazing with the serene indifference of the Past in his passionless eyes upon our wordy counsels. In the midst of an exciting discussion the door opened again, and Miggles re-entered.

But not, apparently the same Miggles who a few hours before had flashed upon us. Her eyes were downcast, and as she hesitated for a moment on the threshold, with a blanket on her arm, she seemed to have left behind her the frank fearlessness which had charmed us a moment before. Coming into the room, she drew a low stool beside the paralytic's chair, sat down, drew the blanket over her shoulders, and saying, " If it's all the same to you, boys, as we're rather crowded, I'll stop here to-night," took the invalid's withered hand in her own and turned her eyes upon the dying fire. An instinctive feeling that this was only premonitory to more confidential relations, and perhaps some shame at our previous curiosity, kept us silent. The rain still beat upon the roof, wandering gusts of wind stirred the embers into momentary brightness, until, in a lull of the elements, Miggles suddenly lifted up her head, and throwing her hair over her shoulder, turned her face upon the group and asked :

" Is there any of you that knows me ? " There was no reply.

"Think again. I lived at Marysville in '53. Everybody knew me there, and everybody had the right to know me. I kept the Polka Saloon until I came to live with Jim. That's six years ago. Perhaps I've changed some."

The absence of recognition may have disconcerted her. She turned her head to the fire again, and it was some seconds before she again spoke, and then more rapidly :

"Well, you see I thought some of you must have known me. There's no great harm done any way. What I was going to say was this : Jim here "—she took his hand in both of hers as she spoke—" used to know me, if you didn't, and spent a heap of money upon me. I reckon he spent all he had. And one day— it's six years ago this winter—Jim came into my back room, sat down on my sofy, like as you see him in that chair, and never moved again without help. He was struck all of a heap, and never seemed to know what ailed him. The doctors came, and said as how it was caused all along of his way of life—for Jim was mighty free and wild like—and that he would never get better, and couldn't last long any way. They advised me to send him to 'Frisco, to the hospital, for he was no good to any one and would be a baby all his life. Perhaps it was something in Jim's eye, perhaps it was that I never had a baby, but I said 'No.' I was rich then, for I was popular with everybody—gentlemen like yourself, sir, came to see me—and I sold out my business and bought this yer place because it was sort of out of the way of travel, you see, and I brought my baby here."

With a woman's intuitive tact and poetry she had, as she spoke, slowly shifted her position so as to bring the mute figure of the ruined man between her and her audience, hiding in the shadow behind it, as if she offered it as a tacit apology for her actions. Silent and expressionless, it yet spoke for her ; helpless, crushed, and smitten with the Divine thunderbolt, it still stretched an invisible arm around her.

Hidden in the darkness, but still holding his hand, she went on :

"It was a long time before I could get the hang of things about yer, for I was used to company and excitement. I couldn't get any woman to help me, and a man I dursen't trust ; but what with the Indians hereabout, who'd do odd jobs for me, and having everything sent from the North Fork, Jim and I managed to worry through. The doctor would run up from Sacramento once in a while. He'd ask to see ' Miggles's baby,' as he called Jim, and when he'd go away, he'd say, ' Miggles, you're a trump—God bless you ' ; and it didn't seem so lonely after that. But the last time he was here he said as he opened the door to go, ' Do you know, Miggles, your baby will grow up to be a man yet, and an honour to his mother ! but not here, Miggles, not here ! ' And I thought he went away sad—and—and——" and here Miggles's voice and head were somehow both lost completely in the shadow.

" The folks about here are very kind," said Miggles after a pause, coming a little into the light again. " The men from the Fork used to hang around here, until they found they wasn't wanted, and the women are kind—and don't call. I was pretty lonely until I picked up Joaquin in the woods yonder one day, when he wasn't so high, and taught him to beg for his dinner ; and then thar's Polly—that's the magpie—she knows no end of tricks, and makes it quite sociable of evenings with her talk, and so I don't feel like as I was the only living being about the ranch. And Jim here," said Miggles, with her old laugh again, and coming out quite into the firelight, " Jim—why, boys, you would admire to see how much he knows for a man like him. Sometimes I bring him flowers, and he looks at 'em just as natural as if he knew 'em, and times, when we're sitting alone, I read him those things on the wall. Why, Lord ! " said Miggles, with her frank laugh, " I've read him that whole side of the house this winter. There never was such a man for reading as Jim."

" Why," asked the Judge, " do you not marry this man to whom you have devoted your youthful life ? "

" Well, you see," said Miggles, " it would be playing it rather low down on Jim to take advantage of his being so helpless. And then, too, if we were man and wife, now, we'd both know that I was *bound* to do what I do now of my own accord."

" But you are young yet and attractive——"

" It's getting late," said Miggles gravely, " and you'd better all turn in. Good-night, boys " ; and, throwing the blanket over her head, Miggles laid herself down beside Jim's chair, her head pillowed on the low stool that held his feet, and spoke no more. The fire slowly faded from the hearth ; we each sought our blankets in silence ; and presently there was no sound in the long room but the pattering of the rain upon the roof and the heavy breathing of the sleepers.

It was nearly morning when I awoke from a troubled dream. The storm had passed, the stars were shining, and through the shutterless window the full moon, lifting itself over the solemn pines without, looked into the room. It touched the lonely figure in the chair with an infinite compassion, and seemed to baptize with a shining flood the lowly head of the woman whose hair, as in the sweet old story, bathed the feet of Him she loved.

It even lent a kindly poetry to the rugged outline of Yuba Bill, half reclining on his elbow between them and his passengers, with savagely patient eyes keeping watch and ward. And then I fell asleep, and only woke at broad day, with Yuba Bill standing over me, and " All aboard " ringing in my ears.

Coffee was waiting for us on the table, but Miggles was gone. We wandered about the house, and lingered long after the horses were harnessed, but she did not return. It was evident that she wished to avoid a formal leave-taking, and had so left us to depart as we had come. After we had helped the ladies into the coach we returned to the house, and solemnly shook hands with the paralytic Jim, as solemnly settling him back into position after each handshake. Then we looked for the last time around the long, low room, at the stool where Miggles had sat, and slowly took our seats in the waiting coach. The whip cracked and we were off!

But as we reached the high road Bill's dexterous hand laid the six horses back on their haunches, and the stage stopped with a jerk. For there, on a little eminence beside the road, stood Miggles, her hair flying, her eyes sparkling, her white handkerchief waving, and her white teeth flashing a last " good-bye." We waved our hats in return. And then Yuba Bill, as if fearful of further fascination, madly lashed his horses forward, and we sank back in our seats. We exchanged not a word until we reached the North Fork and the stage drew up at the Independence House. Then, the Judge leading, we walked into the bar-room and took our places gravely at the bar.

" Are your glasses charged, gentlemen ? " said the Judge, solemnly taking off his white hat. They were.

" Well, then, here's to *Miggles* ; GOD BLESS HER ! "

Perhaps He had. Who knows ?

O. HENRY (1862–1910) *was the name that William Sidney Porter borrowed from the label of a French patent medicine to attach to those great collections of short stories which made him famous. At a time when the short story was in a more or less undeveloped stage he set a new standard and evolved a new technique which profoundly influenced his successors. Here is a good example of his style.*

TOBIN'S PALM

Tobin and me, the two of us, went down to Coney one day, for there was four dollars between us, and Tobin had need of distractions. For there was Katie Mahorner, his sweetheart, of County Sligo, lost since she started for America three months before with two hundred dollars, her own savings, and one hundred dollars from the sale of Tobin's inherited estate, a fine cottage and pig on the Bog Shannaugh. And since the letter that Tobin got saying that she had started to come to him not a bit of news had he heard or seen of Katie Mahorner. Tobin advertised in the papers, but nothing could be found of the colleen.

So, to Coney me and Tobin went, thinking that a turn at the chutes and the smell of the popcorn might raise the heart in his bosom. But Tobin was a hard-headed man, and the sadness stuck in his skin. He ground his teeth at the crying balloons ; he cursed the moving pictures ; and, though he would drink whenever asked, he scorned Punch and Judy, and was for licking the tintype men as they came.

So I gets him down a side way on a board walk where the attractions were some less violent. At a little six by eight stall Tobin halts, with a more human look in his eye.

" 'Tis here," says he, " I will be diverted. I'll have the palm of me hand investigated by the wonderful palmist of the Nile, and see if what is to be will be."

Tobin was a believer in signs and the unnatural in nature. He possessed illegal convictions in his mind along the subject of black cats, lucky numbers, and the weather predictions in the papers.

We went into the enchanted chicken coop, which was fixed mysterious with red cloth and pictures of hands with lines crossing

'em like a railroad centre. The sign over the door says it is
Madame Zozo the Egyptian Palmist. There was a fat woman
inside in a red jumper with pothooks and beasties embroidered
upon it. Tobin gives her ten cents and extends one of his hands.
She lifts Tobin's hand, which is own brother to the hoof of a
drayhorse, and examines it to see whether 'tis a stone in the frog
or a cast shoe he has come for.

"Man," says this Madame Zozo, "the line of your fate
shows——"

"'Tis not me foot at all," says Tobin, interrupting. "Sure,
'tis no beauty, but ye hold the palm of me hand."

"The line shows," says the Madame, "that ye've not arrived
at your time of life without bad luck. And there's more to come.
The mount of Venus—or is that a stone bruise?—shows that
ye've been in love. There's been trouble in your life on account
of your sweetheart."

"'Tis Katie Mahorner she has references with," whispers
Tobin to me in a loud voice to one side.

"I see," says the palmist, "a great deal of sorrow and
tribulation with one whom ye cannot forget. I see the lines of
designation point to the letter K and the letter M in her name."

"Whist!" says Tobin to me; "do ye hear that?"

"Look out," goes on the palmist, "for a dark man and a
light woman; for they'll both bring ye trouble. Ye'll make a
voyage upon the water very soon, and have a financial loss. I
see one line that brings good luck. There's a man coming into
your life who will fetch ye good fortune. Ye'll know him when
ye see him by his crooked nose."

"Is his name set down?" asks Tobin. "'Twill be convenient in the way of greeting when he backs up to dump off the
good luck."

"His name," says the palmist, thoughtful-looking, "is not
spelled out by the lines, but they indicate 'tis a long one, and the
letter 'o' should be in it. There's no more to tell. Good
evening. Don't block up the door."

"'Tis wonderful how she knows," says Tobin as we walk to
the pier.

As we squeezed through the gates a nigger man sticks his
lighted segar against Tobin's ear, and there is trouble. Tobin
hammers his neck, and the women squeal, and by presence of
mind I drag the little man out of the way before the police
comes. Tobin is always in an ugly mood when enjoying himself.

On the boat going back, when the man calls "Who wants
the good-looking waiter?" Tobin tried to plead guilty, feeling

the desire to blow the foam off a crock of suds, but when he felt in his pocket he found himself discharged for lack of evidence. Somebody had disturbed his change during the commotion. So we sat, dry, upon the stools, listening to the Dagoes fiddling on deck. If anything, Tobin was lower in spirits and less congenial with his misfortunes than when we started.

On a seat against the railing was a young woman dressed suitable for red automobiles, with hair the colour of an unsmoked meerschaum. In passing by, Tobin kicks her foot without intentions, and, being polite to ladies when in drink, he tries to give his hat a twist while apologizing. But he knocks it off, and the wind carries it overboard.

Tobin came back and sat down, and I began to look out for him, for the man's adversities were becoming frequent. He was apt, when pushed so close by hard luck, to kick the best dressed man he could see, and try to take command of the boat.

Presently Tobin grabs my arm and says, excited : " Jawn," says he, " do ye know what we're doing ? We're taking a voyage upon the water."

" There now," says I ; " subdue yeself. The boat'll land in ten minutes more."

" Look," says he, " at the light lady upon the bench. And have ye forgotten the nigger man that burned me ear ? And isn't the money I had gone—a dollar sixty-five it was ? "

I thought he was no more than summing up his catastrophes so as to get violent with good excuse, as men will do, and I tried to make him understand such things was trifles.

" Listen," says Tobin. " Ye've no ear for the gift of prophecy or the miracles of the inspired. What did the palmist lady tell ye out of me hand ? 'Tis coming true before your eyes. ' Look out,' says she, ' for a dark man and a light woman ; they'll bring ye trouble.' Have ye forgot the nigger man, though he got some of it back from me fist ? Can ye show me a lighter woman than the blonde lady that was the cause of me hat falling in the water ? And where's the dollar sixty-five I had in me vest when we left the shooting gallery ? "

The way Tobin put it, it did seem to corroborate the art of prediction, though it looked to me that these accidents could happen to any one at Coney without the implication of palmistry.

Tobin got up and walked around on deck, looking close at the passengers out of his little red eyes. I asked him the interpretation of his movements. Ye never know what Tobin has in his mind until he begins to carry it out.

" Ye should know," says he, " I'm working out the salvation

promised by the lines in me palm.   I'm looking for the crooked-nose man that's to bring the good luck.   'Tis all that will save us.   Jawn, did ye ever see a straighter-nosed gang of hellions in the days of your life ? "

'Twas the nine-thirty boat, and we landed and walked up-town, through Twenty-second Street, Tobin being without his hat.

On a street corner, standing under a gas-light and looking over the elevated road at the moon, was a man.   A long man he was, dressed decent, with a segar between his teeth, and I saw that his nose made two twists from bridge to end, like the wriggle of a snake.   Tobin saw it at the same time, and I heard him breathe hard like a horse when you take the saddle off.   He went straight up to the man, and I went with him.

" Good night to ye," Tobin says to the man.   The man takes out his segar and passes the compliments, sociable.

" Would ye hand us your name," asks Tobin, " and let us look at the size of it ?   It may be our duty to become acquainted with ye."

" My name," says the man, polite, " is Friedenhausman—Maximus G. Friedenhausman."

" 'Tis the right length," says Tobin.   " Do you spell it with an ' o ' anywhere down the stretch of it ? "

" I do not," says the man.

" Can ye spell it with an ' o ' ? " inquires Tobin, turning anxious.

" If your conscience," says the man with the nose, " is indisposed toward foreign idioms ye might, to please yourself, smuggle the letter into the penultimate syllable."

" 'Tis well," says Tobin.   " Ye're in the presence of Jawn Malone and Daniel Tobin."

" 'Tis highly appreciated," says the man, with a bow. " And now since I cannot conceive that ye would hold a spelling bee upon the street corner, will ye name some reasonable excuse for being at large ? "

" By the two signs," answers Tobin, trying to explain, " which ye display according to the reading of the Egyptian palmist from the sole of me hand, ye've been nominated to offset with good luck the lines of trouble leading to the nigger man and the blonde lady with her feet crossed in the boat, besides the financial loss of a dollar sixty-five, all so far fulfilled according to Hoyle."

The man stopped smoking and looked at me.

" Have ye any amendments," he asks, " to offer to that

statement, or are ye one too ? I thought by the looks of ye ye might have him in charge."

" None," says I to him, " except that as one horseshoe resembles another so are ye the picture of good luck as predicted by the hand of me friend. If not, then the lines of Danny's hand may have been crossed, I don't know."

" There's two of ye," says the man with the nose, looking up and down for the sight of a policeman. " I've enjoyed your company immense. Good-night."

With that he shoves his segar in his mouth and moves across the street, stepping fast. But Tobin sticks close to one side of him and me at the other.

" What ! " says he, stopping on the opposite sidewalk and pushing back his hat ; " do ye follow me ? I tell ye," he says, very loud, " I'm proud to have met ye. But it is my desire to be rid of ye. I am off to me home."

" Do," says Tobin, leaning against his sleeve. " Do be off to your home. And I will sit at the door of it till ye come out in the morning. For the dependence is upon ye to obviate the curse of the nigger man and the blonde lady and the financial loss of the one-sixty-five."

" 'Tis a strange hallucination," says the man, turning to me as a more reasonable lunatic. " Hadn't ye better get him home ? "

" Listen, man," says I to him. " Daniel Tobin is as sensible as he ever was. Maybe he is a bit deranged on account of having drink enough to disturb but not enough to settle his wits, but he is no more than following out the legitimate path of his superstitions and predicaments, which I will explain to you." With that I relates the facts about the palmist lady and how the finger of suspicion points to him as an instrument of good fortune. " Now, understand," I concludes, " my position in this riot. I am the friend of me friend Tobin, according to me interprctations. 'Tis easy to be a friend to the prosperous, for it pays ; 'tis not hard to be a friend to the poor, for ye get puffed up by gratitude and have your picture printed standing in front of a tenement with a scuttle of coal and an orphan in each hand. But it strains the art of friendship to be true friend to a born fool. And that's what I'm doing," says I, " for, in my opinion, there's no fortune to be read from the palm of me hand that wasn't printed there with the handle of a pick. And, though ye've got the crookedest nose in New York City, I misdoubt that all the fortune-tellers doing business could milk good luck from ye. But the lines of Danny's hand pointed to ye fair,

A. P. HERBERT (1890–   ) *joined the staff of " Punch " in 1924 and became one of its most regular contributors. He left Oxford with a First Class in Jurisprudence, and in 1918 was called to the Bar, but never practised. His intimate knowledge of the British legal system has provided him with varied material for some richly satirical sketches and stories, one of his most successful novels, " Holy Deadlock," being in this vein.*

THE HUMAN HEN

REX *v.* HADDOCK

MR. ALBERT HADDOCK surrendered to his bail at Marlborough Street Police Court to-day.

Mr. Slit, for the prosecution, said :

The police, sir, are anxious that the accused in this case shall be severely dealt with ; but they are not certain what for. It is not the first time that Mr. Haddock has hampered the police by behaving in a manner obviously undesirable but difficult to classify. On the fourteenth of this month he was detained by Constable Boot in Piccadilly and taken to Vine Street Station, and he is now charged with :

(*a*) Assault ;

(*b*) Committing or being a public nuisance ;

(*c*) Conduct calculated to cause a breach of the King's peace ;

(*d*) Causing an obstruction ;

(*e*) Attempt to do bodily harm ;

(*f*) Offensive and insulting behaviour ;

(*g*) Threatening words and gestures ;

and if none of these charges should succeed the Bench will be asked to make an order under the Lunacy Act.

The accused is a very fast runner ; and on the afternoon of the fourteenth, at a time when both the street and the pavement were crowded, he was seen running at a great pace along the pavement——

The Metropolitan Magistrate : Was there any collision with other foot-passengers ?

Mr. Slit : No, sir—no actual collision or injury.

The Magistrate : Then there is no battery.

Mr. Slit : No, sir ; but as you are aware, there may be an assault without battery, indeed, without actual touching. I should tell the Court that the accused was very oddly equipped. He wore running-shorts and rubber shoes, and attached to a belt round his middle was a large motor-horn having an exceptionally raucous and intimidating note. As he bounded along the pavement, darting nimbly between one pedestrian and another, he constantly sounded this horn and shouted, " Look out, I'm coming ! " and even, on one occasion, " If you don't look out you will be hurt ! " Warned or alarmed by these sounds, a great many persons did jump out of the way or change their course to let the accused go by ; and one or two elderly persons, persuaded by the sound of a motor-horn behind them that a motor-car had strayed on to the pavement, ran in alarm to one side with a precipitancy by no means beneficial to tired hearts and aged nervous systems. On these facts, your worship, we ask the Bench for a conviction. Call Constable Boot.

Constable Boot, giving evidence of arrest, said : Accused, when taken into custody, made a statement. He said, " What the —— h—— has it got to do with you ? "

The Magistrate : Come, come, officer, don't beat about the bush. What did the accused say ?

Witness : He said, " What the blank h——"

The Magistrate : No, no, we must have the exact words. This Court is not a kindergarten.

Witness then repeated the alleged expressions of accused, and continued :

I replied, " I want no obscene or obstroperous language from you—see ? "

Accused responded, " I am training pedestrians."

A crowd having collected and which adopted a menacing attitude, I then took accused into custody for his own safety.

Cross-examined : For his *own* safety ? You did not see him endanger the lives or limbs of others ?

Witness : No, sir. He dodged in and out like.

Haddock, in the box, asked leave to make a statement. He said : Speed is the goods, your honour. Speed is nuts. Speed wins the knighthoods. Speed excites the sub-editors. Speed is a front-page story. Speed——

The Magistrate : What is all this about ?

Witness : I was saying, your worship, that rapid movement from place to place was one of the blessings, triumphs, and

Round his middle was a large motor-horn

essentials of modern civilization. There is no old-fashioned speed-limit on the roads or pavements. We may drive our motor-cars as fast as we think fit, provided that we hit nothing and nobody. I was merely behaving like a motor-car.

The Magistrate : Send for the medical officer.

Witness (continuing) : All the motor-cars are going faster. But some go faster than others. And when a faster one overtakes a slow one it makes a rude and unpleasant noise to tell the other to get out of the way——

The Magistrate : To give warning of its approach.

Witness : As you will. And if a fast motor-car sees a man, woman, or child, a nursemaid with a perambulator, a dog or a hen in its path, it makes a loud, rude, and alarming noise to tell the man, woman, child, nursemaid, dog, or hen to get out of the way.[1] The old woman, child, nursemaid, dog, or hen are then expected to proceed to a place of safety as quickly as possible. Many motorists expect them to break into a run ; and in practice most of them *do* break into a run. Nobody thinks that this is bad manners or in any way remarkable. I was merely behaving like a motor-car——

The Magistrate : But——

Witness : The result is that men, women, and children are becoming more and more expert in getting out of the way, though the hen still does it best. And the policy of the Government is not to reduce the speed of motor-cars (for that would be fantastic and fatal), but to increase the speed of pedestrians. It is hoped to educate the pedestrian to such a degree of alertness and alacrity that he will at last approximate to the hen. The hen, your worship—— Your worship, I wish to call a small, middle-aged hen to give evidence——

The Magistrate (kindly) : Very well, Mr. Haddock. The doctor will be here soon and he will bring you a hen.

Witness : The hen, your worship, has a very mobile and flexible neck, and an eye on each side of the head, so that she can look right and look left at the same time. By continual slight movements of the neck she becomes aware of motor-cars approaching noiselessly behind her ; she has exceptional agility and a power of instant acceleration in emergency. In short, the perfect pedestrian. Owing to the difference in natural

---

[1] Contrast the agreeable sounds made by steam-vessels which, as a rule, convey not only warning but useful information about the steamer's intentions—as " I am going to starboard," " My engines are going astern," or " I am about to make a circular movement turning to port." See Strauss on *The Law of Boating*.

advantages, it may be some time before we produce the human hen, but we are advancing.

The trouble is, your honour, that the training is not continuous. The pavements have not kept pace with the roads. On the roads the race is to the swiftest ; but on the pavements there is neither swift nor slow. The man who can run fast has to plod along at the same dull pace as a crowd of people who run more slowly or cannot run at all. There is here, therefore, a vast waste of energy and potential speed ; and speed, as I have said, being the goods, this must be a bad thing. Besides, the dreamy pedestrian who has just had a good shake-up crossing the road is able, when he reaches the pavement, to fall back into his former condition of reverie or stupor and amble along quietly at his own sweet will. Every step he takes on the pavement is a hold-up in his education, a step away from the human hen.

Accordingly, your worship, I was behaving like a motorcar. Though I do not possess a motor-car I have an itch for speed. I love to bound and leap along, delighting in my strength and swiftness, and anxious to show other men that I can run faster than they can. Besides, I have a great many appointments ; and my appointments are more important than other men's. Why should I be held up on a crowded pavement by a lot of slow-moving old trouts who are not in a hurry and couldn't hurry if they were ?

I found, your honour, that when I leaped and bounded through a crowd without giving audible warning I jostled the old trouts, and sometimes knocked them down ; and the old trouts naturally resented it. But now that I sound my little horn they scuttle out of the way and are perfectly safe. And they are kept in good training for the roads, or would be if all the fast-moving men behaved as I do. So what all the fuss is about is frankly baffling, dear old worship, or honour, as the case may be.

The Magistrate : I shall remand the accused for examination as to his mental condition ; but unless the medical report recommends his detention I do not think that there is any case here for the Court to determine.

The accused has not committed an assault ; or, if he has, then every motorist who sounds his horn commits an assault. Nor has he attempted to do bodily harm ; indeed he has taken special measures to avoid it. He has not caused an obstruction, except in the sense that his arrest attracted a crowd ; but the constable is to blame for that, not he. So far from causing an obstruction he made the centre of the pavement clearer for the faster-moving walkers. A fast car which causes a slow one to draw in to the side of the road does not cause an obstruction ; nor, in the absence of offensive words or gestures, would its driver be charged with conduct conducive to a breach of the peace.

The sounding of the horn is not a threat but a warning, benevolent and not offensive in intention, and sanctioned by the law.   Indeed, a man who saw that he might injure another and deliberately refrained from warning him would be a monster and doubly answerable at law if he *did* cause injury.   And, though the sound be unmusical and harsh, the use of a single horn in Piccadilly at a busy hour can hardly be accounted a Common Law nuisance when three or four hundred similar horns are in full blast a few yards away.

The conduct of the accused was admittedly unusual ; but novelty of behaviour is not necessarily a crime, though it may be evidence of imbecility.   The progress of the first motor-car down Piccadilly was, without doubt, as startling and alarming to many as the proceedings of the accused now appear on the Piccadilly pavement.

It seemed, not very long ago, a monstrous thing that a man should bring a swiftly moving machine upon the highway—a machine that roared like a dragon at those who stood in its path, a machine that claimed a superior status to the walking citizen by virtue simply of its speed and strength.   For this looked like the discredited doctrine that Might is Right.   Yet this once monstrous thing is now an accepted and normal part of our lives.   And if we allow extraordinary behaviour to become normal on the roads, we must expect it in the end to leap over the narrow frontier of the gutter and become normal on the pavements.   As the accused has said, there is no speed-limit on the pavements, and, provided he does no damage or wrong, presumably a man may move as fast as he likes.

I have no doubt that as the delicious benefits of speed and noise become more and more appreciated we shall sweep away the old-fashioned and haphazard habits of the pedestrian population.   Every walker will be required to carry lights and a horn and proceed as fast as he can upon the particular foot-track which is allotted to him, according to his capacity and speed. This cannot fail to improve the character of the nation and assist the officers of justice ; for slow walking leads to sauntering, and sauntering to loitering, and from loitering the step is short to loitering with intent to commit a felony.

It is true, however, that we have not yet arrived at that degree of civilization ; and meanwhile it may be that Mr. Haddock, like other pioneers, will have to be put away in a home.   Remanded.

WASHINGTON IRVING (1782–1859), *the son of an Englishman, was born in New York, and made his début as a writer with letters to " The Morning Chronicle " in the manner of Addison and Steele and bearing the pseudonym of Jonathan Oldstyle. His first book, " Diedrich Knickerbocker's History of New York," established him as a humorist. " Rip Van Winkle " comes from " The Sketch Book," a collection of whimsical essays and tales.*

RIP VAN WINKLE

WHOEVER has made a voyage up the Hudson must remember the Kaatskill Mountains. They are a dismembered branch of the great Appalachian family, and are seen away to the west of the river, swelling up to a noble height, and lording it over the surrounding country. Every change of season, every change of weather, indeed every hour of the day, produces some change in the magical hues and shapes of these mountains ; and they are regarded by all the good wives, far and near, as perfect barometers. When the weather is fair and settled, they are clothed in blue and purple, and print their bold outlines on the clear evening sky ; but sometimes, when the rest of the landscape is cloudless, they will gather a hood of grey vapours about their summits, which, in the last rays of the setting sun, will glow and light up like a crown of glory.

At the foot of these fairy mountains the voyager may have descried the light smoke curling up from a village, whose shingle roofs gleam among the trees, just where the blue tints of the up-land melt away into the fresh green of the nearer landscape. It is a little village of great antiquity, having been founded by one of the Dutch colonists, in the early times of the province, just about the beginning of the government of the good Peter Stuyvesant (may he rest in peace !), and there were some of the houses of the original settlers standing within a few years, built of small yellow bricks brought from Holland, having latticed windows and gable fronts, surmounted with weather-cocks.

In that same village, and in one of these very houses (which, to tell the precise truth, was sadly time-worn and weather-beaten), there lived many years since, while the country was yet a province of Great Britain, a simple, good-natured fellow, of the name of Rip Van Winkle. He was a descendant of the Van

Winkles who figured so gallantly in the chivalrous days of Peter Stuyvesant, and accompanied him to the siege of Fort Christina. He inherited, however, but little of the martial character of his ancestors. I have observed that he was a simple, good-natured man ; he was moreover a kind neighbour, and an obedient henpecked husband. Indeed, to the latter circumstance might be owing that meekness of spirit which gained him such universal popularity ; for those men are most apt to be obsequious and conciliating abroad who are under the discipline of shrews at home. Their tempers, doubtless, are rendered pliant and malleable in the fiery furnace of domestic tribulation, and a curtain lecture is worth all the sermons in the world for teaching the virtues of patience and long-suffering. A termagant wife may, therefore, in some respects, be considered a tolerable blessing ; and if so, Rip Van Winkle was thrice blessed.

Certain it is that he was a great favourite among all the good wives of the village, who, as usual with the amiable sex, took his part in all family squabbles, and never failed, whenever they talked those matters over in their evening gossipings, to lay all the blame on Dame Van Winkle. The children of the village, too, would shout with joy whenever he approached. He assisted at their sports, made their playthings, taught them to fly kites and shoot marbles, and told them long stories of ghosts, witches, and Indians. Whenever he went dodging about the village, he was surrounded by a troop of them hanging on his skirts, clambering on his back, and playing a thousand tricks on him with impunity ; and not a dog would bark at him throughout the neighbourhood.

The great error in Rip's composition was an insuperable aversion to all kinds of profitable labour. It could not be from the want of assiduity or perseverance ; for he would sit on a wet rock, with a rod as long and heavy as a Tartar's lance, and fish all day without a murmur, even though he should not be encouraged by a single nibble. He would carry a fowling-piece on his shoulder, for hours together, trudging through woods and swamps, and up hill and down dale, to shoot a few squirrels or wild pigeons. He would never refuse to assist a neighbour even in the roughest toil, and was a foremost man at all country frolics for husking Indian corn or building stone fences. The women of the village, too, used to employ him to run their errands, and to do such little odd jobs as their less obliging husbands would not do for them ; in a word, Rip was ready to attend to anybody's business but his own ; but as to doing family duty, and keeping his farm in order, he found it impossible.

In fact, he declared it was of no use to work on his farm ; it was the most pestilent little piece of ground in the whole country ; everything about it went wrong, and would go wrong in spite of him. His fences were continually falling to pieces ; his cow would either go astray or get among the cabbages ; weeds were sure to grow quicker in his fields than anywhere else ; the rain always made a point of setting in just as he had some outdoor work to do ; so that though his patrimonial estate had dwindled away under his management, acre by acre, until there was little more left than a mere patch of Indian corn and potatoes, yet it was the worst conditioned farm in the neighbourhood.

His children, too, were as ragged and wild as if they belonged to nobody. His son Rip, an urchin begotten in his own likeness, promised to inherit the habits with the old clothes of his father. He was generally seen trooping like a colt at his mother's heels, equipped in a pair of his father's cast-off galligaskins, which he had much ado to hold up with one hand, as a fine lady does her train in bad weather.

Rip Van Winkle, however, was one of those happy mortals, of foolish, well-oiled dispositions, who take the world easy, eat white bread or brown, whichever can be got with least thought or trouble, and would rather starve on a penny than work for a pound. If left to himself, he would have whistled life away in perfect contentment ; but his wife kept continually dinning in his ears about his idleness, his carelessness, and the ruin he was bringing on his family.

Morning, noon, and night her tongue was incessantly going, and everything he said or did was sure to produce a torrent of household eloquence. Rip had but one way of replying to all lectures of the kind, and that, by frequent use, had grown into a habit. He shrugged his shoulders, shook his head, cast up his eyes, but said nothing. This, however, always provoked a fresh volley from his wife, so that he was fain to draw off his forces and take to the outside of the house—the only side which, in truth, belongs to a henpecked husband.

Rip's sole domestic adherent was his dog Wolf, who was as much henpecked as his master ; for Dame Van Winkle regarded them as companions in idleness, and even looked upon Wolf with an evil eye, as the cause of his master's going so often astray. True it is, in all points of spirit befitting an honourable dog, he was as courageous an animal as ever scoured the woods—but what courage can withstand the ever-during and all-besetting terrors of a woman's tongue ? The moment Wolf entered the house his crest fell, his tail drooped to the ground, or curled

between his legs, he sneaked about with a gallows air, casting
many a sidelong glance at Dame Van Winkle, and at the least
flourish of a broomstick or ladle, he would fly to the door with
yelping precipitation.

Times grew worse and worse with Rip Van Winkle as years
of matrimony rolled on : a tart temper never mellows with age,
and a sharp tongue is the only edge-tool that grows keener with
constant use. For a long while he used to console himself, when
driven from home, by frequenting a kind of perpetual club of
the sages, philosophers, and other idle personages of the village,
which held its sessions on a bench before a small inn, designated
by a rubicund portrait of His Majesty George the Third. Here
they used to sit in the shade, of a long lazy summer's day, talking
listlessly over village gossip, or telling endless sleepy stories about
nothing. But it would have been worth any statesman's money
to have heard the profound discussions which sometimes took
place, when by chance an old newspaper fell into their hands
from some passing traveller. · How solemnly they would listen
to the contents, as drawled out by Derrick Van Bummel, the
schoolmaster, a dapper learned little man, who was not to be
daunted by the most gigantic word in the dictionary ; and how
sagely they would deliberate upon public events some months
after they had taken place.

The opinions of this junto were completely controlled by
Nicholas Vedder, a patriarch of the village and landlord of the
inn, at the door of which he took his seat from morning till night,
just moving sufficiently to avoid the sun, and keep in the shade
of a large tree ; so that the neighbours could tell the hour by his
movements as accurately as by a sun-dial. It is true he was
rarely heard to speak, but smoked his pipe incessantly. His adherents, however (for every great man has his adherents), perfectly understood him, and knew how to gather his opinions.
When anything that was read or related displeased him, he was
observed to smoke his pipe vehemently, and to send forth short,
frequent, and angry puffs ; but when pleased, he would inhale
the smoke slowly and tranquilly, and emit it in light and placid
clouds, and sometimes taking the pipe from his mouth, and letting the fragrant vapour curl about his nose, would gravely nod
hi, he d in token of pe fect approbation.

From even this stronghold the unlucky Rip was at length
routed by his termagant wife, who would suddenly break in
upon the tranquillity of the assemblage, and call the members all
to naught ; nor was that august personage, Nicholas Vedder
himself, sacred from the daring tongue of this terrible virago,

who charged him outright with encouraging her husband in habits of idleness.

Poor Rip was at last reduced almost to despair, and his only alternative to escape from the labour of the farm and the clamour of his wife was to take gun in hand, and stroll away into the woods. Here he would sometimes seat himself at the foot of a tree, and share the contents of his wallet with Wolf, with whom he sympathized as a fellow-sufferer in persecution. " Poor Wolf," he would say, " thy mistress leads thee a dog's life of it ; but never mind, my lad, while I live thou shalt never want a friend to stand by thee ! " Wolf would wag his tail, look wistfully in his master's face, and if dogs can feel pity, I verily believe he reciprocated the sentiment with all his heart.

In a long ramble of the kind, on a fine autumnal day, Rip had unconsciously scrambled to one of the highest parts of the Kaatskill Mountains. He was after his favourite sport of squirrel-shooting, and the still solitudes had echoed and re-echoed with the reports of his gun. Panting and fatigued, he threw himself, late in the afternoon, on a green knoll covered with mountain herbage that crowned the brow of a precipice. From an opening between the trees he could overlook all the lower country for many a mile of rich woodland. He saw at a distance the lordly Hudson, far, far below him, moving on its silent but majestic course, with the reflection of a purple cloud, or the sail of a lagging bark, here and there sleeping on its glassy bosom, and at last losing itself in the blue highlands.

On the other side he looked down into a deep mountain glen, wild, lonely, and shagged, the bottom filled with fragments from the impending cliffs, and scarcely lighted by the reflected rays of the setting sun. For some time Rip lay musing on this scene ; evening was gradually advancing ; the mountains began to throw their long blue shadows over the valleys ; he saw that it would be dark long before he could reach the village ; and he heaved a heavy sigh when he thought of encountering the terrors of Dame Van Winkle.

As he was about to descend he heard a voice from a distance hallooing, " Rip Van Winkle ! Rip Van Winkle ! " He looked around, but could see nothing but a crow winging its solitary flight across the mountain. He thought his fancy must have deceived him, and turned again to descend, when he heard the same cry ring through the still evening air, " Rip Van Winkle ! Rip Van Winkle ! "—at the same time Wolf bristled up his back, and, giving a low growl, skulked to his master's side, looking fearfully down into the glen. Rip now felt a vague apprehension stealing over him : he looked anxiously in the same direction, and perceived a strange figure slowly toiling up the rocks, and bending under the weight of something he carried on his back. He was surprised to see any human being in this lonely and unfrequented place, but supposing it to be some one of the neighbourhood in need of his assistance, he hastened down to yield it.

On nearer approach, he was still more surprised at the singularity of the stranger's appearance. He was a short, square-built old fellow, with thick bushy hair and a grizzled beard. His dress was of the antique Dutch fashion—a cloth jerkin strapped round the waist—several pairs of breeches, the outer one of ample volume, decorated with rows of buttons down the sides, and bunches at the knees. He bore on his shoulders a stout keg that seemed full of liquor, and made signs for Rip to approach and assist him with the load. Though rather shy and distrustful of this new acquaintance, Rip complied with his usual alacrity, and mutually relieving each other, they clambered up a narrow gully, apparently the dry bed of a mountain torrent. As they ascended, Rip every now and then heard long rolling peals, like distant thunder, that seemed to issue out of a deep ravine or rather cleft between lofty rocks, toward which their rugged path conducted. He paused for an instant, but supposing it to be the muttering of one of those transient thundershowers which often take place in mountain heights, he proceeded. Passing through the ravine, they came to a hollow, like a small amphitheatre, surrounded by perpendicular precipices, over the brinks of which impending trees shot their branches, so that you only caught glimpses of the azure sky and the bright evening cloud. During he whole time, Rip and his companion had laboured on in silence ; for though the former marvell d greatly what could be the object of carrying a keg of liquor up this wild mountain, yet there was something strange and incomprehensible about the unknown that inspired awe and checked familiarity.

On entering the amphitheatre new objects of wonder presented themselves. On a level spot in the centre was a company of odd-looking personages playing at nine-pins. They were dressed in a quaint outlandish fashion : some wore short doublets, others jerkins, with long knives in their belts, and most of them had enormous breeches, of similar style with that of the guide's. Their visages, too, were peculiar : one had a large head, broad face, and small piggish eyes ; the face of another seemed to consist entirely of nose, and was surmounted by a white sugar-loaf hat, set off with a little red cock's tail. They all had beards, of various shapes and colours. There was one who seemed to be the commander. He was a stout old gentleman with a weather-beaten countenance ; he wore a laced doublet, broad belt and hanger, high-crowned hat and feather, red stockings, and high-heeled shoes with roses in them. The whole group reminded Rip of the figures in an old Flemish painting in the parlour of Dominie Van Schaick, the village parson, and which had been brought over from Holland at the time of the settlement.

What seemed particularly odd to Rip was, that though these folks were evidently amusing themselves, yet they maintained the gravest faces, the most mysterious silence, and were, withal, the most melancholy party of pleasure he had ever witnessed. Nothing interrupted the stillness of the scene but the noise of the balls, which, whenever they were rolled, echoed along the mountains like rumbling peals of thunder.

As Rip and his companion approached them, they suddenly desisted from their play, and stared at him with such a fixed statue-like gaze, and such strange, uncouth, lack-lustre countenances, that his heart turned within him, and his knees smote together. His companion now emptied the contents of the keg into large flagons, and made signs to him to wait upon the company. He obeyed with fear and trembling ; they quaffed the liquor in profound silence, and then returned to their game.

By degrees, Rip's awe and apprehension subsided. He even ventured, when no eye was fixed upon him, to taste the beverage, which he found had much of the flavour of excellent Hollands. He was naturally a thirsty soul, and was soon tempted to repeat the draught. One taste provoked another, and he reiterated his visits to the flagon so often that at length his senses were overpowered, his eyes swam in his head, his head gradually declined, and he fell into a deep sleep.

On waking, he found himself on the green knoll from whence he had first seen the old man of the glen. He rubbed his eyes—it was a bright sunny morning. The birds were hopping and twittering among the bushes, and the eagle was wheeling aloft and breasting the pure mountain breeze. " Surely," thought Rip, " I have not slept here all night." He recalled the occurrences before he fell asleep. The strange man with the keg of liquor—the mountain ravine—the wild retreat among the rocks—the wobegone party at nine-pins—the flagon—" Oh, that wicked flagon ! " thought Rip —" what excuse shall I make to Dame Van Winkle ? "

He looked round for his gun, but in place of the clean, well-oiled fowling-piece, he found an old firelock lying by him, the barrel encrusted with rust, the lock falling off, and the stock worm-eaten. He now suspected that the grave roysterers of the mountain had put a trick upon him, and having dosed him with liquor, had robbed him of his gun. Wolf, too, had disappeared, but he might have strayed away after a squirrel or partridge. He whistled after him, and shouted his name, but all in vain ; the echoes repeated his whistle and shout, but no dog was to be seen.

He determined to revisit the scene of the last evening's gambol, and if he met with any of the party to demand his dog and gun. As he rose to walk, he found himself stiff in the joints and wanting in his usual activity. "These mountain beds do not agree with me," thought Rip, "and if this frolic should lay me up with a fit of rheumatism, I shall have a blessed time with Dame Van Winkle." With some difficulty he got down into the glen ; he found the gully up which he and his companion had ascended the preceding evening ; but to his astonishment a mountain stream was now foaming down it, leaping from rock to rock, and filling the glen with babbling murmurs. He, however, made shift to scramble up its sides, working his toilsome way through thickets of birch, sassafras, and witch-hazel ; and sometimes tripped up or entangled by the wild grape vines that twisted their coils and tendrils from tree to tree, and spread a kind of network in his path.

At length he reached to where the ravine had opened through the cliffs to the amphitheatre ; but no traces of such opening remained. The rocks presented a high impenetrable wall, over which the torrent came tumbling in a sheet of feathery foam, and fell into a broad, deep basin, black from the shadows of the surrounding forest. Here, then, poor Rip was brought to a stand. He again called and whistled after his dog ; he was only answered by the cawing of a flock of idle crows sporting high in air about a dry tree that overhung a sunny precipice, and who, secure in their elevation, seemed to look down and scoff at the poor man's pe plexities. What was to be done ? The morning was passing away, and Rip felt famished for want of his breakfast. He grieved to give up his dog and gun ; he dreaded to meet his wife ; but it would not do to starve among the mountains. He shook his head, shouldered the rusty firelock, and, with a heart full of trouble and anxiety, turned his steps homeward.

As he approached the village he met a number of people, but none whom he knew, which somewhat surprised him, for he had thought himself acquainted with every one in the country round. Their dress, too, was of a different fashion from that to which he was accustomed. They all stared at him with equal marks of surprise, and whenever they cast eyes upon him, invariably stroked their chins. The constant recurrence of this gesture induced Rip, involuntarily, to do the same, when, to his astonishment, he found his beard had grown a foot long !

He had now entered the skirts of the village. A troop of strange children ran at his heels, hooting after him, and pointing at his grey beard. The dogs, too, not one of which he recognized for an old acquaintance, barked at him as he passed. The very village was altered : it was larger and more populous. There were rows of houses which he had never seen before, and those which had been his familiar haunts had disappeared. Strange names were over the doors—strange faces at the windows— everything was strange. His mind now misgave him ; he began to doubt whether both he and the world around him were not bewitched. Surely this was his native village, which he had left but a day before. There stood the Kaatskill Mountains— there ran the silver Hudson at a distance—there was every hill and dale precisely as it had always been—Rip was sorely perplexed—" That flagon last night," thought he, " has addled my poor head sadly ! "

It was with some difficulty that he found the way to his own house, which he approached with silent awe, expecting every moment to hear the shrill voice of Dame Van Winkle. He found the house gone to decay—the roof fallen in, the windows shattered, and the doors off the hinges. A half-starved dog, that looked like Wolf was skulking about it. Rip called him by name, but the cur snarled, showed his teeth, and passed on. This was an unkind cut indeed. " My very dog," sighed poor Rip, " has forgotten me ! "

He entered the house, which, to tell the truth, Dame Van Winkle had always kept in neat order. It was empty, forlorn, and apparently abandoned. This desolateness overcame all his connubial fears—he called loudly for his wife and children—the lonely chambers rang for a moment with his voice, and then all again was silence.

He now hurried forth and hastened to his old resort, the village inn—but it too was gone. A large rickety wooden building stood in its place, with great gaping windows, some of them broken, and mended with old hats and petticoats, and over the door was painted, " The Union Hotel, by Jonathan Doolittle." Instead of the great tree that used to shelter the quiet little Dutch inn of yore, there now was reared a tall naked pole, with something on the top that looked like a red night-cap, and from it was fluttering a flag, on which was a singular assemblage of stars and stripes—all this was strange and incomprehensible. He recognized on the sign, however, the ruby face of King George, under which he had smoked so many a peaceful pipe, but even this was singularly metamorphosed. The red coat was changed for one of blue and buff, a sword was held in the hand instead of a sceptre, the head was decorated with a cocked hat, and underneath was painted in large characters GENERAL WASHINGTON.

There was, as usual, a crowd of folk about the door, but none that Rip recollected. The very character of the people seemed changed. There was a busy, bustling, disputatious tone about it, instead of the accustomed phlegm and drowsy tranquillity. He looked in vain for the sage Nicholas Vedder, with his broad face, double chin, and fair, long pipe, uttering clouds of tobacco smoke, instead of idle speeches ; or Van Bummel, the schoolmaster, doling forth the contents of an ancient newspaper. In place of these, a lean, bilious-looking fellow, with his pockets full of handbills, was haranguing vehemently about rights of citizens—election—members of Congress—liberty—Bunker Hill —heroes of seventy-six—and other words, that were a perfect Babylonish jargon to the bewildered Van Winkle.

The appearance of Rip, with his long, grizzled beard, his rusty fowling-piece, his uncouth dress, and the army of women and children that had gathered at his heels, soon attracted the attention of the tavern politicians. They crowded round him, eyeing him from head to foot with great curiosity. The orator bustled up to him, and drawing him partly aside, inquired " on which side he voted ? " Rip stared in vacant stupidity. Another short but busy little fellow pulled him by the arm, and, rising on tiptoe, inquired in his ear " whether he was Federal or Democrat." Rip was equally at a loss to comprehend the question ; when a knowing, self-important old gentleman, in a sharp cocked hat, made his way through the crowd, putting them to the right and left with his elbows as he passed, and planting himself before Van Winkle, with one arm a-kimbo, the other resting on his cane, his keen eyes and sharp hat penetrating, as it were, into his very soul, demanded in an austere tone " what brought him to the election with a gun on his shoulder, and a mob at his heels, and whether he meant to breed a riot in the village ? "

"Alas ! gentlemen," cried Rip, somewhat dismayed, " I am a poor, quiet man, a native of the place, and a loyal subject of the King, God bless him ! "

Here a general shout burst forth from the bystanders :
" A Tory ! Tory ! a spy ! a refugee ! hustle him ! away
with him ! "

It was with great difficulty that the self-important man in the
cocked hat restored order ; and having assumed a tenfold
austerity of brow, demanded again of the unknown culprit what
he came there for and whom he was seeking. The poor man
humbly assured him that he meant no harm, but merely came
there in search of some of his neighbours, who used to keep
about the tavern.

" Well—who are they ?—name them."

Rip bethought himself a moment and inquired, " Where's
Nicholas Vedder ? "

There was silence for a little while, when an old man replied,
in a thin, piping voice, " Nicholas Vedder ? why, he is dead and
gone these eighteen years ! There was a wooden tombstone in
the churchyard that used to tell all about him, but that's rotten
and gone too."

" Where's Brom Dutcher ? "

" Oh, he went off to the army in the beginning of the war ;
some say he was killed at the storming of Stony Point—others
say he was drowned in the squall, at the foot of Anthony's Nose.
I don't know—he never came back again."

" Where's Van Bummel, the schoolmaster ? "

" He went off to the wars too ; was a great militia general,
and is now in Congress."

Rip's heart died away at hearing of these sad changes in his
home and friends, and finding himself thus alone in the world.
Every answer puzzled him, too, by treating of such enormous
lapses of time, and of matters which he could not understand :
war—Congress—Stony Point !—he had no courage to ask after
any more friends, but cried out in despair, " Does nobody here
know Rip Van Winkle ? "

" Oh, Rip Van Winkle ! " exclaimed two or three. " Oh
to be sure ! that's Rip Van Winkle yonder, leaning against the
tree."

Rip looked, and beheld a precise counterpart of himself as
he went up the mountain ; apparently as lazy, and certainly as
ragged. The poor fellow was now completely confounded. He
doubted his own identity, and whether he was himself or another
man. In the midst of his bewilderment, the man in the cocked
hat demanded who he was, and what was his name ?

" God knows," exclaimed he at his wits' end ; " I'm not
myself—I'm somebody else—that's me yonder—no—that's

somebody else got into my shoes—I was myself last night, but I fell asleep on the mountain, and they've changed my gun, and everything's changed, and I'm changed, and I can't tell what's my name, or who I am ! "

The bystanders began now to look at each other, nod, wink significantly, and tap their fingers against their foreheads. There was a whisper, also, about securing the gun, and keeping the old fellow from doing mischief ; at the very suggestion of which the self-important man with the cocked hat retired with some precipitation. At this critical moment a fresh, comely woman passed through the throng to get a peep at the grey-bearded man. She had a chubby child in her arms, which, frightened at his looks, began to cry. " Hush, Rip," cried she, " hush, you little fool ; the old man won't hurt you." The name of the child, the air of the mother, the tone of her voice, all awakened a train of recollections in his mind.

" What is your name, my good woman ? " asked he.

" Judith Gardenier."

" And your father's name ? "

" Ah, poor man, his name was Rip Van Winkle ; it's twenty years since he went away from home with his gun, and never has been heard of since—his dog came home without him ; but whether he shot himself, or was carried away by the Indians, nobody can tell. I was then but a little girl."

Rip had but one question more to ask ; but he put it with a faltering voice :

" Where's your mother ? "

Oh, she too had died but a short time since : she broke a blood-vessel in a fit of passion at a New England pedlar.

There was a drop of comfort, at least, in this intelligence. The honest man could contain himself no longer. He caught his daughter and her child in his arms. " I am your father ! " cried he—" Young Rip Van Winkle once—old Rip Van Winkle now !—Does nobody know poor Rip Van Winkle ? "

All stood amazed, until an old woman, tottering out from among the crowd, put her hand to her brow, and peering under it in his face for a moment, exclaimed, " Sure enough ! it is Rip Van Winkle—it is himself. Welcome home again, old neighbour ! Why, where have you been these twenty long years ? "

Rip's story was soon told, for the whole twenty years had been to him but as one night. The neighbours stared when they heard it ; some were seen to wink at each other, and put their tongues in their cheeks ; and the self-important man in the cocked hat, who, when the alarm was over, had returned to the field, screwed down the corners of his mouth, and shook his head—upon which there was a general shaking of the head throughout the assemblage.

It was determined, however, to take the opinion of old Peter Vanderdonk, who was seen slowly advancing up the road. He was a descendant of the historian of that name, who wrote one of the earliest accounts of the province. Peter was the most ancient inhabitant of the village, and well versed in all the wonderful events and traditions of the neighbourhood. He re-collected Rip at once, and corroborated his story in the most satisfactory manner. He assured the company that it was a fact, handed down from his ancestor, the historian, that the Kaatskill Mountains had always been haunted by strange beings. That it was affirmed that the great Hendrik Hudson, the first discoverer of the river and country, kept a kind of vigil there every twenty years, with his crew of the *Half-Moon*, being permitted in this way to revisit the scenes of his enterprise, and keep a guardian eye upon the river and the great city called by his name. That his father had once seen them in their old Dutch dresses playing at nine-pins in a hollow of the mountain ; and that he himself had heard, one summer afternoon, the sound of their balls, like distant peals of thunder.

To make a long story short, the company broke up, and re-turned to the more important concerns of the election. Rip's daughter took him home to live with her ; she had a snug, well-furnished house, and a stout, cheery farmer for a husband, whom Rip recollected for one of the urchins that used to climb upon his back. As to Rip's son and heir, who was the ditto of himself, seen leaning against the tree, he was employed to work on the farm ; but evinced a hereditary disposition to attend to any-thing else but his business.

Rip now resumed his old walks and habits ; he soon found many of his former cronies, though all rather the worse for the wear and tear of time ; and preferred making friends among the rising generation, with whom he soon grew into great favour.

Having nothing to do at home, and being arrived at that happy age when a man can do nothing with impunity, he took his place once more on the bench, at the inn door, and was reverenced as one of the patriarchs of the village, and a chronicle of the old times "before the war." It was some time before he could get into the regular track of gossip, or could be made to comprehend the strange events that had taken place during his torpor. How that there had been a revolutionary war—that the country had thrown off the yoke of old England—and that, instead of being a subject of His Majesty George the Third, he was now a free citizen of the United States. Rip, in fact, was no politician ; the changes of states and empires made but little impression on him ; but there was one species of despotism under which he had long groaned, and that was—petticoat government. Happily, that was at an end ; he had got his neck out of the yoke of matrimony, and could go in and out whenever he pleased, without dreading the tyranny of Dame Van Winkle. Whenever her name was mentioned, however, he shook his head, shrugged his shoulders, and cast up his eyes ; which might pass either for an expression of resignation to his fate, or joy at his deliverance.

He used to tell his story to every stranger that arrived at Mr. Doolittle's hotel. He was observed, at first, to vary on some points every time he told it, which was doubtless owing to his having so recently awaked. It at last settled down precisely to the tale I have related, and not a man, woman, or child in the neighbourhood but knew it by heart. Some always pretended to doubt the reality of it, and insisted that Rip had been out of his head, and that this was one point on which he always remained flighty. The old Dutch inhabitants, however, almost universally gave it full credit. Even to this day, they never hear a thunderstorm of a summer afternoon about the Kaatskill but they say Hendrik Hudson and his crew are at their game of nine-pins ; and it is a common wish of all hen-pecked husbands in the neighbourhood, when life hangs heavy on their hands, that they might have a quieting draught out of Rip Van Winkle's flagon.

W. W. JACOBS (1863–   ) *is perhaps the most beloved humorist of our time. The uproarious adventures of his Cockney crews have an extraordinarily wide appeal; he is acknowledged also to be one of the most powerful writers of tales of terror. In " The Dreamer " we find " cookie," a character who can always be relied upon to provide entertainment, once more in the centre of things.*

THE DREAMER

DREAMS and warnings are things I don't believe in, said the night watchman. The only dream I ever 'ad that come anything like true was once when I dreamt I came in for a fortune, and next morning I found half a crown in the street, which I sold to a man for fourpence. And once, two days arter my missis 'ad dreamt she 'ad spilt a cup of tea down the front of 'er Sunday dress, she spoilt a pot o' paint of mine by sitting in it.

The only other dream I know of that come true happened to the cook of a barque I was aboard of once, called the *Southern Belle*. He was a silly, pasty-faced sort o' chap, always giving hisself airs about eddication to sailormen who didn't believe in it, and one night, when he was homeward-bound from Sydney, he suddenly sat up in 'is bunk and laughed so loud that he woke us all up.

" Wot's wrong, cookie ? " ses one o' the chaps.

" I was dreaming," ses the cook, " such a funny dream. I dreamt old Bill Foster fell out o' the foretop and broke 'is leg."

" Well, wot is there to laugh at in that ? " ses old Bill, very sharp.

" It was funny in my dream," ses the cook. " You looked so comic with your leg doubled up under you, you can't think. It would ha' made a cat laugh."

Bill Foster said he'd make 'im laugh the other side of his face if he wasn't careful, and then we went off to sleep agin and forgot all about it.

If you'll believe me, on'y three days arterwards pore Bill did fall out o' the foretop and break his leg. He was surprised, but I never see a man so surprised as the cook was. His eyes was nearly starting out of 'is head, but by the time the other chaps 'ad picked Bill up and asked 'im whether he was hurt, cook 'ad pulled 'imself together agin and was giving himself such airs it was perfectly sickening.

"My dreams always come true," he ses. "It's a kind o' second sight with me. It's a gift, and, being tender-'arted, it worries me terrible sometimes."

He was going on like that, taking credit for a pure accident, when the second officer came up and told 'em to carry Bill below. He was in agony, of course, but he kept 'is presence of mind, and as they passed the cook he gave 'im such a clip on the side of the 'ead as nearly broke it.

"That's for dreaming about me," he ses.

The skipper and the fust officer and most of the hands set 'is leg between them, and arter the skipper 'ad made him wot he called comfortable, but wot Bill called something that I won't soil my ears by repeating, the officers went off and the cook came and sat down by the side o' Bill and talked about his gift.

"I don't talk about it as a rule," he ses, "'cos it frightens people."

"It's a wonderful gift, cookie," ses Charlie Epps.

All of 'em thought the same, not knowing wot a fust-class liar the cook was, and he sat there and lied to 'em till he couldn't 'ardly speak, he was so 'oarse.

"My grandmother was a gipsy," he ses, "and it's in the family. Things that are going to 'appen to people I know come to me in dreams, same as pore Bill's did. It's curious to me sometimes when I look round at you chaps, seeing you going about 'appy and comfortable, and knowing all the time 'orrible things that is going to 'appen to you. Sometimes it gives me the fair shivers."

"Horrible things to us, slushy?" ses Charlie, staring.

"Yes,". ses the cook, nodding. "I never was on a ship afore with such a lot of unfortunit men aboard. Never. There's two pore fellers wot'll be dead corpses inside o' six months, sitting 'ere laughing and talking as if they was going to live to ninety. Thank your stars you don't 'ave such dreams."

"Who—who are the two, cookie?" ses Charlie, arter a bit.

"Never mind, Charlie," ses the cook, in a sad voice; "it would do no good if I was to tell you. Nothing can alter it."

"Give us a hint," ses Charlie.

"Well, I'll tell you this much," ses the cook, arter sitting with his 'ead in his 'ands, thinking ; " one of 'em is nearly the ugliest man in the fo'c's'le and the other ain't."

O' course, that didn't 'elp 'em much, but it caused a lot of argufying, and the ugliest man aboard, instead o' being grateful, behaved more like a wild beast than a Christian when it was pointed out to him that he was safe.

Arter that dream about Bill, there was no keeping the cook in his place. He 'ad dreams pretty near every night, and talked little bits of 'em in his sleep. Little bits that you couldn't make head nor tail of, and when we asked 'im next morning he'd always shake his 'ead and say, " Never mind." Sometimes he'd mention a chap's name in 'is sleep and make 'im nervous for days.

It was an unlucky v'y'ge that, for some of 'em. About a week arter pore Bill's accident Ted Jones started playing catch-ball with another chap and a empty beer-bottle, and about the fifth chuck Ted caught it with his face. We thought 'e was killed at fust—he made such a noise ; but they got 'im down below, and, arter they 'ad picked out as much broken glass as Ted would let 'em, the second officer did 'im up in sticking-plaster and told 'im to keep quiet for an hour or two.

Ted was very proud of 'is looks, and the way he went on was alarming. Fust of all he found fault with the chap 'e was playing with, and then he turned on the cook.

" It's a pity you didn't see *that* in a dream," he ses, tryin' to sneer, on'y the sticking-plaster was too strong for 'im.

" But I did see it," ses the cook, drawin' 'imself up.

" *Wot ?* " ses Ted, starting.

" I dreamt it night afore last, just exactly as it 'appened," ses the cook, in a off-hand way.

" Why didn't you tell me, then ? " ses Ted, choking.

" It 'ud ha' been no good," ses the cook, smiling and shaking his 'ead. " Wot I see must 'appen. I on'y see the future, and that must be."

" But you stood there watching me chucking the bottle about," ses Ted, getting out of 'is bunk. " Why didn't you stop me ? "

" You don't understand," ses the cook. " If you'd 'ad more eddication——"

He didn't 'ave time to say any more afore Ted was on him, and cookie, being no fighter, 'ad to cook with one eye for the next two or three days. He kept quiet about 'is dreams for some time arter that, but it was no good, because George Hall, wot was a firm believer, gave 'im a licking for not warning 'im of a sprained ankle he got skylarking, and Bob Law took it out of 'im for not telling 'im that he was going to lose 'is suit of shore-going togs at cards.

The only chap that seemed to show any good feeling for the cook was a young feller named Joseph Meek, a steady young chap wot was goin' to be married to old Bill Foster's niece as soon as we got 'ome. Nobody else knew it, but he told the cook all about it on the quiet. He said she was too good for 'im, but, do all he could, he couldn't get her to see it.

" My feelings 'ave changed," he ses.

" P'r'aps they'll change agin," ses the cook, trying to comfort 'im.

Joseph shook his 'ead. " No, I've made up my mind," he ses, very slow. " I'm young yet, and, besides, I can't afford it ; but 'ow to get out of it I don't know. Couldn't you 'ave a dream agin it for me ? "

" Wot d'ye mean ? " ses the cook, firing up. " Do you think I make my dreams up ? "

" No, no ; cert'inly not," ses Joseph, patting 'im on the shoulder ; " but couldn't you do it just for once ? 'Ave a dream that me and Emily are killed a few days arter the wedding. Don't say in wot way, 'cos she might think we could avoid it ; just dream we are killed. Bill's always been a superstitious man, and since you dreamt about his leg he'd believe anything ; and he's that fond of Emily I believe he'd 'ave the wedding put off, at any rate—if I put him up to it."

It took 'im three days and a silver watch-chain to persuade the cook, but he did at last ; and one arternoon, when old Bill, who was getting on fust-class, was resting 'is leg in 'is bunk, the cook went below and turned in for a quiet sleep.

For ten minutes he was as peaceful as a lamb, and old Bill, who 'ad been laying in 'is bunk with an eye open watching 'im, was just dropping off 'imself, when the cook began to talk in 'is sleep, and the very fust words made Bill sit up as though something 'ad bit 'im.

" There they go," ses the cook, " Emily Foster and Joseph Meek—and there's old Bill, good old Bill, going to give the bride away. How 'appy they all look, especially Joseph ! "

Old Bill put his 'and to his ear and leaned out of his bunk.

" There they go," ses the cook agin ; " but wot is that 'orrible black thing with claws that's 'anging over Bill ? "

Pore Bill nearly fell out of 'is bunk, but he saved 'imself at the last moment and lay there as pale as death, listening.

" It must be meant for Bill," ses the cook. " Well, pore

Bill ; he won't know of it, that's one thing. Let's 'ope it'll be sudden."

He lay quiet for some time and then he began again.

" No," he ses, " it isn't Bill ; it's Joseph and Emily, stark and stiff, and they've on'y been married a week. 'Ow awful they look ! Pore things. Oh ! oh ! o-oh ! "

He woke up with a shiver and began to groan, and then 'e sat up in his bunk and saw old Bill leaning out and staring at 'im.

" You've been dreaming, cook," ses Bill, in a trembling voice.

" 'Ave I ? " ses the cook. " How do you know ? "

" About me and my niece," ses Bill ; " you was talking in your sleep."

" You oughtn't to 'ave listened," ses the cook, getting out of 'is bunk and going over to 'im. " I 'ope you didn't 'ear all I dreamt. 'Ow much did you hear ? "

Bill told 'im, and the cook sat there, shaking his 'ead. " Thank goodness, you didn't 'ear the worst of it," he ses.

" *Worst !* " ses Bill. " Wot, was there any more of it ? "

" Lots more," ses the cook. " But promise me you won't tell Joseph, Bill. Let 'im be happy while he can ; it would on'y make 'im miserable, and it wouldn't do any good."

" I don't know so much about that," ses Bill, thinking about the arguments some of them had 'ad with Ted about the bottle. " Was it arter they was married, cookie, that it 'appened ? Are you sure ? "

" Certain sure. It was a week arter," ses the cook.

" Very well, then," ses Bill, slapping 'is bad leg by mistake ; " if they didn't marry, it couldn't 'appen, could it ? "

" Don't talk foolish," ses the cook ; " they must marry. I saw it in my dream."

" Well, we'll see," ses Bill. " I'm going to 'ave a quiet talk with Joseph about it, and see wot he ses. I ain't a-going to 'ave my pore gal murdered just to please you and make your dreams come true."

He 'ad a quiet talk with Joseph, but Joseph wouldn't 'ear of it at fust. He said it was all the cook's nonsense, though 'e owned up that it was funny that the cook should know about the wedding and Emily's name, and at last he said that they would put it afore Emily and let her decide.

That was about the last dream the cook had that v'y'ge, although he told old Bill one day that he had 'ad the same dream about Joseph and Emily agin, so that he was quite certain they 'ad got to be married and killed. He wouldn't tell Bill 'ow they was to be killed, because 'e said it would make 'im an old man afore his time ; but, of course, he 'ad to say that *if* they wasn't married the other part couldn't come true. He said that as he 'ad never told 'is dreams before—except in the case of Bill's leg—he couldn't say for certain that they couldn't be prevented by taking care, but p'r'aps they could ; and Bill pointed out to 'im wot a useful man he would be if he could dream and warn people in time.

By the time we got into the London river old Bill's leg was getting on fust-rate, and he got along splendid on a pair of crutches the carpenter 'ad made for him. Him and Joseph and the cook had 'ad a good many talks about the dream, and the old man 'ad invited the cook to come along 'ome with 'em, to be referred to when he told the tale.

" I shall take my opportunity," he ses, " and break it to 'er gentle like. When I speak to you, you chip in, and not afore. D'ye understand ? "

We went into the East India Docks that v'y'ge, and got there early on a lovely summer's evening. Everybody was 'arf crazy at the idea o' going ashore agin, and working as cheerful and as willing as if they liked it. There was a few people standing on the pier-head as we went in, and among 'em several very nice-looking young wimmen.

" My eye, Joseph," ses the cook, who 'ad been staring hard at one of 'em, " there's a fine gal—lively, too. Look 'ere ! "

He kissed 'is dirty paw—which is more than I should 'ave liked to 'ave done if it 'ad been mine—and waved it, and the gal turned round and shook her 'ead at 'im.

" Here, that'll do," ses Joseph, very cross. " That's my gal ; that's my Emily."

" Eh ? " says the cook. " Well, 'ow was I to know ? Besides, you're a-giving of her up."

Joseph didn't answer 'im. He was staring at Emily, and the more he stared the better-looking she seemed to grow. She really was an uncommon nice-looking gal, and more than the cook was struck with her.

" Who's that chap standing alongside of her ? " ses the cook.

" It's one o' Bill's sister's lodgers," ses Joseph, who was looking very bad-tempered. " I should like to know wot right he 'as to come 'ere to welcome me 'ome. I don't want 'im."

" P'r'aps he's fond of 'er," ses the cook. " I could be, very easy."

" I'll chuck 'im in the dock if he ain't careful," ses Joseph, turning red in the face.

10*

He waved his 'and to Emily, who didn't 'appen to be looking at the moment, but the lodger waved back in a careless sort of way and then spoke to Emily, and they both waved to old Bill, who was standing on his crutches farther aft.

By the time the ship was berthed and everything snug it was quite dark, and old Bill didn't know whether to take the cook 'ome with 'im and break the news that night, or wait a bit. He made up his mind at last to get it over and done with, and arter waiting till the cook 'ad cleaned 'imself they got a cab and drove off.

Bert Simmons, the lodger, 'ad to ride on the box, and Bill took up so much room with 'is bad leg that Emily found it more comfortable to sit on Joseph's knee ; and by the time they got to the 'ouse he began to see wot a silly mistake he was making.

" Keep that dream o' yours to yourself till I make up my mind," he ses to the cook, while Bill and the cabman were calling each other names.

" Bill's going to speak fust," whispers the cook.

The lodger and Emily 'ad gone inside, and Joseph stood there, fidgeting, while the cabman asked Bill, as a friend, why he 'adn't paid twopence more for his face, and Bill was wasting his time trying to think of something to say to 'urt the cabman's feelings. Then he took Bill by the arm as the cab drove off and told 'im not to say nothing about the dream, because he was going to risk it.

" Stuff and nonsense," ses Bill. " I'm going to tell Emily. It's my dooty. Wot's the good o' being married if you're going to be killed ? "

He stumped in on his crutches afore Joseph could say any more, and, arter letting his sister kiss 'im, went into the front room and sat down. There was cold beef and pickles on the table and two jugs o' beer, and arter just telling his sister 'ow he fell and broke 'is leg, they all sat down to supper.

Bert Simmons sat on one side of Emily and Joseph the other, and the cook couldn't 'elp feeling sorry for 'er, seeing as he did that sometimes she was 'aving both hands squeezed at once under the table and could 'ardly get a bite in edgeways.

Old Bill lit his pipe arter supper, and then, taking another glass o' beer, he told 'em about the cook dreaming of his accident three days afore it happened. They couldn't 'ardly believe it at fust, but when he went on to tell 'em the other things the cook 'ad dreamt, and that everything 'ad 'appened just as he dreamt it, they all edged away from the cook and sat staring at him with their mouths open.

" And that ain't the worst of it," ses Bill.

" That's enough for one night, Bill," ses Joseph, who was staring at Bert Simmons as though he could eat him. " Besides, I believe it was on'y chance. When cook told you 'is dream it made you nervous, and that's why you fell."

" Nervous be blowed ! " ses Bill ; and then he told 'em about the dream he 'ad heard while he was laying in 'is bunk.

Bill's sister gave a scream when he 'ad finished, and Emily, wot was sitting next to Joseph, got up with a shiver and went and sat next to Bert Simmons and squeezed his coat-sleeve.

" It's all nonsense ! " ses Joseph, starting up. " And if it wasn't, true love would run the risk. I ain't afraid ! "

" It's too much to ask a gal," ses Bert Simmons, shaking 'is 'ead.

" I couldn't dream of it," ses Emily. " Wot's the use of being married for a week ? Look at uncle's leg—that's enough for me ! "

They all talked at once then, and Joseph tried all he could to persuade Emily to prove to the cook that 'is dreams didn't always come true ; but it was no good. Emily said she wouldn't marry 'im if he 'ad a million a year, and her aunt and uncle backed her up in it—to say nothing of Bert Simmons.

" I'll go up and get your presents, Joseph," she ses ; and she ran upstairs afore anybody could stop her.

Joseph sat there as if he was dazed, while everybody gave 'im good advice, and said 'ow thankful he ought to be that the cook 'ad saved him by 'is dreaming. And by and by Emily came downstairs agin with the presents he 'ad given 'er and put them on the table in front of 'im.

" There's everything there but that little silver brooch you gave me, Joseph," she ses, " and I lost that the other evening when I was out with—with—for a walk."

Joseph tried to speak, but couldn't.

" It was six-and-six, 'cos I was with you when you bought it," ses Emily ; " and as I've lost it, it's on'y fair I should pay for it."

She put down 'arf a sovereign with the presents, and Joseph sat staring at it as if he 'ad never seen one afore.

" And you needn't mind about the change, Joseph," ses Emily ; " that'll 'elp to make up for your disappointment.

Old Bill tried to turn things off with a bit of a laugh. " Why, you're made o' money, Emily," he ses.

" Ah ! I haven't told you yet," ses Emily, smiling at him ; " that's a little surprise I was keeping for you. Aunt Emma—

pore Aunt Emma, I should say—died while you was away and left me all 'er furniture and two hundred pounds."

Joseph made a choking noise in his throat, and then 'e got up, leaving the presents and the 'arf-sovereign on the table, and stood by the door, staring at them.

" Good-night all," he ses. Then he went to the front door and opened it, and arter standing there a moment came back as though he 'ad forgotten something.

" Are you coming along now ? " he ses to the cook.

" Not just yet," ses the cook, very quick.

" I'll wait outside for you, then," ses Joseph, grinding his teeth. " Don't be long."

HERBERT JENKINS (1875–1923), *publisher as well as author, achieved instantaneous
success with the first of his books relating the
adventures of the lovable Bindle family, which
he produced in 1916. More Bindle stories were
eagerly demanded, and he was busy conducting
them on fresh adventures until his premature
death. Here we find the Bindles in one of
their most amusing and delicate situations.*

THE SUMMER CAMP FOR
TIRED WORKERS

THE Surrey Summer-Camp for Tired Workers had been
planned by the Bishop of Fulham out of the largeness of
his heart and the plenitude of his inexperience in such
undertakings. He had borrowed a meadow, acquired a cow,
hired a marquee, and wangled fifty army bell-tents and a field-
kitchen, about which in all probability questions would be asked
in the House. Finally, as the result of a brain-wave he had
requisitioned the local boy scouts. Later there would be the
devil to pay with the leaders of the Boys' Brigade ; but the
bishop abounded in tact.

When the time came, the meadow was there, the bell-tents,
the cow, and the boy scouts duly arrived ; but of the marquee
nothing had been seen or heard, and as for the field-kitchen,
the War Office could say little beyond the fact that it had left
Aldershot.

For days the bishop worked indefatigably with telephone
and telegraph, endeavouring to trace the errant field-kitchen
and the missing marquee ; but so much of his time had been
occupied in obtaining the necessary assistance to ensure that
the cow was properly and punctually milked, that other things,
being farther away, had seemed less insistent.

In those days the bishop had much to worry him ; but his
real cross was Daisy, the cow. Everything else was of minor
importance compared with this bovine responsibility. Vaguely
he had felt that if you had a cow you had milk ; but he was
to discover that on occasion a cow could be as unproductive of
milk as a sea-serpent.

None of the campers had ever approached a cow in her
professional capacity. Night and morning she had to be relieved
of a twelve hours' accumulation of milk, all knew that ; but

how? That was a question which had perturbed bishop and campers alike; for the whole camp shared the ecclesiastical anxiety about Daisy. Somewhere at the back of the cockney mind was the suspicion, amounting almost to a certainty, that, unless regularly milked, cows exploded, like overcharged water-mains.

Daisy soon developed into something more than a cow. When other occupations failed (amusements there were none), the campers would collect round Daisy, examining her from every angle. She was a mystery, just as a juggler or the three-card trick were mysteries, and as such she commanded respect.

Each night and morning the bishop had to produce from somewhere a person capable of ministering to the requirements of Daisy, and every one in the neighbourhood was extremely busy. Apart from this, West Boxton was a hotbed of Non-conformity, and some of the inhabitants were much exercised in their minds as to the spiritual effect upon a Dissenter of milking a church cow.

There were times when the bishop felt like a conjurer, billed to produce a guinea-pig from a top-hat, who had left the guinea-pig at home.

Daisy was not without her uses, quite apart from those for which she had been provided by Providence and the bishop. " Come an' 'ave a look at Daisy," had become the conversa-tional forlorn hope of the campers when utterly bankrupt of all other interests. She was their shield against boredom and the spear with which to slay the dragon of apathy.

" No beer, no pictures, only a ruddy cow," a cynic had remarked in summing up the amusements provided by the Surrey Summer-Camp for Tired Workers. " Enough to give a giddy flea the blinkin' 'ump," he had concluded ; but this was only an isolated view. For the most part these shipwrecked cockneys were grateful to Daisy, and they never tired of watching the milk spurt musically into the bright pail beneath her.

The bishop was well-meaning, but forgetful. In planning his camp he had entirely overlooked the difficulty of food and water supplies. The one was a mile distant and could not be brought nearer ; the other had been overcome by laying a pipe, at considerable expense.

In the natural order of disaster the campers had arrived, and in a very few hours became tinctured with the heresy of anti-clericalism. Husbands quarrelled with wives as to who should bear the responsibility for the adventure to which they found themselves committed. One and all questioned the right of a bishop to precipitate himself into the domestic circle as a bearer of discord and summer-camps.

At the time of the arrival of the Bindles, everything seemed chaos. There was a spatter of bell-tents on the face of the meadow, piles of personal possessions at the entrance of the tents, whilst the " tired workers " loitered about in their shirt sleeves, or strove to prepare meals in spite of the handicaps with which they were surrounded. The children stood about wide-eyed and grave, as if unable to play their urban games in a bucolic setting.

When, under the able command of Patrol-leader Smithers, the Bindles' belongings had been piled up just inside the meadow and Mrs. Bindle helped down, sore in body and disturbed in temper, the indefatigable boy scout led the way towards a tent. He carried the Japanese basket in one hand, and the handleless bag under the other arm, whilst Bindle followed with the tin-bath, and Mrs. Bindle made herself responsible for the bundle of blankets, through the centre of which the parrot-headed umbrella peeped out coyly.

Their guide paused at the entrance of a bell-tent, and deposited the Japanese basket on the ground.

" This is your tent," he announced ; " I'll send one of the patrol to help you," and, with the air of one upon whose shoulders rests the destiny of planets, he departed.

Bindle and Mrs. Bindle gazed after him, then at each other, finally at the tent. Bindle stepped across and put his head inside ; but quickly withdrew it.

" Smells like a bus on a wet day," he muttered.

With an air of decision Mrs. Bindle entered the tent. As she did so Bindle winked gravely at a little boy who had wandered up, and now stood awaiting events with blue-eyed gravity. At Bindle's wink he turned and trotted off to a neighbouring tent, from the shelter of which he continued to watch the domestic tragedy of the new arrivals.

" There are no bedsteads." Mrs. Bindle's voice came from within the tent in tones of muffled tragedy.

" You don't say so," said Bindle abstractedly, his attention concentrated upon a diminutive knight of the pole, who was approaching their tent.

" Where's the feather beds, 'Orace ? " he demanded when the lad was within earshot.

" There's a waterproof ground-sheet and we supply mat-tresses of loose straw," he announced as he halted sharply within two paces of where Bindle stood.

" Oh ! you do, do you ? " said Bindle, " an' who 'appens to supply the brass double-bedstead wot me and Mrs. B. is used to sleep on ? P'r'aps you can tell me that, young shaver ? "

Before the lad had time to reply, Mrs. Bindle appeared at the entrance of the tent, grimmer and more uncompromising than ever. For a moment she eyed the lad severely.

" Where am I to sleep ? " she demanded.

" Are you with this gentleman ? " inquired the boy scout.

" She is, sonny," said Bindle ; " been with me for twenty years now. Can't lose 'er no'ow."

" Bindle, behave yourself ! " Mrs. Bindle's jaws closed with a snap.

" We're going to 'ave some sacks of straw in place of that missionary's bed you an' me sleeps on in Fulham," explained Bindle ; but Mrs. Bindle had disappeared once more into the tent.

For the next hour the Bindles and their assistant scout were engaged in getting the bell-tent into habitable condition. During the process the scout explained that the marquee was to have been used for the communal meals, which the field-kitchen was to supply ; but both had failed to arrive, and the bishop had himself gone up to London to make inquiries.

" An' wot's goin' to 'appen to us till 'e runs acrost 'em ? " inquired Bindle. " I'm feelin' a bit peckish myself now—wot I'll be like in a hour's time I don't know."

" I'll show you how to build a scout-fire," volunteered the lad.

" But I ain't a fire-eater," objected Bindle. " I want a bit o' steak, or a rasher an' an egg."

" What's the use of a scout-fire to me with kippers to cook ? " demanded Mrs. Bindle, appearing once more at the entrance of the tent.

At that moment another " tired worker " drifted across to the Bindles's tent. He was a long, lean man with a straggling moustache and three days' growth of beard. He was in his shirt sleeves, collarless, with unbuttoned waistcoat, and he wore a general air of despondency and gloom.

" 'Ow goes it, mate ? " he inquired.

Bindle straightened himself from inspecting the interior of the tin-bath which he was unpacking.

" Oh ! mid ; but I've known wot it is to be 'appier," said Bindle, with a grin.

" Same 'ere," was the gloomy response.

" Things sort o' seem to 'ave gone wrong," suggested Bindle conversationally.

" That's right," said the man, rubbing the bristles of his chin with a meditative thumb.

" 'Ow you gettin' on for grub ? " asked Bindle.

The man shook his head lugubriously.

" What about a pub ? "

" Mile away," gloomed the man.

" Gawd Almighty ! " Bindle's exclamation was not concerned with the man's remark. but with something he extracted from the bath. " Well, I'm blowed," he muttered.

" 'Ere, Lizzie," he called out.

Mrs. Bindle appeared at the entrance of the tent. Bindle held up an elastic-sided boot from which marmalade fell solemnly and reluctantly.

Then the flood-gates of Mrs. Bindle's wrath burst apart, and she poured down upon Bindle's head a deluge of reproach. He and he alone was responsible for all the disasters that had befallen them. He had done it on purpose because she wanted a holiday. He wasn't a husband, he was a blasphemer, an atheist, a cumberer of the earth, and all that was evil.

She was interrupted in her tirade by the approach of a little man with a round, bald, shiny head and a worried expression of countenance.

" D'yer know 'ow to milk a cow, mate ? " he inquired of Bindle, apparently quite unconscious that he had precipitated himself into the midst of a domestic scene.

" Do I know 'ow to wot ? " demanded Bindle, eyeing the man as if he had asked a most unusual question.

" There's a bloomin' cow over there and nobody can't milk 'er, an' the bishop's gone, and we wants our tea."

Bindle scratched his head through his cap, then, turning towards the tent into which Mrs. Bindle had once more disappeared, he called out :

" Hi, Lizzie, jer know 'ow to milk a cow ? "

" Don't be beastly," came the reply from the tent.

" It ain't one of them cows," he called back, " it's a milk cow, an' 'ere's a cove wot wants 'is tea."

Mrs. Bindle appeared at the entrance of the tent, and surveyed the group of three men.

" How did you manage yesterday ? " she demanded practically.

" A girl come over from the farm, missis," said the little man, " and she didn't 'arf make it milk."

" Hold your tongue," snapped Mrs. Bindle.

The man gazed at her in surprise.

" Why don't you get the same girl ? " asked Mrs. Bindle.

" She says she's too busy. I 'ad a try myself," said the man,
" only it was a washout."

" I'll 'ave a look at 'er," Bindle announced, and the three
men moved off across the meadow, picking their way among
the tents with their piles of bedding, blankets, and other impedimenta outside. All were getting ready for the night.

When Bindle reached Daisy, he found the problem had been
solved by one of Mr. Timkins's farm-hands, who was busily at
work, watched by an interested group of campers.

During the next half-hour, Bindle strolled about among the
tents learning many things, foremost among which was that
" the whole ruddy camp was a washout." The commissariat
had failed badly, and the nearest drink was a mile away at The
Trowel and Turtle. A great many things were said about the
bishop and the organizers of the camp.

When he returned to the tent, he found Mrs. Bindle engaged
in boiling water in a petrol-tin over a scout-fire. With the
providence of a good housewife she had brought with her emergency supplies, and Bindle was soon enjoying a meal comprised
of kipper, tea, and bread and margarine. When he had
finished, he announced himself ready to face the terrors of
the night.

" I can't say as I likes it," he remarked, as he stood at the
entrance to the tent, struggling to undo his collar. " Seems to
me sort o' draughty."

" That's right, go on," cried Mrs. Bindle, as she pushed past
him. " What did you expect ? "

" Well, since you asks me, I'm like those coves in religion wot
expects nothink ; but gets an 'ell of a lot."

" Don't blaspheme. It's Sunday to-morrow," was the re-
joinder ; but Bindle had strolled away to commune with the
man with a stubbly chin and pessimistic soul.

" Do yer sleep well, mate ? " he inquired, conversationally.

" Crikey ! sleep is it ?   There ain't no blinkin' sleep in this
'ere ruddy camp."

" Wot's up ? " inquired Bindle.

" Up ! " was the lugubrious response. " Awake all last
night, I was."

" Wot was you doin' ? " queried Bindle with interest.

" Scratchin' ! " was the savage retort.

" Scratchin' ! Who was you scratchin' ? "

" Who was I scratchin' ? Who the 'ell should I be scratchin'
but myself ? " he demanded, his apathy momentarily falling

from him. " I'd like to know where they got that blinkin'
straw from wot they give us to lie on. I done a bit o' scratchin'
in the trenches; but last night I 'adn't enough fingers, damn 'em."

Bindle whistled.

" Then," continued the man with gloomy gusto, " there's
them ruddy chickens in the mornin', a-crowin' their guts out.
Not a wink o' sleep after three for anybody," he added, with
all the hatred of the cockney for farmyard sounds. " Oh ! it's
an 'oliday, all right," he added with scathing sarcasm, " only
it ain't ours."

" Seems like it," said Bindle dryly, as he turned on his heel
and made for his own tent.

That night he realized to the full the iniquities of the man
who had supplied the straw for the mattresses. By the sounds
that came from the other side of the tent-pole, he gathered that
Mrs. Bindle was similarly troubled.

Towards dawn, Bindle began to doze, just as the cocks were
announcing the coming of the sun. If the man with the stubbly
chin were right in his diagnosis, the birds, like Prometheus,
had, during the night, renewed their missing organisms.

" Well, I'm blowed ! " muttered Bindle. " Ole six-foot-o'-
melancholy wasn't swinging the lead neither. 'Oly ointment !
I never 'eard such a row in all my puff. There ain't no doubt
but wot Mrs. Bindle's gettin' a country 'oliday," and with that
he rose and proceeded to draw on his trousers, deciding that it
was folly to attempt further to seek sleep.

Outside the tent, he came across Patrol-leader Smithers.

" Mornin', Foch," said Bindle.

" Smithers," said the lad. " Patrol-leader Smithers of the
Bear Patrol."

" My mistake," said Bindle ; " but you an' Foch is jest as
like as two peas. You don't 'appen to 'ave seen a stray cock,
do you ? "

" A cock," repeated the boy.

" Yes ! " said Bindle, tilting his head on one side with the
air of one listening intently, whilst from all sides came the brazen
blare of ecstatic chanticleers. " I thought I 'eard one just now."

" They're Farmer Timkins's fowls," said Patrol-leader
Smithers gravely.

" You don't say so," said Bindle. " Seem to be in good song
this mornin'. Reg'lar bunch o' canaries."

To this flippancy, Patrol-leader Smithers made no response.

" Does there 'appen to be any place where I can get a rinse,
'Indenberg ? " he inquired.

" There's a tap over there for men," said Patrol-leader
Smithers, pointing to the extreme right of the field, " and for
ladies over there," he pointed in the opposite direction.

" No mixed bathin', I see," murmured Bindle. " Now, as
man to man, Ludendorff, which would you advise ? "

The lad looked at him with grave eyes. " The men's tap is
over there," and again he pointed.

" Well, well," said Bindle, " p'r'aps you're right ; but I ain't
fond o' takin' a bath in the middle of a field," he muttered.

" The taps are screened off."

" Well, well, live an' learn," muttered Bindle, as he made
for the men's tap.

When Bindle returned to the tent, he found Patrol-leader
Smithers instructing Mrs. Bindle in how to coax a scout-fire
into activity.

" You mustn't poke it, mum," said the lad. " It goes out
if you do."

Mrs. Bindle drew in her lips, and folded the brown mackintosh she was wearing more closely about her. She was not
accustomed to criticism, particularly in domestic matters, and
her instinct was to disregard it ; but the boy's earnestness
seemed to discourage retort, and she had already seen the evil
effect of attacking a scout-fire with a poker.

Suddenly her eye fell upon Bindle, standing in shirt and
trousers, from the back of which his braces dangled despondently.

" Why don't you go in and dress ? " she demanded. " Walking about in that state ! "

" I been to get a rinse," he explained, as he walked across
to the tent and disappeared through the aperture.

Mrs. Bindle snorted angrily. She had experienced a bad
night, added to which the fire had resented her onslaught by
incontinently going out, necessitating an appeal to a mere
child.

Having assumed a collar, a coat, and waistcoat, Bindle
strolled round the camp exchanging a word here and a word
there with his fellow-campers, who, in an atmosphere of intense
profanity, were engaged in getting breakfast.

" Never 'eard such language," muttered Bindle, with a grin.
" This 'ere little camp'll send a rare lot o' people to a place
where they won't meet the bishop."

At the end of half an hour he returned and found tea, eggs,
and bacon, and Mrs. Bindle waiting for him.

" So you've come at last," she snapped, as he seated himself
on a wooden box.

" Got it this time," he replied genially, sniffing the air appreciatively. " 'Ope you got somethink nice for yer little love-bird."

" Don't you love-bird me," cried Mrs. Bindle, who had been looking for some one on whom to vent her displeasure. " I suppose you're going to leave me to do all the work while you go gallivanting about playing the gentleman."

" I don't needs to play it, Mrs. B., I'm IT. Vere de Vere with blood as blue as 'Earty's stories."

" If you think I'm going to moil and toil and cook for you down here as I do at home, you're mistaken. I came for a rest. I've hardly had a wink of sleep all night," she sniffed ominously.

" I thought I 'eard you on the 'unt," said Bindle sympathetically.

" Bindle ! " There was warning in her tone.

" But wasn't you ? " He looked across at her in surprise, his mouth full of eggs and bacon.

" I—I had a disturbed night," she drew in her lips primly.

" So did I," said Bindle gloomily. " I'd 'ave disturbed 'em if I could 'ave caught 'em. My God ! There must 'ave been millions of 'em." he added reminiscently.

" If you're going to talk like that, I shall go away," she announced.

" I'd like to meet the cove wot filled them mattresses," was Bindle's sinister comment.

" It—it wasn't that," said Mrs. Bindle. " It was the——" She paused for a moment.

" Them cocks," he suggested.

" Don't be disgusting, Bindle."

" Disgusting ? I never see such a chap as me for bein' lood an' disgustin' an' blasphemious. Wot jer call 'em if they ain't cocks ? "

" They're roosters—the male birds."

" But they wasn't roostin', blow 'em. They was crowin', like giddy-o."

Mrs. Bindle made no comment ; but continued to eat her breakfast.

" Personally, myself, I'm goin' to 'ave a little word with the bishop about that little game I 'ad with wot 'appened before wot you call them male birds started givin' tongue." He paused to take breath. " I don't like to mention wot it was ; but I shall itch for a month. 'Ullo Weary ! " he called out to the long man with the stubbly chin.

The man approached. He was wearing the same lugubrious

look and the same waistcoat, unbuttoned in just the same manner that it had been unbuttoned the day before.

" You was right about them mattresses and the male birds," said Bindle, with a glance at Mrs. Bindle.

" The wot ? " demanded the man, gazing vacantly at Bindle.

" The male birds."

" 'Oo the 'ell—sorry, mum," to Mrs. Bindle. Then turning once more to Bindle he added, " Them cocks, you mean ? "

" 'Ush ! " said Bindle. " They ain't cocks 'ere, they're male birds, an' roosters on Sunday. You see, my missis——" but Mrs. Bindle had risen and, with angry eyes, had disappeared into the tent.

" Got one of 'em ? " queried Bindle, jerking his thumb in the direction of the aperture of the tent.

The man with the stubbly chin nodded dolefully.

" Thought so," said Bindle. " You looks it."

Whilst Bindle was strolling round the camp with the man with the stubbly chin, Mrs. Bindle was becoming better acquainted with the peculiar temperament of a bell-tent. She had already realized its disadvantages as a dressing-room. It was dark, it was small, it was stuffy. The two mattresses occupied practically the whole floor-space and there was nowhere to sit. It was impossible to move about freely, owing to restrictions of space in the upper area.

Having washed the breakfast-things, peeled the potatoes, supplied by Mr. Timkins through Patrol-leader Smithers, and prepared for the oven a small joint of beef she had brought with her, Mrs. Bindle once more withdrew into the tent.

When she eventually reappeared in brown alpaca with a bonnet to match, upon which rested two purple pansies, Bindle had just returned from what he called " a nose round," during which he had made friends with most of the campers, men, women, and children, who were not already his friends.

At the sight of Mrs. Bindle he whistled softly.

" You can show me where the bakers is," she said icily, as she proceeded to draw on a pair of brown kid gloves. The inconveniences arising from dressing in a bell-tent had sorely ruffled her temper.

" The bakers ! " he repeated stupidly.

" Yes, the bakers," she repeated. " I suppose you don't want to eat your dinner raw."

Then Bindle strove to explain the composite tragedy of the missing field-kitchen and marquee, to say nothing of the bishop.

In small communities news travels quickly, and the Bindles soon found themselves the centre of a group of men and women (with children holding a watching brief), all anxious to volunteer information, mainly on the subject of misguided bishops who got unsuspecting townsmen into the country under false pretences.

Mrs. Bindle was a good housewife, and she had come prepared with rations sufficient for the first two days. She had, however, depended upon the statements contained in the prospectus of the S.C.T.W., that cooking facilities would be provided by the committee.

She strove to control the anger that was rising within her. It was the Sabbath, and she was among strangers.

Although ready and willing to volunteer information, the other campers saw no reason to restrain their surprise and disapproval of Mrs. Bindle's toilet. The other women were in their work-a-day attire, as befitted housewives who had dinners to cook under severe handicaps, and they resented what they regarded as a newcomer's " swank."

That first day of the holiday, for which she had fought with such grim determination, lived long in Mrs. Bindle's memory. Dinner she contrived with the aid of the frying-pan and the saucepan she had brought with her. It would have taken something more than the absence of a field-kitchen to prevent Mrs. Bindle from doing what she regarded as her domestic duty.

The full sense of her tragedy, however, manifested itself when, dinner over, she had washed up.

There was nothing to do until tea-time. Bindle had disappeared wtih the man with the stubbly chin and two others in search of the nearest public-house, a mile away. Patrol-leader Smithers was at Sunday-school, whilst her fellow-campers showed no inclination to make advances.

She walked for a little among the other tents ; but her general demeanour was not conducive to hasty friendships. She therefore returned to the tent and wrote to Mr. Hearty, telling him, on the authority of Patrol-leader Smithers, that Mr. Timkins had a large quantity of excellent strawberries for sale.

Mr. Hearty was a greengrocer who had one eye on business and the other eye on God, in case of accidents. On hearing that the Bindles were going into the country, his mind had instinctively flown to fruit and vegetables. He had asked Mrs. Bindle to " drop him a postcard " (Mr. Hearty was always economical in the matter of postages, even other people's postages) if she heard of anything that she thought might interest him.

Mrs. Bindle told in glowing terms the story of Farmer Timkins's hoards of strawberries, giving the impression that he was at a loss what to do with them.

Three o'clock brought the bishop and a short open-air service, which was attended by the entire band of campers, with the exception of Bindle and his companions.

The bishop was full of apologies for the past and hope for the future. In place of a sermon he gave an almost jovial address ; but there were no answering smiles. Every one was wondering what they could do until it was time for bed, the more imaginative going still further and speculating what they were to do when they got there.

" My friends," the bishop concluded, " we must not allow trifling mishaps to discourage us. We are here to enjoy ourselves."

And the campers returned to their tents as Achilles had done a few thousand years before, dark of brow and gloomy of heart.

II

THAT evening, in the sanded tap-room of The Trowel and Turtle, the male summer-campers expressed themselves for the twentieth time uncompromisingly upon the subject of bishops and summer-camps. They were " fed up to the ruddy neck," and would give not a little to be back in London, where it was possible to find a pub " without gettin' a blinkin' blister on your stutterin' 'eel."

It was true the field-kitchen had arrived, that they had eaten their first decent meal, and there was every reason to believe that the marquee was at the station ; still they were " sick of the whole streamin' business."

To add to their troubles the landlord of The Trowel and Turtle expressed grave misgivings as to the weather. The glass was dropping, and there was every indication of rain.

" Rain'll jest put the scarlet lid on this blinkin' beano," was the opinion expressed by one of the party and endorsed by all, as, with the landlord's advice to see that everything was made snug for the night, they trooped out of the comfortable tap-room and turned their heads towards the Summer-Camp.

At the entrance of the meadow they were met by Patrol-leader Smithers.

" You must slack the ropes of your tents," he announced,

" there may be rain. Only just slack them a bit ; don't overdo it, or they'll come down on the top of you if the wind gets up."

" Oh crikey ! " moaned a long man with a straggling moustache, as he watched Patrol-leader Smithers march briskly down the lane.

For some moments the men gazed at one another in consternation ; each visualized the desperate state of discomfort that would ensue as the result of wind and rain.

" Let's go an' 'ave a look at Daisy," said Bindle inconsequently.

His companions stared at him in surprise. A shrill voice in the distance calling " 'Enery " seemed to lend to them decision, particularly to 'Enery himself. They turned and strolled over to where Daisy was engaged in preparing the morrow's milk supply. She had been milked and was content.

" Look 'ere, mates," began Bindle, having assured himself that there were no eavesdroppers, " we're all fed up with summer-camps for tired workers—that so ? "

" Up to the blinkin' neck," said a big man with a dirt-grimed skin, voicing the opinion of all.

" There ain't no pubs," said a burly man with black whiskers, " no pictures, can't put a shillin' on an 'orse, can't do any-think——"

" But watch this ruddy cow," broke in the man with the stubbly chin.

" Well, well, p'rap's you're right, only I couldn't 'ave said it 'alf as politely," said Bindle, with a grin. " We're all for good ole Fulham where a cove can lay the dust. Ain't that so, mates ? "

The men expressed their agreement according to the intensity of their feelings.

" Well, listen," said Bindle, " an' I'll tell you." They drew nearer and listened.

Twenty minutes later, when the voice demanding 'Enery became too insistent to be denied, the party broke up, and there was in the eyes of all that which spoke of hope.

III

THAT night, as Patrol-leader Smithers had foretold, there arose a great wind which smote vigorously the tents of the Surrey Summer-Camp for Tired Workers. For a time the tents withstood the fury of the blast ; they swayed and bent before it, putting up a vigorous defence, however. Presently a shriek told of the first catastrophe ; then followed another and yet another, and soon the darkness was rent by cries, shrieks, and lamentations, whilst somewhere near the Bindles's tent rose the voice of one crying from a wilderness of canvas for 'Enery.

Mrs. Bindle was awakened by the loud slatting of the tent-flap. Pandemonium seemed to have broken loose. The wind howled and whistled through the tent-ropes, the rain swept against the canvas sides with an ominous " swish," the pole bent as the tent swayed from side to side.

" Bindle," she cried, " get up ! "

" 'Ullo ! " he responded sleepily. He had taken the precaution of not removing his trousers, a circumstance that was subsequently used as evidence against him.

" The tent's coming down," she cried. " Get up and hold the prop."

As she spoke, she scrambled from beneath the blankets and seized the brown mackintosh, which she kept ready to hand in case of accidents. Wrapping this about her, she clutched at the bending pole, whilst Bindle struggled out from among the bedclothes.

Scrambling to his feet, he tripped over the tin-bath. Clutching wildly as he fell, he got Mrs. Bindle just above the knees in approved rugger style.

With a scream she relinquished the pole to free her legs from Bindle's frenzied clutch and, losing her footing, she came down on top of him.

" Leave go," she cried.

" Get up orf my stomach then," he gasped.

At that moment, the wind gave a tremendous lift to the tent. Mrs. Bindle was clutching wildly at the base of the pole, Bindle was striving to wriggle from beneath her. The combination of forces caused the tent to sway wildly. A moment later, it seemed to start angrily from the ground, and she fell over backwards, whilst a mass of sopping canvas descended, stifling alike her screams and Bindle's protests that he was being killed.

It took Bindle nearly five minutes to find his way out from the heavy folds of wet canvas. Then he had to go back into the darkness to fetch Mrs. Bindle. In order to effect his own escape, Bindle had cut the tent-ropes. Just as he had found Mrs. Bindle, a wild gust of wind entered behind him, lifted the tent bodily and bore it off.

The suddenness of the catastrophe seemed to strike Mrs.

Bindle cumb. To be sitting in the middle of a meadow at dead of night, clothed only in a nightdress and a mackintosh, with the rain drenching down, seemed to her to border upon the indecent.

" You there, Lizzie ? " came the voice of Bindle, like the shout of one hailing a drowning person.

" Where's the tent ? " demanded Mrs. Bindle inconsequently.

" Gawd knows ! " he shouted back. " Probably it's at Yarmouth by now. 'Oly ointment," he yelled.

" What's the matter ? "

" I trodden on the marjarine."

" It's all we've got," she cried, her housewifely fears triumphing over even the stress of wind and rain and her own intolerable situation.

From the surrounding darkness came shouts and inquiries as disaster followed disaster. Heaving masses of canvas laboured and, one by one, produced figures scanty of garment and full of protest ; but mercifully unseen.

Women cried, children shrieked, and men swore volubly.

" I'm sittin' in somethink sticky," cried Bindle presently.

" You've upset the marmalade. Why can't you keep still ? "

Keep still ! Bindle was searching for the two bottles of Guiness's stout he knew to be somewhere among the débris, unconscious that Mrs. Bindle had packed them away in the tin-bath.

As the other tents disgorged their human contents, the pandemonium increased. In every key, appeals were being made for news of lost units.

By the side of the tin-bath, Mrs. Bindle was praying for succour and the lost bell-tent, which had sped towards the east as if in search of the wise men, leaving all beneath it naked to the few stars that peeped from the scudding clouds above, only to hide their faces a moment later as if shocked at what they had seen.

Suddenly a brilliant light flashed across the meadow and began to bob about like a hundred candle power will-o'-the-wisp. It dodged restlessly from place to place, as if in search of something.

Behind a large acetylene motor-lamp, walked Patrol-leader Smithers, searching for one single erect bell-tent—there was none.

Shrieks that had been of terror now became cries of alarm. Forms that had struggled valiantly to escape from the billowing canvas, now began desperately to wriggle back again to the seclusion that modesty demanded. With heads still protruding they regarded the scene, praying that the rudeness of the wind would not betray them.

Taking immediate charge, Patrol-leader Smithers collected the men and gave his orders in a high treble, and his orders were obeyed.

By the time the dawn had begun nervously to finger the east, sufficient tents to shelter the women and children had been re-erected, the cause of the trouble discovered, and the men rebuked for an injudicious slacking of the ropes.

" I ought to have seen to it myself," remarked Patrol-leader Smithers with the air of one who knows he has to deal with fools. " You'll be all right now," he added reassuringly.

" All right now," growled the man with the stubbly chin as he looked up at the grey scudding clouds and then down at the rain-soaked grass. " We would if we was ducks, or ruddy boy scouts ; but we're men, we are—on 'oliday," he added with inspiration, and he withdrew to his tent, conscious that he had voiced the opinion of all.

IV

LATER that morning three carts, laden with luggage, rumbled their way up to West Boxton railway station, followed by a straggling stream of men, women, and children. Overhead heavy rainclouds swung threateningly across the sky. Men were smoking their pipes contentedly, for theirs was the peace which comes of full knowledge. Behind them they had left a litter of bell-tents and the conviction that Daisy in all probability would explode before dinner-time. What cared they ? A few hours hence they would be once more in their known and under-stood Fulham.

As they reached the station they saw two men struggling with a grey mass that looked like a deflated balloon.

The men hailed the party and appealed for help.

" It's the ruddy marquee," cried a voice.

" The blinkin' tent," cried another, not to be outdone in speculative intelligence.

" You can take it back with you," cried one of the men from the truck.

" We're demobbed, ole son," said Bindle cheerily. " We've struck."

" No more blinkin' camps for me," said the man with the stubbly chin.

" *I trodden on the marjarine* "

" 'Ear, 'ear," came from a number of voices.

" Are we downhearted ? " inquired a voice.

" Noooooooooo ! "

And the voices of women and children were heard in the response.

Some half an hour later, as the train steamed out of the station, Bindle called out to the porters :

" Tell the bishop not to forget to milk Daisy."

" Well, Mrs. B.," said Bindle that evening as he lighted his pipe after an excellent supper of sausages, fried onions, and mashed potatoes, " you 'ad yer 'oliday."

" I believe you was at the bottom of those tents coming down, Bindle," she cried with conviction.

" Well, you was underneath, wasn't you ? " was the response, and Bindle winked knowingly at the white jug with the pink butterfly on the spout.

DOUGLAS JERROLD (1803–1857) *had his first play—" More Frightened than Hurt "—produced when he was eighteen, and he afterwards wrote nearly seventy others, including " Black-Eyed Susan " and " The Bride of Ludgate." He is best remembered, however, for the " Curtain Lectures " of that wretched scold, " Mrs. Caudle," which were highly popular both in " Punch " and as a book.*

THE CAUDLES' SUMMER HOLIDAY

MRS. CAUDLE, WEARIED OF MARGATE, HAS " A GREAT DESIRE TO SEE FRANCE "

" Arn't you tired, Caudle? *No?* Well, was there ever such a man! But nothing ever tires you. Of course, it's all very well for you: yes, you can read your newspapers and—What? *So can I?* And I wonder what would become of the children if I did! No; it's enough for their father to lose his precious time, talking about politics, and bishops, and lords, and a pack of people who wouldn't care a pin if we hadn't a roof to cover us—it's well enough for—no, Caudle, no: I'm not going to worry you; I never worried you yet, and it isn't likely I should begin now. But that's always the way with you—always. I'm sure we should be the happiest couple alive, only you do so like to have all the talk to yourself. We're out upon pleasure, and therefore let's be comfortable. Still, I must say it: when you like, you're an aggravating man, Caudle, and you know it.

" *What have you done now?* There, now; we won't talk of it. No; let's go to sleep: otherwise, we shall quarrel—I know we shall. What have you done, indeed! That I can't leave my home for a few days, but I must be insulted! Everybody upon the pier saw it. *Saw what?* How can you lie there in the bed and ask me? Saw what, indeed! Of course, it was a planned thing!—regularly settled before you left London. Oh yes; I like your innocence, Mr. Caudle; not knowing what I'm talking about. It's a heart-breaking thing for a woman to say of her own husband; but you've been a wicked man to me. Yes: and all your tossing and tumbling about in the bed won't make it any better.

"Oh, it's easy enough to call a woman ' a dear soul.' I must be very dear, indeed, to you, when you bring down Miss Pretty-man to—there now ; you needn't shout like a wild savage. Do you know that you're not in your own house—do you know that we're in lodgings ? What do you suppose the people will think of us ? You needn't call out in that manner, for they can hear every word that's said. What do you say ? *Why don't I hold my tongue then ?* To be sure ; anything for an excuse with you. Anything to stop my mouth. Miss Prettyman's to follow you here, and I'm to say nothing. I know she *has* followed you ; and if you were to go before a magistrate, and take a shilling oath to the contrary, I wouldn't believe you. No, Caudle ; I wouldn't.

"*Very well then ?* Ha ! what a heart you must have, to say ' very well ; ' and after the wife I've been to you. I'm to be brought from my own home—dragged down here to the seaside —to be laughed at before the world—don't tell me ! Do you think I didn't see how she looked at you—how she puckered up her farthing mouth—and—what ? *Why did I kiss her, then ?* What's that to do with it ? Appearances are one thing, Mr. Caudle ; and feelings are another. As if women can't kiss one another without meaning anything by it ! And you—I could see you—looked as cold and as formal at her as—well, Caudle ! I wouldn't be the hypocrite you are for the world !

"There, now ; I've heard all that story. I dare say she did come down to join her brother. How very lucky, though, that you should be here ! Ha ! ha ! how very lucky that—ugh ! ugh ! ugh ! and with the cough I've got upon me—oh, you've a heart like a seaside flint ! Yes, that's right. That's just like your humanity. I can't catch a cold, but it must be my own fault—it must be my thin shoes. I dare say you'd like to see me in ploughman's boots ; 'twould be no matter to you how I disfigured myself. Miss Prettyman's foot, now, would be another thing—no doubt.

"I thought when you would make me leave home—I thought we were coming here on pleasure : but it's always the way you embitter my life. The sooner that I'm out of the world, the better. What do you say ? *Nothing ?* But I know what you mean, better than if you talked an hour. I only hope you'll get a better wife, that's all, Mr. Caudle. What ? *You'd not try ?* Wouldn't you ? I know you. In six months you'd fill up my place ; yes, and dreadfully my dear children would suffer for it.

"Caudle, if you roar in that way, the people will give us warning to-morrow. *Can't I be quiet then ?* Yes—that's like your artfulness : anything to make me hold my tongue. But we won't quarrel. I'm sure if it depended upon me, we might be as happy as doves. I mean it—and you needn't groan when I say it. Good night, Caudle. What do you say *Bless me !* Well, you are a dear soul, Caudle ; and if it wasn't for that Miss Prettyman—no, I'm not torturing you. I know very well what I'm doing, and I wouldn't torture you for the world ; but you don't know what the feelings of a wife are, Caudle ; you don't.

"Caudle—I say, Caudle. Just a word, dear. *Well ?* Now, why should you snap me up in that way. *You want to go to sleep ?* So do I ; but that's no reason you should speak to me in that manner. You know, dear, you once promised to take me to France. *You don't recollect it ?* Yes—that's like you ; you don't recollect many things you've promised me ; but I do. There's a boat goes on Wednesday to Boulogne, and comes back the day afterwards. *What of it ?* Why for that time we could leave the children with the girls, and go nicely. *Nonsense ?* Of course ; if I want anything it's always nonsense. Other men can take their wives half over the world ; but you think it quite enough to bring me down here to this hole of a place, where I know every pebble on the beach like an old acquaintance—where there's nothing to be seen but the same machines—the same jetty—the same donkeys—the same everything. But then, I'd forgot ; Margate has an attraction for you—Miss Prettyman's here. No ; I'm not censorious, and I wouldn't backbite an angel ; but the way in which that young woman walks the sands at all hours—there ! there !—I've done : I can't open my lips about that creature but you always storm.

" You know that I always wanted to go to France ; and you bring me down here only on purpose that I should see the French cliffs—just to tantalize me, and for nothing else. If I'd remained at home—and it was against my will I ever came here —I should never have thought of France ; but,—to have it staring in one's face all day, and not be allowed to go ! it's worse than cruel, Mr. Caudle—it's brutal. Other people can take their wives to Paris ; but you always keep me moped up at home. And what for ? Why, that I may know nothing— yes ; just on purpose to make me look little and for nothing else.

" *Heaven bless the woman ?* Ha ! you've good reason to say that, Mr. Caudle ; for I'm sure she's little blessed by you. She's been kept a prisoner all her life—has never gone anywhere —oh yes ! that's your old excuse,—talking of the children. I want to go to France, and I should like to know what the children have to do with it ? They're not babies *now*—are they ? But you've always thrown the children in my face. If Miss Pretty-man—there now ; do you hear what you've done—shouting in that manner ? The other lodgers are knocking overhead : who do you think will have the face to look at 'em to-morrow morning ? I shan't—breaking people's rest in that way !

" Well, Caudle—I declare it's getting daylight, and what an obstinate man you are !—tell me, shall I go to France ? "

" I forget," says Caudle, " my precise answer ; but I think I gave her a very wide permission to go somewhere, whereupon, though not without remonstrance as to the place—she went to sleep."

  .   .   .   .

MRS. CAUDLE'S FIRST NIGHT IN FRANCE.—" SHAMEFUL INDIFFER-ENCE " OF CAUDLE AT THE BOULOGNE CUSTOM HOUSE

" I SUPPOSE, Mr. Caudle, you call yourself a man ? I'm sure, such men should never have wives. If I could have thought it possible you'd have behaved as you have done—and I might, if I hadn't been a forgiving creature, for you've never been like anybody else—if I could only have thought it, you'd never have dragged me to foreign parts. Never ! Well, I *did* say to myself, if he goes to France, perhaps he may catch a little politeness—but no : you began as Caudle, and as Caudle you'll end. I'm to be neglected through life, now. Oh yes ! I've quite given up all thoughts of anything but wretchedness—I've made up my mind to misery, now. *You're glad of it ?* Well, you must have a heart to say that. I declare to you, Caudle, as true as I'm an ill-used woman, if it wasn't for the dear children far away in blessed England—if it wasn't for them, I'd never go back with you. No : I'd leave you in this very place. Yes ; I'd go into a convent ; for a lady on board told me there was plenty of 'em here. I'd go and be a nun for the rest of my days, and—I see nothing to laugh at, Mr. Caudle ; that you should be shaking the bed-things up and down in that way.—But you always laugh at people's feelings ; I wish you'd only some your-self. I'd be a nun, or a Sister of Charity. *Impossible ?* Ha ! Mr. Caudle, you don't know even now what I can be when my blood's up. You've trod upon the worm long enough ; some day won't you be sorry for it ?

" Now none of your profane cryings out ! You needn't talk about Heaven in that way : I'm sure you're the last person who ought. What I say is this. Your conduct at the Custom House was shameful—cruel! And in a foreign land too! But you brought me here that I might be insulted; you'd no other reason for dragging me from England. Ha! let me once get home, Mr. Caudle, and you may wear your tongue out before you get me into outlandish places again. *What have you done?* There now; that's where you're so aggravating. You behave worse than any Turk to me,—what? *You wish you were a Turk?* Well, I think that's a pretty wish before your lawful wife! Yes —a nice Turk you'd make, wouldn't you? Don't think it.

"*What have you done?* Well, it's a good thing I can't see you, for I'm sure you must blush. Done, indeed! Why, when the brutes searched my basket at the Custom House! *A regular th'ng, is it?* Then if you knew that, why did you bring me here? No man who respected his wife would. And you could stand by, and see that fellow with moustachios rummage my basket; and pull out my night-cap and rumple the borders, and—well! if you'd had the proper feelings of a husband, your blood would have boiled again. But no! There you stood looking as mild as butter at the man, and never said a word; not when he crumpled my night-cap—it went to my heart like a stab— crumpled it as if it was any duster. I dare say if it had been Miss Prettyman's night-cap—oh, I don't care about your groan-ing—if it had been her night-cap, her hair-brush, her curl-papers, you'd have said something then. Oh, anybody with the spirit of a man would have spoken out if the fellow had had a thousand swords at his side. Well, all I know is this: if I'd have married somebody I could name, he wouldn't have suffered me to be treated in that way, not he!

"Now, don't hope to go to sleep, Mr. Caudle, and think to silence me in that manner. I know your art, but it won't do. It wasn't enough that my basket was turned topsy-turvy, but before I knew it, they spun me into another room, and—*How could you help that?* You never tried to help it. No; although it was a foreign land, and I don't speak French—not but what I know a good deal more of it than some people who give them-selves airs about it—though I don't speak their nasty gibberish, still you let them take me away, and never cared how I was ever to find you again. In a strange country, too! But I've no doubt that that's what you wished: yes, you'd have been glad enough to have got rid of me in that cowardly manner. If I could only know your secret thoughts, Caudle, that's what you brought me here for, to lose me. And after the wife I've been to you!

"What are you crying out? *For mercy's sake?* Yes; a

great deal you know about mercy! Else you'd never have
suffered me to be twisted into that room. To be searched,
indeed! As if I'd anything smuggled about me. Well, I will
say it; after the way in which I've been used, if you'd the proper
feelings of a man, you wouldn't sleep again for six months. Well,
I know there was nobody but women there; but that's nothing
to do with it. I'm sure, if I'd been taken up for picking pockets
they couldn't have used me worse. To be treated so—and
'specially by one's own sex!—it's *that* that aggravates me.

"And that's all you can say? *What could you do?* Why,
break open the door; I'm sure you must have heard my voice:
you shall never make me believe you couldn't hear that. Whenever I shall sew the strings on again, I can't tell. If they didn't
turn me out like a ship in a storm, I'm a sinner! And you
laughed! *You didn't laugh?* Don't tell me; you laugh when
you don't know anything about it; but I do.

"And a pretty place you have brought me to. A most respectable place I must say! Where the women walk about
without any bonnets to their heads, and the fish-girls with their
bare legs—well, you don't catch me eating any fish while I'm
here. *Why not?* Why not,—do you think I'd encourage people
of that sort?

"What do you say? *Good night?* It's no use your saying
that—I can't go to sleep so soon as you can. Especially with a
door that has such a lock as that to it. How do we know who
may come in? What? *All the locks are bad in France?* The
more shame for you to bring me to such a place, then. It only
shows how you value me.

"Well, I dare say you are tired. *I* am! But then, see what
I've gone through. Well, we won't quarrel in a barbarous
country. We won't do that. Caudle, dear—what's the French
for lace? I know it, only I forget it. The French for lace, love?
What? *Dentelle?* Now, you're not deceiving me? *You never
deceived me yet?* Oh! don't say that. There isn't a married
man in this blessed world can put his hand upon his heart in
bed, and say that. French for lace, dear? Say it again. *Dentelle?* Ha! Dentelle! Good night, dear. Dentelle! Den—
telle."

"I afterwards," writes Caudle, "found out to my cost wherefore she inquired about lace. For she went out in the morning
with the landlady to buy a veil, giving only four pounds for what
she could have bought in England for forty shillings!"

MRS. CAUDLE RETURNS TO HER NATIVE LAND. "UNMANLY
CRUELTY" OF CAUDLE, WHO HAS REFUSED "TO SMUGGLE A
FEW THINGS" FOR HER.

"THERE, it isn't often that I ask you to do anything for me,
Mr. Caudle, goodness knows! and when I do, I'm
always refused—of course. Oh yes! anybody but your own
lawful wife. Every other husband aboard the boat could behave
like a husband—but I was left to shift for myself. To be sure,
that's nothing new; I always am. Every other man, worthy
to be called a man, could smuggle a few things for his wife—
but I might as well be alone in the world. Not one poor half-
dozen of silk stockings could you put in your hat for me; and
everybody else was rolled in lace, and I don't know what. Eh?
What, Mr. Caudle? *What do I want with silk stockings?* Well,—
it's come to something now! There was a time, I believe, when
I had a foot—yes, and an ankle, too: but when once a woman's
married, she has nothing of the sort; of course. No: I'm *not*
a cherub, Mr. Caudle; don't say that. I know very well what
I am.

"I dare say now, you'd have been delighted to smuggle for
Miss Prettyman? Silk stockings become her! *You wish Miss
Prettyman was in the moon?* Not you, Mr. Caudle; that's only
your art—your hypocrisy. A nice person too she'd be for the
moon; it would be none the brighter for her being in it, I know.
And when you saw the Custom House officers look at me, as
though they were piercing me through, what was your conduct?
Shameful. You twittered about, and fidgetted, and flushed up
as if I really *was* a smuggler. *So I was?* What had that to do
with it? It wasn't the part of a husband I think, to fidget in
that way, and show it. *You couldn't help it?* Humph! And
you call yourself a person of strong mind, I believe? One of the
lords of the creation! Ha! ha! couldn't help it!

"But I may do all I can to save the money, and this is always
my reward. Yes, Mr. Caudle, I shall save a great deal. *How
much?* I sha'n't tell you: I know your meanness—you'd want
to stop it out of the house allowance. No: it's nothing to you
where I get the money from to buy so many things. The money
was my own. Well, and if it was yours first, that's nothing to
do with it. No; I hav'n't saved it out of the puddings. But
it's always the woman who saves who's despised. It's only your
fine-lady wives who're properly thought of. If I was to ruin
you, Caudle, then you'd think something of me.

" I sha'n't go to sleep. It's very well for you who're no sooner
in bed, than you're fast as a church ; but I can't sleep in that
way. It's my mind keeps me awake. And after all, I do feel
so happy to-night, it's very hard I can't enjoy my thoughts. *No :
I can't think in silence !* There's much enjoyment in that to be
sure ! I've no doubt now you could listen to Miss Prettyman—
oh, I don't care, I will speak. It is a little more than odd, I think,
that she should be on the jetty when the boat came in. Ha !
she'd been looking for you all the morning with a telescope, I've
no doubt—she's bold enough for anything. And then how she
sneered and giggled when she saw me,—and said ' how fat I'd
got ' : like her impudence, I think. What ! *Well she might ?*
But I know what she wanted ; yes—she'd have liked to have had
me searched. She laughed on purpose.

" I only wish I'd taken two of the dear girls with me. What
things I could have stitched about 'em ! No—I'm not ashamed
of myself to make my innocent children smugglers : the more
innocent they looked, the better ; but there you with what
you call your principles again ; as if it wasn't given to everybody
by nature to smuggle. I'm sure of it—it's born with us. And
nicely I've cheated 'em this day. Lace, and velvet, and silk
stockings, and other things,—to say nothing of the tumble s and
decanters. No : I didn't look as if I wanted a direction, for fear
somebody should break me. That's another of what you call
your jokes ; but you should keep 'em for those who like 'em.
I don't.

" *What have I made after all ?* I've told you—you shall never
never know. Yes, I know you'd been fin d a hundred pounds if
they'd searched me ; but I never meant that they should. I dare
say you wouldn't smuggle—oh no ! you don't think it worth your
while. You're quite a conjurer, you are, Caudle. Ha ! ha ! ha !
What am I laughing at ? Oh, you little know—such a clever
creature ! Ha ! ha ! Well, now, I'll tell you. I knew what an
unaccommodating animal you were, so I made you smuggle
whether or not. *How ?* Why, when you were out at the *Café*,
I got your great rough coat, and if I didn't stitch ten yards of
best black velvet under the lining I'm a sinful woman ! And to
see how innocent you looked when the officers walked round and
round you ! It was a happy moment, Caudle, to see you.

" What do you call it ? *A shameful trick—unworthy of a wife ?
I couldn't care much for you ?* As if I didn't prove that, by trusting
you with ten yards of velvet. But I don't care what you say :
I've saved everything—all but that beautiful English novel, that
I've forgot the name of. And if they didn't take it out of my

hand, and chopped it to bits like so much dog's-meat. *Served me right?* And when I so seldom buy a book ! No : I don't see how it served me right. If you can buy the same book in France for four shillings that people here have the impudence to ask more than a guinea for—well, if they *do* steal it, that's their affair, not ours. As if there was anything in a book to steal !

"And now, Caudle, when are you going home ! What ? *Our time isn't up?* That's nothing to do with it. If we even lose a week's lodging—and we mayn't do that—we shall save it again in living. But you're such a man ! Your home's the last place with you. I'm sure I don't get a wink of a night, thinking what may happen. Three fires last week ; and any one might as well have been at our house as not. *No—they mightn't?* Well, you know what I mean—but you're such a man !

" I'm sure, too, we've had quite enough of this place. But there's no keeping you out of the libraries, Caudle. You're getting quite a gambler. And I don't think it's a nice example to set to your children, raffling as you do for French clocks and I don't know what. But that's not the worst ; you never win anything. Oh, I forgot. Yes ; a needle-case, that under my nose you gave to Miss Prettyman. A nice thing for a married man to make presents : and to such a creature as that, too. A needle-case ! I wonder whenever she has a needle in *her* hand !

" I know I shall feel ill with anxiety if I stop here. Nobody left in the house but that Mrs. Closepeg. And she is such a stupid woman. It was only last night that I dreamt I saw our cat quite a skeleton, and the canary stiff on its back at the bottom of the cage. You know, Caudle, I'm never happy when I'm away from home ; and yet you will stay here. No, home's my comfort ; I never want to stir over the threshold, and you know it. If thieves were to break in, what could that Mrs. Closepeg do against 'em ? And so, Caudle, you'll go home on Saturday ? Our dear—dear home ! Oh Saturday, Caudle ? "

" What I answered," says Caudle, " I forget ; but I know that on the Saturday we were once again shipped on board the *Red Rover*."

CHARLES LAMB (1775–1834), *across whose own mind fell for a time the shadow of that insanity which had resulted in his sister Mary killing their mother, was the son of a lawyer's clerk, and his sister's sole protection for the greater part of her life. He left innumerable works in prose and poetry, but none are better known than the delightful " Essays of Elia " from which " Roast Pig " is taken.*

A DISSERTATION UPON ROAST PIG

MANKIND, says a Chinese manuscript, which my friend M. was obliging enough to read and explain to me, for the first seventy thousand ages ate their meat raw, clawing or biting it from the living animal, just as they do in Abyssinia to this day. This period is not obscurely hinted at by their great Confucius in the second chapter of his Mundane Mutations, where he designates a kind of golden age by the term Cho-fang, literally the Cooks' Holiday. The manuscript goes on to say that the art of roasting, or rather broiling (which I take to be the elder-brother) was accidentally discovered in the manner following. The swineherd, Ho-ti, having gone out into the woods one morning, as his manner was, to collect mast for his hogs, left his cottage in the care of his eldest son, Bo-bo, a great lubberly boy, who, being fond of playing with fire, as younkers of his age commonly are, let some sparks escape into a bundle of straw, which, kindling quickly, spread the conflagration over every part of their poor mansion, till it was reduced to ashes. Together with the cottage (a sorry antediluvian makeshift of a building, you may think it), what was of much more importance, a fine litter of new-farrowed pigs, no less than nine in number, perished. China pigs have been esteemed a luxury all over the East, from the remotest periods that we read of. Bo-bo was in the utmost consternation, as you may think, not so much for the sake of the tenement, which his father and he could easily build up again with a few dry branches, and the labour of an hour or two, at any time, as for the loss of the pigs. While he was thinking what he should say to his father, and wringing his hands over the smoking remnants of one of those untimely sufferers, an odour assailed his nostrils, unlike any scent which he had before experienced. What could it proceed from? not from the burned cottage—he had smelt that smell before—indeed this was by no means the first accident of the kind which had occurred through the negligence of this unlucky young firebrand. Much less did it resemble that of any known herb, weed, or flower. A premonitory moistening at the same time overflowed his nether lip. He knew not what to think. He next stooped down to feel the pig, if there were any signs of life in it. He burned his fingers, and to cool them he applied them in his booby fashion to his mouth. Some of the crumbs of the scorched skin had come away with his fingers, and for the first time in his life (in the world's life indeed, for before him no man had known it) he tasted—*crackling!* Again he felt and fumbled at the pig. It did not burn him so much now, still he licked his fingers from a sort of habit. The truth at length broke into his slow understanding that it was the pig that smelt so, and the pig that tasted so delicious ; and surrendering himself up to the new-born pleasure, he fell to tearing up whole handfuls of the scorched skin with the flesh next it, and was cramming it down his throat in his beastly fashion, when his sire entered amid the smoking rafters, armed with retributory cudgel, and finding how affairs stood, began to rain blows upon the young rogue's shoulders, as thick as hailstones, which Bo-bo heeded not any more than if they had been flies. The tickling pleasure, which he experienced in his lower regions, had rendered him quite callous to any inconveniences he might feel in those remote quarters. His father might lay on, but he could not beat him from his pig, till he had fairly made an end of it, when, becoming a little more sensible of his situation, something like the following dialogue ensued.

"You graceless whelp, what have you got there devouring ? Is it not enough that you have burned me down three houses with your dog's tricks, and be hanged to you ! but you must be eating fire, and I know not what—what have you got there, I say ? "

"Oh father, the pig, the pig ! do come and taste how nice the burned pig eats."

The ears of Ho-ti tingled with horror. He cursed his son, and he cursed himself that ever he should beget a son that should eat burned pig.

Bo-bo, whose scent was wonderfully sharpened since morning, soon raked out another pig, and fairly rending it asunder, thrust the lesser half by main force into the fists of Ho-ti, still shouting out, "Eat, eat, eat the burned pig, father, only taste—O Lord ! " —with such-like barbarous ejaculations, cramming all the while as if he would choke.

Ho-ti trembled in every joint while he grasped the abominable thing, wavering whether he should not put his son to death for an unnatural young monster, when, the crackling scorching his fingers, as it had done his son's, and applying the same remedy to them, he in his turn tasted some of its flavour, which, make what sour mouths he would for pretence, proved not altogether displeasing to him. In conclusion (for the manuscript here is a little tedious), both father and son fairly set down to the mess, and never left off till they had dispatched all that remained of the litter.

Bo-bo was strictly enjoined not to let the secret escape, for the neighbours would certainly have stoned them for a couple of abominable wretches, who could think of improving upon the good meat which God had sent them. Nevertheless, strange stories got about. It was observed that Ho-ti's cottage was burned down now more frequently than ever. Nothing but fires from this time forward. Some would break out in broad day, others in the night-time. As often as the sow farrowed, so sure was the house of Ho-ti to be in a blaze; and Ho-ti himself, which was the more remarkable, instead of chastising his son, seemed to grow more indulgent to him than ever. At length they were watched, the terrible mystery discovered, and father and son summoned to take their trial at Pekin, then an inconsiderable assize town. Evidence was given, the obnoxious food itself produced in court, and verdict about to be pronounced, when the foreman of the jury begged that some of the burned pig, of which the culprits stood accused, might be handed into the box. He handled it, and they all handled it; and burning their fingers, as Bo-bo and his father had done before them, and Nature prompting to each of them the same remedy, against the face of all the facts, and the clearest charge which judge had ever given—to the surprise of the whole court, townsfolk, strangers, reporters, and all present—without leaving the box, or any manner of consultation whatever, they brought in a simultaneous verdict of Not Guilty.

The judge, who was a shrewd fellow, winked at the manifest iniquity of the decision; and, when the court was dismissed, went privily and bought up all the pigs that could be had for love or money. In a few days his Lordship's town house was observed to be on fire. The thing took wing, and now there was nothing to be seen but fires in every direction. Fuel and pigs grew enormously dear all over the district. The insurance offices, one and all, shut up shop. People built slighter and slighter every day, until it was feared that the very science of architecture would in no long time be lost to the world. Thus this custom of firing houses continued, till in process of time, says my manuscript, a sage arose, like our Locke, who made a discovery that the flesh of swine, or indeed of any other animal, might be cooked (*burned*, as they called it) without the necessity of consuming a whole house to dress it. Then first began the rude form of a gridiron. Roasting by the string, or spit, came in a century or two later, I forget in whose dynasty. By such slow degrees, concludes the manuscript, do the most useful, and seemingly the most obvious arts, make their way among mankind.

Without placing too implicit faith in the account above given, it must be agreed that if a worthy pretext for so dangerous an experiment as setting houses on fire (especially in these days) could be assigned in favour of any culinary object, that pretext and excuse might be found in ROAST PIG.

Of all the delicacies in the whole *mundus edibilis*, I will maintain it to be the most delicate—*princeps obsoniorum*.

I speak not of your grown porkers—things between pig and pork—those hobbydehoys—but a young and tender suckling—under a moon old—guiltless as yet of the sty—with no original speck of the *amor immunditiæ*, the hereditary failing of the first parent, yet manifest—his voice as yet not broken, but something between a childish treble and a grumble—the mild forerunner, or *præludium* of a grunt.

He must be roasted. I am not ignorant that our ancestors ate them seethed or boiled—but what a sacrifice of the exterior teguement !

There is no flavour comparable, I will contend, to that of the crisp, tawny, well-watched, not over-roasted, *crackling*, as it is well called—the very teeth are invited to their share of the pleasure at this banquet in overcoming the coy, brittle resistance —with the adhesive oleaginous—oh, call it not fat ! but an indefinable sweetness growing up to it—the tender blossoming of fat—fat cropped in the bud—taken in the shoot—in the first innocence—the cream and quintessence of the child-pig's yet pure food—the lean, no lean, but a kind of animal manna—or rather, fat and lean (if it must be so) so blended and running into each other, that both together make but one ambrosian result, or common substance.

Behold him, while he is " doing "—it seemeth rather a refreshing warmth, than a scorching heat, that he is so passive to. How equably he twirleth round the string !—Now he is just done. To see the extreme sensibility of that tender age !—he hath wept out his pretty eyes—radiant jellies—shooting stars.

See him in the dish, his second cradle, how meek he lieth !—wouldst thou have had this innocent grow up to the grossness and indocility which too often accompany maturer swinehood ? Ten to one he would have proved a glutton, a sloven, an obstinate, disagreeable animal—wallowing in all manner of filthy conversation—from these sins he is happily snatched away—

> *Ere sin could blight or sorrow fade,*
> *Death came with timely care—*

his memory is odoriferous—no clown curseth, while his stomach half rejecteth, the rank bacon—no coal-heaver bolteth him in reeking sausages—he hath a fair sepulchre in the grateful stomach of the judicious epicure—and for such a tomb might be content to die.

He is the best of savors. Pineapple is great. She is indeed almost too transcendent—a delight, if not sinful, yet so like to sinning that really a tender-conscienced person would do well to pause—too ravishing for mortal taste, she woundeth and excoriateth the lips that approach her—like lovers' kisses, she biteth—she is a pleasure bordering on pain from the fierceness and insanity of her relish—but she stoppeth at the palate—she meddleth not with the appetite—and the coarsest hunger might barter her consistently for a mutton chop.

Pig—let me speak his praise—is no less provocative of the appetite than he is satisfactory to the criticalness of the censorious palate. The strong man may batten on him, and the weakling refuseth not his mild juices.

Unlike to mankind's mixed characters, a bundle of virtues and vices, inexplicably intertwisted, and not to be unravelled without hazard, he is—good throughout. No part of him is better or worse than another. He helpeth, as far as his little means extend, all around. He is the least envious of banquets. He is all neighbours' fare.

I am one of those who freely and ungrudgingly impart a share of the good things of this life which fall to their lot (few as mine are in this kind) to a friend. I protest I take as great an interest in my friend's pleasures, his relishes, and proper satisfaction, as in mine own. " Presents," I often say, " endear Absents." Hares, pheasants, partridges, snipes, barn-door chickens (those " tame villatic fowl "), capons, plovers, brawn, barrels of oysters, I dispense as freely as I receive them. I love to taste them, as it were, upon the tongue of my friend. But a stop must be put somewhere. One would not, like Lear, " give everything." I

make my stand upon pig. Methinks it is an ingratitude to the
Giver of all good flavours, to extra-domiciliate, or send out of the
house, slightingly (under pretext of friendship, or I know not
what), a blessing, so particularly adapted, predestined, I may say,
to my individual palate. It argues an insensibility.

I remember a touch of conscience in this kind at school. My
good old aunt, who never parted from me at the end of a holiday
without stuffing a sweatmeat, or some nice thing, into my pocket,
had dismissed me one evening with a smoking plumcake, fresh
from the oven. In my way to school (it was over London Bridge)
a grey-headed old beggar saluted me (I have no doubt, at this
time of day, that he was a counterfeit). I had no pence to console
him with, and in the vanity of self-denial, and the very cox-
combry of charity, schoolboy-like, I made him a present of—the
whole cake ! I walked on a little, buoyed up, as one is on such
occasions, with a sweet soothing of self-satisfaction ; but before I
had got to the end of the bridge my better feelings returned, and
I burst into tears, thinking how ungrateful I had been to my good
aunt, to go and give her good gift away to a stranger that I had
never seen before, and who might be a bad man for aught I
knew ; and then I thought of the pleasure my aunt would be in
thinking that I—I myself, and not another—would eat her nice
cake—and what should I say to her the next time I saw her—
how naughty I was to part with her pretty present !—and the
odour of that spicy cake came back upon my recollection, and
the pleasure and the curiosity I had taken in seeing her make it,
and her joy when she had sent it to the oven, and how disappointed
she would feel that I had never had a bit of it in my mouth at
last—and I blamed my impertinent spirit of alms-giving and
out-of-place hypocrisy of goodness ; and above all I wished
never to see the face again of that insidious, good-for-nothing,
old, grey impostor.

Our ancestors were nice in their method of sacrificing these
tender victims. We read of pigs whipped to death with something
of a shock, as we hear of any other obsolete custom. The age of
discipline is gone by, or it would be curious to inquire (in a
philosophical light merely) what effect this process might have
towards intenerating and dulcifying a substance, naturally so
mild and dulcet, as the flesh of young pigs. It looks like refining
a violet. Yet we should be cautious, while we condemn the in-
humanity, how we censure the wisdom of the practice. It might
impart a gusto.

I remember a hypothesis, argued upon by the young students,
when I was at St. Omer's, and maintained with much learning

and pleasantry on both sides, " Whether, supposing that the flavour of a pig who obtained his death by whipping (*per flagellationem extremam*) superadded a pleasure upon the palate of a man more intense than any possible suffering we can conceive in the animal, is man justified in using that method of putting the animal to death ? " I forget the decision.

His sauce should be considered. Decidedly, a few breadcrumbs, done up with his liver and brains, and a dash of mild sage. But banish, dear Mrs. Cook, I beseech you, the whole onion tribe. Barbecue your whole hogs to your palate, steep them in shalots, stuff them out with plantations of the rank and guilty garlic ; you cannot poison them, or make them stronger than they are—but consider, he is a weakling—a flower.

STEPHEN LEACOCK (1869–), *a Canadian author of works on political economy, biography, and literary essays, and head of the department of political economy at McGill University, has set half the world laughing with his volumes of delicious ridicule. They are principally short stories burlesquing once popular types of fiction, some of the best known being " Nonsense Novels," and " Literary Lapses." We present here a Nonsense Novel.*

GERTRUDE THE GOVERNESS

Synopsis of Previous Chapters :
There are no Previous Chapters

It was a wild and stormy night on the West Coast of Scotland. This, however, is immaterial to the present story, as the scene is not laid in the West of Scotland. For the matter of that the weather was just as bad on the East Coast of Ireland.

But the scene of this narrative is laid in the South of England and takes place in and around Knotacentinum Towers (pronounced as if written Nosham Taws), the seat of Lord Knotacent (pronounced as if written Nosh).

But it is not necessary to pronounce either of these names in reading them.

Nosham Taws was a typical English home. The main part of the house was an Elizabethan structure of warm red brick, while the elder portion, of which the Earl was inordinately proud, still showed the outlines of a Norman Keep, to which had been added a Lancastrian Jail and a Plantagenet Orphan Asylum. From the house in all directions stretched magnificent woodland and park with oaks and elms of immemorial antiquity, while nearer the house stood raspberry bushes and geranium plants which had been set out by the Crusaders.

About the grand old mansion the air was loud with the chirping of thrushes, the cawing of partridges, and the clear sweet note of the rook ; while deer, antelope, and other quadrupeds strutted about the lawn so tame as to eat off the sun-dial. In fact, the place was a regular menagerie.

From the house downwards through the park stretched a beautiful broad avenue laid out by Henry VII.

Lord Nosh stood upon the hearthrug of the library. Trained

diplomat and statesman as he was, his stern aristocratic face was upside down with fury.

"Boy," he said, "you shall marry this girl or I disinherit you. You are no son of mine."

Young Lord Ronald, erect before him, flung back a glance as defiant as his own.

"I defy you," he said. "Henceforth you are no father of mine. I will get another. I will marry none but a woman I can love. This girl that we have never seen——"

"Fool," said the Earl, "would you throw aside our estate and name of a thousand years? The girl, I am told, is beautiful; her aunt is willing; they are French; pah! they understand such things in France."

"But your reason——"

"I give no reason," said the Earl. "Listen, Ronald, I give one month. For that time you remain here. If at the end of it you refuse me, I cut you off with a shilling."

Lord Ronald said nothing; he flung himself from the room, flung himself upon his horse, and rode madly off in all directions.

As the door of the library closed upon Ronald, the Earl sank into a chair. His face changed. It was no longer that of the haughty nobleman, but of the hunted criminal. "He must marry the girl," he muttered. "Soon she will know all. Tutchemoff has escaped from Siberia. He knows and will tell. The whole of the mines pass to her, this property with it, and I— but enough." He rose, walked to the sideboard, drained a dipper full of gin and bitters, and became again a high-bred English gentleman.

It was at this moment that a high dogcart, driven by a groom in the livery of Earl Nosh, might have been seen entering the avenue of Nosham Taws. Beside him sat a young girl, scarce more than a child, in fact not nearly so big as the groom.

The apple-pie hat which she wore, surmounted with black willow plumes, concealed from view a face so face-like in its appearance as to be positively facial.

It was—need we say it—Gertrude the Governess, who was this day to enter upon her duties at Nosham Taws.

At the same time that the dogcart entered the avenue at one end, there might have been seen riding down it from the other a tall young man, whose long, aristocratic face proclaimed his birth, and who was mounted upon a horse with a face even longer than his own.

And who is this tall young man who draws nearer to Gertrude with every revolution of the horse? Ah, who, indeed? Ah, who, who ? I wonder if any of my readers could guess that this was none other than Lord Ronald.

The two were destined to meet. Nearer and nearer they came. And then still nearer. Then for one brief moment they met. As they passed Gertrude raised her head and directed towards the young nobleman two eyes so eye-like in their expression as to be absolutely circular, while Lord Ronald directed towards the occupant of the dogcart a gaze so gaze-like that nothing but a gazelle, or a gas-pipe, could have emulated its intensity.

Was this the dawn of love ? Wait and see. Do not spoil the story.

Let us speak of Gertrude. Gertrude De-Mongmorenci McFiggin had known neither father nor mother. They had both died years before she was born. Of her mother she knew nothing, save that she was French, was extremely beautiful, and that all her ancestors and even her business acquaintances had perished in the Revolution.

Yet Gertrude cherished the memory of her parents. On her breast the girl wore a locket in which was enshrined a miniature of her mother, while down her neck inside at the back hung a daguerreotype of her father. She carried a portrait of her grandmother up her sleeve and had pictures of her cousins tucked inside her boot, while beneath her—but enough, quite enough.

Of her father, Gertrude knew even less. That he was a high-born English gentleman who had lived as a wanderer in many lands, this was all she knew. His only legacy to Gertrude had been a Russian grammar, a Roumanian phrase-brook, a theodolite, and a work on mining engineering.

From her earliest infancy Gertrude had been brought up by her aunt. Her aunt had carefully instructed her in Christian principles. She had also taught her Mohammedanism to make sure.

When Gertrude was seventeen her aunt had died of hydrophobia.

The circumstances were mysterious. There had called upon her that day a strange bearded man in the costume of the Russians. After he had left, Gertrude had found her aunt in a syncope, from which she passed into an apostrophe and never recovered.

To avoid scandal it was called hydrophobia. Gertrude was thus thrown upon the world. What to do ? That was the problem that confronted her.

It was while musing one day upon her fate that Gertrude's eye was struck with an advertisement :

" Wanted a governess ; must possess a knowledge of French, Italian, Russian, and Roumanian, Music, and Mining Engineering. Salary, £1, 4 shillings and 4 pence halfpenny per annum. Apply between half-past eleven and twenty-five minutes to twelve at No. 41 A Decimal Six, Belgravia Terrace. The Countess of Nosh."

Gertrude was a girl of great natural quickness of apprehension, and she had not pondered over this announcement more than half an hour before she was struck with the extraordinary coincidence between the list of items desired and the things that she herself knew.

She duly presented herself at Belgravia Terrace before the Countess, who advanced to meet her with a charm which at once placed the girl at her ease.

" You are proficient in French ? " she asked.

" *Oh, oui,*" said Gertrude modestly.

" And Italian ? " continued the Countess.

" *Oh, si,*" said Gertrude.

" And German ? " said the Countess in delight.

" *Ah, ja,*" said Gertrude.

" And Russian ? "

" *Yaw.*"

" And Roumanian ? "

" *Jep.*"

Amazed at the girl's extraordinary proficiency in modern languages, the Countess looked at her narrowly. Where had she seen those lineaments before ? She passed her hand over her brow in thought, and spit upon the floor, but no, the face baffled her.

" Enough," she said, " I engage you on the spot ; to-morrow you go down to Nosham Taws and begin teaching the children. I must add that in addition you will be expected to aid the Earl with his Russian correspondence. He has large mining interests at Tschminsk."

Tschminsk ! why did the simple word reverberate upon Gertrude's ears ? Why ? Because it was the name written in her father's hand on the title page of his book on mining. What mystery was here ?

It was on the following day that Gertrude had driven up the avenue.

She descended from the dogcart, passed through a phalanx of liveried servants drawn up seven-deep, to each of whom she gave a sovereign as she passed and entered Nosham Taws.

" Welcome," said the Countess, as she aided Gertrude to carry her trunk upstairs.

The girl presently descended and was ushered into the library, where she was presented to the Earl. As soon as the Earl's eye fell upon the face of the new governess he started visibly. Where had he seen those lineaments ? Where was it ? At the races, or the theatre—on a bus—no. Some subtler thread of memory was stirring in his mind. He strode hastily to the sideboard, drained a dipper and a half of brandy, and became again the perfect English gentleman.

While Gertrude has gone to the nursery to make the acquaintance of the two tiny golden-haired children who are to be her charges, let us say something here of the Earl and his son.

Lord Nosh was the perfect type of the English nobleman and statesman. The years that he had spent in the diplomatic service at Constantinople, St. Petersburg, and Salt Lake City had given to him a peculiar finesse and noblesse, while his long residence at St. Helena, Pitcairn Island, and Hamilton, Ontario, had rendered him impervious to external impressions. As deputy-paymaster of the militia of the county he had seen something of the sterner side of military life, while his hereditary office of Groom of the Sunday Breeches had brought him into direct contact with Royalty itself.

His passion for outdoor sports endeared him to his tenants. A keen sportsman, he excelled in fox-hunting, dog-hunting, pig-killing, bat-catching, and the pastimes of his class.

In this latter respect Lord Ronald took after his father. From the start the lad had shown the greatest promise. At Eton he had made a splendid showing at battledore and shuttlecock, and at Cambridge had been first in his class at needlework. Already his name was whispered in connection with the All England ping-pong championship, a triumph which would undoubtedly carry with it a seat in Parliament.

Thus was Gertrude the Governess installed at Nosham Taws. The days and the weeks sped past.

The simple charm of the beautiful orphan girl attracted all hearts. Her two little pupils became her slaves. " Me loves oo," little Rasehellfrida would say, leaning her golden head in Gertrude's lap. Even the servants loved her. The head gardener would bring a bouquet of beautiful roses to her room before she was up, the second gardener a bunch of early cauliflowers, the third a spray of late asparagus, and even the tenth and eleventh a sprig of mangel-wurzel or an armful of hay. Her room was full of gardeners all the time, while at evening the aged butler, touched at the friendless girl's loneliness, would tap softly at her door to bring her a rye whisky and seltzer or a box of

Pittsburg Stogies. Even the dumb creatures seemed to admire her in their own dumb way. The dumb rooks settled on her shoulder and every dumb dog around the place followed her.

And Ronald ! ah, Ronald ! Yes, indeed ! They had met. They had spoken.

"What a dull morning," Gertrude had said. "*Quel triste matin ! Was fur ein allerverdamnter Tag !* "

"Beastly," Ronald had answered.

"Beastly ! ! " The word rang in Gertrude's ears all day.

After that they were constantly together. They played tennis and ping-pong in the day, and in the evening, in accordance with the stiff routine of the place, they sat down with the Earl and Countess to twenty-five-cent poker, and later still they sat together on the verandah and watched the moon sweeping in great circles around the horizon.

It was not long before Gertrude realized that Lord Ronald felt towards her a warmer feeling than that of mere ping-pong. At times in her presence he would fall, especially after dinner, into a fit of profound subtraction.

Once, at night, when Gertrude withdrew to her chamber and before seeking her pillow, prepared to retire as a preliminary to disrobing—in other words, before going to bed, she flung wide the casement (opened the window) and perceived (saw) the face of Lord Ronald. He was sitting on a thorn bush beneath her, and his upturned face wore an expression of agonized pallor.

Meantime the days passed. Life at the Taws moved in the ordinary routine of a great English household. At 7 a gong sounded for rising, at 8 a horn blew for breakfast, at 8.30 a whistle sounded for prayers, at 1 a flag was run up at half-mast for lunch, at 4 a gun was fired for afternoon tea, at 9 a first bell sounded for dressing, at 9.15 a second bell for going on dressing, while at 9.30 a rocket was sent up to indicate that dinner was ready. At midnight dinner was over, and at 1 a.m. the tolling of a bell summoned the domestics to evening prayers.

Meanwhile the month allotted by the Earl to Lord Ronald was passing away. It was already July 15, then within a day or two it was July 17, and, almost immediately afterwards, July 18.

At times the Earl, in passing Ronald in the hall, would say sternly, " Remember, boy, your consent, or I disinherit you."

And what were the Earl's thoughts of Gertrude ? Here was the one drop of bitterness in the girl's cup of happiness. For some reason that she could not divine, the Earl showed signs of marked antipathy.

Once as she passed the door of the library he threw a bootjack at her. On another occasion at lunch alone with her he struck her savagely across the face with a sausage.

It was her duty to translate to the Earl his Russian correspondence. She sought in it in vain for the mystery. One day a Russian telegram was handed to the Earl. Gertrude translated it to him aloud.

" Tutchemoff went to the woman. She is dead."

On hearing this the Earl became livid with fury, in fact this was the day that he struck her with the sausage.

Then one day while the Earl was absent on a bat hunt, Gertrude, who was turning over his correspondence, with that sweet feminine instinct of interest that rose superior to ill-treatment, suddenly found the key to the mystery.

Lord Nosh was not the rightful owner of the Taws. His distant cousin of the older line, the true heir, had died in a Russian prison to which the machinations of the Earl, while Ambassador at Tschminsk, had consigned him. The daughter of this cousin was the true owner of Nosham Taws.

The family story, save only that the documents before her withheld the name of the rightful heir, lay bare to Gertrude's eye.

Strange is the heart of woman. Did Gertrude turn from the Earl with spurning? No. Her own sad fate had taught her sympathy.

Yet still the mystery remained ! Why did the Earl start perceptibly each time that he looked into her face ? Sometimes he started as much as four centimetres, so that one could distinctly see him do it. On such occasions he would hastily drain a dipper of rum and vichy water and become again the correct English gentleman.

The dénouement came swiftly. Gertrude never forgot it.

It was the night of the great ball at Nosham Taws. The whole neighbourhood was invited. How Gertrude's heart had beat with anticipation, and with what trepidation she had overhauled her scant wardrobe in order to appear not unworthy in Lord Ronald's eyes. Her resources were poor indeed, yet the inborn genius for dress that she inherited from her French mother stood her in good stead. She twined a single rose in her hair and contrived herself a dress out of a few old newspapers and the inside of an umbrella that would have graced a court. Round her waist she bound a single braid of bagstring, while a piece of old lace that had been her mother's was suspended to her ear by a thread.

Gertrude was the cynosure of all eyes. Floating to the strains of the music she presented a picture of bright girlish innocence that no one could see undisenraptured.

The ball was at its height. It was away up !

Ronald stood with Gertrude in the shrubbery.   They looked into one another's eyes.

" Gertrude," he said, " I love you."

Simple words, and yet they thrilled every fibre in the girl's costume.

" Ronald ! " she said, and cast herself about his neck.

At this moment the Earl appeared standing beside them in the moonlight.   His stern face was distorted with indignation.

" So ! " he said, turning to Ronald, " it appears that you have chosen ! "

" I have," said Ronald with hauteur.

" You prefer to marry this penniless girl rather than the heiress I have selected for you."

Gertrude looked from father to son in amazement.

" Yes," said Ronald.

" Be it so," said the Earl, draining a dipper of gin which he carried, and resuming his calm.   " Then I disinherit you. Leave this place, and never return to it."

" Come, Gertrude," said Ronald tenderly, " let us flee together."

Gertrude stood before them.   The rose had fallen from her head.   The lace had fallen from her ear and the bagstring had come undone from her waist.   Her newspapers were crumpled beyond recognition.   But dishevelled and illegible as she was, she was still mistress of herself.

" Never," she said firmly.   " Ronald, you shall never make this sacrifice for me."   Then to the Earl, in tones of ice, " There is a pride, sir, as great even as yours.   The daughter of Metschnikoff McFiggin need crave a boon from no one."

With that she hauled from her bosom the daguerreotype of her father and pressed it to her lips.

The Earl started as if shot.   " That name ! " he cried, " that face ! that photograph ! stop ! "

There ! There is no need to finish ; my readers have long since divined it.   Gertrude was the heiress.

The lovers fell into one another's arms.   The Earl's proud face relaxed.   " God bless you," he said.   The Countess and the guests came pouring out upon the lawn.   The breaking day illuminated a scene of gay congratulations.

Gertrude and Ronald were wed.   Their happiness was complete.   Need we say more ? Yes, only this.   The Earl was killed in the hunting-field a few days after.   The Countess was struck by lightning.   The two children fell down a well.   Thus the happiness of Gertrude and Ronald was complete.

W. J. LOCKE (1863–1930), *one of the most popular of modern novelists, was born at Barbados and educated at Queen's Royal College, Trinidad, and Cambridge. "The Beloved Vagabond" and "The Morals of Marcus Ordeyne" were two of his most successful books. The story below is one of "The Joyous Adventures of Aristide Pujol," the little Frenchman whom he has endued with an irresistibly attractive personality.*

THE ADVENTURE OF
THE PIG'S HEAD

ONCE upon a time Aristide Pujol found himself standing outside his Paris residence, No. 213 *bis*, Rue Saint Honoré, without a penny in the world. His last sou had gone to Madame Bidoux, who kept a small greengrocer's shop at No. 213 *bis* and rented a ridiculously small back room for a ridiculously small weekly sum to Aristide whenever he honoured the French capital with his presence. During his absence she forwarded him such letters as might arrive for him ; and as this was his only permanent address, and as he let Madame Bidoux know his whereabouts only at vague intervals of time, the transaction of business with Aristide Pujol, "Agent, No. 213 *bis*, Rue Saint Honoré, Paris," by correspondence was peculiarly difficult.

He had made Madame Bidoux's acquaintance in the dim past ; and he had made it in his usual direct and electric manner. Happening to walk down the Rue Saint Honoré, he had come upon tragedy. Madame Bidoux, fat, red of face, tearful of eye and strident of voice, held in her arms a little mongrel dog— her own precious possession—which had just been run over in the street, and the two of them filled the air with wailings and vociferation. Aristide uncovered his head, as though he were about to address a duchess, and smiled at her engagingly.

"Madame," said he, "I perceive that your little dog has a broken leg. As I know all about dogs, I will, with your permission, set the limb, put it into splints and guarantee a perfect cure. Needless to say, I make no charge for my services."

Snatching the dog from the arms of the fascinated woman, he darted in his dragon-fly fashion into the shop, gave a hundred orders to a stupefied assistant, and—to cut short a story which

Aristide told me with great wealth of detail—mended the precious dog and gained Madame Bidoux's eternal gratitude. For Madame Bidoux the world held no more remarkable man than Aristide Pujol ; and for Aristide the world held no more devoted friend than Madame Bidoux. Many a succulent meal, at the widow's expense—never more enjoyable than in summer-time when she set a little iron table and a couple of iron chairs on the pavement outside the shop—had saved him from starvation ; and many a gewgaw sent from London or Marseilles or other such remote latitudes filled her heart with pride. Since my acquaintance with Aristide I myself have called on this excellent woman, and I hope I have won her esteem, though I have never had the honour of eating pig's trotters and chou-croûte with her on the pavement of the Rue Saint Honoré. It is an honour from which, being an unassuming man, I shrink.

Unfortunately Madame Bidoux has nothing further to do with the story I am about to relate, save in one respect :—

There came a day—it was a bleak day in November, when Madame Bidoux's temporary financial difficulties happened to coincide with Aristide's. To him, unsuspicious of coincidence, she confided her troubles. He emptied the meagre contents of his purse into her hand.

" Madame Bidoux," said he with a flourish, and the air of a prince, " why didn't you tell me before ? " and without waiting for her blessing he went out penniless into the street.

Aristide was never happier than when he had not a penny piece in the world. He believed, I fancy, in a dim sort of way, in God and the Virgin and Holy Water and the Pope ; but the faith that thrilled him to exaltation was his faith in the inevitable happening of the unexpected. He marched to meet it with the throbbing pulses of a soldier rushing to victory or a saint to martyrdom. He walked up the Rue Saint Honoré, the Rue de la Paix, along the Grands Boulevards, smiling on a world which teemed with unexpectednesses, until he reached a café on the Boulevard des Bonnes Filles de Calvaire. Here he was arrested by Fate, in the form of a battered man in black, who, springing from the solitary frostiness of the terrace, threw his arms about him and kissed him on both cheeks.

" Mais, c'est toi, Pujol ! "

" C'est toi, Roulard ! "

Roulard dragged Aristide to his frosty table and ordered drinks. Roulard had played the trumpet in the regimental band in which Aristide had played the kettle-drum. During their military service they had been inseparables. Since those happy and ear-splitting days they had not met. They looked at each other and laughed and thumped each other's shoulders.

" *Ce vieux Roulard !* "

" *Ce sacré Pujol.*"

" And what are you doing ? " asked Aristide, after the first explosions of astonishment and reminiscence.

A cloud overspread the battered man's features. He had a wife and five children and played in theatre orchestras. At the present time he was trombone in the " Tournée Gulland," a touring opera company. It was not gay for a sensitive artist like him, and the trombone gave one a thirst which it took half a week's salary to satisfy. *Mais enfin, que veux-tu ?* It was life, a dog's life, but life was like that. Aristide, he supposed, was making a fortune. Aristide threw back his head, and laughed at the exquisite humour of the hypothesis, and gaily disclosed his Micawberish situation. Roulard sat for a while thoughtful and silent. Presently a ray of inspiration dispelled the cloud from the features of the battered man.

" *Tiens, mon vieux,*" said he, " I have an idea."

It was an idea worthy of Aristide's consideration. The drum of the Tournée Gulland had been dismissed for drunkenness. The vacancy had not been filled. Various executants who had drummed on approval—this being an out-week of the tour—had driven the chef d'orchestre to the verge of homicidal mania. Why should not Aristide, past master in drumming, find an honourable position in the orchestra of the Tournée Gulland ?

Aristide's eyes sparkled, his fingers itched for the drumsticks, he started to his feet.

" *Mon vieux Roulard !* " he cried, " you have saved my life. More than that, you have resuscitated an artist. Yes, an artist. *Sacré nom de Dieu !* Take me to this chef d'orchestre."

So Roulard, when the hour of rehearsal drew nigh, conducted Aristide to the murky recesses of a dirty little theatre in the Batignolles, where Aristide performed such prodigies of repercussion that he was forthwith engaged to play the drum, the kettle-drum, the triangle, the cymbals, the castagnettes and the tambourine, in the orchestra of the Tournée Gulland at the dazzling salary of thirty francs a week.

To tell how Aristide drummed and cymballed the progress of Les Huguenots, Carmen, La Juive, La Fille de Madame Angot and L'Arlésienne through France would mean the rewriting of a " Capitaine Fracasse." To hear the creature talk about it makes my mouth as a brick-kiln and my flesh as that of a goose. He was the Adonis, the Apollo, the Don Juan, the Irresistible of the Tournée. Fled truculent bass and haughty tenor before him ; from diva to moustachioed contralto in the chorus, all the ladies breathlessly watched for the fall of his handkerchief ; he was recognized, in fact, as a devil of a fellow. But in spite of these triumphs, the manipulation of the drum, kettle-drum, triangle, cymbals, castagnettes and tambourine, which at first had given him intense and childish delight, at last became invested with a mechanical monotony that almost drove him mad. All day long the thought of the ill-lit corner, on the extreme right of the orchestra, garnished with the accursed instruments of noise to which duty would compel him at eight o'clock in the evening hung over him like a hideous doom. Sweet singers of the female sex were powerless to console. He passed them by, and haughty tenor and swaggering basso again took heart of grace.

" *Mais, mon Dieu, c'est le métier !* " expostulated Roulard.

" *Sale métier !* " cried Aristide, who was as much fitted for the merciless routine of a theatre orchestra as a quagga for the shafts of an omnibus. " A beast of a trade ! One is no longer a man. One is just an automatic system of fog-signals ! "

In this depraved state of mind he arrived at Perpignan, where that befell him which I am about to relate.

Now, Perpignan is the last town of France on the Gulf of Lions, a few miles from the Spanish border. From it you can see the great white monster of Le Canigou, the pride of the Eastern Pyrenees, far, far away, blocking up the valley of the Tet, which flows sluggishly past the little town. The Quai Sadi-Carnot (is there a provincial town in France which has not a *something* Sadi-Carnot in it ?) is on the left bank of the Tet ; at one end is the modern Place Arago, at the other Le Castillet, a round, castellated red-brick fortress with curiously long and deep machicolations of the fourteenth century with some modern additions of Louis XI, who also built the adjoining Porte Notre Dame which gives access to the city. Between the Castillet and the Place Arago, the Quai Sadi-Carnot is the site of the prefecture, the Grand Hôtel, various villas and other resorts of the aristocracy. Any little street off it will lead you into the seething centre of Perpignan life—the Place de la Loge, which is a great block of old buildings surrounded on its four sides by narrow streets of shops, cafés, private houses, all with balconies and jalousies, all cramped, crumbling, Spanish, picturesque. The oldest of this conglomerate block is a corner building, the Loge de Mer, a thirteenth-century palace, the cloth exchange in the glorious days when Perpignan was a seaport and its merchant princes traded with Sultans and Doges and such-like magnificoes of the Mediterranean. But nowadays its glory has departed. Below the great gothic windows spreads the awning of a café, which takes up all the ground floor. Hugging it tight is the Mairie, and hugging that, the Hôtel de Ville. Hither does every soul in the place, at some hour or other of the day, inevitably gravitate. Lawyers and clients, doctors and patients, merchants, lovers, soldiers, market-women, loafers, horses, dogs, wagons, all crowd in a noisy medley the narrow cobble-paved streets around the Loge. Of course there are other streets, tortuous, odorous and cool, intersecting the old town, and there are various open spaces, one of which is the broad market square on one side flanked by the Théâtre Municipal.

From the theatre Aristide Pujol issued one morning after rehearsal, and, leaving his colleagues, including the ever-thirsty Roulard, to refresh themselves at a humble café hard by, went forth in search of distraction. He idled about the Place de la Loge, passed the time of day with a café waiter until the latter, with a disconcerting " *Voila! Voila!* " darted off to attend to a customer, and then strolled through the Porte Notre Dame on to the Quai Sadi-Carnot. There a familiar sound met his ears— the roll of a drum followed by an incantation in a quavering, high-pitched voice. It was the Town Crier, with whom, as with a brother artist, he had picked acquaintance the day before.

They met by the parapet of the Quai, just as Père Bracasse had come to the end of his incantation. The old man, grizzled, tanned and seamed, leant weakly against the parapet.

" How goes it, Père Bracasse ? "

" Alas, mon bon Monsieur, it goes from bad to worse," sighed the old man. " I am at the end of my strength. My voice has gone and the accursed rheumatism in my shoulder gives me atrocious pain whenever I beat the drum."

" How much more of your round have you to go ? " asked Aristide.

" I have only just begun," said Père Bracasse.

The southern sun shone from a cloudless sky ; a light, keen wind blowing from the distant snow-clad Canigou set the blood tingling. A lunatic idea flashed through Aristide's mind. He whipped the drum strap over the old man's head.

"Père Bracasse," said he, "you are suffering from rheumatism, bronchitis, fever and corns, and you must go home to bed. I will finish your round for you. Listen," and he beat such a tattoo as Père Bracasse had never accomplished in his life. " Where are your words ? "

The old man, too weary to resist and fascinated by Aristide's laughing eyes, handed him a dirty piece of paper. Aristide read, played a magnificent roll and proclaimed in a clarion voice that a gold bracelet having been lost on Sunday afternoon in the Avenue des Platanes, whoever would deposit it at the Mairie would receive a reward.

" That's all ? " he enquired.

" That's all," said Père Bracasse. " I live in the Rue Petite-de-la-Réal, No. 4, and you will bring me back the drum when you have finished."

Aristide darted off like a dragon-fly in the sunshine, as happy as a child with a new toy. Here he could play the drum to his heart's content with no score or conductor's bâton to worry him. He was also the one and only personage in the drama, concentrating on himself the attention of the audience. He pitied poor Roulard, who could never have such an opportunity with his trombone. . . .

The effect of his drumming before the Café de la Loge was electric. Shopkeepers ran out of their shops, housewives craned over their balconies to listen to him. By the time he had threaded the busy strip of the town and emerged on to the Place Arago he had collected an admiring train of urchins. On the Place Arago he halted on the fringe of a crowd surrounding a cheap-jack whose vociferations he drowned in a roll of thunder. He drummed and drummed till he became the centre of the throng. Then he proclaimed the bracelet. He had not enjoyed himself so much since he left Paris.

He was striding away, merry-eyed and happy, followed by his satellites when a prosperous-looking gentleman with a very red face, a prosperous roll of fat above the back of his collar, and the ribbon of the Legion of Honour in his button-hole, descending the steps of the great glass-covered café commanding the Place, hurried up and laid his finger on his arm.

" Pardon, my friend," said he, " what are you doing there ? "

" You shall hear, monsieur," replied Aristide, clutching the drumsticks.

" For the love of Heaven ! " cried the other hastily interrupting. " Tell me what are you doing ? "

" I am crying the loss of a bracelet, monsieur ! "

" But who are you ? "

" I am Aristide Pujol, and I play the drum, kettle-drum, triangle, cymbals, castagnettes and tambourine in the orchestra of the Tournée Gulland. And now, in my turn, may I ask to whom I have the honour of speaking ? "

" I am the Mayor of Perpignan."

Aristide raised his hat politely. "I hope to have the pleasure," said he, "of Monsieur le Maire's better acquaintance."

The Mayor, attracted by the rascal's guileless mockery, laughed.

"You will, my friend, if you go on playing that drum. You are not the Town Crier."

Aristide explained. Père Bracasse was ill, suffering from rheumatism, bronchitis, fever and corns. He was replacing him. The Mayor retorted that Père Bracasse being a municipal functionary could not transmit his functions except through the Administration. Monsieur Pujol must desist from drumming and crying. Aristide bowed to authority and unstrung his drum.

"But I was enjoying myself so much, Monsieur le Maire. You have spoiled my day," said he.

The Mayor laughed again. There was an irresistible charm and roguishness about the fellow, with his intelligent oval face, black Vandyke beard and magically luminous eyes.

"I should have thought you had enough of drums in your orchestra."

"Ah! there I am cramped!" cried Aristide. "I have it in horror, in detestation. Here I am free. I can give vent to all the aspirations of my soul!"

The Mayor mechanically moved from the spot where they had been standing. Aristide, embroidering his theme, mechanically accompanied him; and, such is democratic France, and also such was the magnetic, Ancient Mariner-like power of Aristide—did not I, myself, on my first meeting with him at Aigues-Mortes fall helplessly under the spell—that, in a few moments, the amateur Town Crier and the Mayor were walking together, side by side, along the Quai Sadi-Carnot, engaged in amiable converse. Aristide told the Mayor the story of his life—or such incidents of it as were meet for Mayoral ears—and when they parted—the Mayor to lunch, Aristide to yield up the interdicted drum to Père Bracasse—they shook hands warmly, and mutually expressed the wish that they would soon meet again.

They met again; Aristide saw to that. They met again that very afternoon in the café on the Place Arago. When Aristide entered he saw the Mayor seated at a table in the company of another prosperous, red-ribboned gentleman. Aristide saluted politely and addressed the Mayor. The Mayor saluted and presented him to Monsieur Quérin, the President of the Syndicat d'Initiative of the town of Perpignan. Monsieur Quérin saluted and declared himself enchanted at the encounter. Aristide stood gossiping until the Mayor invited him to take a place at the table and consume liquid refreshment. Aristide glowingly accepted the invitation and cast a look of triumph around the café. Not to all mortals is it given to be the boon companion of a Mayor and a President of the Syndicat d'Initiative !

Then ensued a conversation momentous in its consequences.

The Syndicat d'Initiative is a semi-official body existing in most provincial towns in France for the purpose of organizing public festivals for the citizens and developing the resources and possibilities of the town for the general amenity of visitors. Now Perpignan is as picturesque, as sun-smitten and, in spite of the icy tramontana, even as joyous a place as tourist could desire ; and the Carnival of Perpignan, as a spontaneous outburst of gaiety and pageantry, is unique in France. But Perpignan being at the end of everywhere and leading nowhere attracts very few visitors. Biarritz is on the Atlantic coast at the other end of the Pyrenees ; Hyères, Cannes and Monte Carlo on the other side of the Gulf of Lions. No English or Americans—the only visitors of any account in the philosophy of provincial France—flock to Perpignan. This was a melancholy fact bewailed by Monsieur Quérin. The town was perishing from lack of Anglo-Saxon support. Monsieur Coquereau, the Mayor, agreed. If the English and Americans came in their hordes to this paradise of mimosa, fourteenth-century architecture, sunshine and unique Carnival, the fortunes of all the citizens would be assured. Perpignan would out-rival Nice. But what could be done ?

" Advertise it," said Aristide, " Flood the English-speaking world with poetical descriptions of the place. Build a row of palatial hotels in the new part of the town. It is not known to the Anglo-Saxons."

" How can you be certain of that ? " asked Monsieur Quérin.

" Parbleu ! " he cried, with a wide gesture. " I have known the English all my life. I speak their language as I speak French or my native Provençal. I have taught in schools in England. I know the country and the people like my pocket. They have never heard of Perpignan."

His companions acquiesced sadly. Aristide, aglow with a sudden impudent inspiration, leant across the marble table.

" Monsieur le Maire and Monsieur le Président du Syndicat d'Initiative, I am sick to death of playing the drum, the kettledrum, the triangle, the cymbals, the castagnettes and the tambourine in the Tournée Gulland. I was born to higher things. Entrust to me "—he converged the finger-tips of both hands to

his bosom—" to me, Aristide Pujol, the organization of Perpignan-Ville de Plaisir, and you will not regret it."

The Mayor and the President laughed.

But my astonishing friend prevailed—not indeed to the extent
of being appointed a Petronius, *arbiter élegantiarum*, of the town of
Perpignan ; but to the extent of being employed, I fear in a sub-
ordinate capacity, by the Mayor and the Syndicat in the work of
propagandism. The Tournée Gulland found another drum and
went its tuneful but weary way ; and Aristide remained gloriously behind and rubbed his hands with glee. At last he had
found permanence in a life where heretofore had been nought
but transience. At last he had found a sphere worthy of his
genius. He began to nourish insensate ambitions. He would
be the Great Benefactor of Perpignan. All Roussillon should
bless his name. Already he saw his statue on the Quai Sadi-
Carnot.

His rise in the social scale of the town was meteoric, chiefly
owing to the goodwill of Madame Coquereau, the widowed
mother of the Mayor. She was a hard-featured old lady,
with a face that might have been made of corrugated iron
painted yellow and with the eyes of an old hawk. She dressed
always in black, was very devout and rich and narrow and iron-
willed. Aristide was presented to her one Sunday afternoon at
the Café on the Place Arago—where on Sunday afternoons all
the fashion of Perpignan assembles—and—need I say it ?—she
fell at once a helpless victim to his fascination. Accompanying
her grandmother was Mademoiselle Stéphanie Coquereau, the
Mayor's niece (a wealthy orphan, as Aristide soon learned),
nineteen, pretty, demure, perfectly brought up, who said " *Oui,
Monsieur* " and " *Non, Monsieur* " with that quintessence of
modest grace which only a provincial French Convent can
cultivate.

Aristide's heart left his body and rolled at the feet of
Mademoiselle Stéphanie. It was a way with Aristide's heart.
It was always doing that. He was of Provence and not of
Peckham Rye or Hoboken, and he could not help it.

Aristide called on Madame Coquereau, who entertained him
with sweet Frontignan wine, dry sponge cakes and conversation.
After a while he was invited to dinner. In a short space of time
he became the intimate friend of the house, and played piquet
with Madame Coquereau, and grew familiar with the family
secrets. First he learned that Mademoiselle Stéphanie would go
to a husband with two hundred and fifty thousand francs.

Aristide's heart panted at the feet of Mademoiselle Stéphanie. Further he gathered that, though Monsieur Coquereau was a personage of great dignity and importance in civic affairs, he was as but a little child in his own house. Madame Coquereau held the money-bags. Her son had but little personal fortune. He had reached the age of forty-five without being able to marry. Marriage unauthorized by Madame Coquereau meant immediate poverty and the testamentary assignment of Madame Coquereau's fortune to various religious establishments. None of the objects of Monsieur Coquereau's matrimonial desire had pleased Madame Coquereau, and none of Madame Coquereau's blushing candidates had caused a pulse in Monsieur Coquereau's being to beat the faster. The Mayor held his mother in professed adoration and holy terror. She held him in abject subjection. Aristide became the confidant, in turn, of Madame's sour philosophy of life and of Monsieur's impotence and despair. As for Mademoiselle Stéphanie, she kept on saying, " *Oui, Monsieur* " and " *Non, Monsieur,*" in a crescendo of maddening demureness.

So passed the halcyon hours. During the daytime Aristide, in a corner of the Mayor's office, drew up flamboyant circulars in English which would have put a pushing Land and Estate Agent in the New Jerusalem to the blush, and in the evening played piquet with Madame Coquereau, while Mademoiselle Stéphanie, model of modest piety, worked pure but nameless birds and flowers on her embroidery frame. Monsieur le Maire, of course, played his game of manilla at the café, after dinner, and generally came home just before Aristide took his leave. If it had not been for the presence of Mademoiselle Stéphanie, it would not have been gay for Aristide. But love gilded the moments.

On the first evening of the Carnival, which lasts nearly a fortnight in Perpignan, Aristide, in spite of a sweeter " *Oui, Monsieur* " than ever from Mademoiselle Stéphanie, made an excuse to slip away rather earlier than usual, and, front door having closed behind him, crossed the strip of gravel with a quick step and flung out of the iron gates. Now the house had an isolated position in the new quarter of the town. It was perky and modern and defaced by all sorts of oriel windows and tourelles and pinnacles which gave it a top-heavy appearance, and it was surrounded by a low brick wall. Aristide, on emerging through the iron gates, heard the sound of scurrying footsteps on the side of the wall nearest to the town, and reached the corner, just in time to see a masquer, attired in a Pierrot costume and wearing what seemed to be a pig's head, disappear round the further angle. Paying no heed to this phenomenon, Aristide lit a cigarette and walked, in anticipation of enjoyment, to the great Avenue des Plantanes where the revelry of the Carnival was being held.   Aristide was young, he loved flirtation, and flirtation flourished in the Avenue des Plantanes.

The next morning the Mayor entered his office with a very grave face.

"Do you know what has happened?   My house was broken into last night.   The safe in my study was forced open, and three thousand francs and some valuable jewellery were stolen.   *Quel malheur!*" he cried, throwing himself into a chair, and wiping his forehead.   "It is not I who can afford to lose three thousand francs at once.   If they had robbed *maman* it would have been a different matter."

Aristide expressed his sympathy.

"Whom do you suspect?" he asked.

"A robber, *parbleu!*" said the Mayor.   "The police are even now making their investigations."

The door opened and a plain-clothes detective entered the office.

"Monsieur le Maire," said he, with an air of triumph, "I know a burglar."

Both men leapt to their feet.

"Ah!" said Aristide.

"*A la bonne heure!*" cried the Mayor.

"Arrest him at once," said Aristide.

"Alas, Monsieur," said the detective, "that I cannot do.   I have called on him this morning and his wife tells me that he left for the North yesterday afternoon.   But it is José Puégas that did it.   I know his ways."

"*Tiens!*" said the Mayor reflectively.   "I know him also, an evil fellow."

"But why are you not looking for him?" exclaimed Aristide.

"Arrangements have been made," replied the detective coldly.

Aristide suddenly bethought him of the furtive masquer of the night before.

"I can put you on his track," said he, and related what he knew.

The Mayor looked dubious.   "It wasn't he," he remarked.

"José Puégas, Monsieur, would not commit a burglary in a pig's head," said the policeman, with the cutting contempt of the expert.

"It was a vow, I suppose," said Aristide, stung to irony.   "I've always heard he was a religious man."

The detective did not condescend to reply.

" Monsieur le Maire," said he, " I should like to examine the premises, and beg that you will have the kindness to accompany me."

" With the permission of Monsieur le Maire," said Aristide, " I too will come."

" Certainly," said the Mayor. " The more intelligences concentrated on the affair the better."

" I am not of that opinion," said the detective.

" It is the opinion of Monsieur le Maire," said Aristide rebukingly, " and that is enough."

When they reached the house—distances are short in Perpignan —they found policemen busily engaged with tape-measures around the premises. Old Madame Coquereau in a clean white linen dressing-jacket, bare-headed, defying the keen air, stood grim and eager in the midst of them.

" Good morning, Monsieur Pujol, what do you think of this ? "

" A veritable catastrophe," said Aristide.

She shrugged her iron shoulders. " I tell him it serves him right," she said cuttingly. " A sensible person keeps his money under his mattress and not in a tin machine by a window which any one can get at. I wonder we've not been murdered in our beds before."

" Ah, Maman ! " expostulated the Mayor of Perpignan.

But she turned her back on him and worried the policemen. They, having probed, and measured, and consulted with the detective, came to an exact conclusion. The thief had climbed over the back wall—there were his footsteps. He had entered by the kitchen door—there were the marks of infraction. He had broken open the safe—there was the helpless condition of the lock. No one in Perpignan, but José Puégas, with his bad, socialistic, Barcelona blood, could have done it. These brilliant results were arrived at after much clamour and argument and imposing procès verbal. Aristide felt strangely depressed. He had narrated his story of the pig-headed masquer to unresponsive ears. Here was a melodramatic scene in which he not only was not playing a leading part, but did not even carry a banner. To be less than a super in life's pageant was abhorrent to the nature of Aristide Pujol.

Moodily he wandered away from the little crowd. He hated the police and their airs of gods for whom exists no mystery. He did not believe in the kitchen-door theory. Why should not the thief have simply entered by the window of the study, which like the kitchen was on the ground floor ? He went round the house and examined the window by himself. No ; there were no traces of burglary. The fastenings of the outside shutters and the high window were intact. The police were right.

Suddenly his quick eye lit on something in the gravel path and his heart gave a great leap. It was a little round pink disc of confetti.

Aristide picked it up and began to dance and shake his fist at the invisible police.

"Aha ! " he cried, " now we shall see who is right and who is wrong ! "

He began to search and soon found another bit of confetti. A little farther along he discovered a third and a fourth. By using his walking-stick he discovered that they formed a trail to a point in the wall. He examined the wall. There, if his eyes did not deceive him, were evidences of mortar dislodged by nefarious toes. And there, *mirabile visu !* at the very bottom of the wall lay a little woollen pompon or tassel, just the kind of pompon that gives a finish to a pierrot's shoes. Evidently the scoundrel had scraped it off against the bricks while clambering over.

The pig-headed masquer stood confessed.

A less imaginative man than Aristide would have immediately acquainted the police with his discovery. But Aristide had been insulted. A dull, mechanical bureaucrat who tried to discover crime with a tape-measure had dared to talk contemptuously of his intelligence ! On his wooden head should be poured the vials of his contempt.

" *Tron de l'air !* " cried Aristide—a Provençal oath which he only used on sublime occasions—" It is I who will discover the thief and make the whole lot of you the laughing-stock of Perpignan."

So did my versatile friend, joyously confident in his powers, start on his glorious career as a private detective.

" Madame Coquereau," said he, that evening, while she was dealing a hand at piquet, " what would you say if I solved this mystery and brought the scoundrel to justice ? "

" To say that you would have more sense than the police, would be a poor compliment," said the old lady.

Stéphanie raised cloistral eyes from her embroidery frame. She sat in a distant corner of the formal room discreetly lit by a shaded lamp.

" You have a clue, Monsieur ? " she asked with adorable timidity.

Aristide tapped his forehead with his fore-finger. " All is there, Mademoiselle."

They exchanged a glance—the first they had exchanged—while Madame Coquereau was frowning at her cards ; and Aristide interpreted the glance as the promise of supreme reward for great deeds accomplished.

The Mayor returned early from the café, a dejected man. The loss of his hundred and twenty pounds weighed heavily on his mind. He kissed his mother sorrowfully on the cheek, his niece on the brow, held out a drooping hand to Aristide, and, subsiding into a stiff imitation Louis XVI chair, rested his elbows on its unconsoling arms and hid his face in his hands.

" My poor uncle ! You suffer so much ? " breathed Stéphanie in divine compassion.

" Little Saint ! " murmured Aristide devoutly, as he declared four aces and three queens.

The Mayor moved his head sympathetically. He was suffering from the sharpest pain in his pocket he had felt for many a day. Madame Coquereau's attention wandered from the cards.

" *Dis donc*, Fernand," she said sharply. " Why are you not wearing your ring ? "

The Mayor looked up.

" *Maman*," said he, " it is stolen."

" Your beautiful ring ? " cried Aristide.

The Mayor's ring, which he usually wore, was a remarkable personal adornment. It consisted in a couple of snakes in old gold clenching an enormous topaz between their heads. Only a Mayor could have worn it with decency.

" You did not tell me, Fernand," rasped the old lady. " You did not mention it to me as being one of the stolen objects."

The Mayor rose wearily. " It was to avoid giving you pain, *maman*. I know what a value you set upon the ring of my good Aunt Philomène."

" And now it is lost," said Madame Coquereau, throwing down her cards. " A ring that belonged to a saint. Yes, Monsieur Pujol, a saint, though she was my sister. A ring that had been blessed by His Holiness the Pope——"

" But, *maman*," expostulated the Mayor, " that was an imagination of Aunt Philomène. Just because she went to Rome and had an audience like any one else——"

" Silence, impious atheist that you are ! " cried the old lady. " I tell you it was blessed by His Holiness—and when I tell you a thing it is true. That is the son of to-day. He will call his mother a liar as soon as look at her. It was a ring beyond price. A ring such as there are few in the world. And instead of taking care of this precious heirloom, he goes and locks it away in a safe.

Ah ! you fill me with shame. Monsieur Pujol, I am sorry I can play no more, I must retire. Stéphanie, will you accompany me ? "

And gathering up Stéphanie like a bunch of snowdrops, the yellow, galvanized iron old lady swept out of the room.

The Mayor looked at Aristide and moved his arms dejectedly.

" Such are women," said he.

" My own mother nearly broke her heart because I would not become a priest," said Aristide.

" I wish I were a Turk," said the Mayor.

" I, too," said Aristide.

He took pouch and papers and rolled a cigarette.

" If there is a man living who can say he has not felt like that at least once in his life he ought to be exhibited at a fair."

" How well you understand me, my good Pujol," said Monsieur Coquereau.

The next few days passed busily for Aristide. He devoted every spare hour to his new task. He scrutinized every inch of ground between the study window and the wall ; he drew radiating lines from the point of the wall whence the miscreant had started homeward and succeeded in finding more confetti. He cross-examined every purveyor of pierrot shoes and pig's heads in Perpignan. His researches soon came to the ears of the police, still tracing the mysterious José Puégas. A certain good-humoured brigadier whose Catalan French Aristide found difficult to understand, but with whom he had formed a derisory kind of friendship, urged him to desist from the hopeless task.

" *Jamais de la vie !* " he cried—" The honour of Aristide Pujol is at stake."

The thing became an obsession. Not only his honour but his future was at stake. If he discovered the thief, he would be the most talked of person in Perpignan. He would know how to improve his position. He would rise to dizzy heights. Perpignan-Ville de Plaisir would acclaim him as its saviour. The Government would decorate him. And finally, both the Mayor and Madame Coquereau would place the blushing and adorable Mademoiselle Stéphanie in his arms and her two hundred and fifty thousand francs dowry in his pocket. Never before had so dazzling a prize shimmered before him in the near distance.

On the last Saturday night of the Carnival, there was a special *corso* for the populace in the Avenue des Plantanes, the long splendid Avenue of plane trees just outside the Porte Notre Dame, which is the special glory of Perpignan. The masquers danced to three or four bands. They threw confetti and *ser-*

pentins. They rode hobby-horses and beat each other with bladders. They joined in bands of youths and maidens and whirled down the Avenue in Bacchic madness. It was a *corso blanc,* and every one wore white—chiefly modifications of Pierrot costume—and every one was masked. Chinese lanterns hung from the trees and in festoons around the bandstands and darted about in the hands of the revellers. Above, great standard electric lamps shed their white glare upon the eddying throng casting a myriad of grotesque shadows. Shouts and laughter and music filled the air.

Aristide in a hideous red mask and with a bag of confetti under his arm, plunged with enthusiasm into the revelry. To enjoy yourself you only had to throw your arm round a girl's waist and swing her off wildly to the beat of the music. If you wanted to let her go you did so ; if not, you talked in the squeaky voice that is the recognized etiquette of the carnival. On the other hand any girl could catch you in her grip and sweep you along with her. Your mad career generally ended in a crowd and a free fight of confetti. There was one fair masquer, however, to whom Aristide became peculiarly attracted. Her movements were free, her figure dainty and her repartee, below her mask, more than usually piquant.

" This hurly-burly," said he, drawing her into a quiet eddy of the stream, " is no place for the communion of two twin souls."

" *Beau masque,*" said she, " I perceive that you are a man of much sensibility."

" Shall we find a spot where we can mingle the overflow of our exquisite natures ? "

" As you like."

" *Allons ! Hop !* " cried he, and seizing her round the waist danced through the masquers to the very far end of the Avenue.

" There is a sequestered spot round here," he said.

They turned. The sequestered spot, a seat beneath a plane tree, with a lonesome arc-lamp shining full upon it, was occupied.

" It's a pity ! " said the fair unknown.

But Aristide said nothing. He stared. On the seat reposed an amorous couple. The lady wore a white domino and a black mask. The cavalier, whose arm was around the lady's waist, wore a pig's head, and a clown or Pierrot's dress.

Aristide's eyes fell upon the shoes. On one of them the pompon was missing.

The lady's left hand tenderly patted the cardboard snout of her lover. The fierce light of the arc lamp caught the hand and revealed, on the fourth finger, a topaz ring, the topaz held in its place by two snakes' heads.

Aristide stared for two seconds ; it seemed to him two centuries. Then he turned simply, caught his partner again, and with a " *Allons, Hop !* " raced back to the middle of the throng. There, in the crush, he unceremoniously lost her, and sped like a maniac to the entrance gates. His friend the brigadier happened to be on duty. He unmasked himself, dragged the police agent aside, and breathless, half-hysterical, acquainted him with the astounding discovery.

" I was right, *mon vieux !* There at the end of the Avenue you will find them. The pig-headed prowler I saw, with *my* pompon missing from his shoe, and his *bonne amie* wearing the stolen ring. Ah ! you police people with your tape-measures and your José Puégas ! It is I, Aristide Pujol, who have to come to Perpignan to teach you your business ! "

" What do you want me to do ? " asked the brigadier stolidly.

" Do ? " cried Aristide. " Do you think I want you to kiss them and cover them with roses ? What do you generally do with thieves in Perpignan ? "

" Arrest them," said the brigadier.

" *Eh bien !* " said Aristide. Then he paused—possibly the drama of the situation striking him. " No, wait. Go and find them. Don't take your eyes off them. I will run and fetch Monsieur le Maire and he will identify his property—*et puis nous aurons la scène à faire.*"

The stout brigadier grunted an assent and rolled monumentally down the Avenue. Aristide, his pulses throbbing, his heart exulting, ran to the Mayor's house. He was rather a panting triumph than a man. He had beaten the police of Perpignan. He had discovered the thief. He was the hero of the town. Soon would the wedding bells be playing. . . . He envied the marble of the future statue. He would like to be on the pedestal himself.

He dashed past the maid-servant who opened the door and burst into the prim salon. Madame Coquereau was alone, just preparing to retire for the night. Mademoiselle Stéphanie had already gone to bed.

" *Mon Dieu*, what is all this ? " she cried.

" Madame," shouted he, " glorious news. I have found the thief ! "

He told his tale. Where was Monsieur le Maire ?

" He has not yet come back from the café."

" I'll go and find him," said Aristide.

"And waste time? Bah!" said the iron-faced old lady, catching up a black silk shawl. "I will come with you and identify the ring of my sainted sister Philomène. Who should know it better than I?"

"As you like, Madame," said Aristide.

Two minutes found them on their journey. Madame Coquereau, in spite of her sixty-five years, trudged along with springing step.

"They don't make metal like me, nowadays," she said scornfully.

When they arrived at the gate of the Avenue, the police on guard saluted. The mother of Monsieur le Maire was a power in Perpignan.

"Monsieur," said Aristide, in lordly fashion, to a policeman, "will you have the goodness to make a passage through the crowd for Madame Coquereau, and then help the Brigadier Pésac to arrest the burglar who broke into the house of Monsieur le Maire?"

The man obeyed, went ahead clearing the path with the unceremoniousness of the law, and Aristide giving his arm to Madame Coquereau followed gloriously. As the impressive progress continued the revellers ceased their revels and followed in the wake of Aristide. At the end of the Avenue Brigadier Pésac was on guard. He approached.

"They are still there," he said.

"Good," said Aristide.

The two police-officers, Aristide and Madame Coquereau turned the corner. At the sight of the police the guilty couple started to their feet. Madame Coquereau pounced like a hawk on the masked lady's hand.

"I identify it," she cried. "Brigadier, give these people in charge for theft."

The white masked crowd surged around the group, in the midst of which stood Aristide transfigured. It was his supreme moment. He flourished in one hand his red mask and in the other a pompon which he had extracted from his pocket.

"This I found," said he, "beneath the wall of Monsieur le Maire's garden. Behold the shoe of the accused."

The crowd murmured their applause and admiration. Neither of the prisoners stirred. The pig's head grinned at the world with its inane, painted leer. A rumbling voice beneath it said:

"We will go quietly."

"*Attention s'il vous plaît*," said the policeman, and each holding a prisoner by the arm they made a way through the crowd. Madame Coquereau and Aristide followed close behind.

" What did I tell you ? " cried Aristide to the brigadier.

" It's Puégas, all the same," said the brigadier, over his shoulder.

" I bet you it's not," said Aristide, and striding swiftly to the back of the male prisoner whipped off the pig's head, and revealed to the petrified throng the familiar features of the Mayor of Perpignan.

Aristide regarded him for two or three seconds open-mouthed, and then fell back into the arms of the Brigadier Pésac screaming with convulsive laughter. The crowd caught the infection of merriment. Shrieks filled the air. The vast mass of masqueraders held their sides, swayed helplessly, rolled in heaps, men and women, tearing each other's garments as they fell.

Aristide, deposited on the ground by the Brigadier Pésac, laughed and laughed. When he recovered some consciousness of surroundings, he found the Mayor bending over him and using language that would have made Tophet put his fingers in its ears. He rose. Madame Coquereau shook her thin fists in his face.

" Imbecile ! Triple fool ! " she cried.

Aristide turned tail and fled. There was nothing else to do.

And that was the end of his career at Perpignan. Vanished were the dreams of civic eminence ; melted into thin air the statue on the Quai Sadi-Carnot ; faded, too, the vision of the modest Stéphanie crowned with orange-blossom ; gone for ever the two hundred and fifty thousand francs. Never since Alnaschar kicked over his basket of crockery was there such a hideous welter of shattered hopes.

If the Mayor had been allowed to go disguised to the Police Station, he could have disclosed his identity and that of the lady in private to awe-stricken functionaries. He might have forgiven Aristide. But Aristide had exposed him to the derision of the whole of Roussillon and the never-ending wrath of Madame Coquereau. Ruefully Aristide asked himself the question : why had the Mayor not taken him into the confidence of his masquerading escapade ? Why had he not told him of the pretty widow, whom, unknown to his mother, he was courting ? Why had he permitted her to wear the ring which he had given her so as to spite his sainted Aunt Philomène ? And why had he gone on wearing the pig's head after Aristide had told him of his suspicions ? Ruefully Aristide found no answers save in the general chuckle-headedness of mankind.

It was his supreme moment

" If it hadn't been such a good farce I should have wept like a cow," said Aristide, after relating this story. " But every time I wanted to cry, I laughed. *Nom de Dieu !* You should have seen his face ! And the face of Madame Coquereau ! She opened her mouth wide showing ten yellow teeth and squealed like a rabbit ! Oh, it was a good farce ! He was very cross with me," he added after a smiling pause, " and when I got back to Paris I tried to pacify him."

" What did you do ? " I asked.

" I sent him my photograph," said Aristide.

L. W. M. LOCKHART (1831–1882) *was the nephew of John Gibson Lockhart, the biographer of Sir Walter Scott. As a soldier he served in many parts of the world, and was correspondent to " The Times " during the Franco-Prussian war. He wrote a number of novels distinguished for their humour and delicacy of perception, and was a celebrated contributor to " Blackwood's Magazine," in which this rollicking tale of the military reserves appeared.*

A NIGHT WITH THE VOLUN-TEERS OF STRATHKINAHAN

O NE autumn day, a good many years ago, I was taking mine ease in mine inn in Edinburgh, when it was announced to me that a visitor, by the name of Captain Cumming, was waiting below. I occupied the interval between the announcement and his appearance in the room in mentally calling the roll of my acquaintances, but failed to discover any one answering to this description ; nor could I tax myself with knowing any member of the clan. From the Red Comyn who was made " siccar " end of in the olden time, to the Black Cumming who threatens us with the immediate end of Time itself, all the clan Cumming " were to me like shadows." The difficulty was (not immediately) solved by the entrance of Tom Finlayson, not a few years ago my friend and brother subaltern in the —th Hussars.

" Hulloa, Peter ! " I exclaimed, using his regimental misnomer—which, written in full, was " Blue Peter "—" I'm delighted to see you ; and how are you ? and what are you ? and where are you ? and what will you drink ? Take a weed and bring yourself to an anchor ; and, by the quality of mercy, let my hand alone and spare at least my trigger finger ; " for Peter was strong in his friendly feelings, and expressed them strongly upon such occasions by collecting one's fingers into a sort of fascine and then squeezing them with the full power of his vice-like grasp. " But where is your friend ? " I went on.

" What friend ? " replied Peter.

" Why, Captain Cumming, of course ; I suppose he came with you."

" Captain Cumming ! " said Peter ; " why, hang it !—I'm —you don't mean to say you don't—eh ? "

366

Peter had never been a lucid expositor of his ideas, but there was a haziness about this which led my gaze to his nose, the tints on which had given rise to his sobriquet, and had undoubtedly derived their own origin from habits not unconnected with a rather hurried close of his military career.

Peter, still sensitive about his tints, read my eye like a book and laid his fingers nervously on the many-coloured feature. " Hang it ! " he cried, " don't stare so, and listen to the end of a fellow's sentence. I was going to say that you don't positively assert that you don't know who Captain Cumming is ? "

" Yes, I do assert that I know nothing about him."

" Well, he is in this room."

" Oh ! is he ? " said I banteringly, now convinced of Peter's melancholy state, but determined to humour him for the sake of the furniture. " Of course—not so bad—ha ! ha !—pray introduce me."

" Now then, look here," burst out Peter, " I'm Captain Cumming ! "

" Oh ! I understand now. All right, Peter ; the rose by any other name, etc., and of course I'm safe ; but you're not half disguised. Let me recommend a beard, a dark wig, and a lick of flesh-coloured paint on the—you know ; and what have you broken for ? and where are you off to ? in short, let me hear all about it ; " and I drew two chairs to the fire, and prepared to receive in comfort a recital of my friend's pecuniary embarrassments and his scheme of flight from the Philistine.

" Tut, tut ! there's no deception, no mystery ; can't you understand ? I've changed my name for good and all—got a property by my wife, and taken her name."

I congratulated him heartily on his good fortune, and added, " I suppose the ' Captain ' is a little honorary prefix of your own invention built on the ruins of that cornetcy which——"

" No, it isn't."

" What ! did you acquire that by your wife too ? "

" No ; I'll tell you. You see, though in right of my wife I'm a landed proprietor, the property in question does not yield a very large revenue, and, moreover, what there is of it is a good deal burdened ; and so, when we went down to take up our abode there, we found it rather difficult to make the ends meet, and therefore, to supplement our income, and give me some occupation at the same time, I accepted the appointment of Adjutant of the 2nd Administrative Battalion of Keltshire Volunteers. My property lies in that county, so it suits very well ; and that's how I stand before you, transformed from ex-Cornet Tom Finlayson into Captain Cumming."

" And how do you like the work ? " I inquired.

" Oh, very well ; the colonel does very little, so I have the corps pretty much in my own hands, and can work out my own system."

This was said with some dignity, and I had much difficulty in repressing a grim smile as I thought of Tom's military antecedents and the system likely to spring from them.

" Nothing like system," he went on. " I carry out old Chalk's —th Hussar system as much as possible. I hated Chalk, and he hated me ; but I recognize his military talent, and I have made use of him I can tell you ; and, though I say it that shouldn't, you'll find few corps that can walk round the 2d Ad. Batt. of the Keltshire Volunteers. I took 'em over, sir, like a lump of clay, and my what-d'ye-call-it hand has moulded them into a—a—moulded them, sir ! The worst of the business is that the fellows won't stick to it. You drill them up to the highest pitch of perfection and then they leave you. You never saw such a fickle, captious set of devils as I have to deal with. They're always taking offence—sometimes with their officers, sometimes with me, and very often with my system—and then they resign ; so that though the corps is a crack corps, it is a very small one. Three companies have already been broken up, and if another goes, the 2d Ad. Batt. of the Keltshire Volunteers will collapse—the adjutancy will collapse—and Captain Cumming will also collapse financially. Now another company is in a very shaky state, which makes me horribly anxious and uneasy. It (the shaky company, the Strathkinahan company) has lately been transferred from the Kippershire county corps to ours. Strathkinahan is in our county, but in a part of it which dovetails itself far into Kippershire, so that the men are in feeling rather Kippershire than Keltshire men, more especially that they are all on the property of Lord Worrycow, the great Strathkinahan proprietor. Well, these fellows don't like the transfer, and won't co-operate at all. They lost their captain some time before they joined us, and being ordered to select his successor from our county, they keep shilly-shallying and doing nothing, much provoked thereto (I understand) by their lieutenant and ensign— the one a fellow who distils whisky on a large scale, and the other a sheep-farmer who largely consumes it—both, I believe, so thoroughly inefficient, that either the corps will not select them for promotion or they themselves decline to be promoted. I'll be hanged if I know what they want ! but the result of it will certainly be that if they don't get a good captain to keep them together they will fade away like the other three companies, and then good-bye to my appointment.

"Well, I've done what I could by writing threats and re-monstrances—all to no purpose; so now I am going down to beat up their quarters in person. I have a man in my eye who would make a first-rate captain for them; and if I can only get them to elect him, the company will be saved, and so will be my adjutancy; so I am determined that they *shall* elect him, by fair means or foul. Couldn't you make a run down with me, and then come on for a few days to my place and try your hand at grouse-driving? It's a glorious district—splendid scenery, and all that—and I'm sure the natives will amuse you; and then your diplomatic talents might be of immense assistance in helping an old friend out of a difficulty."

I had some ten days at my disposal at the time, so I readily agreed to Tom's proposal, and the next day saw us *en route* for Strathkinahan.

It will not do, for obvious reasons, to describe too accurately the geographical position of Strathkinahan. Suffice it to say that it lies far away out of the beaten tracks of men, and that he who would behold it must undergo a varied yet tedious journey, with perils by land and perils by water, and the equally important Highland element of whisky. Everything, however—even a Highland journey—must have an end, and at last, amid pelting rain and howling wind, our jaded horses were pulled up in the dark opposite the "Bodach-beg Inn and Hotel."

"Here we are," said Tom; "we are to sleep here, and have our meeting with the corps in the barn behind the house. I wonder if the officers have come; I asked them to dine with us. How infernally dark and quiet it all is! Kick the door, driver, and rouse them up."

A long onslaught by the driver's hoofs on the door produced no effect.

"Break the window," shouted Tom; and the driver, finding no other missile handy, again had recourse to his left boot, which he hurled through a lower pane. This destruction of property at once had the desired effect.

Lights shone in the windows, dogs barked, and at last the door was half opened and a head showed itself warily in the aperture. It was the head of an angry man, and from it pro-ceeded winged words of wrath.

"Gang on! gang on! this meenut; I've tell't ye a'ready there's nae mair whusky in the inns, and if there was, there's

nane for a drucken auld carle like you. A Collector ! a bonny
Collector ! I'll collect ye ! and it'll be fower and saxpence for
the peen o' glass, and if ye dinna pay it this meenut ye shall
march hame on your hose, for deil a sicht o' yer damned auld
brogue shall ye get this nicht without the siller."

"The man's a maniac," cried Tom, springing past me and
pouncing on the orator like a tiger, whom throttling, he thrust
back into the house. "What in the name of all the whiskies do
you mean, you jabbering idiot ? Whisky ! I don't want any
of the abomination. We want the dinner and the rooms and the
beds we ordered. Don't you know me—Captain Cumming ?
I was here fishing last summer ; and didn't you get my letter,
you numskull ? "

"Captain Cumming ! is it you, sir ? Wha wad have
expeckit yer honour at siccan a time o' year ? I made sure it
was the Collector ; he's on the ramble this eight days past,
drinking three days here till I pit him oot, and five up i' the
bothy, and noo he's hunting for drink heigh and laigh—ragin'
like a bear ; for he would soom the Spey in spate if it ran wi'
Talusker or Glenleevat."

"But my letter, man, my letter ? Did you not get it ? "

"I got nae letter, sir. Ye see, the postman gaed aff a week
sin' to see his freens up Appin way, and there's been nae chance
tae get a letter without sending ance errand the fifteen mile.
But come in, gentlemen ; beds ye shall ha'e and rooms, but for
the denner I dinna ken what to say ; but I'll speak to the wife."
With which he ushered us into a room, fireless and cold, yet
stuffy withal, and pregnant with the odours of departed peat
and whisky long ago consumed. Leaving his candle, he retired
hastily to consult the guidwife upon the serious crisis.

"Well, this is a nice state of things," said Tom ; "but I wrote
to the Volunteers a fortnight ago, so they must have had time to
get their warning before the confounded postman went off for
his holiday—fancy a single-handed postman daring to have a
holiday !—so we're sure to have them here ; and even if we
have a bad dinner and unaired rooms, it's only for one night,
for we'll get the business over this evening and be off home
to-morrow morning."

The landlord shortly after returned and told us, with many
apologies, that ham and eggs, a fowl, and perhaps "a bit braxy"
would be our dinner, assuring us at the same time that his
statement as to the whisky, outside, was only a humane fiction
devised for the Collector's own good, and that there was an
abundance of the best Glenlivet down below. He added ruefully

that " the bodach " (meaning the Collector) had been lurking about the premises, and had taken advantage of the temporary confusion consequent on our arrival to effect a lodgment in the kitchen, where he was again " makin' himself most ootrageous " and resisting all attempts at eviction—physically with his fists, and morally with the argument that he was there on military duty.

" Ye see," explained the landlord, " he's in thae Strath-kinahan Volunteers, and bein' ' on the beer,' as ye may say, he's gotten it into his head that he has a tryst here this night wi' his commandin' offisher—the Earl, I'm thinking'—which shows that the Collector is far through ; for when he's in his ordinary he cares for nane, and wad break tryst wi' the archangel Gabriel himsel', if he had the chance."

A light seemed to break on Tom (who, by-the-bye, had never visited the corps since its incorporation with his battalion). " Who is this Collector ? " he inquired.

" Weel, sir, he's no exacklee a Collector himsel', but he aye gets it as a kin' o' title ; his fayther aye got it, but I'm thinking it wad be his grandfayther was the Collector."

" And what is his name ? "

" Shooliter."

" Shoeleather ? "

" Shooliter."

" That's a queer name ; I never heard it before."

" It's no exacklee his name jist, but a byname from the bit farm. ' Hamish Shooliter, the Collector,' that's him in full," said the landlord, as if summing up and closing the discussion.

" But he must have a name—a surname I mean," said Tom.

" Weel, I suppose he wull ; it'll be Cawmill maist likely."

Tom hurriedly consulted his notebook. " By Jove ! just as I expected," he exclaimed ; " ' Ensign James Campbell, Shooliter Farm, Glencroaky ; ' why, this beastly Collector is the ensign, and his tryst is to dine with us here to-night ! "

" Aweel," said the landlord, " nensign's the word ; for he's been aye croonin' to himsel' as if he was discoorsin' with some ither body. He's been aye sayin' in a fierce voice, ' Nensign ! Nensign Hamish ! Nensign Shooliter, you're drunk, sir ! You're not fit for t' nensign ! Shoulder arms and faal oot, Nensign Cawmil ! ' and then he answers himsel' in a quate fleeching way, ' Jist anither glass o' tuddy afore I fall, my lord ; the tuddy's goot ; it's easy to tak'. I'm a Collector and a nensign, and anither glass can hairm naither the tane nor the tither.' And aye the fierce voice again, ' Shooliter ! attention ! to the right

half face ! to the devil with you, Shooliter ! quick march ! '
And syne he greets.''

Tom now shortly explained to the landlord the new position
which he occupied to the Volunteers of Strathkinahan—told him
of the meeting arranged for that evening, and that the officers
were expected to join us at dinner. " The lieutenant,'' he
continued, " is a Mr. McTavish of Glensnork ; do you know
him ? ''

" I ken him weel,'' replied the landlord ; " he was here wi'
Shooliter for his first three days, preparing, he aye said, for his
' prospection ' ; but he wearied o' the Collector and misca'd
the whusky for having nae bite wi' it ; sae he gaed aff wi' the
doctor to the new inns at Mairdroukit, for a chainge o' scene and
speerits ; but he'll be here, the corby, when he smells drink for
naething.''

" And the doctor, he was invited too—do you know anything
of him ? ''

" Fine that—a dacent nice man ; he'll be wi' Glensnorruk,
nae doot, and they'll be comin' thegither. If the doctor was to
come it'll be a' richt, for he'll baith come himsel' and bring the
tither.''

I was this day a travelled and a hungry man ; it was now
past seven o'clock, and I by no means saw the advantage of
hanging my dinner-hour on such a vague contingency as the
arrival of these worthies, so with some decision I asked Tom
" in how many minutes we should order dinner to be served ? ''

" Well,'' said Tom, " I asked these fellows for seven o'clock
sharp, but we must give them a little law. The roads are bad,
and an engagement in Strathkinahan is different from an engagement in Belgravia ; besides, the cooking will take time : we'll
give them three-quarters of an hour and then sit down. Dinner
at a quarter to eight, landlord—places for five ; you must have
another fowl and more ham and eggs ; and look here, if your
friend the Collector has not collected his senses by dinner-time,
don't let him come up—d'ye hear ? ''

" I'll see to him, sir, nae fear ; and now I'll show you your
rooms, gentlemen.''

When I was finishing my toilette Tom appeared. His air
was mysterious, and he shut the door carefully.

" You see,'' he said, " what a queer lot of people I have got
to do with here ; the chances are we shall have no meeting at
all, or if we do, that the meeting will be, like the ' United Brick
Lane Temperance Association,' drunk ; but if they *do* come,
confound them ! drunk or sober, I'll carry my point and make

them elect my man, Sir William M'Vittie—I swear I will.   I have
had another talk with the landlord, and he now admits that he
knows more of the politics of the matter than he pretended at
first.   They're all dead against the transfer—which, however, is
a *fait accompli*—and I suppose they have got it into their woolly
brains that by refusing to elect a Keltshire man as captain they
will prevent the practical working out of the matter.   The landlord thinks they'll come, however, for the sake of the liquor—
which it appears their late captain used to stand freely—but,
being come, will give fair words and try to evade any decision.
But we'll take the fowler in his own gin ; and I've been thinking
of a dodge, if you'll help me—will you ? "

" Of course I will," I replied ; " I'll assassinate the Collector
if necessary, or anything."

" Well, then, I'll introduce you to the meeting as a tremendous
swell of some sort—something between a Field-Marshal and a
Prime Minister, but, above all things, as a special friend and
confidant of the Queen's—stay, why shouldn't you be the
Inspector-General of the Volunteers ? The very thing ; so you
shall be.   When the right moment comes you'll address them ;
and if, with this hint, you don't carry my point for me, all I can
say is, you've degenerated since the old Newbridge days, when
you canvassed two Roman Catholic parishes successfully in the
Orange interest as The O'Clancy More. What did it then ?
why, blarney and poteen. With the Irish Celt these are specifics.
Try his Caledonian brother with the same. Of course you'll
feel your way and be cautious, and take your time from me.
I'm a little nervous about the doctor ; we must feel his pulse at
dinner, and either make him a conspirator or not, according to
his symptoms.   Now, let us go down ; I'm as hungry as a hunter.
Stay, we must christen you first—what are you to be ? Not
more than a general and a knight, I think, to begin with. We
can easily promote you as public enthusiasm warms up. So
come along, General Sir Hercules O'Halloran, K.C.B.—that
ought to fetch them. You're a trifle young for a colonel even,
but you're big and burly, and the doctor's the only one who's
the least likely to suspect, and I can tell him, if necessary, that the
Queen insisted on your promotion for services at Court. Come on."

We had not been long in the sitting-room when a sound of
approaching wheels was heard, and a confused murmur of many
voices, and on looking out of the window, we beheld, by the
dusky light of a torch, a gig which had drawn up at the door.
It contained two human figures, and was surrounded by a crowd
of indistinct forms, who had apparently arrived with it.

"The doctor and the lieutenant, of course," said Tom, "thank goodness ; and these weird shapes must be the corps : well, they shall have a captain to-night ; and now for dinner." He rang the bell, which the landlord answered. "Is that the lieutenant who arrived just now ? " inquired Tom.

"It's Glensnorruk himsel', sir, and the doctor wi' him safe enough ; and there's a drove o' billies come alang wi' them. Maist likely they'll ha'e been waitin' up at the bothy till he cam' by ; between oorsel's, I'm thinkin' there's mair gangs on at that bothy than the gauger kens o', but it's no' for the like o' me——"

"Oh, hang the bothy ! ask the lieutenant and the doctor to come up."

In a few moments we heard a peculiar sound on the wooden stairs—a hurtling, grinding, bumping sound—suggesting the idea that some heavy body was being propelled upwards by an agency not altogether successful in resisting the tendency of the said body to gravitate to the bottom of the stairs. Occasional crashes took place, when both appeared to be involved in a common downfall. These crashes were succeeded by guttural sounds of the human voice, which I conjectured to be profane swearing in Gaelic. The ascent was, however, achieved, and there was a repetition of the sounds along the passage leading to our room, alternated with quick whispers of entreaty, expostulation, and wrath. A heavy bump against our door announced that the expedition, whatever it might be, had arrived. There was a pause. Tom and I looked at each other.

"What the deuce can it be ? " he said.

"Somebody very drunk," I replied, "taking care of somebody rather worse ; the Collector, for choice."

At this moment the door was slowly opened, and an arm, terminating in a very evil and claw-like hand, was extended into the room and commenced a sawing vertical action in the air, that might mean deprecation, but was probably the result of heavy leverage going on at some other part of its proprietor's unseen body.

"Come in," cried Tom, "come in " ; but the saw only worked more vigorously, and the fingers were clinched as if in intense muscular exertion.

"Stay out then," shouted Tom in a rage, whereupon the saw worked for a few strokes with terrific vehemence, and a shoulder and eventually a head made their appearance. The head was a bald head, decorated on either side with a high and tapering horn of black hair ; the face was swarthy and dingy, pierced with a pair of Chinese-looking eyes, and corrugated with a wild assortment of smiles, or rather grins, which broke out independently all over the face, cancelling and neutralizing the expression of each other in a most puzzling manner. The arm continued to saw, and the horned head was butted backwards and forwards as if in salutation.

" Mephistopheles ! " I exclaimed involuntarily.

" Her name's McTaveesh, sir—McTaveesh of Glenschnorruk, sir ; Rifled Lifteenant, sir," said the head.

" Oh ! Mr. McTavish," said Tom, " how do you do ? I'm glad to see you ; won't you come in, though ? "

" How doo yew doo ? and how are yew ? and how doo yew doo?" went the head, as if mechanically repeating some formula.

" Very well, thanks ; but come in," said Tom.

" Can't," replied the head.

" What ? " said Tom.

" Not able," said the head.

" Why not ? " said Tom.

The head tossed one of its horns back indicatively to the door and murmured, " The Collecthur."

" Where ? " cried Tom.

" On her ither airm and leg," replied the head.

" Why, damme ! he's a regular old man of the sea, this infernal Collector ! " shouted Tom.

" Run him in, Mr. McTavish, and let's see him ; give a tug ; pull away—all your strength—there ! " and the head, followed by its body, shot comet-like into the room and subsided on the floor, leaving behind it, inside the door, and on the perpendicular, an Apparition.

" The Collector ! " said McTavish, picking himself up and extending another claw, by way of introduction, in the direction of the new arrival. It was satisfactory to see this historical character at last.

He was a tallish elderly man, with a very red face, a fixed and flaming eye, and white hair, on the top of which was perched, somewhat defiantly, a round drum-shaped boy's cap with a tassel at the side—a head-dress evidently filched from the nursery below.

He wore tartan trousers and a black dress-coat, with what are called " weepers " on the cuffs. On the whole, his appearance was not disappointing. We tried to keep our gravity, and Tom to be courteous.

" How do you do, Mr. a—a—Collector ? " he said.

The Collector spoke not a word, but elevated his arm with the gesture of a minister bespeaking attention for grace before meat, and remained in this attitude, like the lion rampant in the Scottish shield. I think he had some hazy notion of performing a military salute, but was deterred by considerations of equilibrium.

" Won't you sit down ? " said Tom, trying to look as if the attitude of the lion rampant was perfectly normal and expected. There was no answer. The fixed eye had shifted its angle and glued itself to a bottle of sherry which stood on the table ; and the mind, such as it was, that shone through that eye was in that bottle and nowhere else.

" Hadn't he better sit down, Tom ? " I interposed, treating the Collector as a lay figure.

" Certainly," said Tom.

" Well, then, here goes ; " and I poured out a glass of sherry and advanced towards the Collector. " Take a glass of sherry, ensign ? " I said. He shot out the paw to its full extent, and slid one foot forward in my direction. I took a step back, still holding out the shining bait. Out went the paw again, and another shuffling pace was effected ; and so on and so on till we got opposite the sofa, when I turned upon him and decanted him into it, giving him the wine by way of reward.

This he devoured, and then letting the glass fall and break on the floor, again, as if nothing had happened, fastened his burning orbs on the bottle. It was evidently fruitless to attempt any conversation with the wretch, so we left him to his contemplation, and Tom turned his attention to Mr. McTavish.

This gentleman was, no doubt, according to the Strath-kinahan standard, very sober. By comparison he certainly was, but I am inclined to think he was indebted for this happy state of things less to personal abstinence than to the quelling influence of two sober Sassenachs and a certain feeling of being on a superior moral elevation to the Collector. He stood up with his thumbs stuck into the arm-holes of his waistcoat, his head carried low, as if preparing to butt, and every particular square inch of his visage working with a spasmodic action.

His English was broken and almost unintelligible, and every sentence was preceded, accompanied and followed by a series of sputterings and hootings which, with the working of his face, I could refer to no mental emotion whatsoever.

Mephistopheles, the Black Dwarf, the Gorilla, Waterton's Nondescript, the laughing hyena, the horned screech-owl, and the vampire were a few of the ideas instantly suggested by the contemplation of this Highlandman.

" Well, Mr. McTavish," said Tom, " so you got my letter

all right ; I suppose you warned the corps, and I hope we shall have a good meeting and get through our business ? "

" Shess, captain—that's adjutant, shess, sir. Letter ? shess, Corps come ? shess. Business ? tit, tit, tit ! no business." Then after a pause, and with an insinuating assortment of puckers playing all over his face, " Bheil Gaelig a'gad ? "

" What ? " said Tom.

" Spoke Gaelic ? tit hish ! "

" No," said Tom.

" No spokes ? act tit ! no spoke Gaelic ? "

" But we *have* business, Mr. McTavish, and very important business too."

" Shess, sir, shess, to be certainly, captain, major, adjutant, but no spokes ? none ? not a few ? "

" Devil a word," said Tom testily.

" To be surely, tevil a word, ach tit ! "

" This is healthy," said Tom, forgetting his manners and looking round at me with a shrug. The lieutenant also looked at me, and, catching his eye, I thought I read in it symptoms that he might speak better and stick more to the point if he chose. The instant our eyes met he fired off his " bheil Gaelig a'gad ? " at me.

" No," said Tom ; " this is a general, and a great friend of the Queen's, and he couldn't think of speaking it."

" Ach ! she's a Queen's freend ? and no spokes ? Queen spoke a few ? "

" Not a single one," said Tom ; " she'd be ashamed to do it."

" Tit, tit, tit ! to be surely, Sassenach Queen—no spoke."

" But about business, Mr. McTavish——" A diversion in his favour was, however, created by the entrance of the dinner and a sudden movement on the part of the Collector. He had sat perfectly motionless and staring at the bottle ; but his line of vision being intersected by the waiter, he uttered a low moan, rose from the sofa, and, with a stride and a plunge, made the door and lurched out of the room.

In the depths of his drunken Celtic inner-consciousness, the fellow was probably offended.

" Ensign Cawmil—jist a little peety, she's no greatly hersel' the nicht," said the lieutenant. " She's a pretty fellow, ferry pretty, a good offisher, a good ensign—in Gaelic ; but the nicht she's no jist hersel' ; no, sir, no jist hersel'. But we'll not be angry or quarrel her, no, no ; tit, tit ! hish ! " The last was semi-interrogative, semi-deprecatory.

" Well," said Tom, " I can't say I think it creditable. Being drunk and speechless may make a very excellent officer in Gaelic, but in any other language he would be considered a disgrace to his commission ; and when I was only to be here for one night, he might, I think, have contrived to be sober."

" To be surely," replied the lieutenant ; " and she'd be trying for four days to do it."

" To do what ? "

" To lay the whisky, to be sure."

" To lay it in, I suppose you mean—and he seems to have succeeded to a marvel."

" Ach ! no, tit, tit ! to lay it with bitters *and more.*"

" Well, hang me if I ever heard such a recipe ! more whisky, do you mean ? "

" Most certaintlee, bitters and more," in the indignant tone of one who heard an infallible specific for the first time called in question.

The landlord here announced Dr. M'Kinlay, and a little, meek, elderly, and apparently somewhat sober man walked into the room.

" How do you do, doctor ? " said Tom. " As I had invited the other officers to dine, I took the liberty of asking you to join us as the honorary assistant-surgeon, and I'm delighted to see you."

" Much obliged, sir, and very proud I am to come ; it's an honour, sir, to me to make your acquaintance."

" Let me present you," continued Tom, " to Sir Hercules O'Halloran, who has come down to have a look at the Scotch Volunteers." Then, in a whispered aside, " A very eminent man, particular friend of the Queen's ; might do you all a deal of service ; he reports everything, sir, everything—medical service and all."

" God bless me ! " said the unsuspecting doctor ; " it's a great honour, Sir Hercules, to see you, and to dine with you makes me very proud indeed. I never expected such a distinction, I'm sure. May I make so bold, Sir Hercules, as to ask how you left her Majesty the Queen ? "

Trying to combine the air of camps and courts, I replied with bland condescension that my royal mistress was, at the date of my last telegram from Windsor that forenoon, in the enjoyment of excellent health and spirits ; had lunched in private ; was to drive to Eton College for inspecting purposes in the afternoon, " and by this time," looking at my watch, " is entertaining, with her usual condescension, the Archbishop of Canterbury and the Pope's Legate at dinner."

" God bless me ! " cried the doctor ; " this is wonderful !

And you heard all this to-day, Sir Hercules ? here, far away in the Highlands ? Excuse the freedom, but there's something awful in meeting the like of you, Sir Hercules."

" Oh ! I'm a very humble person, doctor ; don't imagine " (with great humility) " I'm anybody to be afraid of. Her Majesty is good enough to keep me posted up in her movements. Three telegrams a-day, that's all. There's so much I have to be consulted about, you see ; you understand me ? eh ? "

" Unquestionably, Sir Hercules, of course. It must be a great comfort to her Majesty, although I say it to your face, sir, to have such a fine, affable, pleasant nobleman to consult with ; and she'll miss you much, no doubt."

" Tut, tut, doctor, you flatter me and make a great man of a mere nobody—a poor soldier, sir, nothing more, who is glad to make your acquaintance, doctor."

I concluded with an access of condescension, extending my hand, which the doctor took in a tumult of delight and awe.

Tom warned me by a look not to go too far ; but as he had given me my *rôle*, I was determined to play it for myself. Besides, indeed, the doctor was evidently prepared to swallow anything.

" Now let us sit down to dinner," said Tom. " Sir Hercules, will you kindly face me ? Gentlemen, pray be seated. I'm afraid the dinner won't be very choice."

Nor, in truth, was it. He who hath bent his hungry head over dinner in a Highland inn, even in the tourists' season, may remember how much that meal is indebted to the keen mountain air and the appetite with which it is approached ; and he may therefore form some idea of a similar banquet out of the season. Fowl there was, but such as reminded one of the feathered spectre which, on arriving at a dhâk bungalow in India, the traveller inevitably sees led shrieking to the slaughter, to serve as the *pièce de resistance* fifteen minutes after. Eggs were there, but such as " Brother Sam " describes as having been " very nice little eggs six weeks ago " ; and as for the ham, it painfully suggested the universal adaptability of the driver's boot.

Our guests, however, seemed to enjoy it thoroughly. The doctor, though perched, timid and bird-like, on the edge of his chair, contrived to play an excellent knife and fork ; and the lieutenant, his head almost flush with the table, ate like a ghoul, albeit sorely impeded therein by an attempt to reconcile the normal position of his hands in the arm-holes of his waistcoat with their duties of wielding knife, fork, and spoon.

I had taken a quiet opportunity of hinting to Tom my suspicion that the lieutenant was hiding his light under a bushel with a view to evading business ; and that if the conversation was to be kept off it for a time, the scoundrel would be found comparatively fluent, especially under the immediate influence of meat and drink. In pursuit of these tactics, therefore, we contrived to make the conversation (if such it could be called) general.

" Well, McTavish," he said, dinner being now some time over, " I'm very glad to have made your acquaintance in this pleasant sort of way. Here's to your very good health ; and now I think it's time to discuss the *real business* of the evening."

" Goot life, captain ! business already ? You must be ferry heavy on the speerits, if you would be for beginning already," said the lieutenant. " No, surr ; my thanks to you, but not a trop of tuddy will the wine settled herself. It was a mighty fine surprise for Mr. Lauchy when she obsairved herself in the lock-up. ' It will be your fun, Glenschnorruk,' says she, ' that—— ' "

" I beg your pardon," interrupted Tom ; " you misunderstood my meaning ; what I wished to express was that we should lose no time in looking at the concern which has brought us here to-night."

" Hoosh, captain ! you would not be thinkin' of that. If the postboy cannot look at his own horse and his own concern, he must be a ferry poor cratur inteed, and the doctor's powney Callum, she looks at herself. ' It will be your fun, Glenschnorruk,' says Mr. Lauchy, ' that you are putting on to my head.' ' My teer goot friend,' says I—— "

" You misunderstand me again, Mr. McTavish," said Tom firmly. " You must be aware that it is now six months since you lost your captain, and—— "

" Six months, captain ? will it be six months sin' the cratur died ? "

" Six months," said Tom.

" Well, maybe, maybe ; oich ! oich ! six months. Well, well, she was a nice bit cratury. ' Yes, Mr. Lauchy,' says I, ' you are ferry right, and you will have—— ' "

" The devil seize Mr. Lauchy ! " thundered Tom in a fury. " I'll tell you what it is, Mr. McTavish, I have come here to discuss business and not to waste time, and if you had the proper spirit—— "

" Well, well, captain," said the irrepressible, in the tone of one yielding to excessive importunity, " if you must set to the speerits, goot life ! let us yoke to them, but be ferry strict with Mr. Stew-art to give them out of his own brown pig.[1] As the

---

[1] An earthenware vessel called a " grey-beard " in the Lowland dialect, and containing a gallon.

meenister says, 'Stew-art's pig is like the cask o' the weedy woman, with a last drop always into it.' You will ken the meenister, captain ? "

Tom's wrath melted away at the peal of laughter with which I greeted the lieutenant's last flank movement ; he joined in it, but denied all knowledge of the divine, and outmanœuvred McTavish by plunging *in medios res*.

" Now, Mr. McTavish," he said, " have the goodness to listen without interrupting me. I have come here to-night to see that the corps *does* elect a captain, and I mean to see that it does, and I wish to know if you will support Sir William McVittie. The Lord-Lieutenant is anxious that he should be nominated, and what is more, so is the Queen. You must elect a Keltshire man ; he is a Keltshire man, and the best, and indeed the only, man you can get in the district. Now I have said my say ; let me hear yours, but let it be to the point. We have had quite enough of Mr. Lauchy and his salmon, and I won't listen to another word except on business."

" Ferry well, to be certaintlee, surr, ferry well ; but you will likely be ringin' for Stew-art's pig first ? "

" Certainly," said Tom, ringing the bell, " and now go on."

" Ferry well, I was just saying to me ownself and to the Collecthur lately that it would be incaatious to be in a tremendeous hurry aboot the business. ' Collecthur,' says I, ' we cannot chump over crayt big hetches and titches withoot a look into them.' ' What you say is a true case,' says the Collecthur. ' You are a cliver man, Glenschnorruk,' says he ; ' and we must not chump over a captain ferry hastily.' "

" Well," said Tom, " that's all very true ; but I'll be hanged if six months isn't long enough to look at the biggest hedge or ditch that was ever jumped over, and in fact there *is* to be no more delay in the matter. I tell you I won't stand this humbug any longer, and you mistake your man if you think you can play the fool with me. Will you support Sir William or will you not ? and if not, will you propose some one else, in opposition to the Queen's wishes, and the Lord-Lieutenant's, and mine ? " Tom added demurely.

" I am sure," said the doctor, on whom the fiery sherry was working its effect perceptibly—" I am sure such a statement would be sufficient for the corps ; the Queen's wish and the Lord-Lieutenant's and yours, captain, and I may add yours, Sir Hercules (for, of course, your feeling will be her Majesty's), would weigh with them against any other suggestion ; and I will say this, that if Glensnork were to set himself up in an opposition to these wishes of yours, he would pan himself, pan himself, Sir Hercules, I do assure you."

" I don't doubt it," I said, assuming that the process of ' panning' was equivalent to ostracism in Strathkinahan ; " and serve him right too," I added rather fiercely.

" But he may be sure of this," continued the doctor, " that Strathkinahan will refuse to be panned with him."

" Hoosh, doctor ! " said the lieutenant, whose normal attitude towards the doctor was that of an honoured patron evidently ; " you are a ferry cliver man, but you are incaatious to speak when you are not asked to spoke. Ailsie McLeod is in crayt trouble with her tooth-gums ; you had petter " (with a dignified wave) " go and make them heal—tit, tit ! "

" The opinion of a sober professional man," cried the doctor in high wrath, " is at least as valuable as that of a being who forgets himself daily with the bottle."

" Deed, doctor, he'll be a ferry smart man that forgets the pottle when you are into the room. Go away—go and sing a song to Ailsie's tooth-gums."

" Come, come, gentlemen," cried Tom, as the doctor was bursting out in huge wrath at this *tu quoque*, " we are forgetting ourselves ; to business, business, business. What do you say, Mr. McTavish—will you support Sir William ? "

" Well, well, Sir William is a fine man, a ferry fine nice nobleman ; but, for God's sake, captain, is Stew-art niver bringing his pig ? "

" Oh yes ! this will bring him " (ringing the bell) ; " and now go on, for heaven's sake ! "

A diversion was, however, again created in the lieutenant's favour by the entrance of the landlord, who informed us that the corps had been for a considerable time awaiting us in the barn, and were beginning to get a " little troublesome " ; and as it appeared to Tom and myself that perhaps more might be done by a direct appeal to the whole body than by fencing with their impracticable officer, we decided to descend at once.

A strange scene presented itself to our eyes as we entered the barn. It was dimly lighted by a few tallow candles stuck into bottles, and by a stable-lantern suspended from a cross-beam in the centre. A heavy cloud of tobacco-smoke brooded over all, through which were hazily revealed the figures of the Volunteers. We had a dim panorama of shaggy crests of hair, of red faces, of tobacco-pipes, and of all manner of improvised drinking-vessels ; while the hum of many voices, the puffing of many pipes, and the glugging of lips that drank greedily were the sounds that met our ears. When our entrance was observed, suddenly uprose from the mist the form of a tall man with an outstretched arm, and from his lips proceeded a sound much resembling an ill-executed sneeze—" Att-itshun ! " The form and the voice were those of the Collector, who seemed to have partially succeeded in " laying the spirit," and who now, in the exercise of his military function, was calling the room to " attention."

The men all rose, looking like the peaks of hills appearing above the morning mist.

" Saloot ! " cried the Collector, still favouring the attitude of the lion rampant ; whereupon the corps all began to make what looked like mesmeric passes with their right arms in the air. " Dooble saloot ! " shouted the Collector again ; and then each man employed his left arm also, which gave the pleasing general effect of about fifty men swimming for their lives in an ocean of tobacco-smoke. This movement had for me such a delightful novelty that I could not help remarking on it to the lieutenant, who explained with great pride that it was an invention of his own devised to meet a difficulty he had felt in receiving merely the same salute as the Collector. " So I doobled it for my nanesel' ; and if the craturs had more airms, they would use plenty more of them for the captain and yoursel'."

Tom now told the lieutenant that he would like to see the company fallen in in their ranks for a minute or two, just to get an idea of the general appearance of the men.

" Would you put the craturs into rangks withoot their sojer's clothes on, captain ? and withoot their guns ? Tit, tit ! begging your grace, that would be a ferry fulish-like trick, to be sure."

" I don't want to see their clothing or their rifles ; I want to see the men themselves. Have the goodness to fall them in," said Tom firmly, " and get them into single rank."

" Ferry goot, ferry well," said the lieutenant, with a shrug. " Shooliter, be craytly kind and put the craturs into a single rank." The Collector had, however, apparently succumbed to his old enemy again, for he only waved his arm feebly, and muttered, with a sort of imbecile snigger, " She kens naething aboot it."

" Very well," said Tom. " I'll do it myself ; give me a sergeant."

" Is there a sergeant among ye ? " cried McTavish.

" No," shouted the collective voice of Strathkinahan from the mist.

" Very well, a corporal will do," said Tom.

" Is Corporal McIldhu thereaboots ? " inquired McTavish, perring into the haze.

"He's at the bothy," shouted a score of voices.

"Why did he not take heed to come doon?" said the lieutenant.

"He had words wi' the Collector," explained the chorus again.

"Well, well, that's a peety—a sore peety—and the captain here and all."

I understood the chorus to admit, by a sort of rumbling growl, that it *was* a pity.

"Well, never mind," said Tom; "give me a ' coverer ' of some sort, and we'll get on."

"Deed, and it's a thing the corps never had, captain. There was a taak of sairvin' them oot at our own costs; and they would be ferry goot in the wat nichts if they were happenin' to be McIntoshe's clothes, and cheap."

"Isn't this nice?" said Tom grimly, looking round at me. "Give me your right-hand man, then; I suppose the company had a right and a left?"

"Shess, sir! most notoriouslee, most certaintlee. Hand me oot the richt-hand man," he cried into the mist.

"She is not into here," replied the chorus.

"Who is she then, at all?" cried the lieutenant.

"Lauchy Fraser," shouted the chorus, with a roar of laughter.

"Ach! deed, and it is trooth," cried the lieutenant, heartily joining in the mirth; "she is on a veesit to the shirra"; where-upon there was another roar, which put Tom quite out of temper, and he pounced personally into the mist, and, seizing the first man he found there, stood him up against the wall.

"This is the right-hand man," he said; "and now come on, all the rest of you, and fall in." And what with the doctor's assistance and mine, he at length contrived to get them into a row against the wall, all continuing to smoke their pipes and to retain their drink-vessels in their hands. Tom winked at these delinquencies, however, for the purpose, as he explained to me after, of keeping them in good humour and carrying his point. "Now, Mr. McTavish, take command of them; and if your ensign can stand, which seems doubtful, he may as well take his place—it may keep him out of mischief, at least."

"I am to command them, captain?"

"If you please, Mr. McTavish."

The lieutenant waddled out in front of the line, his hands in the arm-holes of his waistcoat, his head low, and shooting backwards and forwards like a large gander waddling heavily to a pond, while from his lips came a sort of preliminary hissing also suggestive of that bird. The hissing gradually " boiled up," so to speak, till it bubbled into a cry of " Oarter arrums ! " whereupon the men gave an apologetic plunge in their ranks, apparently to imply that if they had the means, the lieutenant's wish would be cheerfully complied with.

" Tut, tut ! Mr. McTavish," said Tom, struggling between laughter and indignation, " I don't mean that ; take command in the regular way."

" Shoolter arrums ! " shouted the bewildered lieutenant, and again the corps executed a sort of *pas d'extase.*

" Fall in on the right, Mr. McTavish," said Tom, with a desperate effort to keep his countenance ; " and, for the love of heaven, take your hands out of your waistcoat, and hold up your head, and try to look like a reasonable being for three minutes ! " he added, as the lieutenant moved sulkily to his position.

The arrangements being at last completed, including the position of the Collector, who, by the way of compromise, was accommodated with a stool on the left flank, Tom and I walked slowly down the rank and inspected the men. They were a fine set of fellows, certainly—tall, sinewy, broad-shouldered, and athletic-looking. Many, indeed, bore very unequivocal traces of the manner in which they had occupied their time at " the bothy " ; but there was no disgraceful case like that of the Collector, the intermittent nature of whose inebriety made it difficult to deal with on any uniform system. The men, as a rule, stood steadily enough in the ranks, though in one or two exceptional cases an attempt was made to shake hands with the inspecting officer as he passed.

" Gentlemen," said Tom, when the inspection was completed, " I have to congratulate you on your fine, I may say your soldier-like, appearance. I had often heard of the fine *physique* you have in this district——" [" It could not have been the feesick of Dr. McKinlay," interpolated McTavish, still rankling at his medical friend], " and I am not disappointed. A fine *physique,* and the mental intelligence which you evidently possess, are immense advantages ; but they must be properly applied, and there are two things that can alone compass this end—drill and discipline. As it is with the regular, so it is with the volunteer soldier. I am sorry to find, with regard to the first, that you have been unfortunate in losing your drill-sergeant ; but I am now making arrangements to supply his place. With regard to the second, the grand essential is that the corps should be fully and efficiently officered ; above all things, that there should be at its head a competent captain—a man of intelligence, energy, and, I may add, social position. A long period has elapsed since the death of your late captain, and no step has been taken to elect and nominate his successor to the Lord-Lieutenant. I have made frequent representations to your officers on this score, but without any result. I have therefore personally visited you for the double purpose of inspecting the corps and of impressing upon you all the necessity of at once proceeding to elect a captain. When I say that *I* am inspecting the corps, I do not speak correctly, for I am in reality on this occasion only the attendant of the distinguished General Sir Hercules O'Halloran, who, in his capacity of Inspector-General of Reserves, does you the honour of being present here to-night, and may not improbably feel himself called upon to address a few words of advice to you on the subject I have been insisting upon. When I mention that Sir Hercules, in addition to his great military distinction, is so highly honoured as to be the confidential adviser of our beloved Sovereign, you will, I am sure, concur with me in the propriety of at once giving three cheers for that eminent officer. Hip ! hip ! hip ! hurrah ! " The cheers were given with right good-will, till roof and rafters rang ; and then Tom gravely continued his oration : " The Lord-Lieutenant will not appoint a gentleman to that position without your nomination, and I must tell you that he is not a little surprised and disappointed at the delay which has taken place. It would not be right for me to conceal from you, and I have Sir Hercules's sanction to mention, that pain and surprise have also been excited in far more august quarters, by what he has felt himself compelled to stigmatize as ' this unseemly tardiness ' ; but to-night I am confident this stigma will be removed, and I now propose that we proceed at once to elect a gentleman to the vacant position. I will not trouble you to stand in the ranks while this goes on ; but I earnestly request you to sit down in an orderly manner and discuss the matter in a business-like way. To the right face ! Break off ! " The men tumbled out of their ranks and reseated themselves on the benches ; the Collector obeyed the order by turning a back somersault off his stool ; and the lieutenant waddled back into civil life much relieved, to lay aside the crown of office. " Now," said Tom, " let us discuss the matter quietly. I say Sir William McVittie is our best man, and that we ought to elect him at once. Light your pipe, McTavish, and give us your opinion."

" Sir William is no doot a ferry fine, nice, parteecular, pretty fellow, captain," said the lieutenant, emphasizing each epithet with a draw at his pipe, in which an inordinate amount of suctional power was employed ; " but if a captain is to be aal the goot things that you have spoke into your bit speech, Sir William will not be our man."

" How d'ye mean ? " inquired Tom.

" Angus McRioch, will you be craytly kind, and tell the captain whether Sir William is for the dipping or for the smearing of the sheeps ? " said the lieutenant, in a voice of the deepest solemnity.

" Dipping ! " bellowed the whole room as one man.

" Ferry well, captain, you will not, after that, again be speaking for Sir William," said McTavish, with an air of one who has got rid of the first of a series of difficulties, and proceeds to handle the next, confident of success.

" But I don't see what that has got to do with the question," urged Tom. " As he has neither got to dip nor smear the Volunteers, I don't think it matters what he does with his sheep."

" There niver was a yowe, there niver was a tupp, there niver was a wedder dipped yet at aal on to the holdings of my father's son ; there niver will be a yowe, there niver will be a tupp, there niver will be a wedder dipped on to his holdings," said a lantern-jawed old fellow in a sort of chant ; and the somewhat irrelevant statement was received with much applause, and evidently held to strengthen the case against Sir William.

" What would the old red man, Colin-with-the-crooked nose, have said to all the dippings and the trash, Angus ? " inquired another anti-Sir William-ite ; but the Nestor only smoked with ineffable grimness. He had uttered, and that, he evidently thought, should settle the matter without further parley.

" There was once a pollis-offisher, by the name of McArdle, in the Strath," suggested another of the party, " but he is not into it now. Will somebody be ferry kind, and say who pit him oot ? "

" Sir William ! " cried a dozen voices.

" I suppose a pollis-offisher is to have no mouth in this Strath," observed a gentleman largely provided in respect of that feature, and with complexional indications that neither in eating nor in speaking was it principally employed.

" McArdle was not a drucken man," hiccoughed the Collector. " He tasted—at a time—like me ; it was his dewty— Sir William pit him oot for—for his dewty. His name was Peter." And much honour was done to these decidedly hazy propositions.

" If Sir William is to be captain in the Strath, the Volunteers may ferry quickly put their mouths into the store wi' the guns, and not bring them oot again," suggested another satirist.

"After the shearin', when the ball was in the barn at Craig-Vittie, there was plenty of tea, but I did not obsairve anything for a manbody to drink," said another.

"If Sir William is to be captain, he will have to list the auld wives into the company. Betty McCandlish will make a ferry parteecular fine lieutenant to him, and Ailsie McLeod will be ensign instead of the Collector."

"Sir William is a temperanst man at his heart."

"And a temperanst man is a teirant."

"And we will have no teirants and no teiranny here."

Loud applause followed these heroic sentiments, and the lieutenant, turning to Tom, observed, "You see, captain, Sir William is a parteecular nice goot nobleman, but the Volunteers will not be for having a teirant for their captain."

"But there is no one else in the district you can elect, and as you must elect some one, why, you must elect Sir William. It's all nonsense about tyranny. Sir William is an excellent man, and no more a teetotaller than I am, though, of course, he doesn't think that every parade is to be turned into a drinking bout. When you know him better, when he is mixed up with you as your captain, you will find all these things you've been hearing about him are nonsense, and I hear he is going to reside regularly at Craig-Vittie."

"If I might make bold to say a word," said a diplomatist, whose opinion was evidently held in high esteem, "I would say this, that if we must elect a captain, we must elect him ; but if there is no one into the Strath who is shootable for the poseetion, then, for Got's sake, let us not at aal forget that there is other places with shootable people into them. We will elect some ferry crayt man ; we will elect the Prince of Whales. He will be captain to the company ; but we will not be troubling him, and he will not be troubling himself to come down to the Strath for the dreels ; and so we will have a captain and no teiranny."

This novel method of solving the difficulty found universal favour ; and McTavish at once abandoned his Fabian policy and became clamorous for instant action as to the Prince's election.

Tom took me out of the room for consultation. "Did you ever see such an impracticable set of devils ? " he said. "What's to be done ? "

"Arguing won't mend matters, that's clear," I replied. "Give me some particulars about this Sir William and I'll see

what I can do." Tom did so, and I learned that Sir William
had quite recently succeeded to the property ; that he had lived
principally abroad in the diplomatic service, and was as yet
almost unknown in the Strath ; but that he was about to settle
on his acres, and that his co-operation and assistance would be of
the greatest importance in saving the Volunteer movement in
the locality from death by alcoholic drowning. He was reported
to be a very sensible man ; and though neither the tyrant nor
the ascetic he was alleged to be by the corps, he had, on a recent
short visit to the Strath, been not a little startled and scandalized
at the extraordinarily chronic state of fuddlement in which its
inhabitants lived, and had expressed himself pretty broadly
on the subject, and, in one or two instances, made a clearance
of the most inveterate offenders. *Hinc illæ lacrymæ.* " In
fact," Tom concluded, " he is just the man to keep these dipso-
maniacs in order ; and I know he will accept if he is elected."

" Very well," said I, " you had better let me speak to them.
Just say that ' the General ' will address a few observations to the
corps."

When we returned to the meeting we found that they had
just elected the Prince of Wales *nem. con.*, and were expecting
with flaming eyes the arrival of the " glasses round " with which
the lieutenant had suggested they should celebrate the event
" at their own costs."

Three cheers for " our captain, the Prince," were given
somewhat defiantly on our entrance ; and, on the whole,
matters bore a decidedly unsatisfactory aspect.

" Gentlemen," cried Tom, " Lieutenant-General Sir Hercules
O'Halloran, K.C.B., Inspector of the Reserve Forces, will address you " ; and I stepped forward, desperately determined
that if unscrupulous impudence could avert the collapse of the
Keltshire " Ad. Batt." and the loss of my friend Tom's appointment, it should not be wanting to me on this occasion.

" Gentlemen," I said, " first of all I must express to you, as
representing the Royal Family, my very sincere thanks for the
honour which you have so loyally and so very properly bestowed
upon us—I mean, upon the Prince of Wales. Gentlemen, you
have done honour to yourselves in honouring him—(cheers)—
and before I go further I beg that you will allow me, on behalf of
the Queen, to defray the expense of the further honour which
you propose to offer him in drinking his health." (Loud and
protracted cheering, during which I tried to look as if the Privy
purse was at that moment in my portmanteau upstairs.)   " But
having said thus much, it deeply grieves me to add that duty and

my instructions compel me to decline, with every expression of gratitude, the honour which you have done to his Royal Highness." (Murmurs, soothed by the arrival of the liquor, during which I paused for a second or two.) "Yes, gentlemen," I resumed, "it is my painful duty to be obliged to decline. You must all be aware, of course, that the Prince, from his position and natural affability, is perpetually importuned to accept situations similar to that which you have offered him to-night. In such great numbers are they offered to him, indeed, that to fill one tithe of them, even in a nominal and honorary way, would strain and overtax his royal energies most insupportably. Under these circumstances we were obliged to come to a fixed determination ; and I assure you that in coming to it I experienced the greatest hesitation and difficulty, but having been come to, it cannot be deviated from. It was this—that the Prince should only consent to take command of one corps at a time. What that corps should be it was, of course, left for me to decide ; and after renewed hesitation, my choice fell upon—upon—upon the corps which—now enjoys that distinction.

"The Prince himself, with that self-abnegation which characterizes him, has frequently implored me to reconsider the matter, and bring him into a wider connection with a movement which he honours and admires.

"Supported by her Majesty, I have, however, remained firm ; and you must pardon me if I say that even the impression which you as a corps have made upon me to-night, and the *absorbing* interest which you clearly take in your duties, cannot make me waver.

"On Monday night, the night before I left London, I was dining in private with the Prince and the Duke of Cambridge ; and his Royal Highness, understanding that I was about to proceed northward on my tour of inspection, again reverted to the subject. 'Give me a Scotch corps, General,' said the Prince— 'there's a good fellow.' 'It cuts me to the heart to say "No," sir,' I replied. 'But what am I to say to all these fine fellows ?' he inquired, pulling out a bundle of papers, which were requisitions from the Kirkintilloch, Kilbogie, Slamannan, Cowcaddens, and other corps. 'You can show your interest in them by nominating the gentleman you would wish to fill the post instead of your Royal Highness,' I replied. 'It is a happy thought,' said the Prince ; 'but it is impossible for me to go down to Kilbogie and Cowcaddens at present, and I would not nominate a substitute without being sure of him, as, of course, where *I* nominate, the corps can't refuse to elect.' 'Leave it all to Sir

Hercules,' said the Duke ; ' his judgment in all military matters is simply the best in the country.' ' Your Highness does me infinite honour,' I replied. ' Pooh, pooh ! only your due, O'Halloran,' said the Duke. ' Well, O'Halloran, would you mind going to these places for me,' said the Prince, ' to say that I thank the corps with all my heart, and that I leave you to act for me and nominate a substitute ? ' ' It is my duty and delight to do what your Royal Highness wishes,' I replied. ' But you must be very careful in your selection, General ; you must be sure that the man is fit in every way—above all, that he is a district proprietor—and when you have made your choice you must be firm. Remember that for the moment you are the Prince of Wales ; and if any other corps should elect me while you are in the north, pray go to them also and select a substitute for me. I am ashamed to give you so much trouble.' ' Don't mention it, Prince,' I replied ; ' I will carry out your instructions to the letter.'

" Now, gentlemen, by your selection of the Prince to-night you have virtually thrown, as you must see, the appointment of your captain into my hands ; for though, as a matter of form, I shall simply propose a gentleman to you, you will, as a matter of course, accept him ; and standing in this position, I feel the grave responsibility which rests upon me. On the one hand, it is most unpleasant to me to run counter to your inclinations ; but on the other, the duty I owe to the Prince is paramount.

" As far as my own convictions go, however, I have no hesitation in making my selection. In many districts where I might be called upon to act as I am to-night, I should require time for inquiry and consideration ; but here, in Strathkinahan, I find ready to my hand the right man, and that in the person of one of my oldest and dearest friends, a man of great distinction, high character, probity and Presbyterian principles—a man, in fact, every inch a man and a soldier. I allude to my honourable friend Sir William McVittie of Craig-Vittie, Baronet."

A perfect howl of indignation rose from the party, upon whom this came like a thunderclap. It was necessary to take a high tone at once, so " Volunteers ! " I cried, raising my voice sternly, " you forget in whose presence you virtually are. Situated as you are, this unseemly demonstration is very nearly approaching to a seditious cry, and I trust " (with grim emphasis) " that I shall never have to report or to punish sedition in Strathkinahan. I propose to you Sir William McVittie. I am sorry there is a prejudice against him, but I can't help it.   How groundless it is I well know.

" His views upon certain practical matters, such as the dipping of sheep, may not be as healthy as I could wish, but a residence in Strathkinahan will correct them.   As to his being a temperance man, *that* I repudiate, on behalf of my old friend, as a personal insult ; and when I tell you that at Court, where he is known well, his singular power of consuming claret and other fluids has procured for him the nickname of ' Gallon ' McVittie, you will, I think, acquit him of any such baseness."   (" Hurrah ! hurrah ! " from the doctor and Tom, slightly joined in by a few converts.)

" I beg to propose him, then, as a fit and proper person to be Captain of the Strathkinahan Volunteers, and I *expect* the proposal to be seconded and carried unanimously."

" I second it, Sir Hercules ! " cried the doctor at once.

" And it is carried *nem. con.*," I added hastily.   " Get paper, pen, and ink, and I will draw the requisition."

" I make so bold as to make a protest against it," said the diplomatist.

It was necessary to nip this sort of thing in the bud by a *coup d'état*, so I replied, with fierce energy, advancing and gobbling at the fellow, " Hold your tongue, sir ! you ought to be ashamed of yourself, sir ! All your brother volunteers blush for you, sir ! Another word, and I shall turn you out of the corps, and out of the room, and send you to the lock-up, sir ! "

This quelled the fellow ; and the rest of them accepted me as apparently a sort of dictator, endowed with the fullest legislative and executive powers. No further difficulty was made ; and after I had ordered another round of liquor to the health of the Queen, another to the health of Sir William, and a third in honour of Tom and myself, certain hieroglyphs were dashingly appended to the requisition ; and the meeting broke up in the highest delight after singing " Auld Lang Syne " and dancing hand in hand round the prostrate and senseless form of the Collector.

Next morning we departed at daybreak, and posted the requisition at the first village.   I confess I had many misgivings as to what the morning feelings of the Volunteers might be, and whether, in my wish to serve Tom, I might not have run him into a serious scrape. All, however, went well, and in three weeks I had the satisfaction of seeing Sir William gazetted. And I can assure my readers that the pious fraud has turned out to admiration.

E. V. LUCAS (1868–   ) *has given to a grateful world a host of delicate essays to which it is a delight to turn from the bustle of everyday life. The fellowship of animals, the inspiration of a walk, the friendliness of inns, the strangeness of what is new, and the lingering beauty of what is old—among such things as these his pen rambles in a querying and reflective spirit. The charming quality of his humour is shown in this epistolary tale.*

THE CHRISTMAS DECORATIONS

The Rev. Lawrence Lidbetter to his curate, the Rev. Arthur Starling

DEAR STARLING,—I am sorry to appear to be running away at this busy season, but a sudden call to London on business leaves me no alternative. I shall be back on Christmas Eve for certain, perhaps before. You must keep an eye on the decorations, and see that none of our helpers get out of hand. I have serious doubts as to Miss Green.—Yours,

L. L.

II

Mrs. Clibborn to the Rev. Lawrence Lidbetter

DEAR RECTOR,—I think we have got over the difficulty which we were talking of—Mr. Lulham's red hair and the discord it would make with the crimson decorations. Maggie and Popsy and I have been working like slaves, and have put up a beautiful and effectual screen of evergreen which completely obliterates the keyboard and organist. I think you will be delighted. Mr. Starling approves most cordially.—Yours sincerely,

MARY CLIBBORN.

III

Miss Pitt to the Rev. Lawrence Lidbetter

MY DEAR MR. LIDBETTER,—We are all so sorry you have been called away, a strong guiding hand being never more needed. You will remember that it was arranged that I should have sole charge of the memorial window to Colonel Soper— we settled it just outside the Post Office on the morning that poor Blades was kicked by the Doctor's pony. Well, Miss Lockie now says that Colonel Soper's window belongs to her, and she makes it impossible for me to do anything. I must implore you to write to her putting it right, or the decorations will be ruined. Mr. Starling is kind, but quite useless.—Yours sincerely,

VIRGINIA PITT.

IV

Miss Lockie to the Rev. Lawrence Lidbetter

MY DEAR MR. LIDBETTER,—I am sorry to have to trouble you in your enforced rest, but the interests of the church must not be neglected, and you ought to know that Miss Pitt not only insists that the decoration of Colonel Soper's window was entrusted to her, but prevents me carrying it out. If you re-collect, it was during tea at Mrs. Millstone's that it was arranged that I should be responsible for this window. A telegram to Miss Pitt would put the matter right at once. Dear Mr. Starling is always so nice, but he does so lack firmness.—Yours sincerely,

MABEL LOCKIE.

V

Mrs. St. John to the Rev. Lawrence Lidbetter

DEAR RECTOR,—I wish you would let Miss Green have a line about the decoration of the pulpit. It is no use any of us saying anything to her since she went to the Slade School and acquired artistic notions, but a word from you would work wonders. What we all feel is that the pulpit should be bright and gay, with some cheerful texts on it, a suitable setting for you and your helpful Christmas sermon, but Miss Green's idea is to drape it entirely in black muslin and purple, like a lying-in-state. One can do wonders with a little cotton-wool and a few yards of Turkey twill, but she will not understand this. How with all her *nouveau art* ideas she got permission to decorate the pulpit at all I cannot think, but there it is, and the sooner she is stopped the better. Poor Mr. Starling drops all the hints he can, but she disregards them all.—Yours sincerely,

CHARLOTTE ST. JOHN.

VI

Miss Olive Green to the Rev. Lawrence Lidbetter

DEAR MR. LIDBETTER,—I am sure you will like the pulpit. I am giving it the most careful thought, and there is every promise of a scheme of austere beauty, grave and solemn and yet just touched with a note of happier fulfilment. For the most part you will find the decorations quite conventional—holly and evergreens, the old terrible cotton-wool snow on crimson back-ground. But I am certain that you will experience a thrill of satisfied surprise when your eyes alight upon the simple gravity of the pulpit's drapery and its flowing sensuous lines. It is so kind of you to give me this opportunity to realize some of my artistic self. Poor Mr. Starling, who is entirely Victorian in his views of art, has been talking to me about gay colours, but my work is done for *you* and the few who can *understand*.—Yours sincerely,   OLIVE GREEN.

VII

Mrs. Millstone to the Rev. Lawrence Lidbetter

DEAR RECTOR,—Just a line to tell you of a delightful device I have hit upon for the decorations. Cotton-wool, of course, makes excellent snow, and rice is sometimes used, on gum, to suggest winter too. But I have discovered that the most perfect illusion of a white rime can be obtained by wetting the leaves and then sprinkling flour on them. I am going to get all the others to let me finish off everything like that on Christmas Eve (like varnishing-day at the Academy, my husband says), when it will be all fresh for Sunday. Mr. Starling, who is proving himself such a dear, is delighted with the scheme. I hope you are well in that dreadful foggy city.—Yours sincerely,

ADA MILLSTONE.

VIII

Mrs. Hobbs, charwoman, to the Rev. Lawrence Lidbetter

HONOURED SIR,—I am writing to you because Hobbs and me dispare of getting any justice from the so-called ladies who have been turning the holy church of St. Michael and all Angels into a Covent Garden market. To sweep up holly and other green stuff I don't mind, because I have heard you say year after year that we should all do our best at Christmas to help each other. I always hold that charity and kindness are more than rubys, but when it comes to flour I say no. If you would believe it, Mrs. Millstone is first watering the holly and the lorrel to make it wet, and then sprinkling flour on it to look like hore frost, and the mess is something dreadful, all over the cushions and carpet. To sweep up ordinery dust I don't mind, more par-ticulerly as it is my paid work and bounden duty ; but unless it is made worth my while Hobbs says I must say no. We draw the line at sweeping up dough. Mr. Starling is very kind, but as Hobbs says, you are the founting head.—Awaiting a reply, I am, your humble servant,   MARTHA HOBBS.

IX

Mrs. Vansittart to the Rev. Lawrence Lidbetter

DEAR RECTOR,—If I am late with the north windows you must understand that it is not my fault, but Pedder's. He has suddenly and most mysteriously adopted an attitude of hostility to his employers (quite in the way one has heard of gardeners doing), and nothing will induce him to cut me any evergreens, which he says he cannot spare. The result is that poor Horace and Mr. Starling have to go out with lanterns after Pedder has left the garden, and cut what they can and convey it to the church by stealth. I think we shall manage fairly well, but thought you had better know in case the result is not equal to your anticipation.—Yours sincerely,   GRACE VANSITTART.

X

Mr. Lulham, organist, to the Rev. Lawrence Lidbetter

DEAR SIR,—I shall be glad to have a line from you authorizing me to insist upon the removal of a large screen of evergreens which Mrs. Clibborn and her daughters have erected by the organ. There seems to be an idea that the organ is unsightly, although we have had no complaints hitherto, and the effect of this barrier will be to interfere very seriously with the choral part of the service. Mr. Starling sympathizes with me, but has not taken any steps.—Believe me, yours faithfully,

WALTER LULHAM.

XI

The Rev. Lawrence Lidbetter to Mrs. Lidbetter

MY DEAREST HARRIET,—I am having, as I expected, an awful time with the decorations, and I send you a batch of letters and leave the situation to you. Miss Pitt had better keep the Soper window. Give the Lockie girl one of the autograph copies of my *Narrow Path*, with a reference underneath my name to the chapter on self-sacrifice, and tell her how sorry I am that there has been a misunderstanding. Mrs. Hobbs must have an extra half-a-crown, and the flouring must be discreetly discouraged— on the ground of waste of food material. Assure Lulham that there shall be no barrier, and then tell Mrs. Clibborn that the organist has been given a pledge that nothing should intervene between his music and the congregation. I am dining with the Lawsons to-night, and we go afterwards to the *Tempest*, I think.— Your devoted   L.

PHILIP MACDONALD *has to his credit a long list of skilfully constructed detective stories, starting with " The Rasp " in 1926 and including such outstanding successes as " Patrol," which has twice been screened. With " Glitter," however, he set out on an entirely new path, and in this hilarious and brilliantly original story of the adventures of a Novel has given full play to that rich gift of humour which is such a pleasant feature of his thrillers.*

" GLITTER "

STUDIO FLAT, 9 DIGBY STREET,
RUSSELL SQUARE, LONDON, W.C.2.
April 21st, 193–.

DEAR MR. KANE,

I am sorry to trouble you, but I should be very glad if you would let me know whether or not your firm intends to publish my novel, *Glitter*, the manuscript of which I sent you as long ago as the 25th December last.

If you could let me know by return I shall be much obliged.

Yours sincerely,

E. MANORY KING.

WM. H. KANE, ESQ.,
MESSRS. KANE & FEATHERSTONE,
123 ST. JAMES'S COURT,
LONDON, S.W.1.

STUDIO FLAT, 9 DIGBY STREET,
RUSSELL SQUARE, LONDON, W.C.2.

DEAR CLEEVER,

I return the manuscript of *Less Than The Dust*. This is the worst you have ever sent me. It is so extraordinarily bad that I am not troubling to write a separate report. I think that in spite of the name on the book, which doesn't look much like a pseudonym, the writer must be a woman. If so, can't you do something about having her put away ?

397

Although I have not given you a report, my two guineas have been well earned, because, with my usual zeal, I have read every word of the clotted ullage.

Yours ever,

E. M. K.

P.S.—Very sorry to trouble you, but should take it very kindly if you will tell your people to send me the reading fees due on *Crime of Harley Simpson*, *Mud*, and *Wild Rosemary*. If you could at the same time let me have the two guineas for *Less Than The Dust*, it would be better than ever.

R. E. CLEEVER, ESQ.,
MESSRS. BOLTON,
    (Publishing Department),
182X STRAND,
LONDON, W.C.

STUDIO FLAT, 9 DIGBY STREET,

RUSSELL SQUARE, LONDON, W.C.2.

April 21st, 193–.

DEAR SIR,
    I much regret that I have to-day been forced to draw a cheque for £5.
    In view of your letter to me of the 19th April last, I thought I had better mention this to you in the hope that you will be able to see your way to meeting this in spite of my overdraft.
    I need hardly say that I am expecting very shortly to pay in considerable sums to my account, otherwise I should not, of course, have taken this action.
    I am just concluding negotiations for the publication of my new novel, *Glitter*, and expect to receive a substantial advance within the next few days.

Yours faithfully,

E. MANORY KING.

THE MANAGER,
ST. STEPHEN'S BANK, LTD.,
214 NEW ROAD,
WESTMINSTER, S.W.1.

STUDIO FLAT.
April 21st, 193–.

DEAR MRS. EDWARDS,

I regret to say that I shall have to ask you to leave over the rent for the flat for just a few days longer ; until I receive an overdue cheque, in respect of my next book, from my publishers.

I hope you will be able to agree to this slight postponement.

Yours faithfully,

E. MANORY KING.

THE HOUSEKEEPER.

STUDIO FLAT, 9 DIGBY STREET,
RUSSELL SQUARE, LONDON, W.C. 2.
April 21st, 193–.

DEAR JACK,

Herewith thirty bob in bank-notes. I am sorry I can't run to more at the moment, but there's another crisis. If you could let me have this back on Friday, so much the better.

Am leaving this at the *Planet's* office in case you want it before to-night. Assume you'll be at the Club as usual.

Yours,

E. M. K.

P.S.—Have a very good front-page article in my head—" Do Wives Make Good Mothers ? " Would Bobsworth use it ?

E. M. K.

STUDIO FLAT, 9 DIGBY STREET,
RUSSELL SQUARE, LONDON, W.C. 2.
April 21st, 193–.

DEAR BUSTER,

I'm sorry, I can't possibly. If your letter had come by one post earlier, you should have had something, but as it is a man got in before you and as I'd already promised him all I could spare—there it is.

I shall see you on Saturday after all. I've cashed a very doubtful one for the fare and will be home by lunch-time. Am writing to our maternal parent by this post, but for obvious reasons in another envelope. How's your young man getting on in Africa ? Tell me on Saturday.

Love,

E.

P.S.—For God's sake keep the talk during the week-end off my writing and what I get for it. There's nothing to be said on this—especially on what I get for it.

STUDIO FLAT, 9 DIGBY STREET,
RUSSELL SQUARE, LONDON, W.C.2.
April 21st, 193–.

DEAREST MOTHER,

So very sorry I haven't answered your letter before. Yes ! Of course I'll come for the week-end. I'll catch the eight-forty from Paddington, getting in at twelve-thirty.

That's very sad news about Brander ; I'm sure the garden won't look the same without his southern aspect showing like a black moon in the middle of the rose-beds. But perhaps you'll be able to get some one cheaper now. Brander must have been a bit of a strain on you, and as he's all right you won't have to worry about him any more.

Yes : things are going pretty well with me. I've just finished a book—*Glitter*—which, privately, I *think* will knock 'em. It's not like anything I've done before, but I've put a devil of a lot of work into it.

Yes : it will be published by Kane and Featherstone.

No : I don't regret having chucked up the job with Marable. I've said that from the beginning and I still say it. Some are born " yes-men," others though yessir-ship is thrust upon them will never properly achieve it, and I'm one of the others. I can work, by myself for myself, like a nigger. For other men I can't—or, at any rate, not willingly and well. I gave a good imitation of it for two years, but that was enough.

Look after yourself until the week-end ; then I'll do it for you.

A very great deal of love,

E.

KANE AND FEATHERSTONE, LIMITED,
PUBLISHERS.

Directors :
WILLIAM HAVERSTOCK KANE.
CHARLES FEATHERSTONE.
SIR BAYNIT CHEESEBOROUGH.

Telephone : Gerrard ooX4 (3 lines).   " *Omnes Arti.*"
Telegrams : Crashingdon, Piccy, London.
Cablegrams : Ohar, London.

123 St. JAMES's COURT, LONDON, S.W.1.
22nd April, 193–.

DEAR MR. KING,

Many thanks for your letter of yesterday : I was about to write to you in any case.

Whilst we much admire the indubitable cleverness of your new book—*Glitter*—we have reluctantly come to the conclusion that, so far at least as we are concerned, it is not a publishable proposition. As you know, we are not averse to taking chances or to losing money in the effort to give good work a chance ; but we really feel that there would be so little demand for a book of the type of *Glitter* that—after lengthy consideration—we have, as I say, come very reluctantly to the conclusion that we cannot take the risk of complete loss in which publication would, to our minds, indubitably involve us.

Our attitude, I would like to add, might have been different had any one of the three novels published under your late contract with us been more profitable than they turned out to be. *Glitter* is indubitably good work ; but there is also—if you will allow me to say so—so large a quality of " cleverness " —and subsequent lack of *general* appeal—about it that it would only appeal to a very small circle of readers.

May I conclude by assuring you of our hope that we shall soon see another manuscript upon more orthodox lines from your pen : you may be assured that we shall give it the fullest and most favourable consideration possible. We are by no means blind to the indubitable possibilities of your work.

Your MS. is being returned to you under separate cover.

Yours sincerely,

WILLIAM H. KANE.

E. MANORY KING, ESQ.

(*Unposted.*)

THE STUDIO FLAT, 9 DIGBY STREET,
RUSSELL SQUARE, LONDON, W.C.2.
April 23rd, 193–.

So's your old man !

E. M. K.

WM. H. KANE, ESQ.

The St. Stephen's Bank, Limited
(NEW ROAD BRANCH)

Tel. : Skip 1234.

214 NEW ROAD,
WESTMINSTER,
LONDON, S.E.1.

E. MANORY KING, ESQ.,
The Manager acknowledges receipt of favour to hand,
of the 21st instant, and will reply to the same in due course.

22nd April, 193–.

E. V. WINSOME
Provision Merchant

13 VILLIPER STREET, LONDON, W.C.2

To A/c rendered   .   £3 19s. 8½d.

A cheque in settlement by return is requested for this long
overdue A/c.

GAUNTLET & HARRIS
Tailors and Breeches Makers
120b SAVILLE ROW, LONDON, W.1.

Telephone : Gerrard 81320.
Telegrams : Seatingly, London

22nd April, 193–.

DEAR SIR,
We note with surprise that your long overdue account of
£17 17s. 0d. has not yet been met, in spite of our frequent
applications for payment.
We trust that you will make it unnecessary for us to take
other action in the matter by letting us have a cheque for the
amount per return of post.

Yours faithfully,

HENRY GAUNTLET.

CAPTAIN E. MANORY KING,
9 DIGBY STREET, W.C. 2.

THE MAN IN THE MOON

RUSSELL SQUARE, W.C.

MR. KING,

		£	s.	d.
To :—				
6 Botts. P.A.	. . . .		3	9
1 Bott. Walker	. . . .		12	6
3 Rounds Drinks (Monday)	. .		6	2½
2 ,, ,, (Tuesday)	. .		6	2½
20 Cigs. (Sunday)	. . .		1	0
Carried fd. (from March)	. .	2	11	4
		4	8	5½

Boy will call for empties Sat. Stock-takers come Mon.
Settmt. wld. ob.

B. BUNN.

THE YARD OF ALE CLUB

Tel : Gerrard 12345.   ALE YARD,
                                                     DALROY ST., W.1.
                                                     22nd April, 193–.

E. M. KING, ESQ.
  The Committee begs to call your attention to Rule 160,
which provides that unless yearly subscriptions are paid within
two calendar months from the 1st of January in each year, the
member or members failing to pay will cease to enjoy membership if the subscription due be not forthcoming within seven
days after receipt of the official notification.

                                  (Subscription due £2 2s. 0d.)

HYGIENIC DAIRIES, LIMITED

                                  Head Office : 44 MELROSE ROAD,
Telephone : Golders 84.   LONDON, N.W.14.
                                       April 22nd, 193–.

MR. KING,
9 DIGBY STREET, W.C. 2.

DEAR SIR,
  I am instructed to apply to you for immediate payment
of your account (£7 12s. 6d.) with our Russell Square Branch.
  Your cheque by return will oblige.

                              Yours faithfully,
                                  CHARLES A. BARRY
                                  (Head Cashier).

ARTHUR HAMBLETON

NEWSAGENT.   **TOBACCO.**

April 22.

To MR. KING,

DR. SIR,
    I have honour enclose ac/t (£5 6s. 4d.) herewith and the same paid would give satisfaction.

                              Truly,

                                   A. HAMBLETON.

FOX & DOUBLEDAY

(EVERYTHING FOR THE HOUSE)

TOTTENHAM COURT ROAD, W.1.

Tel. : Court 8765.

FINAL APPLICATION.

    To instalments due upon Goods *

	£	s.	d.
February instalment . .	3	12	6
March do. . .	3	12	6
April do. . .	3	12	6
	10	17	6

E. M. KING, Esq.,
9 Digby Street, W.C.

        * 1 Wardrobe. 2 Tables. D.R. Chairs (6).
        2 Carpets. 1 Bed. Plate. Linen, etc.

NEW READERS BEGIN HERE

MANORY KING, a young and handsome novelist, who, having been a successful soldier during the war, is now an unsuccessful writer, has, after much delay, had his fourth novel refused by

KANE AND FEATHERSTONE, his erstwhile Publishers.

He is in debt to

BANK, LANDLORD, and various importunate creditors. He has, after facing the possible refusal of Bank to keep his honour intact, gathered sufficient money to lend thirty shillings to

JOHN HARRINGTON, a journalist, but his friend, and to buy a return ticket to Soliton, where he intends to spend the week-end with his mother,

MRS. KING, and his sister,

MISS KING, and his brother,

HENRY KING, who does not come into the story at all.

NOW READ ON

FIRST STOP EXETER

" One week-end return Soliton, please. How much ? "

" Thirty-eight an' six."

" Here ! You've given me fourpence too much change."

" No, I . . . Sorry, sir. Thank you, sir."

" Right. . . . Which platform's the eight-forty go from ? "

" Number six. . . ."

" Thanks."

" Porter, sir ? "

" No, thanks. Which side's Number Six ? "

" Rahnd top end, sir. Better 'urry if y' want the ite-foary. On'y couple o' minutes."

" Good God ! "

" Hallo, Bob ! Thought you'd missed it."

" Oh, I've been in the station matter of a quarter of an hour. Been at the bookstall. We're in luck ; carriage to ourselves."

" Never many first-class on this early one. Cigarette ? "

" Thanks. . . . Paper ? . . . Seen the *Onlooker* ? "

" Not yet. Yes . . . ought to be off soon, she's a minute late already."

" Um ! "

" Good God ! "

" What's up ? "

" The *Onlooker's* got Gorm for book-reviewing."

" Ha ! Yes, I saw they had. Don't you like it ? "

" *Like* it ! *Like* it ! Just because the scrofulous, swollen-headed pooh's bluffed the public, via the *Planet*, into thinking he's a critic of drama, here's what used to be a sober-headed, quite intelligent weekly like the *Onlooker* taking him on as their star bookman. . . . It's—it's . . . No wonder no good work ever gets a fair show nowadays. Hallo, we're off."

" Yes. Better shut the window, hadn't we, till we've passed the turn ? . . . Good Lord, the silly ass, he'll never do it ! Look here ! Look at this chap sprinting. . . ."

" He *will* do it. Turn of speed. . . . Here ! Open our door and hold it for him or that porter'll stop . . ."

" Ste—ady ! . . . Grab his arm, Howard. . . ."

" Gottim. . . . Hee—ave away ! . . . Slam door, Bob . . ."

" *There* you are, sir ! "

" Much . . . foof. . . . Much obliged . . . foof ! Thanks awfully. Damn . . . foof . . . good of you . . . foof . . ."

" Look *out*, Howard. His suit-case'll be on your head. . . ."

" Foof. Just caught it. Sorry. Damn clumsy. Afraid I'm a bit of a nuisance. And there's my third-class ticket on the floor, so it's no good pretending I'm entitled to travel with you. I'll change at Exeter."

" Why ? They never send an inspector on to this one. Do they, Bob ? "

" Never. You sit tight, sir. You've earned your seat. Care for a paper ? "

" Thanks. I was too rushed to get anything. Very kind of you."

" Got the time, Bob ? "

" Ten minutes to Exeter. What's the book ? Seems to've got hold of you."

" Has—almost. Thing called *First to the Left*. It starts extraordinarily well. Amazing. But it begins to weaken about the middle. And I'll bet the end's going to be right off it."

" That's the worst of you literary blokes. So critical you can't enjoy . . ."

" Don't be silly. Fancy calling a publisher ' literary.' My dear man, that's the last thing a publisher is. No *real* publisher ever reads a book. I do sometimes—that's why I'll never be a success. Old Flewin's never read anything in his life except *Little Arthur's History of England* and the *Morning Pòst*."

" You'd better follow his example. Give up reading and play more golf. You're getting fat, anyhow."

" If your stomach's a sample of what golf will do for the average man, I'll stick to books . . . I tell you what, though. If you find me the book for the firm to publish—which is the book I am looking for, I won't read another for six months and I'll play six rounds a week with you."

" If you know the sort of book you're looking for, why not write it yourself ? Or get some clever lad to do it to specification."

" You've got a draper's soul in a stockbroker's carcass. . . .
Seriously, though, I've been looking for something for two years
and can I find it ? I can't."

" What sort of a book ? "

" No particular *sort*. Something fairly good *and* utterly
new. Above all, utterly new. . . . Very difficult to put what
I mean—what I know I mean—into words. All I know is that
if it ever comes along I shall know it. It may be an old story ;
in fact, it will be, but something about it will be *new*—angle or
method or technique or all three. I don't mean I'm after
another Gertrude Stein. Far from it. I *think* what I want
will turn out to be something like a story of Ethel M. Dell's
recast by Arnold Bennett and written by Anita Loos. *Something*
like that, only more so, if you follow me. . . ."

" I don't. But carry on."

" I—I can't. Damn it ; it comes to this—that I'm waiting
for something and I don't know what it is, but I shall when I
see it, whatever it is. Follow ? "

" What you really mean is that you want something no one's
done before. . . . Hal-lo ! Here we are. That chap still
asleep ? "

" Leave him ; he's going on. Soliton, the ticket was. . . .
Ah, he's coming to. . . . This is only Exeter, sir."

" Thanks. Thanks. Just—just remembered something.
Got—got to telephone."

" Steady there. She always pulls up with a jerk here. . . .
Oops ! There we are. . . . Come on, Howard. . . . Good-
day, sir."

" Porter ! . . . Hi, you, there ! . . . Porter ! *Porter !* "

" Zir ? "

" Telephone and telegraph. Is there an office at the
station ? "

WHAT HAS HAPPENED

MANORY KING, a young, handsome, and impecunious Novelist who has only been successful as a Soldier, has had his latest MS. refused by his erstwhile publishers. Having precariously obtained sufficient money for his journey, he is on his way to spend the week-end in Devonshire with his Mother and Sister and Brother,

MRS. KING, MISS KING, AND HENRY KING, all members of the same family.

Nearly missing his train, he gets into a first-class compartment, in which are already seated

HOWARD GARTH, the junior partner of the publishing firm of Flewin, Mile & Garth, and his friend

ROBERT GRAMERCY FORFOLD PAGE, a prosperous and entirely unimportant Stockbroker.

Manory, apparently asleep but in reality working out complicated financial calculations behind closed eyelids, overhears a conversation between Garth and Page which makes him determined to submit his MS. *Glitter*, to Garth's firm. He accordingly breaks his journey at Exeter, telephones to his friend,

JOHN HARRINGTON, an almost honest journalist, asking him to collect the MS. and deliver it to the offices of Flewin, Mile & Garth, and telegraphs to Mrs. King, his Mother, that his arrival has been delayed.

NOW BEGIN

FIRST GLEAMS

Title :	*Date Submitted :*	*Author :*
Glitter.	25th April, 193–.	E. M. King.

In accordance with request, I have read this book within twenty-four hours.

I do not recommend its publication. I suppose it is clever but am not very sure of this. In my opinion the form of the book is sufficient to condemn it. This form—or lack of form—may be apprehended in a casual glance through the pages. The author seemed to be striving after a new method and to have achieved only an indigestible mixture of a dozen old ones.

As for the story, it might, conceivably, be interesting if directly written ; but even then it would be so wild a combination of realism and fantasy ; character and crime ; action and reflection that I think it would almost surely fail with the critics and certainly with the public.

A. J. FARQUHAR-SMYTHE.

" Miss Frost."
" Yes, Mr. Garth ? "
" Mr. A. J. Farquhar-Smythe's a blasted old fool ! "
" Yes, Mr. Garth."

MEMORANDUM

From Mr. Garth.   *To* Mr. Flewin.

Send you herewith F.-S.'s report on *Glitter*, the MS. I have spoken to you about. F.-S. is entirely wrong. I think he is getting too old for reading ; certainly he is too set in his opinions. Have told you my opinion of *Glitter*, which has not changed. We *must* have a try with this. It will either flop or go to ten thousand. Can't we have a little gamble on it ?   H. G.

28th April.

MEMORANDUM

From Mr. Flewin.   *To* Mr. Garth.

Re *Glitter*. I never gamble. See author. Offer him £80 outright. If he sells will authorize heavy initial advertising. If he won't sell : usual first novel terms ; only 2.5 per cent. extra for publicity.

G. A. F.

28th April.

" *Miss Frost.*"
" *Yes, Mr. Garth ?* "
" *Mr. Flewin . . .*"
" *Yes, Mr. Garth ?* "
" *Never mind.   Get him on the phone.*"
" *He's still got it disconnected, Mr. Garth.*"
" *He . . .*"

MEMORANDUM

From Mr. Garth.   *To* Mr. Flewin.

Yours noted.   But this is King's *fourth* novel.

H. G.

28th April.

MEMORANDUM

From Mr. Flewin.   *To* Mr. Garth.

I know.

G. A. F.

" *Miss Frost.*"

" *Yes, Mr. Garth ?* "

" *Ring up this man King.   Fix an appointment.*"

" *To-day ?* "

" *If he can.   I expect he will.   Three-thirty.*"

" *Very well, Mr. Garth.*"

MEMORANDUM

From Mr. Garth.   *To* Mr. Flewin.

Glitter.   In order not to waste time I had King up here to-day.   Pleasant fellow ;   young, with any amount of good work in him.   Put your proposals to him.   He will not sell. He boggled at the " first novel " terms, but will take them, if we pay the advance on signing agreement and not on publication.   I think we should do this.   I imagine he is hard up.

H. G.

29th April.

MEMORANDUM

From Miss Moreland.   *To* Mr. Garth.

Mr. Flewin tells me to write, re *Glitter*, that he agrees to the suggestion in your last memo.

I. M.

Flewin, Mile & Garth

Telephone : Gerrard 34560.   ADAM HOUSE,
                                                                ADELPHI, W.
                                                          29th April, 193–.

DEAR MR. KING,

Confirming our conversation of yesterday in regard to *Glitter*, we would be willing to publish this book, provided you will agree to the following terms :

A payment of £35 in advance, on account of a royalty of 10% (ten per cent.) of the published price, such royalty to increase to twelve and a half per cent. on all copies which might be sold after 5000. The publishers to retain the U.S. rights and pay to the Author 50% (fifty per cent.) of the monies received for such rights.

All other rights, e.g., Film, Dramatic, and Serial to be retained by the Author.

The publishers to have the option of publishing the Author's next six books on the same terms.

In regard to the question of the date for payment of the advance, I have consulted with my partners, and find that we could make a special instance and pay you this sum on signature of the contract.

Yours sincerely,

HOWARD GARTH.

P.S.—I wonder whether you would care to lunch with me on Wednesday next at one-fifteen, at the Junior Universities ? I think, after the extraordinary coincidence of our meeting in the train last Saturday, we should further the acquaintance.

" *Miss Frost !* "

" *Yes, Mr. Garth ?* "

" *E. Manory King should go a long way.*"

" *Yes, Mr. Garth.*"

" *He seizes opportunities, also he can give the best imitation of a man asleep that I've ever seen.*"

DRAFT

DEAR MR. GARTH,

Many thanks for your letter. I wonder whether you could get your Secretary to let me know over the telephone how quickly the contract could be prepared for signature, as I

DRAFT

DEAR MR. GARTH,

While there are certain points about your suggested contract that I do not quite like, e.g., the next six books and the amount of the advance

DRAFT

DEAR MR. GARTH,

I agree to the terms set out in your letter, and I should be very much obliged indeed if you would have the contract prepared at once so that we could complete within as short a time as possible.

I am sorry to be so urgent, but the fact of the matter is

DEAR JACK,

I only heard last night that you had been sent to Glasgow on that job. Many thanks for returning the thirty bob, badly needed.

Have had a bit of luck ; *Glitter* is placed at last—with the people you took it to after my phone message from Exeter. Funny thing, I nearly missed my train on Saturday and shot into a first-class carriage in which were Garth, the junior partner, and some friend of his. His talk—while I was feigning slumber—made me think he was the man for *Glitter*, and sure enough he has turned out to be. I saw him yesterday and we were both very amused at the coincidence of my having sent the MS. !

Seems quite a nice fellow, fairly honest for a publisher. They have given me rather bad terms but I can't dictate at the moment.

Ring me up as soon as you get back as I think a little cheque swapping seems indicated.

Yours,

E. M. K.

P.S.—Many thanks for getting the MS. in so promptly. It must have quite prevented Garth having any suspicion about my sleep in the train.

DRAFT

DEAR MR. GARTH,

Thanks for your letter. The terms are perfectly satisfactory. This is rather a bad way to begin business relations, but I wonder whether I might ask you to let me have the cheque for the advance at once without waiting for the preparation and signature of the

DEAREST MOTHER,

I can't think how I came to make the mistake, but I seem to remember telling you that my new book was going to be published by my old publishers. This was very silly of me, because it is to be done by Flewin, Mile & Garth, a very much better firm from whom I get much better terms than I ever did from the others.

The week-end was as good as ever. I hated having to come back, but as you know, I have a lot of work on hand and must get on with it.

Love to everybody, will see you again soon.

E. M.

DRAFT

DEAR MR. GARTH,

Many thanks for your letter. I think that I can agree to the terms you suggest, provided that the contract only binds me for ~~three~~ four more novels, and that the advance is raised from £35 to ~~£50~~ £40. Also I would like to suggest that owing to a temporary delay in payment of ~~large royalties due to me from my U.S. publishers~~ other sources the contract is prepared and completed at once so that the advance can be paid to me forthwith. ~~matter of the advance may be completed without delay.~~

STUDIO FLAT, 9 DIGBY STREET,
RUSSELL SQUARE, LONDON, W.C. 2.
April 30*th,* 193–.

DEAR MR. GARTH,

Many thanks for your letter of yesterday.

I quite agree to the terms set out therein. I wonder whether you would be good enough to have the contract drawn up at once so that I can feel the matter is definitely settled. I could call at any time to sign the contract and save you posting it.

I would like to lunch very much with you on the date you suggest, and will be at the Junior Universities at one-fifteen unless I hear from you to the contrary in the meantime.

Yes, it was certainly an odd coincidence that I should have sent you the manuscript of *Glitter* before struggling into your carriage on Saturday.

Yours sincerely,

E. MANORY KING.

" Is that Gerrard 34560 ? "
" Yes."
" Flewin, Mile & Garth ? "
" Yes."
" Can I speak to Mr. Garth's secretary, please ? "

GBH

14

" Hold on a minute. . . ."

" Mr. Garth's secretary speaking."

" Manory King this end."

" Yes, Mr. King."

" I wrote to Mr. Garth a couple of days ago. . . ."

" Yes, Mr. King ? "

" I was wondering . . . could you let me know . . . do you, by any chance, happen to know whether the contract for *Glitter's* been made out yet ? "

" They're working on it now, Mr. King."

" Oh, thanks. . . . Er . . . have you any idea when it will be finished ? I should probably be passing your office this afternoon and could come in to sign it."

" I am afraid it wouldn't be this afternoon, but it should be ready to-morrow."

" Oh . . . thanks. . . ."

```
┌─────────────────────┐
│  ENQUIRIES:         │
│  PLEASE RING        │
└─────────────────────┘
```

" Good-morning. . . . My name's King—Manory King. Could I see Mr. Garth ?   Or his secretary ? "

" One moment, please. . . . Ay'm sorry. Mr. Garth is engaged and Miss Frost is at lunch.   Can ay do anything ? "

" I wonder if you'd kindly find out whether the contract for my book, *Glitter*, is ready for signature ?   They told me it would be to-day.   I happened to be passing, and I . . ."

" One moment, please. . . . Ay'm sorry ; the contract is with Mr. Flewin for approval."

" Oh. . . . I see. . . . Perhaps Mr. Flewin could spare me . . ."

" Ay'm sorry, Mr. Flewin is not in to-day. The contract will have been sent down to the country with the rest of Mr. Flewin's peepers."

" Oh. . . . Right. . . . It doesn't matter. . . . I just happened to be passing. . . . Good-afternoon."

MISS MORELAND: PLEASE CLOSE DOOR

" Good-morning, Miss Moreland ? "

" Good afternoon. Mr. King, is it ? . . . I'm *very* sorry, Mr. King, but I fear that I have dragged you up here upon a wild-goose chase."

" But your note . . ."

" I *know* ; that is the trouble. When they informed me yesterday that you had called. I spoke to Mr. Flewin upon the telephone. And he stated—or I understood him to state—that he would either bring your contract back with his other papers this morning, or would, if he did not return to the office to-day, send it, by messenger, with his other papers. Accordingly I asked you by letter. . . ."

" But when do you . . ."

" Mr. Flewin, however, followed neither of these courses. And as I was unable to trace your telephone . . ."

" I'm not on the telephone just at present. I . . ."

" As I was unable to trace your telephone number, and so could not get a word with you over the wire, I had a telegram despatched . . ."

" I'm afraid I've been out all the . . ."

" But since you are here, I presume that either it miscarried or that you have been away from home. I am really exceedingly . . ."

" That's quite all right. But I'd like to get this matter settled up. Could you tell me when . . ."

" Mr. Flewin will be with us to-morrow, Mr. King. So soon as I see him, I will put . . ."

" So if I were to give you a ring . . ."

" If you would be so good as to have a word with me over the wire, let us say late in the forenoon, I could then inform you with . . ."

" Thanks, thanks. Yes. I'll ring up just before twelve. Thanks."

" *Thank* you, Mr. King. If, then, you will do as you say and call me upon the tel . . ."

" I will. I will. Thanks. Thanks. . . . Afternoon."

" Hold the line, please, and I'll switch you through. . . . Here you are."

" Miss Moreland."

" Speaking.   That is Mr. King ? . . . Mr. King, I have had a word with Mr. Flewin. . . ."

" Over the wire ? "

" No.   Not over the wire.   Mr. Flewin is here.   Mr. Flewin asks me to say that he would be glad if you could manage to make it convenient to call here and see him sometime to-morrow or the next day.   Or should either of these days prove inconvenient, then shall we say Friday next ?   I . . ."

" The HELL we . . ."

" I beg your pardon. . . ."

" So sorry.   So sorry.   I—I hurt myself. . . ."

" Dear me !   How did . . ."

" Nothing.   Nothing at all.   A—a dog came into the box and snapped . . ."

" Goodness gracious.   I . . ."

" GO AWAY, you little beast. . . . He's gone now. . . . A very small dog. . . . Miss Moreland, will you please give Mr. Flewin my compliments and tell him that I am afraid I have to go to Scotland to-morrow.   Would it be best if Mr. Flewin could spare me a moment this afternoon ?   I want to get this contract off my mind before I go away."

" I see.   I appreciate the situation.   If you will hold the line a moment I will . . ."

" Do.   Do."

" Your time is up.   Will you have another three minutes ? "

" Don't be silly !   I haven't been talking for two . . ."

" Your time is up !   Will you have another three minutes ? "

" Yes.   Only it's a damn . . ."

" Th-rrree   pennies,   please. . . . One. . . . Two. . . . Thrrree. . . . Press button A. . . . You are through again."

" Hallo.   Hal-*lo*.   *Hal*-lo ! "

" Mr. King ? "

" Yes."

" I have had a word with Mr. Flewin.   He desires me to state that he is very pressed this afternoon, but that if you could make it convenient to call in at four-thirty he would be delighted to . . ."

" Thanks, thanks.   Four-thirty.   I'll be there.   G'bye."

" If you would step this way, Mr. King. . . . Mr. King, Mr. Flewin."

" Ah !   How d'ye do, Mr. King ? "

" How do you do ? "

" Sit down, won't you ? . . . That's right. . . . Fine weather, Mr. King."

" Yes. A pity it's raining."

" Yes. Yes. Wretched day."

" Yes."

" Now, let me see. About this series of wrappers you were to . . ."

" Wrappers ? "

" Wrappers, yes. The point I wish to . . ."

" *Wrappers ?* "

" Jackets, then. I want to make it per . . ."

" I think there's some mistake."

" Mistake ? "

" Yes."

" Mistake ? "

" Yes. My name is King—Manory King. I understand that you are going to publish my . . ."

" Of course ! Of course ! Stupid of me, Mr. King. My thoughts were wandering. Now, about this book of yours— *Tinsel.* . . ."

" *Glitter.*"

" Yes ; this book, *Glitter*. Now, Mr. King, we have decided to publish this book. We like it. We think it has possibilities, distinct possibilities. But with—er—with this type of book, we have to be careful. Very careful, Mr. King. Very careful."

" Ye-es ? "

" Yes. Very careful. It is a book which . . . Come in. Ah ! Afternoon, Garth."

" Afternoon. Hallo, King, how are you ? "

" Very well, thanks."

" Garth ; I was just discussing with Mr. King his book, *Spangles* . . ."

" *Glitter.*"

" Yes. His book, *Glitter*. I was saying that, although we think a lot of its possibilities, we have, with a book of this type . . ."

" Excuse me a moment, Mr. Flewin. I dare say authors' opinions of their own work aren't worth much, but it does seem to me that whatever value there is in *Glitter* lies in its being of no ' type ' at all."

" There's a lot in what he says, Flewin. I agree with him."

" Yes. Yes. Perhaps I didn't make myself clear. I didn't

intend to refer to the—er—style of the writing, but to the *story*. There . . ."

" I say, Flewin . . ."

" One moment, Garth, one moment. . . . As I was saying, Mr. King, I did not intend to refer to—er—the *style* but to the *story*. Now, with these modern stories dealing with stage-life . . ."

" Stage-life ? "

" Yes. Yes. Stage-life and—er—night clubs . . . and—er—or, let me see . . . let me see . . . am I confusing . . ."

" You are, Flewin. King's book doesn't deal with the stage. In fact, the stage is almost the only thing it isn't about."

" Yes. Yes. I'm sorry, Mr. King. But you will understand how easy it is for us to become temporarily confused. . . ."

" Quite. Quite."

" Well, I don't think there's anything else, Mr. King. We shall publish your book and give it a fair showing. Yes. So we needn't keep you any long . . ."

" Half a moment, Flewin. I think King really dropped in to see you about his contract. . . ."

" Quite. Quite. Well, Mr. King, we are giving you our usual terms. You know them, I believe. They are generous."

" Yes. I . . ."

" Yes. We will have the contract prepared and sent to you for your signature. . . ."

" The contract's ready, Flewin. I sent it down to you for approval. I think we might as well sign it now and get it done with."

" Well . . . yes. One moment. . . . Where is the woman ? Why can't she answer when I ring ? . . . Ah, Miss Moreland, I believe you will find in my bag, with the other papers, a contract in respect of Mr. King's novel, *Twinkles* . . ."

" *Glitter*."

" Mr. King's novel, *Glitter*. Please bring it in."

" The two copies are before you, Mr. Flewin. I laid them upon your desk after lunch. I thought . . ."

" Ah ! Yes. Here it is. Thank you, Miss Moreland. Now then, business. I sign here. . . . And give you this, Mr. King. You read through this copy and sign it, and return it to me. . . . So. . . . Now our business is completed. . . . Good-day, Mr. King. I hope we shall have the pleasure of seeing you again up here and telling you how many thousands of copies of *Gilt* we are selling per week. Ha ! "

" There's the matter of Mr. King's cheque yet, Flewin.

The advance clause makes it payable now and not on publication."

"Very well, Mr. King. I will give instructions that the cheque is prepared and sent on to you in due course. Goodday."

"Er . . . I . . . well, thanks very much. Good-bye."

POST OFFICE TELEGRAPH

Handed in at STRAND.   *6th May*, 193–.
      2.15 p.m.

To : Hollington. c/o *Scottish Planet.* Glasgow.

S.O.S. somehow wire at least three ideas urgent sending letter now with duplicate to cover.

KING.

STUDIO FLAT,
6. v. 3–.

DEAR JACK,

Hope to God you got my wire : I think you'll understand it ; know you will. Here's a cheque for the three. If you couldn't raise it, and haven't wired, burn cheque. If you have (please the Lord !) cash cheque—as late as possible. It should take over two days from now to get to my bank, and in the meantime I'll fix things with them.

Having the hell of a time trying to get my advance out of F. M. & G. Cheque yesterday, cheque to-morrow, but *never* cheque to-day. That's their technique. Devil of it is, it's such bad business to look as if one's tongue was hanging out over a matter of thirty-five quid. I've succeeded (or perhaps I haven't) in disguising anguish ; but can't last out any longer. If they don't give it to me to-morrow, I'll pinch their petty-cash or something. Mossy lot of illegitimates ! Especially Flewin—the

Big Noise. Hæmorrhage of words and a stricture of ideas. And he's got a secretary—oh, my Creator ! Same complaints as her boss, worse ; face like the back of a dragon.

Did you ever tell Bobsworth about my " Do Wives Make Good Mothers ? " article ? I *must* get some hack work. For Mike's sake hurry up and come back. I've got that all-alone-in-the-great-city-and-the-streets-*aren't*-paved-with-gold sort of feeling.

Yrs.,

E. M. K.

FINANCIAL POSITION (1)

Credit.	£	s.	d.		*Debit.*	£	s.	d.	
F. M. & G.	35	0	0	(to come)	*	15	0	0	(Bank. Ex. O/D)
		4	7	(in hand)	†	3	19	8½	(Booze—
Cleever	4	4	0	(to come)					Winsome)
(Reading fees.)					†	5	8	5½	(do. &c. Man in
									Moon)
	39	8	7		†	2	2	0	(Yard of Ale)
					*	7	12	6	(Dairy)
					†	5	6	4	(Hambleton)
					***	10	17	6	(Fox &
						3	12	6	Doubleday)
						17	17	0	(Tailor)
* Nasty One.						70	16	0	
† Do Something.						8	10	6	(Rent)
						79	6	6	
						39	8	7	
					Minus	39	17	11	

FINANCIAL POSITION (2)

Credit.					Debit.			
	£	s.	d.		£	s.	d.	
F. M. & G.	35	0	0	(to come)	10	0	0	(Bank)
		4	7	(in hand)	1	0	0	Winsome)
Cleever	4	4	0	(to come)	2	0	0	(M. in Moon)
					5	0	0	(Dairy)
	39	8	7		2	10	0	(Hamb.)
					10	17	6	(F. & D.)
					5	0	0	(Rent)
					36	7	6	

£	s.	d.
39	8	7
36	7	6
3	1	1

STUDIO FLAT, 9 DIGBY STREET,
RUSSELL SQUARE, LONDON, W.C. 2.
May 8th, 193–.

DEAR JACK,

Many thanks for the three quid. They tell me at the *Planet* office that you will be back on Tuesday. Don't be surprised but you may find me on the sofa in your rooms.

I am very ill, and have been ordered away to the country by my doctor.

Yours,

E. M. K.

P.S.—Have £35 in hand, enough to share expenses for a bit.

PART TWO

READ THIS FIRST

E. MANORY KING, a young and handsome novelist, has at last succeeded in placing his newest novel,

" GLITTER," with

FLEWIN, MILE & GARTH, a well-known but moderately scrupulous firm of publishers.

King, pressed on all sides by

CREDITORS, people to whom he owes money, manages at last to extract, five days late, a cheque for £35 from his publishers. Examining his financial position he finds that if he is to pay out anything at all it will leave him with insufficient money. He therefore arranges with his friend,

JOHN HARRINGTON, a journalist, but pleasant, that he shall share Harrington's rooms until such time as the financial situation has been relieved.

NOW READ ON.

Flewin, Mile & Garth

Adam House, Adelphi, W.
September 2nd, 193–.

Dear Mr. King,

Mr. Garth has asked me to send you the enclosed cuttings, showing our advertisements in *The Times Literary Supplement*, *Planet*, *Observer*, and *The Sunday Times*.

Yours sincerely,

A. Frost.

ENC : 1. *Times Lit. Sup.*

Flewin, Mile & Garth
Autumn Announcements

GLITTER
by
E. MANORY KING

An unusual and trenchant book by this rising young author. The publishers are convinced that a great success awaits this arresting and individual work.

ENC : 2. *The Planet*

FLEWIN, MILE & GARTH
Autumn Announcements

GLITTER
E. MANORY KING

E. Manory King—*Glitter*—Love and Satire ! Realism and Fantasy ! ! Laughter and Suspense ! ! ! Mystery and Romance ! ! ! ! Farce and Melodrama ! ! ! ! !

All England will soon be talking about this book. It *MUST* be read !

ENC : 3.   *The Observer*

FLEWIN, MILE & GARTH
Autumn Announcements

GLITTER

by

E. MANORY KING

A penetrating and original study, in a style altogether its own, of life as it is and as it should be.

ENC : 4.   *The Sunday Times*

Flewin, Mile & Garth
Autumn Announcements

GLITTER

E: MANORY KING

In *Glitter* Mr. E. Manory King has given us a book so unusual, so compelling, so vivid and yet so delicate that we have no hesitation whatsoever in advancing the opinion that it is not only a book which everybody should read, but a book which everybody will read.

> 8 RUSSELL ROAD, BLOOMSBURY, W.C.
> *September 5th, 193–.*

UNITED PRESS AGENCY,
143 MORTIMER STREET,
W.C. 3.

DEAR SIRS,
   I believe that I have inadvertently allowed my subscription to fall in arrear. I accordingly send you herewith a cheque for 15*s.* 6*d.* and would be glad if you would continue your press-cutting service, to the address above, with particular reference to my new novel *Glitter.*

> Yours faithfully,
>
> E. MANORY KING.

FLEWIN, MILE & GARTH
Early Autumn Announcements

General :

SHOULD AMERICA BE ABOLISHED

by

FATHER ROBERT KNOWLES

A trenchant powerful series of essays by the well-known cleric, graced with even more than his usual happy satire.

Fiction :

THE CORPSE IN THE CONSERVATORY

by

FRED LUTYENS

Another clever thriller from this king of mystery writers.

LOVE ON THE HIGH SEAS

by

MURIEL EMSWORTH DAKIN

A charming story, alight with the blaze of romance and played out against a vivid background of life in Honolulu.

GLITTER

by

E. MANORY KING

Mr. Manory King has already firmly established his reputation. This new book, which is entirely unlike anything he has done before, should go far towards setting him among the very first rank of our present-day novelists. It is something *NEW!*

Flewin, Mile & Garth

Telephone : Gerrard 34560.　　　　ADAM HOUSE,
　　　　　　　　　　　　　　　　　　　ADELPHI, W.
　　　　　　　　　　　　　　　　　　June 2nd, 193-.
Publicity Department.

DEAR SIR,
　　We should be much obliged if you would let us have for
publicity purposes a recent photo of yourself and some biographical notes. If possible, we should like the photo to be a
novel one, *e.g.,* sitting at your desk writing, and should like the
biographical notes to include such tit-bits of interest as your
favourite author, how I do my work, etc.
　　We may not require this material just at present, but we like
to have such information to hand upon our files.

　　　　　　　　　　　　　Yours very truly,
　　　　　　　　　　　　　　　F. G. BLIGHT
　　　　　　　　　　　　　　　　(Publicity Manager).

E. MANORY KING, ESQ., 9 DIGBY STREET,
　　RUSSELL SQUARE, W.C.2.

Flewin, Mile & Garth

Telephone : Gerrard 34560.　　　　ADAM HOUSE,
　　　　　　　　　　　　　　　　　　　ADELPHI, W.
　　　　　　　　　　　　　　　　　　June 30th, 193-.
Publicity Department.

DEAR SIR,
　　I have to hand this morning the artist's rough for the jacket
we intend to use upon your novel, *Glitter.* I should very much
like to have a word with you on this matter, and am wondering
whether you could make it convenient to call at the office some
time during this week when you can look at the rough, and we
can discuss it.
　　I enclose herewith (1) a copy of my letter of the 2nd of June,
which was returned marked " Address unknown " from Digby

Street, and which I wrote before receiving your card stating that
all letters should be sent c/o J. Harrington, Esq., and (2) a copy
of the matter which it is proposed to print upon the dust jacket
of *Glitter*.

I should be much obliged if you could read over this last and
tell us whether it meets with your approval.

Yours very truly,

F. G. BLIGHT
(Publicity Manager).

E. MANORY KING, ESQ., c/o J. HARRINGTON, ESQ.,
8 RUSSELL ROAD, BLOOMSBURY, W.C.

8 RUSSELL ROAD, BLOOMSBURY, W.C.
July 1st, 193–.

DEAR SIR,

Many thanks for your letter of the 30th June. I am afraid
I have no photographs of myself at all, except one taken by my
sister when I was fifteen years old, and which would certainly
do nothing towards furthering any sales which my work might
have.

As to biographical details, I think the best thing to do is to
tabulate as follows :

Born (in wedlock), 1896.

Height : 6 ft. Weight : 12 st. 10 lb. 8 oz.

Educated : St. James's School and Trinity, Cambridge.
Left Cambridge after one year on the outbreak of War.

1915–16. Active service in France with 8th Hussars, R.E.
Signals, and Machine Gun Corps.

1916–18. Service in Egypt. With 2nd Lancers and Cavalry
Machine Gun Corps.

Bachelor. Recreations : boxing, fencing, watching polo.

Hobbies : none.   Vices : usual.

In regard to the wrapper, would it be suitable if I called at
your office next Tuesday afternoon at about three ?

As to the blurb, I have been wondering whether it is it not
possible to avoid anything of this sort. In my opinion blurbs

are never of value as they either mislead the intending reader entirely as to what he is going to get or else disappoint him bitterly with the book, because they have raised his expectations to such a pitch that no writer could possibly live up to them.

> Yours faithfully,
> E. MANORY KING.

P.S.—I wonder whether you could tell me exactly when *Glitter* will be making its appearance ?

DEAR E.,
   Hadn't the heart to wake you up. Billiter very sniffy about rent. Could you give him something this morning ? See you about squaring up to-night. Shall be in about seven-thirty. Your book's come.

Flewin, Mile & Garth

Telephone : Gerrard 34560.   ADAM HOUSE,
                                            ADELPHI, W.
                                   August 29th, 193–.

DEAR SIR,
   We have pleasure in sending you herewith six presentation copies of *Glitter.*
   Trusting that this will be satisfactory.

> We are,
> Yours faithfully,
> FLEWIN, MILE & GARTH.

E. MANORY KING, ESQ.,
9 RUSSELL ROAD,
BLOOMSBURY, W.

DEAR J.,
   Have given B. my last four to keep him quiet. Think he will be all right until Sat. Have to go out to-night—freeman's dinner.   M. K.

" Well, s'long, King, ol' man. Ca—ca—can't give you lif' ! Love to give you lif' ! Gug—going my way.

" No No. I thank you. It is all all right. I will walk. Many, many thanks for your hos—hos—hos . . ."

" But's a hellofa night. Lemme . . . lemme . . . givalif'."

" No. No. But you—you must dine with *me* sho—soon, Jardine."

" Ri-oh. When. . . . Awri, cabby, don' start. . . . When ? "

" I—I—I will give you a ring. . . ."

" This is *sho* sudden, Man'ry. . . ."

" Upon the telephone. . . . I—I—am *berry* vizzy at—at—the moment."

" Ri-oh. Give us tinkle. Carn give you a lif' then ? "

" No. No. No. . . . No. No, I thank you. . . . Walk. Prefer. The—the fresh air. . . . The rain in one's face. What—what the doc—doctor most def—def—most definitely ordered."

" Well, good-bye, King."

" Farewell. . . ."

" Taxi for you, sir ? "

" Eh, I beg . . . I beg your pardon ? "

" You require another taxi, sir ? "

" Do I *look* as if I required a taxi-meter cab ? "

" Yes, sir."

" Oh. . . . Yes, you are right, sergeant. I do require a taxim . . . taxim . . . taxim . . ."

" I'll get one, sir."

" Stop ! You—you will not get one. Please sergeant, do not get one. I would rather that you followed any other course than that. I require a cab, sergeant, because it is probably going to rain ; it is cold and I have a long and weary way to go. But I cannot have a cab, sergeant. Is that not sad ? "

" Sad, sir ? Yessir."

" Why cannot I have a cab, sergeant ? Answer adjudged correct, because I have no money with which to pay the cab-driver. . . . Good-night, sergeant."

" Good-night, sir."

" Sergeant ! "

" Yessir ? "

" I feel a little better."

" That's good, sir."

" Is not it ? Sergeant, if I were to take the first turning to the right, would I not come into Fair Street ? And would Fair Street not lead me narrowly to Piccadilly ? "

" Yessir."

" Thank you. Good-night."

" Good-night, sir."

" And, sergeant ? "

" Yessir ? "

" God bless you."

" Thank you, sir."

" Good-night. I am about to walk. Watch me walk. . . . There ! "

" Very creditable, sir."

" Thank you. I shall now keep on walking. . . . My girl ! My girl ! She ain't no I-ngel fair ; if Eving's the plice fer a bee-ootiful fice, you'll never find 'er there. . . . First right. *Should* be Fair Street. 'Tis. . . . She's orlright at night, but in the daylight, she's a norrible sight ter see ; but she's got. . . . *Hell and Death !* . . . 'Struth ! . . ."

" Oh, *have* you hurt yourself ? "

" Hurt myself, madam. *Hurt* myself ? Not, as we say, to notice. I've only broken my right shin-bone in sixteen places. . . . What *is* this ? Your car—oh, *gosh* ! . . . May I hold on to it ? . . ."

" I'm *so* sorry. I'd only switched the lights off for a moment. . . . There they are. May I look ? I know . . ."

" Good *Lord* ! "

" Is it worse ? . . . you're standing on it. P'r'aps you oughtn't to put weight . . ."

" No. No. It's better. I can't feel it. It wasn't anything worse than a hack on the shin. . . ."

" I'm so glad. But the way you exclaimed . . ."

" Something took my breath away."

" Oh ! . . . Not your leg ? "

" Not my leg."

" Oh ! Well, I'm extremely sorry I had the car for a moment without lights. I hope your bruise won't be serious. Good-night ! "

" Er—please forgive me . . . I. . . . What are you doing ? . . . Could I . . . might I . . . can I be of any use ? "

" Are you still here ? No ; I can attend to this, thank you."

" Please let me help you. I'm very good with cars."

" Really ? How interesting. Thank you ; I can manage."

" But, please . . ."

" *Thank you !* I would prefer to be alone. May I suggest

that as your leg is not serious damaged, you depart as you came, singing."

" Look here ! I was . . ."

" Yes. And you are still."

" I am *not*. . . . See here ; it's beginning to rain ; that cloak'll get spoilt if you don't take care. You sit in the car while I tinker. I'm really first-class with cars—first-class. I'm even better with cars than I am with w—— Please sit in the car, while . . ."

" So you're *even* better with cars than you are with—— ? "

" Horses. Horses, I was going to say."

" It wasn't what you started to . . ."

" Yes, it was. Yes. *Wild* horses I was going to say."

" O-oh ! It *is* beginning to rain. . . . Thank you. . . . Well, here I am inside."

" Yes. Splendid ! . . . Er—have you a light in there ? "

" Two. A saloon light and a dash-light."

" Would you mind switching them both on ? "

" Both ? "

" Please."

" Why ? "

" To see by."

" But neither will light the engine."

" I want to—er—very technical, I'm afraid. . . . I may have to—er—follow the wiring through . . ."

" Really ? . . . There you are, then. That do ? "

" Will it do ? . . . Yes. . . . That's *beautiful* ! "

" You won't get very far, will you, until you've at least looked at the engine ? "

" I'm afraid you'll have to let me work my own way."

" I suppose I . . . You're getting *soaked*."

" Am I ? Yes, I suppose it is raining. I like it."

" Have you the time ? The clock on this dash has stopped."

" I haven't. My watch is . . . in dock. Does it matter ? "

" Mere curiosity. I was wondering how long it would take for you to put the car right. Because if you stand there much longer it will probably . . ."

" I was considering. . . . Now, you have been driving the car ; am I right ? "

" Entirely."

" And she has suddenly jibbed with you ? Suddenly stopped running—ceased to function ? "

" Hardly that. She's been parked here, not more than half an hour. And now she won't start. The self-starter seems all

right. And I know there's plenty of petrol. What is it, d'you
think ? Carburettor ? "

" No. No. Not carburettor."

" Ignition ? "

" We-ell, hardly. I'll just . . . perhaps I'd better have a
look. . . ."

" That bonnet-catch just unscrews. Don't wrestle with
it."

" Ah ! I see. Thank you. . . . There you are, then ; let's
have a look at your vitals."

" What're you doing now ? "

" Er—looking . . ."

" Sorry ; I can't quite hear. Could you come here a
moment. Found the trouble ? "

" Yes, I think so. Fairly certain."

" Have you, really ? What is it ? Can you put it right ? "

" I'm afraid not. I shall have to walk to the nearest garage
and get . . ."

" But what *is* the trouble ? "

" Piston."

" *Piston ?* "

" Yes. Piston-casing furred."

" Dear me ! Will you do something for me ? "

" Anything ! "

" *Don't* push so far in. You'll crack this window ! What I
want you to do is to screw that bonnet-cover down, walk round
to the other side, and get in. Will you ? "

" *Will* I ? . . . I say, these seats *are* comfortable. . . . What
did you—— ? Good God ! The engine's started ! "

" Yes. That piston-casing of yours doesn't seem to be matter-
ing much. What had happened was that I had forgotten to
switch on."

" Oh ! "

" Yes. I say, are you *very* good at cars ? "

" No."

" Do you know anything about cars at all ? "

" No."

" Do you know the difference between a piston and a carburettor ? "

" Academically, yes. In practice, no."

" Why did you fool like that then ? "

" You don't like ' fooling about ? ' "

" No. . . . And must you glare like that ? "

" Please leave the light on ! I won't glare. And I'll tell you why I ' fooled about '—although you know quite well already. I fooled about because if I hadn't fooled about I couldn't have been able to stay, and if I hadn't been able to stay I might not have seen you again."

" Now that you have stayed you may not."

" May not what ? "

" See me again."

" I must."

" Must ? "

" I mean that I've *got* to. Got to in the sense that a man has got to have water to drink and bread to eat."

" Oh ! I—I——"

" What ? Say it ! Say it ! Please say it ! "

" Where do you want to go ? "

" There. Or as near to it as I may."

" I don't understand you. Where ? "

" Wherever you're going."

" When you say foolish things you should be careful not to sound as if you meant them. . . ."

" Why ? "

" Because then they sound even—even . . ."

" Even what ? "

" Even more foolish than they are. Where are you going ? "

" I've told you where I *want* to go."

" Let's say : where have you got to go ? "

" Home."

" Which is ? "

" In the purlieus."

" But what purlieus ? . . . You silly man, can't you see I'm offering you a lift ? "

" I *thought* I could. But, to tell the truth, I couldn't believe my luck."

" Are you a lucky person ? "

" I've always said I was the unluckiest devil in the world— until now."

" What made you say that ? "

" D'you want me to tell you ? Really tell you, I mean ? Bear in mind that if I speak the truth you may think I'm crazy. *Do* you want to be told ? Do you ? "

" I . . . I . . . But you. . . . I think you . . ."

" I *can* tell you ? "

" I . . . think . . . you know, you didn't understand my question."

" How ? "

" What I *meant* was : why *used* you to think you were the unluckiest devil in the world ? "

" That *may*'ve been what you meant.   But if I tell you that, may I tell you, after, why I don't think so now ? "

" Y-yes, if you must."

" I used to think I was unlucky because, although I was on active service for four years, I never got killed. . . ."

" What a dreadful thing to say ! "

" Is it ?   I don't think so."

" But why ?   Why ? "

" Because, since the war, everything's gone wrong with me. . . . I see, now, why it has."

" Why ? "

" Law of compensation.   No one can have all the luck—so if there's an enormous lump coming to you, you have to have a lot of rough first. . . . Now don't—please, please don't !—pretend to misunderstand what I'm saying ; don't pretend you don't know that *you*'re the great, the tremendous piece of luck I was talking about."

" I won't.   But I . . ."

" Stop. . . . Look here ; when I ran into this car, I was tight.   Quite tight. . . ."

" I know.   You were singing. . . ."

" But I'm not now.   Am I ? "

" I . . . I don't think so."

" Thank you.   I'm not.   But neither am I normal.   By that I mean that I'm—how shall I put it ?—*released*. . . . D'you think I'm drivelling ? "

" No.   I know exactly what you mean.   You mean that you're enough out of yourself to be able to say, to a stranger, what you think is the truth."

" You darling. . . . I *will* say it.   You darling !   You're right. There were two mis-statements only in what you said—I don't *think* it's the truth ; I *know* it is ; and you aren't a ' stranger.' "

" But . . ."

" You *know* you aren't.   Could you sit here, talking like this, or listening to me talk, with a *stranger* ?   Could you ? "

" N-no."

" You *know* we aren't strangers. . . . You only say so because of the *time*. . . . In time, which is purely a conventional expedient, like bathrooms and Thou Shalt Not Kill, we are strangers.   But Time doesn't *mean* anything ; in *fact*, we know each other.   I *know* that I know you—that lovely shell of you and that still more lovely you that's inside. . . ."

"Oh, *please*."

"What's the matter? What is it, my darling? Tell me. Why do you look like that? Don't turn your head away! Don't! Let me see you!"

"Oh, *please*. . . . please don't look at me. . . . I don't know what's the matter with me. . . . I think I'm going to cry or something. . . . Let me look at *you*. . . ."

"*Now then, 'ere, 'ow much longer's this car to stay 'ere? This ain't an auth'rised park.*"

"All right, officer, all *right*. We're not obstructing any traffic. . . ."

"*This ain't no auth'rised park!*"

"All right, all right. In a minute we'll. . . . Gosh! I say, that was a quick start! I thought my tummy was going out at the back."

"I had to do *something*. I had to do *something*. Pig of a man! Peering in like that, with that silly, beery voice. And me being a *damned* little fool and . . . and . . . piping my eye. . . ."

"But *why* were you . . . crying?"

"You wouldn't understand. Not sure that I do myself. I was being a fool anyhow. . . ."

"God! Don't stop like that. . . . Sorry, but I nearly went through the windscreen."

"I want to say something to you. And I can't drive properly. I can't see."

"Dar . . ."

"Please be quiet. I want to know : is this your idea of a joke?"

"Now you be quiet, you little devil! . . . No, I'm not sorry for saying that. . . . You *know* that was a beastly implication. . . . Look at me."

"Don't! You're hurting my shoulder!"

"Well, look at me then!"

"There!"

"God! You are lovely! . . . Look here ; something's happened to us. Hasn't it? . . . Hasn't it? . . ."

"Yes."

"You know it and I know it. And it's a wonderful and quite miraculous something. Can't we get rid of our beastly every-day-ness enough to admit it? I can. Won't you? Here's a sudden blazing wonder in a damned drab, machine-made world! Can't we—as we ought to—be thankful for it instead of hiding sheep's faces and pretending we're mad when we really know it's the others who're mad and only we who're

wonderfully sane ? Can't we ? . . . Can't we ? . . . Tell me
we can and I'll leave you now—to show how I believe—and not
see you until to-morrow, which is years and years away. . . .
Look at me, just once more, and say we can ! . . . Look at me
and say. . . . please look at me and . . ."

"We can. . . . Oh, I *know* we can . . . dear ! "

"Thank God ! . . . I'm going now. . . . How does this
door ? . . . Got it ! "

"When shall I see you ? When shall I see you ? . . . I'm
quite shameless, you see ? "

"When can you . . . darling ? And where ? "

"Come . . . come and see me to-morrow evening. . . .
I've got a little . . . a little party. But it won't . . . it needn't
be there all the time. . . . Will you come ? "

"Where ? Time ? "

"Any time after half-past eight. . . . Here's a card ; take
it. I *must* go. If I stay I shall . . ."

"Darling ; I'd forgotten . . ."

"What ? Tell me ! Don't look so harassed. . . . Tell me
at once ! "

"It's only . . . it's only . . . I haven't got . . . got any
money. I'm practically a beggar. . . . I mean it. . . . I . . .
I *will* make some. . . . I . . . can . . . but . . ."

"And who, may I ask, was talking just now about the mad
world and the sane—us ? Don't be a dear idiot. I know money
does matter—sometimes . . . but it *can't* to us . . . can it ? "

"You beloved. . . . Don't go ! . . . Don't. . . . Good-
night then. . . . Good-night. . . ."

"Bless you ! "

"Good . . ."

"I passed by your window when the morning was red, the
lark on the something, the dew overhead, and though I sang
softly that no one might hear . . ."

"For the love of Mike, shut up that row ! "

"Sorry, Jack. Sorry ! "

"What's the matter with you ? Tight or something ? "

"Both, laddie. Both."

"*Although you sang softly !* What's the big idea, coming in
about nine making a noise like a rusty mangle ? "

"Sorry, old boy ; sorry ! Have we got any beer ? "

" Where d'you think you are ?   *Have we got any beer ?*   Where d'you think you are ?   Buckingham Palace ? "

" Sorry, boy ; sorry !   We got any tea ? "

" We have, in the larder, some dried shavings from the Board School pencil-sharpeners which Billiter pretends is tea.   We have also just about enough gas to boil half a kettle.   We have no sugar and no milk.   If the prospect appeals to you, make the bloody stuff yourself.   Coming in at half-past three making a damn' row !   What's the matter with you ? "

" I'll tell you, Jack.   What is the matter with me is that there's nothing the matter.   Anything the matter. . . . Oh, *gosh* ! "

" Gosh what ? "

" Where did I put that last lot of pop-tickets ? "

" How the devil should I know where you put your last lot of tickets ?   I keep all mine at the office.   What d'you want to get out ?   Jug of milk, or something ? "

" No.   Tails."

" What for ?   Isn't your own enough ? "

" Jack, I've got to go out disguised as a gentleman to-morrow evening.   Got to !   This week's problem.   Will that clean dress shirt of yours fit me ?   Can Mrs. Billiter iron a tie ?   And how does A get his coat out of jug ?   Answer adjudged correct :   I *will* wear that clean dress shirt of yours ; Mrs. Billiter *must* iron a tie, and A sell something to get his coat out of jug."

" What's the matter with you to-night ? "

" I've told you already.   The matter is that there's nothing the matter.   The matter is that I've been making a mistake in thinking that there was something the matter with the world, and really, you know, there isn't."

" You've been talking to a fairy ! "

" I've been spoken to by an angel ! "

" Don't get muddled, my lad.   Birds 've got wings, too."

" Don't be so coarse ! "

" Coarse ?   You telling me not to be coarse !   Here, let's have a look at you. . . . Yes, authentic baa-lamb look, slight suffusion of eyes, practically no smell upon the breath. . . . You bloody idiot, Manory, I believe you're in love ! "

" You silly ass, that's what I've been trying to tell you for the last twenty minutes.   Got a sheet of notepaper ? "

" What the hell d'you think I am ?   Woolworths ?   Coming in here about eight in the middle of the night, singing !   I'm going back to bed.   I'll pound your face in if you make another whisper, coming in here . . ."

" I say, Jack ! "

" Yah ? "

" Where's your fountain pen ? . . . Steady ! That might've hit me ! "

" The next one will.   Pen's in the desk drawer."

" Never mind, I've got a pencil."

" Just as well, 'cause there isn't any ink."

" Dear Buster, I believe I did throw out some hint about gracing the home with my presence for this week-end.   If I did, disregard it.   I can't afford the fare and if I could, I'm afraid I should use it for a very different purpose.   Life is not real, Buster, but equally it is not an empty dream.   Life, I am inclined to think, is really rather fun if you look at it in the proper way. . . . Jack. . . . JACK ! "

" What the—— ? "

" Have you got a bob ?   The light's gone."

" *Don't speak to me !* "

" Why not ? "

" I can't speak ! "

" Hallo ! . . . Hallo ! . . . Hallo ! . . . Exchange. . . . Exchange, *please* wake up ! . . . Hallo ! . . . HALLO ! "

" Are you calling ? "

" Not so's you'd notice it !   Please get me Gardens 0423."

" Gardens 0324 ? "

" No, Gardens 0423."

" I said Gardens 3420."

" Please go away and send your brother !   The number I'm asking for is Gardens owe—four—two—three."

" . . . Hallo, yes ? "

" Is that Gardens 0423 ? "

" Yes.   Mrs. Mather speaking."

" Sally, darling, this is Susan."

" Hallo, dear !   What's the matter ? "

" Nothing, only I knew you'd be up because I knew you belonged to the Philimore party.   Sal, I want you to do something for me."

" 'Course I will, dear.   Anything."

" Come and be a party at my flat to-morrow night."

" But, Susan, I've got to go out."

" Yes, I know you have—to me. . . . *Please*, Sally ! "

" Well, if you put it like that . . ."

" I do. . . ."

" What's the great urgency ? "

" Guess ! "

" Man ? "

" Yes."

" What's his name ? "

" Haven't the faintest idea."

" *Susan !* . . . Where's he come from ? "

" Haven't the remotest."

" What on earth ! . . . What's he do ? "

" My dear, how should I know ? "

" Susan, what *have* you been doing ? "

" Come to dinner to-morrow night and I'll tell you. I must tell you—I shall burst if I don't tell somebody . . . and I told him that I'd got a little party to-morrow night and he could come if he wanted to, so for God's sake come and be my party ! "

" I think I'd better."

" And, Sally, if I say to you to-morrow night ' D'you remember Stuttgart ? . . .' "

" Do I remember *what* ? "

" Stuttgart."

" What is he ? "

" Don't be silly. If I say that to you—' Do you remember Stuttgart ? '—please remember that I want you to go in ten minutes."

" Look here, Susan, I'll come on one condition—you *lunch* here to-morrow."

" Love to. . . . And I'll tell you all about it ! "

" What the hell's this ? "

" What's what ? "

" This."

" Here, that's mine ! "

" I dare say. What the hell is it ? "

" Well, you can see, can't you ? It's a lady's visiting card."

" Yes, I can see that ! And what's it doing here at breakfast-time."

" Dropped out of my pocket."

" Here ! You're in high circles, aren't you ? "

" Not noticeably."

" Well, I mean to say, all these small double f's and what

not, pretty good ! ' Margery ffolliatt-Wilson '—that's old ffolliatt-Wilson's daughter, isn't it ? "

" My dear Holmes, you astonish me."

" And this is the calico you were all het up about, is it ? "

" The longer I know you, Holmes, the more baffled I . . ."

" Shut up ! What did you say to me just now, before all this card stuff ? "

" I said, how much money have you got ? "

" Dunno. I'll see . . . three . . . four . . . here's a tanner, four and six . . . five . . . five and threepence ha'penny. Be better off to-morrow when the screw comes along. After I've paid out I shall have ten bob.

" To-morrow's not a damn' bit of good to me, nor's your five and threepence ha'penny."

" That's good, because you couldn't have it."

" Jack ! You know that great ulster that that uncle of yours sent you and that you never wear ? "

" I do."

" Lend it to me, will you ? "

" Going to a fancy dress ball ? "

" No, you coot ! You don't want it ; I'll sell it. As soon as I touch next I'll give you the price back."

" All right, you stiff."

" Thanks awfully."

" Shut up. Look here. . . . If it's any good to you I might be able to raise a quid at the office."

" Don't worry, old thing. I'd rather you didn't, anyhow, and you see, I've got to get those tails out this morning and spend the day with Billiter's iron. It'll take me a couple of hours to clean it, I expect. . . . Iron, I mean."

" Right. S'pose I shan't see you to-night then ? "

" 'Fraid not, old thing."

" Well, whatever you do, don't come in singing ! And don't wake up to ask me if we've got any beer or champagne, or anything like that. . . . And good luck, blast you ! "

" Good-morning ! Can I see the proprietor ? "

" The whath ? "

" The proprietor."

" Ithn't one."

" Oh. Do you—er—look after—er—do the business ? "

" Yeth."

" Oh."

" Whath you wanth ?   Whath in the bag ? "

" In that bag is a very good ulster, practically brand new, and a slightly worn suit by one of the best tailors in London. I wanted to see whether I could sell them."

" Thell them !   *Thell* them !   You can't *give* thecond-hand thtuff away."

" Can't you ?   That seems a pity."

" You gettin' freth ? "

" With you ? . . . Well, good-morning ! "

" 'Ere, mithter—mithter ! "

" What is it ? "

" Ath yer 'ere, may'th well thee woth you got in the bag. . . ."

" . . . Now look here, all bunkum apart, that's a damn' fine coat.   You can see it's hardly been used.   It's big enough and heavy enough to keep a rhinoceros warm, made by a good tailor—look in the pocket—and I happen to know that that coat cost nineteen guineas."

" Yeth.   Ten guineath for credit, sixth guineath for rent, two guineath blood money to the unionth, and a quid for the coat.   Whath the good of a coat like that ?   Who'th goin' to wear a coat like that ?   You can't thee anybody walkin' about in a coat like that.   Only uth for a coat like that'th to put on the bed inthtead of an eiderdown."

" Right-o !   If you don't want it, I'll take it away.   What about the suit ? "

" Let'th 'ave a look !   Thuit, d'you call it ?   Thuit !   Thuit ! It *wath* a thuit, but what'th it fit for now ? "

" Wearing."

" What'th it fit for now, I thay !   Fit for thipping."

" Thipping ? "

" Thipping."

" What d'you mean—thipping ? "

" Thipping to the blackth."

" Shipping to the blacks ? "

" Yeth.   That'th all that thuit'th fit for.   Thipping to the blackth.   They don't know the differenth between a thuit that'th a thuit and a thuit that wath wunth a thuit."

" Well—shipping or no shipping—how much ? "

" I tell you what, mithter—I tell you what I'll do.   I'll give you half a guinea for the thuit and you throw in the coat."

" Here, give's it back ! "

"Mithter! Mithter! . . . We wathted a lot o' time talkin', we'd better do a deal. I'll give you fifteen and thix for the lot."

"You can keep your fifteen and six, and . . . and . . . put it on the mantelpiece in the spare room! I'll take 'em along somewhere else."

"Oh, you'll take 'em thomewhere elth! There ithn't another thomewhere elth nearer than Bethnal Green, and thath'th a bit of a thtep if you haven't got the buth fare."

"Never mind that. I like walking. Good-morning!"

"Mithter! . . . Mithter! . . . My latht word—a quid!"

"What for? The suit?"

"Don' be thilly! A quid I thaid. A quid for a coat thath no good to god, beatht or man, and a thuit thath only fit for thipping to the blackth."

"Oh, all right! Where's the quid?"

"Ahem! . . . I say! . . . Anybody there? . . . Hallo-allo-allo!"

"Wait a minute. Wait a minute! Bit of a hurry, aren't you?"

"For once you are right!"

"What d'you want?"

"I want to give you this ticket and this pound, and this shilling, and get out that dress coat that the ticket stands for."

"All right. Wait a minute. . . ."

". . . Hallo-allo-allo!"

"All right. All right! 'Ere y'are!"

"Thanks. Haven't got a bit of paper, I s'pose? Or a box or anything like that?"

"Paper and string tuppence."

"My God! Give's the coat!"

"Is you watch going, Sally?"

"Yes, dear."

"What's it say?"

"It says what your clock says, darling. Twenty-past nine."

" Oh. . . . Sally ! "

" Yes, dear ? "

" Sally, I think I shall . . . I shall . . . I shall *burst* if he doesn't turn up ! "

" Is Lady Margery ffoliatt-Wilson at home ? "

" I will see, sir.   What name, sir ? "

" King.   Manory King."

" Very well, sir.   Will you please step this way ? "

" Thank you."

" I am sorry, sir.   Lady Margery is not at home."

" Oh . . . thank you . . . thank you. . . . I see . . . '

" This way, sir."

" Oh . . . thank you. . . . I say ! I've just remembered something."

" Sir ? "

" Look here, you look fairly human. No, no ! I don't mean that, you know what I mean ! "

" Yes, sir."

" I have just remembered Lady Margery may not—er—recognize—er—my name. She *is* in, isn't she ? "

" My instructions were, sir, that Lady Margery was not at home."

" Exactly. Now, you be a good fellow and just tell Lady Margery that . . . just give Lady Margery. . . . Just say to Lady Margery. . . . Say Mr. King is the man who knows nothing about motor-cars."

" Sir ? "

" Say that—Mr.—King—is—the—man—who—knows—nothing—about—motor—cars."

" Very well, sir."

" Sir ! "

" Hallo ! "

" If you will come this way Lady Margery will see you   If you would give me your hat and coat, sir. . . . Thank you."

" Mr. Manory King, my lady ! "
" Good-evening ! "
" Good God ! "
" I *beg* your pardon ? "
" I . . . I . . . I . . . I was thinking. . . . I was hoping. . . . I think . . ."
" Let me help you. You've made some mistake, haven't you ? "
" Thank you. That was . . . what I wanted to say. . . . But to save me from madness, will you please tell me whether this card is one of yours ? "
" What an extraordinary thing ! Yes, it certainly is. But . . . but . . ."
" I'm not after the silver. There's just one thing in this world that I want to know. And that is who gave me that card. Can you help me ? "
" I'm terribly sorry, Mr. King, I can't. I haven't the foggiest idea. I use rather a lot of cards."
" Yes. . . . Yes. . . . I s'pose so. . . ."
" Perhaps could I . . . I should like to help. . . . How did you get it ? "

" I'm very sorry—more sorry than ever, but it just means nothing to me. You see, Mr. King, I don't want to be rude, and I know you've described her beautifully . . . but what you tell me . . . I know it's very difficult . . . would fit at least twenty girls I know, and I may not even know this one."
" Yes. Yes. I see. You have been—been very, very kind to me. I am—I'm awfully sorry I have been such a nuisance."

" Sally ! "
" Yes ? "
" I s'pose that damn' clock *is* right ? "
" Yes, dear. . . . Don't look so white."
" I think you'd better go, Sal. No point in your waiting."
" I'll go if you'll come back and spend the night with us. Don't bite it like this, you silly child."
" I . . . I . . . Sally, *please* go ! "

WHAT HAS GONE BEFORE

MANORY KING, young and handsome novelist, whose fourth novel is about to be published, falls deeply in love with

SUSAN MAINWARING, a charming and beautiful girl, whom he imagines to be

LADY MARGERY FFOLLIATT-WILSON, somebody quite different.

Susan, who, owing to the comparative poverty of her father,

SIR JERROLD MAINWARING, whom there is no need to worry about, makes her income sufficient for her needs by means of literary and journalistic work. She leaves her car in Fair Street one evening and on returning to drive it away, finds that it will not start. While tinkering, she accidentally switches off the lights, and Manory King, who has been dining, perhaps a little injudiciously, with

FLENBOROUGH WATKINS, a one-time fellow-officer, walks into the back of the car, bruising his leg.

Manory and Susan find, each in the other, an instantaneous attraction. More than this, for they have at first sight fallen in

LOVE, an ecstatic state.

When they part, Susan, telling Manory that if he wishes he may call upon her the following evening, gives him a card from her bag. Unknowingly, she gives him one of Margery ffolliatt-Wilson's (the merest acquaintance), which happens to be in her bag. They part, Manory's name not having been mentioned.

The next evening Manory calls at the address upon the card, to find that Margery ffolliatt-Wilson is not the woman he wants, while in her flat Susan, with her bosom friend,

MRS. MATHER (SALLY), waits in vain.

Now start to read this enthralling tale of

LOVE, LIFE AND LITERATURE
IN LONDON.

UNITED PRESS AGENCY.

Cutting from the   MERCURY.
Issue dated   10th September.

The Book-Table.

I have been unlucky this week. I have read four highly
advertised novels, *Passion-Fruit* by Katharine Marle ; *Cocktails and Toothpaste* by Nichol E. Bevells ; *Rocks of Atonement*
by Edith P. Sewell ; and *Glitter* by E. Manory King.

This is a bad bunch. The best of them—which is not saying
anything at all—is *Rocks of Atonement.* If Miss Sewell could
have something done about her adjectives, would write about
places of which she at least knew something, and would concoct
a story in which there were real people instead of Hollywood
types, she might do something worth reading.

She has a certain narrative gift and a tremendous—almost
frightening—belief that what she finds so well worth writing
will be worth reading.

Cocktails and Toothpaste is Mr. Bevells at his worst.
When you have read the title you have read the book.

Passion Fruit is one of these novels about Sex, with two
capital S's, which, aspiring to be " fearless," merely succeed in
being fearful.

Glitter by E. Manory King is completely incomprehensible
from first page to last.

                                              F.F.

UNITED PRESS AGENCY.

Cutting from   FASHION.
Issue dated   15th September.

Potted Reviews.

Mary Goes West by Philimore Hopkins. Arizona. Re-
volvers. Mustangs. Beautiful girl. Fair.

Glitter by E. Manory King. Very clever, very amusing,
good mental exercise. Read it.

UNITED PRESS AGENCY.

Cutting from
MERTHYR TYDVIL & DISTRICT ALBION.
Issue dated September 14th.

Glitter, by E. Manory King, which comes to us under the ægis of that well-known and enterprising firm, Flewin, Mile & Garth, is not a book which does credit to this usually astute firm. It is very modern in tone and the author would appear to deliberately and of set purpose set out to achieve flippancy anent the serious matters of life, and seriousness with regard to those matters looked upon by the civilized world as fit and proper subjects for mirth. (7s. 6d. net.)

UNITED PRESS AGENCY.

Cutting from the OBSERVATOR.
Issue dated September 18th.

I find that I have not left myself much space in which to do justice to an extraordinary work by an author of whom I regret to say I have never before heard. This is Mr. E. Manory King, and his book *Glitter* should most certainly be read, if only for his extremely interesting and ably carried out experiment in technique.
(*Glitter*—Flewin, Mile & Garth. 7s. 6d.)

UNITED PRESS AGENCY.

Cutting from WEEKLY POST.
Issue dated September 21st.

Books.

Not a very interesting week. The two detective stories which head my list are neither better nor worse than the majority of their egregious kind.

Glitter, by Mr. E. Manory King (Flewin, Mile & Garth, 7s. 6d.), is an appalling hotch-potch. The author does not seem to know what he is aiming at, and the reader is consequently bewildered. A poor attempt to disguise the lack of something to write about by writing about it obscurely.

UNITED PRESS AGENCY.

Cutting from   DAILY COURIER.
Issue dated   September 19th.

Glitter—E. Manory King. (Flewin, Mile & Garth. 7*s*. 6*d*.
net.)

Mr. King—at least I am assuming him to be a Mister—
has written a book *Glitter*. On finishing its first chapter I
was irresistibly reminded of an incident which took place in my
recent visit to the United States. It is a strange thing—so
strange that I have never, even with all my powers of concentra-
tion, been able to dissociate the two—but there is something in
me which makes my mind react, *vocally*, to the *written* word, and
silently to the *spoken*. There can be no doubt—I will not admit
of any doubt—that this is wrong. But there it is.

And so it is *in* me, as it were, to regard every book which I
read as a play and every play which I see as a book. Now,
although this is perhaps unfair to the author of *Glitter*, it is not
so with the classics. Nor is it so with such a book, for instance,
as Mr. Bantock's new novel *Hipsworth*. My sensations, after
the third chapter of *Hipsworth*, were very similar to those which
I once enjoyed, I remember, upon an occasion which shall be
nameless. Mr. Bantock's book is not so good as his next will be.
But it is better than Mrs. Neville's *Twice Upon a Time*.

UNITED PRESS AGENCY.

Cutting from   EVENING SENTINEL.
Issue dated   September 24th.

Glitter by E. Manory King. Published by Flewin, Mile &
Garth. 7*s*. 6*d*. *net*.

I had the impression after reading the first half of Mr. King's
book—which I must confess was the only half which I read—
that he was striving to do for his times what Meyerbeer did for
Holland at the end of the last century—striving, but by no means
succeeding.

I do not like being merely condemnatory, but I must say
that I regard *Glitter*—which has in a way to be regarded
seriously—as a poor imitation of a really great book.

FLEWIN, MILE & GARTH

GLITTER

by

E. MANORY KING

WHAT THE REVIEWERS SAY :

Fashion.—Very clever, very amusing, good mental exercise. Read it.

Merthyr Tydvil & District Albion.—*Glitter* . . . is a book which . . . does credit to this astute firm.

Observator.—. . . Should most certainly be read.

Evening Sentinel.—. . . A really great book.

Daily Courier.—. . . Mr. King has written a Book !

> 9 RUSSELL ROAD,
> BLOOMSBURY, W.
> *October 2nd,* 193–.

DEAR GARTH,

The reviews of *Glitter* have been very mixed, with a preponderance on the side, I should say, of bad. Also, I notice the size of your advertisements is dropping. In the circumstances I am naturally very anxious to learn how the book is going on and hope you will forgive me for troubling you. The sooner you can let me know, the better.

Yours sincerely,

E. MANORY KING.

HOWARD GARTH, ESQ.,
MESSRS. FLEWIN, MILE & GARTH,
ADAM HOUSE,
ADELPHI, W.C.

Flewin, Mile & Garth

Telephone : Gerrard 34560.   ADAM HOUSE,
                                                ADELPHI, W.C.
                                        October 3rd, 193–.

MY DEAR KING,

Your letter of yesterday—I was going to write you to-day, anyhow, about *Glitter.* I am very sorry indeed to have to tell you so, but it is not going at all as well as I had hoped, and, moreover, believed that it would.

To put matters bluntly, it is, so far at least, a flop. We printed 1000 to start with and of these we have sold only 240.

We have not entirely given up hope yet, and I am going to see whether we cannot give it at least a couple of weeks more good advertising, but I must warn you that you ought not to base any expectations upon this.

                            Yours sincerely,
                                HOWARD GARTH.

P.S.—This is a beastly letter to have to write. *Glitter* is a
        damn fine book, but it seems to me nowadays that the better
        the book the less chance it has, especially if it is something
        that the sheep are not used to. At the end of the fortnight
        I will write you again whatever happens.   H.G.

E. MANORY KING, ESQ., 9 RUSSELL ROAD,
        BLOOMSBURY, W.

Flewin, Mile & Garth

Telephone : Gerrard 34560.   ADAM HOUSE,
                                                ADELPHI, W.C.
                                        October 6th, 193–.

Publicity Department.

DEAR MR. KING,

Gabriel of Bond Street, having failed to obtain a reply from you to their offer of a free sitting, have asked me to take the matter up with you.

I wonder whether I could not persuade you to let them take a photograph of you? They will not try to sell you any copies afterwards. I am sure it will be to your own interest, more particularly as we ourselves are badly wanting an up-to-date and pleasing photograph of yourself for use in connection with fresh publicity which we are about to give to your book *Glitter*.

Yours very truly,

F. M. BLIGHT

(Publicity Manager).

E. MANORY KING, ESQ.,
9 RUSSELL ROAD,
BLOOMSBURY, W.

GABRIEL

" *The Camera for Art's sake.*"

Telephone : Gerrard 04481.

1234 BOND STREET, W.1.
October 8th, 193–.

DEAR SIR,

We are delighted to hear from Messrs. Flewin, Mile & Garth that you would be willing to sit to us for a free camera portrait study of yourself. As we understand that our photograph will be urgently required for publicity purposes, may we suggest that you call here at eleven-thirty to-morrow morning? If this is convenient to you, please do not trouble to communicate with us. If, however, it should be inconvenient, perhaps you would kindly give us a ring upon the telephone.

Yours very faithfully,

RAYMOND BATOUX

(Director).

E. MANORY KING, ESQ.,
9 RUSSELL ROAD,
BLOOMSBURY, W.

E. Manory King's New Novel
GLITTER

Photo : Gabriel.

Mr. E. MANORY KING, the well-known Novelist.

GLITTER

MR. KING's latest book has achieved an instantaneous and overwhelming success, which his Publishers confidently predicted. Every one is reading *Glitter*. Have you bought YOUR copy ? If not, order it to-day.
All Booksellers, 7s. 6d. net.

Flewin, Mile & Garth

ADAM HOUSE,
ADELPHI, W.C.

Telephone : Gerrard 34560.

October 15th, 193–.

Publicity Department.

DEAR MR. KING,

I send you herewith a block of the new advertisement of *Glitter* which is going to be shown in various papers during the next fortnight. You will, I am sure, agree that the reproduction of Gabriel's admirable photograph of yourself is excellent.

Yours very truly,

F. M. Blight

(Publicity Manager).

E. Manory King, Esq., 9 Russell Road,
　　　Bloomsbury, W.

P.S.—I regret that at the time of posting the block had not reached us. Your photograph will, however, be reproduced in the space indicated.

" You look bored, Susan."

" Always am in this sort of place. Why are hosts always late ? "

" Seen *The Point of View* this week ? "

" No. Don't want to."

" For heaven's sake take it and hide your face in it. Here ! "

" *My God !* "

" Susan ! What's the matter ? "

" Well, I'm . . ."

" What *is* it ? "

" What an extraordinary . . ."

" What is it ? "

" How perfectly amazing. . . ."

" Susan, if you don't tell me *at once* what you're . . . "

" Well, to think . . ."

" What is it you're staring at ? "

" This ! "

" The patent food or the photograph ? "

" Don't be a fool ! "

READ THIS FIRST

MANORY KING, an unsuccessful novelist, young and handsome, is desperately in love with

SUSAN MAINWARING, a young and lovely girl, but does not know how to find her as she inadvertently gave him, at their only meeting, the wrong card. She is heartsore because he has not found her, and since his name had not been mentioned between them, she cannot find him. She is, however, intuitive enough to realize that his failure to find her is due to some mischance.

Susan is sitting in the lounge of the

SAVOY, a good pull-up for Carmens, with her friend,

WHOSE NAME I CANNOT REMEMBER, when she sees in a paper Manory's photograph, showing him to be a novelist whose new book

" GLITTER " is obtainable for 7s. 6d.

Susan, realizing now that she can, at any time she wants to, find Manory, decides not to do so at the moment, but rather to use all her knowledge, influence, and ability to pull strings to make this new book of his so great a success that he will, when the time comes, not be backward in coming forward. She cuts a luncheon appointment and immediately starts to work on her self-imposed campaign.

NOW YOU CAN START!

(*By Hand*)

Wm. H. James, Esq.,
General Editor, *Fashion*,
40x Bouverie Street, E.C. 4.

Dear Bill,

Do me a favour ! I enclose a review of a book called *Glitter* : put this in for me instead of the long one I did about Hugh Walpole's latest. If you think you can't do it, would you be a dear and let me know by wire to the Amazon Club. It's no good 'phoning that place, because they never find you.

Yrs.,

Susan.

Post Office Telegram

Susan Mainwaring c/o Amazon Club, Piccadilly.
YOU HAVE ALREADY DONE *GLITTER*.   BILL.

Post Office Telegram

James   Fashion   Bouverie Street   E.C.
I KNOW READ NEW NOTICE DON'T BE SILLY.

Susan.

Post Office Telegram

Susan Mainwaring c/o Amazon Club, Piccadilly.
RIGHTO.   BILL.

UNITED PRESS AGENCY

Cutting from   *Fashion*.
Issue dated   October 18th, 193–.

Glitter. E. Manory King (Flewin, Mile & Garth. 7s. 6d. net). Some weeks ago, in my Potted Reviews, I made mention of this book. What I said, exactly, was " Very clever, very amusing, good mental exercise, read it."

This still applies to the book which has been on my mind. So much so, indeed, that a few days ago I succumbed to the temptation to read it again—a temptation which does not often occur in a reviewer's life.

On my second reading I was to discover that my first had been merely superficial. What I said about it then I say about it now, but now I add a very great deal.

Glitter is that very rare thing, a book in which the reader will find with every reading some merit which he did not notice before. I hold myself much to blame for having dismissed this work so lightly the first time it came to my notice. I cannot now speak too highly of it. I don't know the author, nor whether the author be a man or a woman, but I predict here and now that for E. Manory King there awaits—perhaps to-morrow, perhaps in six months, perhaps in five years—a very great and universal success.

Glitter is the work of a genius. Not only by reason of the amazing manner in which the strange tale is unfolded but by reason also of the tale itself, the firm and delicate etching of its characterization, the Olympian humanity with which its widely diverse incidents are presented, and finally, the mind which one can sense all the time behind the drama and pathos, comedy and character, fantasy and wit.

POST CARD

You asked me some time ago whether, when you went away this month, I would write your weekly column for *The Reader*. Now find shall not be so busy as had supposed. Will be delighted do this for you.

SUSAN M.

MRS. GORDON WRIGHT,

144 QUEEN VICTORIA MANS.,

SOUTH KENSINGTON,
S.W. 7.

POST CARD

Darling,—How too sweet of you ! Copy must deal with at least 4 books and not more than 7—¾ of 2-column page. Please sign copy " for " me and sent in before Sat. next.
E. W.

Miss Susan Mainwaring,

13 Cheyne House,

Chelsea,

S.W.

" Hallo ! . . . Piccadilly 1230. . . . Palace Chambers ? Is Lord Foresthill there ? "

" Hold the line, please."

" Hallo. Foresthill speaking."

" Who's this, Charles ? . . . Three guesses only."

" I'm not going to guess, because I know."

" Pretty good, but not good enough. Say who it is or I'll ring off."

" . . . Susan."

" You're right, Charles, but that's the biggest fluke even you've ever pulled off ! Will you do something for me ? "

" Anything, my delight ! "

" Take me out to lunch."

" Mean it ? "

" 'Course I mean it. I warn you I want something, but I think my company ought to be fair exchange."

" Generous ! Will the Naples Grill one-fifteen suit you ? "

" Charles, sometimes I almost like you ! "

" Butterworth ! "

" Yes, madam ? "

" Do they ever give you an afternoon off ? "

" Yes, madam."

" Wher. is the next one, Butterworth ? "

" Er . . ."

"Don't look so frightened ; you haven't got to take me to the Pictures ! "

"No, madam.   My next afternoon, madam, is on Wednesday, that is to say to-morrow."

"Got any half-sections, Butterworth ? "

"Half-sections, madam ? "

"Side-kickers ;   friends . . . what you'd probably call cronies."

"My due proportion, madam."

"Will any of you be all boys together to-morrow ? "

"To some extent, madam."

"Would ten pounds between you be any good for three of you for an easy afternoon's work, pleasant travelling about London, doing the heavy in clean shops ? "

"For you, madam, yes.   But perhaps if you would indicate the nature of this task . . ."

"Here, Butterworth, is a list of bookshops.   I've divided it into three.   If there are more than three of you divide it yourselves into whatever the number may be.   I want each one of you, working individually, to go to each one of these shops and there to ask for a copy of the book that you will see written at the head of the list.   If they have a copy, buy it.   Most of them won't.   When they haven't, be very snuffy about it and say that Lord this or Lady that, or any one you like, must have a copy immediately, and that you really can't wait while they order one, as you can easily get one in another shop.   That's all, Butterworth.   Follow ? "

"Yes, madam.   And when shall I report ? "

"I'll come in here on Wednesday morning, about the usual time.   Sure to see you then.   Here's three fivers, that's ten for your band, and five for expenses.   Any change from the five thankfully received.   Good-afternoon, Butterworth ! "

"Good-day, madam ! "

"And Butterworth ! "

"Madam ? "

"Cheer up ! "

"Certainly, madam."

Flewin, Mile & Garth

ADAM HOUSE,

Telephone : Gerrard 34560.
ADELPHI, W.C.

October 23rd, 193–.

DEAR KING,

Am writing you before I said I would because there are some slight indications that things are on the mend. I am afraid that we can't expect the really large sale I had hoped for, but the improvement which has taken place in the last week does seem to warrant my telling you that I think there is a chance of the book still enjoying some measure at least of success.

I expect you will have seen the very good reviews in last week's *Fashion* and *The Reader*, but your Press Cutting Agency may not have sent you the enclosed cutting from the *Sunday Messenger*.

For the first time, the sales instead of declining or at least remaining stationary at a single figure a week, have made a decided jump. Only yesterday we received orders from seventeen bookshops, all, curiously enough, on this side of London. This is quite a good sign, however, for, in our trade at least, what Piccadilly thinks to-day, Ponders End will uphold to-morrow.

Yours sincerely,

HOWARD GARTH.

E. MANORY KING, ESQ., 9 RUSSELL ROAD,
BLOOMSBURY, W.

ENC : 1.

A Driveller's Diary
By LORD FORESTHILL

Chiming Clocks.—It is possible for me to hear, and sometimes I do—if I am awake —the chiming of Big Ben as I lie in my bed. I like it.

It is not long since I saw a very eminent personage stand stock-still in the middle of Parliament Square, however, and shake an irate fist at Big Ben, who then was striking noon. He cried out for all to hear : " Who would live in Westminster ? " I cannot imagine what he meant.

Swaffer Resartus.—At the wedding the other day of Lord Crimpnellys (which as you may, but probably do not, know, is pronounced Crimpney) to the Hon. Adelaide Smith (pronounced as written) I sat behind a somewhat meagre and stooping person whose back and black hair was rather longer than is usually permitted by the dictates of Fashion. Upon my right I had an eminent Cabinet Minister who was suffering from a peculiarly distressing (to me, at least) bronchial catarrh.

The perpetual and harrowing noise seemed to distress my long-haired fellow-guest in front of me, for after about the fourth bombardment he began to turn round. I did not recognize the face, and it was not until at the reception afterwards that Lady Portobello clutched me by the arm and said : " Look ! Can that be Hannen Swaffer ? " and I saw that Swaffer indeed it was, only what a Swaffer ! Swaffer without that hat of black velour and without that death-defying Swaffer stock. In morning clothes, like any other working man, and a nice, new, white, high, shiny, upstanding collar.

Clothes indeed make the man !

All is Gold that Glitters ! I believe a Mr. Chesterton once made the remark at the head of this paragraph. It is certainly sometimes true. I have been very much interested lately in the rapid rise of that most brilliant of our younger novelists, Manory King.

I liked his first book, I liked his second book, I even liked his third book. But with his fourth book, *Glitter*, which is on every intelligent person's tongue, he has jumped clean out of his previous rank and set himself very near to that small peak at present held, though precariously, by such ill-assorted companions as Walpole and Arlen, Kipling and Eric Linklater, Galsworthy and Wells.

I am very glad at Mr. King's success. He certainly deserves it. If any of you who read these drivellings of mine every Sunday are still so uneducated that they have not read *Glitter*, I implore them at once to do so.

Piper ! Piper ! 6.30 Enos ! Extra ! War in the East !
6.30 Enos ! WAR ! WAR ! EXTRA ! All the Runners an'
Riders !

Evening News

Grave Egyptian Crisis

BIMBAM BEY DECLARES WAR !

40,000 Dervishes already in arms

EVENING STANDARD

WAR !

STAR

UNREST IN EGYPT!

Evening Planet

WAKE UP! ENGLAND!

Fate of the East in the Balance !

BLOW TO BRITISH PRESTIGE

PITIFUL PLIGHT OF ARMY OF OCCUPATION

"Harrington."

"Hal-lo!"

"Chief wants you."

"Oh, God!..."

"Ah! Come in, Harrington. Look here, I want you to go down to Wapping on that warehouse fire. See if there's any hocus.... Come in! Yes, Busby, what do you want?"

"It's impossible to get Maxwell, sir."

"Hell! What did you offer him?"

"Wasn't a question of price, sir. He's in a nursing-home for appendicitis."

"Blast!! What the hell are we going to do? Haven't got a man on the staff who could touch him.... What *is* it, Harrington?"

"You talking 'bout H. J. Maxwell, sir? War Correspondent?"

"Yes, yes, but..."

"'Scuse me, sir, but I know just the man for the job. Knows East, been soldier, writes well. Done a bit of work for the paper, too, on and off."

"Who's that?"

"Wake up, will you? Wake up!"

"Get to perdition out of it!"

"Wake up, you blasted owl!"

"Why should I? Go away!"

"Damn you! If you don't wake up I'll..."

"All right! All *right*! You've waked me now. What the devil is it?"

"You'll soon see what it is. Get into some clothes...."

"Well, that's that, Mr. King. Harrington, much obliged to you. Miss Fairley, make out a cash slip for Mr. King for £150. Mr. King, if you present this at the Cashier's Office as you go out you can draw the money as you like. If you want more, cable. Harrington, take him down to the Cashier's Office and after that to see Duprez. Duprez will tell him about the sailing arrangements."

" Here, Jack, take this quick."

" Good Lord, man ! I don't want as much as that ! "

" Don't be a stiff ! If you don't want it now you will about Friday fortnight. Go on ! "

" This is Mr. Manory King, Duprez. You'll have heard that he is going out on the Egyptian job."

" Yep. Park y'r sterns a shake. . . . Hallo ! Hallo ! Mr. Travers. . . . Travers, Duprez here. Fix up that correspondent's passage to Cairo ? . . . Yep. . . . Nothing quicker ? . . . Nope. . . . Yep. . . . *Castrella* ? . . . Right. . . . That's that. Mr. King, they wanna get you there quick. The passenger line's gone bluey. Fastest thing we can do is to shove you super-cargo on the *Castrella*. She's a 2000-ton tramp. She'll get you across three or four days quicker than anything else in the present state."

" When does she sail ? "

" You'll have to jump, laddie. She sails from the Kettering Dock, Quay 7, at eleven forty-five to-night. You'll just have time to buy y'r kit, kiss Momma good-bye and get something into yourself to be sick on. Here's a ticket, first-class, platform 12, main line Victoria. . . ."

" Come on, Jack, come out and have a real dinner."

" My dear bloke, I can't. Got to go to Wapping."

" Good God ! "

" What'll I do about your letters ? "

" Open the lot. Bills in the fire, you won't get any receipts ; I'll wire the family. Anything about *Glitter* or other books leave if you can or else write and tell 'em where I am.

Shan't trouble to notify 'em myself. Good-bye, old thing ! "

" Good-bye. Best of luck ! "

" Taxi ! "

" Where to, sir ? "

" Justin Creed's, Regent Street."

" Outfitters you mean, sir ? "

" That's right."

" Well, I think that's everything, sir, and I hope you are satisfied."

" Entirely. Now, you have got it, haven't you ? All that new stuff in the trunks to be put on the eight-fifteen from Victoria—you've got the labels ? "

" Yes, sir. You heard me give the instructions."

" And the old stuff I've taken off can be bunged in a parcel and sent to J. Harrington, Esq., at 9 Russell Road, Bloomsbury."

" Very good, sir."

" . . . Good-night ! You've looked after me very well."

" Thank you very much, sir, I'm sure. Good-night ! "

" Table for two, sir ? "

" One."

" Alone to-night, Captain King ? "

" Good God ! It's Charles ! Charles, you've got a memory like Datas ! It must be at least six years since I've been in here, and yet you remember me ! Head of the class ! "

" I don't remember all the customers, Captain King."

" Very handsome, Charles. Look after me like a mother, Charles, will you ? Let your first maternal act be, very properly, to give me a drink. Is Porkie still here ? "

" No, Captain King, but we have a very good man indeed."

" I want a double Dry Martini, Charles, and while you're getting it, slide behind some screen and have one yourself."

" Very good, sir. Thank you, sir."

" Everything to your liking, Captain King ? "

" Very much so. All I wanted was some company. Pity you had those Yanks to look after as well as me. From my point of view, I mean."

" I hope we shall have the pleasure of seeing you a lot now, sir."

" Your hopes are dashed. You will *not* have the pleasure of seeing me a lot or at all, Charles. As a matter of fact, I'm off to Egypt to-night."

" Active service again, sir ? Nasty business this Egyptian business."

" Yes and no to active service. Correspondent, as a matter of fact. Wretched business, I should imagine. Get shot at by the enemy, not allowed to shoot back, and about as popular with the army as a very bad smell."

" May I suggest another liqueur brandy, sir ? If I may say so, sir, you seem rather depressed."

" No more brandy, Charles. No more anything. I haven't got the head I used to have. . . . Yes, I am depressed. Hellish depressed ! Not about the job, but because I've had to rush off in such a hurry. . . . There's some one I particularly would have liked to see before I went away and I . . . Don't know why I'm boring you with all this."

" Not boring, sir. I think I may say without impertinence that we are old friends."

" If you feel that way, Charles, I'm delighted."

" Very nasty to have to go away without . . . May I ask . . . is it . . . ? "

" No, Charles, it is not. That lady is now the Countess . . . You've probably seen . . . Well, anyway, if she doesn't come in here a lot it's because she doesn't want to see you. A splendid example of Chorus to Court."

" Well, there's something refreshing about that nowadays, sir. It is generally Court to Chorus in these times."

" Charles, for God's sake stop that band playing that waltz. I think you've made me a bit tight or something, Charles. If they don't stop I shall probably burst into tears ! Ask them to play . . . Ask them to play . . . Ask them not to play at all ! "

" Certainly, sir."

" Don't be an ass, Charles—I believe you would ! But I've got to go, anyhow. That the bill ? "

" Yes, sir."

" Right. . . . Pheew ! . . . Never mind, it was worth it.

And, here, Charles, have a bit of a celebration or something, will you ? "

"Thank you, sir, very much indeed. I will. I hope we shall see you again, sir, when you get back from the East. . . . Good-night, sir. Good luck. . . ."

Have to report that at 7.59 p.m. assisted at serious street accident. Was proceeding north along east side of Piccadilly at 7.58½ (at which time was opposit Larki & Sorrentz, Jewellers) when saw gentleman in brown hat, fawn overcoat, standing on edge of kerb. (Distance between self and gent approx. 20 yds.) Pavement was clear, time being what it was, so that had uninterrupted view of gent. Same stood apeariently waiting for taxi. At this time no traffic in road, owing to block being held at top of Haymarket. Single taxi, occupied, came out of turning by Pavilion Theatre and swung right. Just previous to taxi coming abrest of gent block at Haymarket top released. Saw gent look at taxi but not signal, flag being down. Then as taxi slowed, gent seemed to recognize occupant, apeariently lady. Gent waved arms like a manniac and jumped out into road as if to stop taxi, shouting something. As he landed in road, lorry coming up from released Haymarket block struck him on right side, herling him several ft. then pulling up just in time to avoid near wheel traversing g's neck.

Small crowd formed (paper-boys, etc.) before I could reach spot. Ordering crowd aside, examined body and found life not extinck. Procured ambulance and went with casuality to St. George's Hospital where he was taken into Casuality Ward. At Hospital endeavoured to ascertain from casuality's clothing identity of same. Failed owing to there being no distingwishing marks upon body or clothes and nothing in pockets safe cigarette case, pocket knife, 1 piece twine, 1 cigarette picture, 15/7½ in silver, 1 pipe, 1 tobacco pouch, 2 1½ stamps (unused) 1 pocket h'chf (clean) 1 pocket h'chf (soiled).

Casuality's clothing was brand new. Underwear Cromwell type. Suit good material, good finish, no distinguishing marks.

Was informed by surgeon that casuality suffering from concussion, 3 broken ribs, dislocated shoulder, simple fracture left leg, severe bruising, abrasions, etc. Long superficial wound in scalp.

(Signed)   X4342.
P. C. BIGGLESWADE.

26th October, 193-.

PART THREE

THIS IS WHAT HAS BEEN TOLD

MANORY KING, a young and handsome novelist, whose last book has achieved a tremendous success, is lying unconscious and without identification in St. George's Hospital. He was about to leave—not yet knowing of the huge vogue his book was about to enjoy—for Egypt as War Correspondent to

"THE PLANET," a sensational newspaper, when he was run over by a lorry manufactured by

HENRY FORD, quite a well-to-do man.
Manory was run over by the lorry because he had jumped into the road to try to intercept a taxi containing

SUSAN MAINWARING, a young and lovely girl whom he does not know by her real name, and whom he has been despairingly searching for.
Susan has, off her own

BAT, a winged mammal, and because she loves him, done a great deal towards furthering the imminent success of his book

" GLITTER, A REALISTIC FANTASY."
The situation now is that

NOBODY knows where Manory is. *The Planet* know he has not reached Egypt ; his publishers think him at home. His friend,

JOHN HARRINGTON, a journalist, does not know what to think, while Susan—who knows nothing of the disappearance—is beginning to think it is time to reveal herself to Manory.

KEEP THAT IN YOUR HEAD AND BEGIN.

GLITTER

BY

E. MANORY KING

Messrs. Flewin, Mile & Garth have to apologise to all those who have not their desire for immediate possession of this book satisfied. The orders received have been so stupendous that, although the printers are working day and night, the publishers cannot at the moment cope with the demand. They hope, however, that this situation will have been satisfactorily met within a few days, by which time the new arrangements for printing should be working sufficiently smoothly to allow of the supply being equal to the immense demand which shows no sign of diminution.

" Send Harrington here, and tell him to hurry ! "

" Want me, sir ? "

" I don't want *you*, I want your friend, King."

" King, sir ? "

" Yes, King. What the blistering hell has that fellow done with himself ? "

" Done with himself, sir ? "

" Don't keep repeating what I say ! Here I get this cable this morning to say your precious friend never sailed on that boat after all. His luggage went aboard all right. They waited for him as long as they could and then they went without him. If he missed the damn boat, why couldn't he let us know ? Where is he ? "

" Haven't any idea, sir. . . . It's a shock to me. I thought he was in Cairo by this time."

" Can't think what the fellow's playing at—and what's all this fuss about that book, *Glitter* ? "

" Yes, sir, that's his last book. Going very well, I should think."

" *Very well !* Seems to be going like bubonic plague ! Two days off for you. Find out what's happened to him, but don't go about with your mouth wide open. Keep quiet. We don't want all Fleet Street laughing at us. First, we haven't a correspondent. Then we get one and lose him ! Get off now, and as you go out ask Mr. Huxley to come and see me."

" Huxley ! Our infernal correspondent's gone and lost himself. Get somebody else at once—some one fit to travel by himself ! And get him this evening—we're a week out on this job. Some of you people'll get the sack quick if this office doesn't change ! "

" This is the case, sir."

" H'm. . . . How long has he been like this ? "

" Hasn't changed at all, sir, since they brought him in. We've set the leg and ribs, put the shoulder back, dressed the wounds ; but what I can't make out is this coma."

" Has he been like this all the time, Sister ? "

" All the time, sir. We've kept a special watch on him. There's one thing, sir, he hasn't shown any deterioration."

" H'm ! . . ."

Flewin, Mile & Garth

Telephone : Gerrard 34560.

ADAM HOUSE,
ADELPHI, W.C.
November 20th, 193-.

DEAR KING,

What has become of you ? I expected to see you up here before this, or at least to have had a reply to my notes of Monday and Tuesday. I don't think I mentioned it then—perhaps I thought you would imply it—but if, by any chance, you would like to have some money, we should be only too delighted to accommodate you.

Glitter is going as I have never known a book go before. Heartiest congratulations ! Do let's hear from you.

Yours sincerely,
HOWARD GARTH.

P.S.—We are sending along such stacks of correspondence to you that I think you will soon have to get a secretary. Such is fame !

H. G.

" THE HOLLYHOCKS,"
ACACIA ROAD, WYRBLETON, SURREY.
November 15th, 193-.

E. MANORY KING, ESQ., Author,
c/o MESSRS. FLEWIN, MILE & GARTH,
ADAM HOUSE, ADELPHI, LONDON, W.C.

DEAR MR. KING,

I hope you will not think me rude for writing to you, but I have enjoyed your book, *Glitter,* so very much and so have my friends (Miss) Irene Stubbs and (Miss) Winnie Smithson. We were wondering whether it would be troubling you too much to ask you to let us have your autograph (three times) because we collect autographs. We have enclosed three pieces of paper for this purpose together with stmpd. addsd. envp.

Yours very sincerely,
(MISS) ERICA HOBHOUSE.

CHAPEL COTTAGE,
STONY ROAD, LIPSY COAD,
NR. LLANDUDIDRIDNYCH WELLS,
November 12th, 193–.

E. MANORY KING, ESQ.,
c/o MESSRS. FLEWIN, MILE & GARTH,
ADAM HOUSE, ADELPHI, W.C.

DEAR SIR,

As a minister of the South Wales Congregational and Anabaptist Church, may I take the liberty of remonstrating with you over your rather terrible work, *Glitter*. It is a sad thing that one of your undoubted abilities should so far give himself over to the heathen and flesh-pots.

Hoping that you will in future present to your great public work more worthy of your gifted pen.

I remain,

Yours always truthfully,
WILLOUGHBY SPRAGGETT
(Revd.).

THE DOVECOT, LESSER BUSTLEFORTH,
NR. TEDBURY, SOMERSET.
November 9th, 193–.

MR. KING, Author of *Glitter*,
c/o Publishers,
LONDON.

DEAR SIR,

What pleasure your ennobled work has given me and my family (4 boys, 2 girls). It is so hard nowadays for a lonely widow, such as I am, to find suitable reading matter for her chicks, but your uplifting and ennobled writing makes in this case the Mother's task only too delightfully easy.

I am really writing to you because my husband, Jefferson Plinth, of whom you will doubtless have heard, when he was on This Side, was a writer too ; not perhaps so great a writer as yourself, but in his way undoubtedly a genius. Writing of him in the *Yeovil Parish Gazette*, the Revd. C. D. Ponsonby once remarked : " In a different age, with only a slightly different pen, our popular churchwarden would have been hailed as one of a nation's literary geniuses."

I know from my dear Jefferson's talk only too well how literary people hang together, and I have been wondering whether you, from the pinnacle of the great success to which your achievements have brought you, could reach down a hand to help the hard-pressed widow of a fellow genius, who never received his just dues while he was with us.

Times are so very, very hard that I am sure I and the chicks would be grateful for even the smallest sign of that generosity which your ennobled writing proves you to have in such abundant quantities.

Hoping you will not think I have taken any undue liberty.

Yours fraternally,
HARRIET PLINTH.

FULCRUM & COMPANY

" Clean as a Whistle "

Publicity Offices.   MOONBEAM CITY,
November 10th, 193–.

E. MANORY KING, ESQ.,
c/o MESSRS. FLEWIN, MILE & GARTH,
ADAM HOUSE, ADELPHI, LONDON, W.C.

DEAR SIR,
In approaching you we would like to draw your attention to the fact that such eminent personages as Miss Edith Hell, Miss Cutey Goldflesch, Sir Henry Sidebottom, F.R.Z.S., Lady Lieberhundt, and Mr. Marcus Stromburg, have already, as you may have noticed, favourably received our application that they should help us in our good work of pushing forward the sales of Moonbeam Soap.

We do not, of course, know whether your goodself makes use of this product, but we feel certain that one exercising so much influence over the general public will appreciate that his testimony could not but go a long way towards influencing the public.

We should feel honoured and obliged if you would allow us to publish your photograph over an advertisement stating that you habitually use and recommend our product. We should like to point out that, while the advertisement would undeniably be great, the Directors are also prepared to reimburse you for your trouble to the extent of a sum of £50.

I remain, Sir,

Yours obediently,

SAMPSON SAVERHOUSE

(Chief Deputy Assistant Publicity Manager).

Raoul de Bondieu

Telephone : Seine 88-x-Bonlit 23.
RUE DE DUMAS 44,
PARIS.
le 18 *Novembre,* 193–.

SIR,

We have honour to approach in re your novel *Glitter*. We are agents literary dealing with perfectly all the countries of present-day Europe. When we have the honour to express to you that we have handled the output of such terrific authors as Wallace (Edgar) ; Ruck (Berta) ; M. Dell (Ethel) ; Bennett (Eileen) ; and Boswell (Johnson), throughout all the asabove-mentioned countries of modern-day Europe, we hope that you will appreciate readily that we are in super position to handle your stuff jolly well.

Hoping to receive reply favourably without much delay.

We are, Honoured Sir,

Your obedient servants,

RAOUL DE BONDIEU

(Rene Chatnoir, Directeur).

Empire Educational Films, Ltd.

Telephone : Norbit 100.   PARKVIEW STUDIOS,
                                                      NORBITON.
                                            November 11th, 193–.

E. MANORY KING, ESQ.,
c/o MESSRS. FLEWIN, MILE *&* GARTH,
ADAM HOUSE, ADELPHI, W.C.

DEAR SIR,
    We are extremely interested in your novel *Glitter* from the
point of view of its possibilities for adaptation to the screen.
    We are assuming that the film rights are retained by your-
self. If they are, we wonder whether you could make it convenient to come along and see me at some time, or, if you are
too busy to make the journey to this somewhat out-of-the-way
spot and would give my secretary a ring, stating when you are
free, I shall be delighted to come and have a few minutes' chat
with you.
    I would like to add that we have undoubtedly the finest
cortege of Directors in the country ; among those particularly
interested in your work are William Winters, so well known for
his battle pictures ; Arthur Disraeli, whose recent picture,
In The Air, was so favourably received ; and Ian Morton.

                              Yours very truly,
                                    WALLACE LUPUS
                                    (Managing Director).

Western Union Cablegrams

MANORY KING c/o FLEWGAR PICCY LONDON.

    OFFER TWELVE THOUSAND DOLLARS WORLDS FILM RIGHTS
GLITTER REPLY TIGER FILMS NEW YORK.

" Mr. 'Arrington ! "

" What is it ?   Can't you see I'm busy ? "

" Orl right, sir.   No need to bite a body's 'ead orf ! "

" Sorry, Mrs. Billiter, sorry.   It's all this stuff . . ."

" You may well say *all*, Mr. 'Arrington. . . ."

" What do you want, Mrs. Billiter ? "

" Well . . . there's a lidy for yer."

" Lady for *me* ? "

" Yes, Mr. 'Arrington, and if I *may* say so, a very pleasant-spoken, nice-lookin' young party."

" For me ?   What's the name ? "

" Well, *she* sez Mannering, but she gives us this here card, and it seems to say Main-waring."

" Mainwaring ? . . . Well, I s'pose you had better show her up.   This room's in a hell of a mess.   No, don't stop to tidy up.   I've got all these letters where I know they are."

" Is it . . . Mr. Harrington ? "

" Harrington's my name, certainly.   Miss Mainwaring ? "

" Yes. . . . I'm terribly sorry to worry you—I can see you're very busy, and it seems a silly time to call, but . . . but . . ."

" Won't you sit down, Miss Mainwaring ?   Here, I'll take those papers off that chair. . . . Sorry the place is in such an awful mess."

" Thank you. . . . Mr. Harrington, I believe you're a great friend of Mr. King's."

" That's quite right. . . ."

" Mr. Harrington, where is Mr. King ?   I got his address and came here to see him, but downstairs the landlady told me he hadn't been here for weeks and weeks."

" He hasn't."

" Where is he ?   Do you know ? "

" Well—er—Miss Mainwaring . . . you'll appreciate, of course, that—er—well, the fact is—er—as you—er—no doubt know, Mr. King has suddenly jumped into the limelight and as a matter of fact—er—it's rather up to me to—er—keep his present whereabouts . . ."

" Mr. Harrington, that's no good.   I rather suspected it downstairs, but I know now.   You haven't the foggiest idea where he is, have you ? "

"If you put it like that, I haven't, and I'm damn' worried about it."

"Worried?"

"Well, wouldn't you be worried? Just look round this room! All you can see is his bl . . . his correspondence, and also I can't think what the poor old stiff's gone and done with himself."

"You don't think . . . you don't think . . . Mr. *Harrington*!"

"No, no . . . no! Of course I don't. King's very well able to look after himself. Don't for heaven's sake get worried over anything, I said. Good Lord!"

"What's the matter?"

"Are you the girl that . . . that he . . ."

"I expect I am."

"Well, I used to curse him about you, but I didn't know what . . ."

"Thank you very much, Mr. Harrington!"

"Well, I'm jiggered! You're the girl who wasn't ffolliatt-Wilson!"

"Wasn't who?"

"Some name like ffolliatt-Wilson."

"Whatever *do* you mean?"

"Only that night when you . . . you probably know what night I mean, anyway, King came home here as if somebody had just given him the earth on a plate. Woke me up. Flashed a great card all over the place. Covered with small f's."

"My goodness me! *That's* what it was! D'you know, Mr. Harrington, what I did? I *am* a fool! . . . I . . . he and I . . . what I mean . . . is . . . we had arranged . . . This sounds perfectly awful . . . but we had arranged to . . . Anyhow, we were to see each other again and he had somehow forgotten to tell me his name. . . . Just before he got out of the car he . . . that is to say . . . Anyhow, just before we said—er—just before we left each other I gave him a card and I s'pose I was a bit hurried or something, and I just picked one out of my bag and Margery ffolliatt-Wilson's must've been in there. It was, now I come to think of it! What a *damn* little fool I am!"

"Oh, very natural mistake. Anybody might make it. But I must say it was a slip that caused poor old King a pretty rotten time. I couldn't do anything with him until I suddenly got him a job to go out as War Correspondent for the *Planet* to Egypt."

" Oh, is that where he is, then ? D'you think . . . is there any chance . . . Is there any danger ? "

" Miss Mainwaring, he has *not* gone there ! That's just the trouble. If he was nice and safely sitting in some mess tent, drinking his head off, I wouldn't mind, but that's not it ! It's not knowing where he is and all *this* . . . and trying to keep it quiet. . . ."

" Trying to keep it quiet ? "

" Well, in a way I've got to. For a bit, anyhow. You see, I don't believe anything's happened to him. I've known the stiff for a long time and he always bobs up, and as I feel certain he's all right . . . *and* as my editor is almost certain to sack me if I go opening my mouth about his disappearance . . . *and* with all this literature . . . *and* my landlord and landlady are wearing out their boots answering the door, what with postmen and reporters, and touts and what not . . ."

" So, really, you and I, Mr. Harrington, are the only people that *really* know that he's . . . he's . . . missing. . . . Tell me something ! "

" Tell you anything."

" Did he know before he apparently went off to Egypt that *Glitter* was going to make him a rich man ? "

" He did *not* ! He was still living here with me—you can see what this place is like for yourself ; he used to sleep on the sofa there. . . . I should never even have thought of getting him that job if we had known there was going to be all this money knocking about, though I expect he would have taken it before for other reasons. You, to be exact."

" Oh ! . . . It's very odd, Mr. Harrington, but here he is—gone—and both you who are his great friend, and me who . . . well, both of us . . . we neither of us seem to be really worried about him. It's almost as if we know that, whatever's happening, he is really all right. I mean, though I am terribly *worried*, I haven't got that beastly sick sort of feeling."

" I think you're quite right not to have it. If you want to know what I *really* think, I think poor old Manory's judiciously gone off to the country to get away from the bulls."

" The *bulls* ? "

" You know what bulls are ! Animals with long blue papers ! "

" Of course. Why, was he—— ? "

" He certainly was. And so am I, to a certain extent. But King was up against a very bad patch."

" But couldn't he have let you know something ? "

" *That's* the only odd part about the whole business. I've got a theory about it, though. I think that he thought that if I didn't know where he was, I shouldn't have to be perpetually lying about him. That would be rather like him, you know—though I suppose you don't, really."

" But I do ! "

" Sorry ! "

" Mr. Harrington ! "

" Yes ? "

" Is he a good business man ? "

" Rotten ! Poor devil's never had any opportunity to be good."

" Mr. Harrington ! Will you come into a partnership with me ? "

" What is it ? "

" You've *got* to ! I know you will. You've been so awfully nice already. You and I, we're going to be Manory King Limited, until Mr. King, Managing Director, comes back again. Follow ? "

" Dimly. You might elucidate a bit, though."

" What I mean exactly is this. Just about now is the time he ought to be grabbing all his opportunities with both hands and feet. Is that right ? "

" It is."

" And as he's away, he can't, can he ? "

" No."

" Well, don't you think that somebody, you and me, ought to do it for him before he loses all the opportunities that there are going about ? . . . Also, it would be rather fun, you know. Are you very busy ? "

" Busy ! Well, I'm on the staff of the *Planet*, and their idea is that for every shilling a week you draw you do two hours' hard work. It's not mine, but still . . ."

" Couldn't you throw it up ? "

" We-e-ell ! Tell you what I *can* do, though ! I'm overdue for my fortnight's holiday. I can insist on taking that, and see how we go."

" Is that a bet, Mr. Harrington ? "

" A bet it is."

" Will you shake hands on it ? "

" I will."

" Well, we ought to get down to business at once, oughtn't we ? "

" Yes."

" Well, s'pose we take these letters off here and put them on
top of that pile over there.   Does that matter ? "

" Not a bit ! "

" *That's* right, then.   Now . . ."

" Hallo !   Is that 34560 Gerrard ? "

" Yes.   Flewin, Mile & Garth."

" Can I speak to Mr. Garth, please ? "

" Who is that speaking ? "

" Mr. Manory King's secretary."

" Oh !   Hold the line, please. . . ."

" Hallo !   Mr. Garth's secretary speaking.   Who is that ? "

" Mr. Manory King's secretary here."

" Oh !   I'm afraid Mr. Garth is engaged.   Can I do anything ? "

" I'm afraid not.   Perhaps you would ask Mr. Garth whether
he could telephone later."

" If you wouldn't mind holding the line I'll see if Mr. Garth
can speak. . . ."

" Thank you."

" Garth speaking.   Who's that ? "

" Mr. Manory King's secretary, Mr. Garth."

" Oh ! . . . Yes ? "

" Mr. Garth, Mr. King has asked me to tell you that he has
gone into the country for a rest."

" Yes ?   Where's he gone ? "

" I'm sorry, Mr. Garth, but I have had strict instructions from
Mr. King not to divulge his address.   I hope you will understand that he doesn't mean anything personally, but he has just
told me that he doesn't want any one to know, so you'll understand. . . ."

" Yes.   Yes.   Yes !   What can I do for you ?   I suppose
you are transacting all his business ? "

" That is so, Mr. Garth.   I and his financial representative."

" Oh !   Well, what can I do for you ? "

" It's about the American rights, Mr. Garth.   The contract, Mr. Garth, states that the American rights belong to your firm, but that you shall pay Mr. King fifty per cent. of any monies you receive.   Mr. King did not notice this figure when he signed the contract.   He assumed, quite naturally, I think, that the figure was ninety per cent.   He has asked me to see whether I could not adjust this matter with you."

" Oh, has he ? "

" Mr. King asked me to say, Mr. Garth, that he thinks the English royalty terms are so advantageous to your firm that he is sure you will meet him on this question of the American rights.   Have you got a publisher yet ? "

" We have got several offers in front of us, but haven't decided which one to accept.   This is rather strange of Mr. King, I must say, to raise this point at this stage."

" Oh, do you think so, Mr. Garth ?   All previous contracts with his other publishers have been for a larger percentage, and I think he is feeling rather strongly about this.   In fact, he said to me that he hoped it would not mean any litigation."

" Oh, did he ?   Would you mind giving me your 'phone number ? "

" Certainly.   The number is Studios 9766."

" I'll ring you at half-past three."

" Is that Studios 9766 ? "

" Yes."

" Can I speak to Mr. Manory King's secretary, please ? "

" I'm afraid she is out.   This is Harrington speaking, Mr. King's representative.   Can I take a message ? "

" Hold on one moment.   Flewin, Mile & Garth here."

" Hallo !   Is that Mr. King's secretary ? "

" No, his representative.   His secretary is out."

" What !   Representative ? . . . Sorry, I didn't know that he . . ."

" Mr. King has just employed me . . . I'm an old friend of

his . . . to look after certain aspects of the financial side of his affairs. Is it about the American rights question you want to speak ? "

" Yes, that's it. I have had a talk with my partners and though they say that they think it odd that Mr. King didn't notice this matter at the time, they are prepared to meet him by changing his fifty per cent. on the U.S. rights to seventy-five per cent. Will that do ? "

" I think I am empowered to say on Mr. King's behalf that that would be suitable. It was just that he thought that fifty per cent. for you rather excessive."

" All right. I'll have the contract altered. If you will send Mr. King's to me I will sign the alteration. What about Mr. King's signature on our copy ? "

" If you will send the copy to this address, 13 Cheyne House, Chelsea, I will send it down to the country with Mr. King's other papers and get him to sign and return it."

" How's that for a signature, Mr. Harrington ? "

" We-ell ! . . ."

" Tell me honestly, now."

" Well, honestly, it's no good at all. Wouldn't deceive a blind puppy."

" Don't be *too* severe about it ! "

" I'm not really. Here, give that to me ! I'll show you how to forge."

" How ? "

" Where's that signature of his own ? "

" Here. . . ."

" Right ! Now, I'll show you something. Got that, put it in front of you, upside down, then get the thing you want to forge on, put the upside down signature just above it, and copy it backwards . . . drawing . . . like this. . . . How's that ? "

" Marvellous ! You're a treasure ! "

13 CHEYNE HOUSE, CHELSEA, S.W.
November 23rd, 193–.

DEAR SIRS,

I am instructed by Mr. Manory King to thank you for your letter of yesterday's date, enclosing the interim Royalty Statement showing the sales as 145,000 copies to date. This is a figure which Mr. King notes with satisfaction.

In reply to your kind offer as to whether Mr. King desires any immediate payments, he instructs me to thank you for this, but to say that at the moment he will not avail himself of it. If he should wish to at any future date, he will either write to you himself or through me.

Yours faithfully,

S. MAINWARING

(Secretary).

MESSRS. FLEWIN, MILE & GARTH, ADAM HOUSE,
ADELPHI, W.C.

" Sister ! Sister ! Are you awake ? "

" Ye-ah. . . ."

" Sister ! Number 66 is talking ! Not delirious, seems quite all right. Strange, of course, but I thought perhaps you had better see him."

" Aw-ri ! . . ."

" So you are better, are you ? "

" Have I . . . where . . . what is this place ? "

" St. Joseph's Hospital. You've been ill, very ill."

" What . . . happened ? Something . . . hit me."

" Something hit you all right ! You were knocked down in the road."

" Oh . . . yes . . . I . . . I . . . Can't seem . . . seem to . . . remember . . . it . . ."

" Don't try. Go to sleep. In the morning you can tell us everything."

" But . . . but . . . I'm not trying, but . . . but my . . . head . . . keeps . . . trying . . . and, O God ! . . . I want to remember ! "

" Go to sleep. Go to sleep, there's a good boy. You're quite all right now."

" How long . . . how long . . . have I—— ? "

" Never mind ! Never mind ! Go to sleep. Nurse ! "

" Yes, Sister ? "

" Call the House-surgeon. . . ."

" My . . . how long . . . Cairo ! . . . Cairo ! . . . Cairo ! . . . What . . ."

" Keep quiet, there's a good boy ! It's quite all right. Everything's all right."

" But I . . . Nurse ! Nurse ! Nurse ! "

" Most astonishin' thing, that coma case ! Fellow just woke up out of it last night like a baby."

" Really ? "

" Absolute fact ! Right as a trivet this morning. Pretty wobbly trivet, but quite all right."

" Damned odd case that ! Even old Rumble-guts couldn't make head or tail of it."

" He won't now. Here's this chap, as you might say, quite all right."

" Found out who he is ? "

" Well, that's the funny part. He's got his name all right. Odd name—Kelso—Christopher Kelso. Comes from Liverpool. Comes out pat all right, but something seems to worry him about it, and he can't remember what he does in life."

" Dam' queer ! "

Telephone : Studios 9766.

13 CHEYNE HOUSE,
CHELSEA, S.W.
November 24th, 193–.

MRS. PETER GALE, Hon. Sec., N.I.B. Club,
143 MAITLAND STREET, W.

DEAR MADAM,

I am instructed by Mr. Manory King to say that he much regrets that he will be unable to attend the dinner of the N.I.B. Club at which you so kindly invited him to be the guest of honour.

Mr. King is at present recuperating after a nervous breakdown, and under his Doctor's orders is living an entirely undisturbed life in the country.

Mr. King is very sensible of the honour which you have done him, but as he cannot defy his Doctor's orders, much regrets that he is unable to attend the dinner, and speak to the N.I.B. Club.

Yours faithfully,
S. MAINWARING
(Secretary).

N. I. B.

143 MAITLAND STREET, W.
November 25th, 193–.

DEAR MR. KING,

So sorry to hear through your secretary that your health forbids your attending our next monthly dinner as the guest of honour.

I wonder whether you would be so very good as to send some little message, together with the donation towards the Club funds which doubtless you would have made during the evening, had you been able to attend ?

Yours faithfully,
IRMA GALE
(Hon. Sec.).

E. MANORY KING, ESQ., 13 CHEYNE HOUSE,
CHELSEA, S.W.

Star Performers' Pesky Corporation Inc.

Cablegrams : PESK. N. Y. OFFICE : 1084 382ND STREET,
NEW YORK CITY, N.Y.

DEAR SIR,

Referring to previous correspondence, I am desired by Mr. Pesky to state that after careful consideration it has been decided by the Corporation that your book *Glitter* is not suitable for production.

Yours very truly,
DUKE P. HAREWASCH
(Chief Assistant Secretary to Mr. Pesky).

E. MANORY KING, ESQ., 13 CHEYNE HOUSE,
CHELSEA, LONDON, ENGLAND.

Western Union Cablegrams.

To : MANORY KING c/o FLEWGAR PICCY LONDON.

DEAL OFF BOARD DECIDED AGAINST *GLITTER*.

TIGER FILMS.

Western Union Cablegrams.

To : MANORY KING c/o FLEWGAR PICCY LONDON.

OFFER CANCELLED TALKIE SITUATION PRECLUDES EXPENSE *GLITTER* AT PRESENT.

PHOTO-GOLDBRICK-SPEYER.

13 CHEYNE HOUSE, CHELSEA, S.W.
November 26th, 193–.

DEAR SIR,

Mr. Manory King desires me to say, in answer to your communication of Nov. 11th, that he cannot enter into any definite contract in regard to the film rights for his book *Glitter* just at the moment as counter-negotiations are proceeding with three or four American firms.

Yours faithfully,

JOHN HARRINGTON.

WALLACE LUPUS, ESQ., E. E. FILMS LTD.,
NORBITON.

Post Office Telegrams.

HARRINGTON 3 CHEYNE HOUSE CHELSEA.

ADVISE KING NOT CLOSE ANY AMERICAN DEAL WITHOUT APPROACHING E. E. F.

LUPUS.

16*

Post Office Telegrams.

WALLACE LUPUS FLICKERING NORBITON.

SEVEN AMERICAN OFFERS FOR *GLITTER* TO HAND. SUGGEST MEETING YOUR LONDON OFFICE TWO P.M. TO-DAY.
                                                HARRINGTON.

Post Office Telegrams.

HARRINGTON 13 CHEYNE HOUSE CHELSEA.

WILL BE THERE. LUPUS.

Mr. Harrington, this is Mr. Winters, the producer, who is so anxious to do *Glitter*, Mr. King's book."

" How d'you do ? "

" How d'you do, Mr. Harrington. Yes, as Mr. Lupus was saying, I'm very keen to do *Glitter* as my next picture. My last was *Bloodshed !* . . . Don't suppose you happen to've seen it ? "

" Sorry ; I'm afraid I haven't."

" H'm ! It went round pretty nearly everywhere, I think. 'Course, *I* wasn't satisfied with it. Dam' well received and all that, of course—but I'm one of those poor unfortunates who can never lie back and be pleased with what he's done ; I'm always after something better, something better and something new and, above all, something with THEME. Theme's the thing—Theme ! . . . and that's what *Glitter's* got. As soon as I'd read the book, I said to myself there's a book with a Theme. I went down to the studio full of it the next morning—full of it. Didn't I, Lupus ? "

" Yes. Yes, you did, Winters. Now I think perhaps Mr. Harrington . . ."

" Absolutely full of it. I remember driving my car down to the Studio at twenty ! Just think of that ! Twenty ! I looked at the speedometer just as I got into the straight, and I generally take that bend somewhere between fifty and fifty-five. I tell you, all I could do was to lie back and laugh. But it was all because I was so wrapped up in *Glitter*. In this job, Mr. Harrington, if one wants to make a good picture, one *must* have *Theme*.

I don't know whether you ever saw a picture of mine called *Carnage* ? "

" I can't say that I did."

" H'm ! Well, that was a fairly early picture of mine. Wasn't satisfied with it, of course ; I never am satisfied with my work, once it's done it's done and my mind's on the next job ; I'm afraid that's the way with me. Well, in *Carnage*—I had the whole of the Air Force out for that picture by the way ; dam' interesting work, and I must say they played up dam' well. Very pleasant boys ; they seemed to like working under me— I don't want to sound pleased with myself, of course, but I must say I've very pleasant memories of shooting that picture. They gave me a dinner at the end of it—glad to see the back of me, I expect, what ?—a good dinner, some of 'em were so tight they were just lying about. Old Blanket-Blanket was there too ; made a speech ; said they'd told him that if all the Operation Orders in the Force were as good as the ones I'd been getting out, things would be better. . . . Well, I suppose I'd better be push-ing off ; got a whole cast waiting for me down at Norbiton on the set. Been very pleasant to've met you. I hope you'll fix the business up with Mr. Lupus ; I'm very anxious to get on to *Glitter* ; it's got *Theme*. Tell you how I should treat it—shall treat it if I get the chance : did you ever happen to see a picture of mine called *Slaughter* ? Had the whole of the R.A.F. and about half the Navy out for that picture. I must say . . ."

" I say, Winters, time's getting on. Your light'll go . . ."

" I say ! I'd no idea it was so late. I must be getting along. Can't have that lot drawing salaries just for lying about. Had enough of that when I made *Destruction !* in India. That was dam' funny. Talk about people just lying around. . . . But I *must* push off ; remind me to tell you about shooting that picture some time. . . . I say, I'm late ! Good thing I brought the Bentley to-day, get on to the set in twenty minutes. . . . Good-bye, sorry I've got to rush like this, breaks up our chat. See you again soon perhaps. . . ."

" Now, Mr. Lupus, perhaps we might get down to business. I'm a busy man, you know."

" I'm sorry about Winters . . . but I'll give him his due, Mr. Harrington, he's a very able director—brilliant."

" Yes ? Now ; I understand from your wire yesterday that you wanted to see me before I clinched with any American firm."

" One moment, Mr. Harrington, I take it you are fully empowered to act for Mr. King in this matter ? "

" Entirely.　Here's a letter, signed by Mr. King, giving me full authority.　Now let's get to business as quick as we can, if you don't mind."

" I'll be very brief.　How much do you want for the world film rights of *Glitter*, Mr. Harrington ? "

" As much as we can get."

" Ha-ha !　Very natural.　Well, what's your top offer from the Yankees ? "

" The biggest offer we have ever definitely received was £3000, but as you can see from this cable here, in which the offer was made, it was some time ago, since when other negotiations have been opened with other firms and corporations, and I've no doubt I can push it a great deal higher without much trouble. Let's say £5000's the figure you've got to beat."

" Phe-ew !　Steep, Mr. Harrington ! "

" For *Glitter*—the best best-seller ?　It's not even an incline."

" We're a British company, Mr. Harrington."

" So I've perceived.　We'd better call the deal off, then, and I'll be getting back.　Sorry to've wasted your time ;　I didn't think you could rise to it, but Mr. King was anxious to have the book filmed by an English company if possible ; but I'm afraid he's not so foolishly patriotic as to throw away thousands. Good-afternoon, Mr. Lupus ! "

" Just a moment, Mr. Harrington ; just a moment.　Please ! How long can you give me to put the matter before my board ? "

" I don't think it's worth doing that.　It'd be best to call the deal off now, I think. . . ."

" Could you give us till six—that's only a matter of three hours !　Surely you could do that !　Surely ? "

" Very well ;　I don't see how that could hurt.　But it *is* only till six, Mr. Lupus. . . ."

" I'll do my best to get word to you before."

" Jack ! "

" Hallo.　Don't ask me anything difficult, I'm sweating too much on old Lupus.　What's the time ? "

" Five-thirty.　All I was going to ask was what you thought about old Prideaux's letter."

" I *think* we'd better play him a bit longer. . . ."

" I suppose you're right.　You're one of these annoying people who always is.　All right, I'll do a letter now."

13 Cheyne House,
Chelsea, S.W.
December 2nd, 193–.

Dear Sir,

I am instructed by Mr. Manory King to thank you for your letter of the 5th ulto.

Mr. King much regrets that his health still will not permit him to give sufficient attention to business really to consider your proposal. He wishes me to express his apologies for this delay upon his part in replying to your offer ; so soon as he is fully recovered he will communicate with you again.

Yours faithfully,

S. Mainwaring

(Secretary).

Sir John Prideaux, Princess Elizabeth's Theatre,
Haymarket, S.W.1.

" How'll that do ? "

" Very good. Send it. . . . My God ! Was that the bell ? "

" Yes. I'll go."

" Jack ! Jack ! It's a wire ! Open it quick, I daren't. I'm sure it's from E.E.F."

" You're dead right, my dear. Here, look at it ! "

Post Office Telegrams.

Harrington 13 Cheyne House Chelsea.

Offer Six Thousand Please Wire Reply Immediately.

Lupus.

The St. Stephen's Bank, Limited

(NEW ROAD BRANCH.)

Tel. : Skip 1234.

214 NEW ROAD, WESTMINSTER,
LONDON, S.E. 1.
16th December, 193–.

DEAR SIR,

I would like to call your attention to the state of your account. The account is a Current one and is now standing at the rather unwieldy figure of Fifteen Thousand Pounds (£15,000).

As we note that although these large amounts continue to be paid in there has been no drawings against the account, we respectfully suggest that some at least of the total figure standing to your credit should be forthwith transferred to a Deposit account.

Yours faithfully,
H. G. SIMPSON
(Manager).

E. MANORY KING, ESQ., 13 CHEYNE HOUSE,
CHELSEA, S.W.

13 CHEYNE HOUSE, CHELSEA, S.W.
December 17th, 193–.

DEAR SIR,

Mr. King instructs me to thank you for your letter of the 8th instant, in which you offer him £600 for a short story of approx. 5000 words. Mr. King has, as you may know, been unwell, and consequently is not seriously doing any work at present. He has by him, however, a short story, copy of which is enclosed, entitled *Butterfingers*, which he would be willing for you to publish. Seeing that this is not absolutely up-to-date work, Mr. King would be willing also to accept the rather poor remuneration which you offer.

Mr. King would be glad to have a reply from you by return of post.

Yours faithfully,
S. MAINWARING
(Secretary).

P.S.—Mr. King is fully aware that this story is not in the style of his other work, but he thinks it none the worse for this.

THE EDITOR,
ST. JAMES'S MAGAZINE,
HENRIETTA STREET, W.C.2.

13 CHEYNE HOUSE, CHELSEA, S.W.
December 19*th*, 193–.

DEAR SIR,

I am instructed by Mr. Manory King to inform you that he has decided to accept your offer of £100 per article (for twelve Turf articles), to be supplied to him for his signature only, provided that the whole twelve of the articles in the series shall appear within twelve weeks, and that, should be object to any of the copy to which he has to append his name, you will agree to make such alterations as he may consider necessary.

Yours faithfully,

S. MAINWARING

(Secretary).

THE EDITOR,
THE MORNING MERCURY,
MERCURY HOUSE,
FLEET COURT, E.C.

" 'Oy ! "

" 'Ul-lo ! "

" Lend us that piper you 'ad."

" Ain't got it. Lent it ter Ginger."

" An' I s'pose 'e's walked round to the other end of the courtyard with it. . . . Six ! . . . Six ! . . . Six ! . . . *Six !* "

" Carn't you see 'e's busy writing ? "

" 'E's always writing, that fellow. Wot yer scribblin', cock ? "

" I s'pect 'e's an author—*The Corpse in the Copse* or *The Perils of Love*."

" Naow, it ain't ! I know wot 'e's writin'. *The Nick of Time or Born in the Vestry !* "

" Trying to make 'is forchune, I s'pose. Wants to be another Manory King."

" MY GOD ! . . . Sister ! Sister ! "

" But you said it was Kelso ! "

" But it had always worried me. You know it had worried me."

" Now, don't get excited."

" I won't, Sister, I won't. But I can prove it easily enough, and if you don't let me prove it now, I shall probably go mad and be here for life ! "

" That's right enough, Doctor, this is Mr. Manory King all right. What *I* want to know is—well, never mind. Perhaps I'd better not excite him."

" You won't hurt him, whatever you say. Will he, King ? You see, Mr. Garth, it's like this. His body's been mended for a long time, but there was just a shutter down in his mind. Then something he heard this morning just lifted that shutter— and here he is—himself again ! . . . And a very lucky self to wake up to find, I should say ! Treat him just as if nothing had happened—eh, King ? But don't take him out for any long walks, because that leg's not quite right yet."

" If you gentlemen would come this way, please, Chief-Inspector Tivett will see you. . . ."

" Sure you want to rush into it like this, King ? "

" Damn and blast it all ! If I don't do something now, they might hear about me and do a bunk, with all that dough."

" Yes, s'pose you're right."

" Mr. Garth and Mr. Manory King, sir."

" Good-morning, gentlemen ! Won't you sit down ? . . . How can I help you ? "

" Shall I do the talking, King ? "

" Well, you might start off for me, like a good fellow."

" Chief Inspector, this is a most extraordinary affair. I know you're used to 'em, but I think even you will agree. This is Mr. Manory King, the novelist."

" Oh yes. The author of *Glitter* ? "

"Yes. On the 26th October Mr. King had the misfortune to be knocked down in Piccadilly and very seriously injured by a lorry. He had a broken leg, and concussion of the brain. The concussion left him with an impaired memory, which largely took the form of his not knowing his own name and being under the impression that this was Christopher Kelso, which, by the way, he tells me is the name of the leading character in a book he had been planning before the accident. Since the 26th October, until to-day, Mr. King has been, unidentified, in St. Joseph's Hospital ; but—and here comes the extraordinary part—we, his publishers, in common with a great many other people have understood that Mr. King was away in the country having a rest cure under doctor's orders, which prevented him from divulging his address. . . . We were led to suppose this by communications with a woman signing herself S. MAIN-WARING. The deception was so normally and easily carried out that I'm afraid no one ever even suspected it. Now the point is this, that all this time all payments due to Mr. King from us, and I expect from a good many other sources also, have been paid over to this woman. The total sum involved must be a good many thousand pounds. In addition to the other parts of the deception, I must say that the forgeries constantly in evidence of Mr. King's signature were very, very good. So good that I doubt whether he would know them as forgeries himself. . . . That's the whole story, as far as we know it at present. Mr. King is naturally very anxious to have something done about these people at once, before they get wind of his reappearance, and try to get away with the money. . . . I don't think there's anything else we can tell him, is there, King ? "

"Didn't you say something about some man as well as this woman ? "

"Oh yes, I'd forgotten that ! Somewhere near the beginning of this fraud I rang up his supposed secretary—the woman—and was answered by a man, who said he was King's ' representative.' He did give a name over the 'phone, but either I didn't catch it at the time or else it has completely slipped my memory. That was the only time I, or any one in my office, have been in communication with any one except the woman."

"Well, that certainly *is* a rum start ! . . . If I might ask you gentlemen to wait here a moment, I'll go and see my chief."

" This is number thirteen Cheyne House ? "

" Y-y-y-yes ? "

" Party of the name of Main-waring live here ?   S. Main-waring ? "

" Ye—ye—ye—yes, sir ! "

" She in ? "

" Ye—ye—ye—yes, sir ! "

" These gentlemen and I will come in."

" B-b-b-bu—but . . ."

" You stand out o' the way, my girl !   Any back entrance to this flat ? "

" N-n-n-no—no—sir ! "

" Sure ? "

" N-n-nun—nun. . . . I   mum—mum—mum—mean y-y-yes ! "

" Tell Main-waring a police officer wants to see her."

" Ye—ye—yes, sir.   Wh—wh—wha—what fuf—fuf-fur ? "

" Never you mind !   Get Main-waring here ! "

" What *is* all this ? . . . How dare you come in here, frightening my servants. . . . *You ?* "

" My . . . *God !* . . . My *darling !* "

" Talk about a rum start ! "

NEW READERS BEGIN HERE

MANORY KING, a handsome and very successful novelist, is in love with, and newly wedded to

SUSAN, *née* **MAINWARING,** a charming and lovely girl who has, until the time of her engagement to Manory, earned her own living as a reviewer of books and free-lance journalist. In co-operation with Manory's friend,

JOHN HARRINGTON, a real newspaper-man, she has, by skill and chicanery, brought Manory to his present pinnacle of fame, bullying the

GENERAL PUBLIC, a body of perhaps well-intentioned but certainly sheep-headed persons, into appreciation, assumed and/or real, of Manory's work. She and Manory, after their wedding, go for their honeymoon to

SCOTLAND, a wild and mountainous country where they have been lent the ancient castle of

SIR LESLIE PHILLIPS, a racehorse owner *inter alia*.

After their honeymoon, the young couple return to

LONDON, a big city in their native land, where they have taken a house. Life seems to lie before them like a gay carpet for their joyous feet.

NOW WRITE ON!!

DENIS MACKAIL (1892–   ) *is one of the most energetic and popular contributors of the magazine story dealing with love and laughter, whilst his books, such as " Bill the Bachelor," " The Flower Show," and " Greenery Street " are noted for their intuitive and amusing characterization. He is at his funniest in this tale of romance and rancour.*

SAY IT WITH CHEESE

FORMALITY, they say, has gone out of modern life. Church-parade and chaperons have vanished from the face of the earth. Soft shirts and high necks are seen in the stalls. Visiting-cards are left almost exclusively by canvassers for carpet sweepers. Hustle, and with it a general loosening of all the old rules and conventions, has shaken society from top to bottom— so much so, indeed, that it's difficult any longer to say which of these extremes is which. New eras dawn so fast in these stirring times that even yesterday's bad manners are thought just a trifle over-punctilious this morning.

Yet still there are backwaters and creatures that dwell in them. Though road-houses spring up in the suburbs and snack-bars have penetrated to the heart of Mayfair, there is still at least one Club in St. James's where tradition lingers, barley-water is brewed, and the members are united in that utter negation of social intercourse which was once the hall-mark of the Englishman's greatest gift to the history of fug.

The Crabapple, it's called, and on the day when you hear that they've introduced mixed squash-rackets at the Crabapple you will also know that your informant has gone off his head. For it won't and it can't be true. The Crabapple may—and, indeed, must—eventually break ; but it will never bend. The air which its members have breathed for well over a century may one day be released by the picks of the workmen who are sent to destroy it ; but there'll be no change in its atmosphere until that happens, for the average age of the Committee is sixty-nine, and each one of them is a club-conservative to the core.

And the waiting-list may dwindle, but there are still no actual vacancies, and if there were, do you think that the Committee would stoop to any popularizing or modernizing tactics ?

Not while they can still lift an ear-trumpet or drop a blackball. Why, three years ago a young fellow of barely sixty made an entry in the suggestion-book proposing that smoking should be allowed in the smaller dining-room after nine o'clock, and the Committee had him up, and of course nobody knows what they said to him because there's a tradition of secrecy just as strong as that of stick-in-the-mud. But the page was removed, and the rash innovator resigned, and that's the kind of Club that the Crabapple was three years ago, and it hasn't altered, so that anyone would notice it, since.

An assembly, you may possibly feel, which it is better to hear about than to join. Quite so ; but we're only suggesting that you should be implicated in the former alternative. For that was just the preface, and this is the story.

L UNCH-TIME on a day towards the end of March. All the windows shut, of course. Fires flickering, radiators roasting, the tape-machine ticking, stuffed heads staring ; two page-boys standing by the swing-doors from the street—ready to pluck them open whenever a muffled member appears on the steps ; the porter writing mysteriously in a mysterious ledger, with one eye on the point of his pen and the other cocked penetratingly on each fresh arrival.

The smoking-room nearly deserted, and quite silent save for the rustling of a newspaper and the heavy breathing of a major-general. The double dining-room, on the other hand, filling up rapidly with characters who have nearly all entered with varying degrees of stoop, hobble, stagger or shuffle ; have glared at the framed menus on the big desk in the middle ; and having written and signed their orders, have disposed themselves at the separate tables—alone, if possible, but as the room gets fuller still, with a stiff nod at the other occupant.

This nod means : " Do you mind if I join you ? " and, unless the two members are known to each other elsewhere, is acknowledged with another nod signifying : " Not in the least, as long as you don't talk to me." Thus, at about half-past one, Mr. Mortimer Murbles, who was already a little annoyed about an appointment which had been thrust on him for three o'clock, was still further put out to find that there was no longer a table where he might lunch by himself. Yet having snarled at the steward, accepted the chair which was drawn out for him. And gave that nod which has just been described, and received another one which was no more genial—only no one could say that he'd invited anything else—and thus Mr. Murbles sat down.

And a tall waiter appeared with his luncheon-bill (to which some figures had now been added) and a basket of bread. And Mr. Murbles said : " Hey ! Take that away, and get me some toast ! " And the tall waiter said : " Very good, sir," and came back almost instantly with a toast-rack and a plate of soup. And Mr. Murbles executed a fantasia on the cruet, and began lapping and gobbling. And the other member continued to munch and absorb a helping of roly-poly pudding.

And presently Mr. Murbles was brought a plate of roast mutton, accompanied by vegetables in a small, plated dish, and to the short waiter who performed this service the other member said : " Hi ! Stilton ! "

Whereupon the short waiter departed, and returned with a cylindrical trophy modestly wrapped in a napkin, and shifted the cruet, and set it on the centre of the table. And the other member began digging and delving with an ivory-handled trowel, and Mr. Murbles gave a distinct sniff through his rather large nose.

This sound, in Mr. Murbles's opinion, should have been quite enough to indicate that he found the proximity of the Stilton displeasing ; to make it quite clear that the centre of the table was no place for it while he was still eating roast mutton. As, however, the other member failed to take any action, he sniffed again. But the other member, who had stopped scooping by this time, merely started chewing. Mr. Murbles saw that the situation must be tackled still more firmly.

" Waiter ! " he said, ferociously. " Hey ! Waiter ! "

A third waiter instantly clapped on all his brakes, and swung round to the right.

" Yessir ? " he said.

" Waiter ! " said Mr. Murbles. " Take that cheese away. It smells."

" Very good, sir," said the waiter ; and was just bending over to get a grip on it, when the other member spoke sharply and curtly.

" Waiter ! " he said. " Leave that cheese where it is. I haven't finished with it."

" Beg pardon, sir," said the waiter, straightening himself out again.

" Waiter ! " snapped Mr. Murbles. " Did you hear me just then ? Remove that cheese."

" Waiter ! " said the other member, instantaneously. " Leave that Stilton alone ! "

" Waiter ! " barked Mr. Murbles ; but the waiter had had

enough of it, and as there was obviously no possibility of putting the cheese in two places at once, he fled as precipitately as he had arrived, and for the next twenty minutes kept well out of sight in the smaller dining-room, where—he might conceivably be thanking Heaven—his regular duties lay.

But for the next ten minutes it was also touch and go in the larger dining-room whether or not Mr. Murbles would choke with rage, as he gnashed his way through the rest of his roast mutton and drank splutteringly from his beaker of burgundy. Of course, he didn't speak to his enemy across the table—how could he when they didn't know each other?—any more than his enemy spoke to him. But if covert glances could kill, there would have been more than one corpse in the Crabapple that day, while the heat engendered by these two elderly gentlemen as they sat there in silence could easily have started a large steam-engine.

Yet it was obvious which of them must leave the field first. Presently the cheese-eater rose, pushed back his chair, and hobbled off to pay his bill. Mr. Murbles instantly thrust the Stilton away from him, at the same time calling loudly to yet another waiter to clear up that disgusting mess; but he could hardly regard this as a victory, and his blood-pressure was still dangerously high.

" Monstrous ! " he kept muttering. " Impertinence ! Offensive bounder ! " And then presently he, also, rose with an effort, and lumbered across to the desk with his bill, and the cashier glanced at it and said : " Seven shillings, if you please, sir." And Mr. Murbles planked down a ten-shilling note, and, as he did so, it came into his mind that there would be more satisfaction in hating his enemy if he knew his name.

So he said : " Hey, you ! Banks ! Who was that member who was lunching at my table just now ? "

And the cashier gave him three shillings, and said : " That gentleman, sir ? Mr. Mulvey, sir. Funny thing, sir, the gentleman was just asking me your name, sir, too."

" Umph ! " said Mr. Murbles—anything but tickled, it would seem, by this type of humour. " I see," he said. " Mulvey. Never heard of him. Thanks, Banks."

And he passed across the landing into the library for his coffee and brandy, and was slightly soothed to find his favourite corner unoccupied, and sank on to a leather sofa in it. And closed his eyes presently, and was on the point of dropping into a light if stertorous slumber, when he suddenly gave a convulsive movement and jerked out his watch.

" Dash ! " he muttered—hoisting himself on to his feet again. " That girl. Nearly forgot about her. Better be getting along."

A girl and Mr. Murbles, you exclaim. Mr. Murbles and a girl ! Impossible, you say. Romance behind that protuberant waistcoat ? Sentiment behind that angry, red face ? A soft spot in this horny and typical old member of the Crabapple ? And you shudder ; but there was no need for you to shudder, for your first impression was perfectly correct. The girl—her name was Phœbe—was merely Mr. Murbles's orphaned niece. Mr. Murbles was her guardian and trustee. She was a kennel-maid near Kenilworth, which relieved him of almost all responsibility under the first head, and since her unearned income amounted to just twenty pounds a year, he'd very little trouble under the second.

Nevertheless, he frequently complained of the thoughtlessness and selfishness of her parents in dying and putting him in this onerous position, and he'd frequently stated that he'd be glad when she was twenty-one and relieved him of it. But she wasn't twenty-one yet, and she'd written and said she was coming up to see him, and he'd been very irritable ever since, because why couldn't she have said what she wanted, and wasn't it obvious that she wanted something that she hadn't liked to say ?

Umph, in fact, and deep suspicion in Mr. Murbles's little pig's eyes, as he entered his study and as his niece Phœbe came forward and kissed him.

" Well ? " he said. " Well ? What about it ? What's the matter ? What have you been up to ? You haven't lost your job, I hope ? "

" Oh, no," said Phœbe—and some dogs, it may strike us, were extremely fortunate in having so attractive an attendant. " Oh, no, Uncle Mortimer," she said. " At least," she added, a little nervously, " I mean, not exactly."

" Heh ? " said Mr. Murbles. " Not exactly ? What on earth do you mean ? "

" Well," said Phœbe, with a bit of an effort and a bit of a gulp, " what I mean is—— Well, you see ; I'm engaged."

" Heh ? " said Mr. Murbles again. " Nonsense," he said. " You can't do anything like that without my permission. Are you forgetting I'm your guardian ? "

" No," said Phœbe. " But that's just why I'm telling you. I want to get your permission, so that we can be married. Oh, and by the way——"

" Wait a minute, wait a minute ! " boomed Mr. Murbles.

" Not so fast, my girl. Married, indeed ! Why, who *is* this fellow ? "

" He's called Giles Burton," said Phœbe—and she tried not to blush, but she had to, it seemed, whenever she mentioned this marvellous name. " And I've known him quite a long time now, and he's terribly nice, and he's learning farming near Warwick, and——"

" Hey ! " interrupted her Uncle Mortimer. " Learning farming ? Do you mean to say that's all he's doing, and he thinks he can marry you without any money, and——"

" Oh, no. He's got lots of money."

" Heh ? How much ? "

" Oh, masses. And a big house, and a lot of land. Only, you see, his father died, and he left it him so that he won't really have it till he's twenty-five. Unless he marries, I mean—only then his father's old lawyer has got to give his approval. He's gone to see him to-day. Oh, and that reminds me——"

" Wait ! Stop ! " said Mr. Murbles. " Gone to see him to-day, has he ? And is there any reason," he asked, " why a niece of mine shouldn't be good enough to satisfy a lawyer ? Heh ? Who is this fellow ? What's his name ? "

" He's called Mulvey."

" Mulvey ? Did you say Mulvey ? "

" Yes, and isn't it funny, Uncle Mortimer, because Giles told me he belonged to the same club as you. Oh, and by the way—— Why, what's the matter, Uncle Mortimer ? What is it ? "

" Heh ? " said Mr. Murbles, and his pig's eyes had become much more like those of an infuriated ferret. " *That* fellow ! And I'm supposed to countenance your engagement to a boy who can't support you without leave from—— You're suggesting that I should discuss the settlement with—— But it's preposterous ! " said Mr. Murbles. " I won't hear of it. It's quite out of the question. I'll have nothing to do with it. I absolutely decline to give my consent to anything so objectionable and abominable. Poph ! ! " said Mr. Murbles, and blew his big nose violently. " Umph ! " he said, and glared at his niece like an old basilisk.

" But—but, Uncle Mortimer——"

" No. That's my last word. And if you try and do anything behind my back——"

" I see. You mean you'd stop us."

" Certainly. Have a cup of tea."

" No, thank you. Perhaps I'd better go in that case."

" The whole thing——" began Mr. Murbles ; but his niece

and ward didn't wait to hear any further comments on her love-affair. She ducked her head, to hide her swimming eyes, and she turned and bolted out of the study, and blundered across the hall, and slammed the front door behind her and rushed down the steps into the street. Nor did she pause, though her uncle was still bellowing after her like a bull, until she had reached a popular tea-shop near Piccadilly Circus, which she entered rapidly and emotionally, and where a young gentleman rushed forward and gripped her by the elbow.

" Hi ! " he said. " Phœbe ! Here I am. What happened ? "

" Nothing," she said. " Oh, Giles, darling, I told him everything, and I thought it was going to be all right, but then suddenly he became perfectly horrible, and he's absolutely forbidden it, and—— And, oh, Giles—what did Mr. Mulvey say ? "

" About the same," said the young gentleman, a bit ruefully. " I mean, he was all right at first, and then suddenly he flew clean off the handle and put his foot down. I say, dash ! I say, I adore you, you know, and this is ghastly. I say, what on earth are we to do ? "

" It—it'll be all right next year," said Phœbe. " I mean, if you still—— "

" Of course I will. But a year. A whole year. I say, darling—— "

" What ? "

" Then the cheese didn't do any good ? "

" The cheese ? Oh, Giles—how awful ! I put it on his hall table, and I tried to tell him about it—three times, I tried. But he kept on interrupting me, and then I was so upset that I forgot about it, and it's still there, and I'm not going back for it, and I hope he eats it and it chokes him ! Darling—what did you do with the other one ? Did that horrible Mr. Mulvey just take it, and then treat you like that ? What ? Do you mean he didn't even thank you ? "

" Well," said the young gentleman, a little awkwardly ; " well, no, he didn't because—Well, as a matter of fact, I did just what you did. I mean, I put it on a chair in the passage— meaning to give it him at the right moment—and then we had such a row that it went clean out of my head. I suppose it's still there, but I'm not going to call for it. Well, for one thing there isn't time, if we're going to catch that train."

" Oh, Giles. Your two lovely cheeses. Just wasted."

" Can't be helped. Sha'n't have to lug 'em about any more. Well ; I suppose we'd better have some tea."

"Yes. I mean, thank you. Darling, it's a bit of a blow, isn't it?"

"Good for us, perhaps?"

"You don't really think that?"

"No."

"Nor do I. But they've got us in a hole, you know. I can just see Uncle Mortimer forbidding the banns or setting the bloodhounds on us if we tried to dodge him. He'd simply love it, and he's got nothing else on earth to do."

"And old Mulvey," said the young gentleman, "can stop my allowance any second he wants to, and I'm not going to have you starving."

"Darling Giles, that's awfully sweet of you."

"Well, I mean it. Try one of those cakes."

And they laughed—a bit sadly, because they'd come up to London so full of hope, and they'd been so quickly and thoroughly disappointed. Yet they were young, and deeply in love, and it was rather exciting to be in a popular tea-shop together. And perhaps they weren't really surprised, either, because they each knew the old man whom they had to deal with, and perhaps it had been rather foolish to imagine that gifts of cheese—even if actually proffered—could soften the hearts of old men like that.

Could they wait a year, then? They'd got to. Could they bear it? No; but they'd still got nearly three hours with each other, and they'd be meeting again in a few days, and so on, and perhaps it might be worse. Only when they actually separated, to return to the kennels and the farm, did terrible pangs assail this simple and devoted pair. And one of them wept while combing a cocker-spaniel, and the other was abnormally downcast while feeding a delicate calf out of a bottle.

For they adored each other, and a year was eternity, and they'd certainly had two terrible blows. Nor did they think about the cheeses—and, still less, of course, did they consider that other cheese which was so largely responsible for their misfortunes.

Yet cheese was still distinctly associated with their two lines of fate.

Because if there's one thing that's more natural than another, when you're excited and in love, surely it's a little vagueness and wool-gathering and inattention to pettifogging detail. Isn't it notorious, for instance, that three-quarters of the articles brought to lost property offices are owned by lovers? And, if these two particular victims had come up to London with two similar drum-shaped parcels on the luggage-rack, you might almost call it inevitable that—if they didn't forget them altogether—they should each take the wrong one when they parted at Paddington.

Not that one cheese was better or worse than the other—they were both, as a matter of fact, excellent—but one was marked " Mortimer Murbles, Esq.," and the other " Murdoch Mulvey, Esq." Well, with initials like these, even calm and collected characters might have had to look twice to distinguish them, and neither Giles nor Phœbe had been in the mood to look at all carefully even once.

You see the situation, then. There was now one cheese in each elderly gentleman's hall bearing the name of his latest and bitterest enemy. And presently Mr. Murbles spotted the parcel on his own table, and conceived it to be a hat which his servant might have sent to the cleaner's ; and, as it was still there when he looked again some hours later, he bawled at his servant, and his servant came running.

" Billington ! " said Mr. Murbles, forcefully. " Take that hat and put it away ! Do you think," demanded Mr. Murbles, " that that's the kind of place to leave it ? "

" Beg pardon, sir," said Billington. " Very good, sir." And since he, in his turn, conceived that his master had bought a new billycock, trilby, or gibus, he took it away—though it seemed unusually heavy—and began unwrapping it on the shelf outside his pantry.

Whereupon it became obvious to more than one of Billington's senses that it wasn't a hat at all, but a large and fully developed cheese. And he scratched his head, and he examined the super-scription again, and he gasped, and ran back to his employer.

" Excuse me, sir," he said, flourishing a rather pungent piece of paper.

" Heh ? " said Mr. Murbles. " What the blazes do you want now ? "

" That parcel, or package, sir," said Billington. " I've just opened it, sir, and I find it contains a cheese."

" What ! " said Mr. Murbles.

" A cheese, sir," repeated Billington. " And I fancy there might be some mistake, or error, sir, because I found this gentle-man's name on it when I looked again, sir."

" Heh ? " said Mr. Murbles, grabbing the piece of paper and glaring at it. And then it certainly seemed to Billington that his dear old master was in grave danger of spontaneous combustion, so crimson was his countenance and so dreadful his demeanour. " Insufferable ! " he snorted. " Infernal impudence ! " he bellowed. " If I were a younger man," said Mr. Murbles, thickly and threateningly, " or if I had a horse-whip——" He broke off, clutching at his collar with one hand, and flinging the crumpled paper at his servant with the other. " Billington ! " he said, hoarsely and horribly. " You'll do that parcel up again —do you hear me ? And you'll find out this—this fellow's address. And you'll take it round there—No ; wait a minute, Billington ; there'll be no misunderstanding about this. I'll write a message. Stay where you are."

" Very good, sir," said Billington ; and Mr. Murbles puffed and blew, and sat down at his writing-table, and took up his pen, and pulled out one of his cards. " Please keep this reminder of your own bad manners," he scrawled. And he was more than delighted with this snappy sentence, and he grinned diabolically, and handed the card to his man.

" There ! " he said. " Put that inside when you tie it up again, and take it round there first thing in the morning. Do you hear me, Billington ? "

" Yes, sir," said Billington. " Very good, sir. I'll see to it, sir."

And off he went to find a clean bit of paper and some more string, and Mr. Murbles alternately growled when he thought of the insult that he had been offered, and wheezed repulsively when he thought of his masterly retort. On the whole, however, he was satisfied that he had more than defended his own honour, and his growls diminished until finally he took a stiff night-cap and heaved himself off to bed.

So, in the morning, while Phœbe was washing some puppies and Giles was trundling round on a tractor, and both of them were thinking of each other, with a good deal of longing and despair, Billington put on his bowler, and wedged the parcel under his left arm, and set forth as he had been instructed, and rang at Mr. Mulvey's door, and handed his burden to the maid who opened it, and turned round again and came home.

So that now Mr. Mulvey had two cheeses ? Not a bit of it. He'd had one yesterday, certainly ; he'd found it himself, and he'd opened it, and for the moment he hadn't known what to make of it. But then he, also, had looked at the paper again, and he'd started and he'd ground his false teeth, and the deduction which he'd drawn was as false, though as natural, as that formulated by his enemy, Mr. Murbles.

The cheese, he took it, was intended as a commentary, and an outrageously offensive commentary on his action at the Crabapple. The size and strength of it were supposed to underline and mock his perfectly rational conduct at lunch ; and, as this became clearer and clearer to Mr. Mulvey, so did his veins swell, his blood boil, and a passion seize him for revenge.

If he hadn't been a retired lawyer, and therefore steeped in caution, he would probably have done what he ultimately did even sooner. Yet the longer he thought about it, the more furious he became, and the message which he finally drafted and wrapped up in the parcel certainly didn't err on the side of either courtesy or insipidity.

In cold, legal language, and at considerable length, he gave Mr. Murbles exactly the same advice which Mr. Murbles was at that very moment giving him—namely, to keep the cheese as a souvenir of his own incivility ; and, having done this, Mr. Mulvey summoned his butler and gave him strict injunctions to take the parcel round to his enemy's establishment at the earliest possible opportunity.

So that this butler actually passed Billington, twice, in the street, and when Billington got back again, what was his astonishment to find that an apparent miracle had taken place. A package virtually indistinguishable from the one which he had just left was there on the hall table. It even smelt the same, and he was just on the point of questioning his colleague the housemaid as to how on earth it had got there, when his dear old master himself burst out of the dining-room, and saw it, and became purple in the face.

" Hey ! You ! Billington ! " he thundered. " Why's that still here ? Why haven't you taken it as I told you ? Heh ? "

" Beg pardon, sir," said Billington. " I did take it, sir. And I see this isn't my paper or string, sir, and it's got your name on it, sir."

" Heh ? " said Mr. Murbles, and rushed at the package and wrenched it open, and very nearly exploded as he saw, or thought he saw, the same cheese back again ; but was comparatively calm at this moment compared with his condition when he'd read Mr. Mulvey's letter.

Then, indeed, did Billington and his colleague the housemaid fly to their respective quarters, though the sound of their dear old master's frenzy followed them up to the attic and down to the basement. Mere adjectives no longer availed, but savage ejaculations accompanied by strangled curses flowed from Mr. Murbles as he stormed to and fro, as he clenched his gouty fists, as he kicked the lighter articles of his furniture.

Thus he continued until nearly twelve o'clock—as did Mr. Murdoch Mulvey, about half a mile away—at which hour both characters set forth to call on each other, and therefore naturally found each out. Nor, since in their haste and fury they had both taken taxis, did they meet, or even see each other, as they bounced up and down on their respective seats—though at one moment their two vehicles were separated by nothing more than a policeman.

"Heh?" said Mr. Murbles to Mr. Mulvey's butler. "Gone out, has he? What? Might be at the Club?" He turned, and stumbled down the steps. "Crabapple," he snapped at the driver, and bounced up and down again, and was out and clambering up more steps almost before the vehicle had stopped.

"Hey!" he said, addressing the porter. "You! Webster! Has Mr. Mulvey come in yet?"

"No, sir. Not yet, sir," said the porter; yet even at the same moment his other eye spotted Mr. Mulvey struggling out of a second taxi, and he would have informed Mr. Murbles, but that Mr. Murbles had already flung his coat and hat at a page-boy, and vanished round the corner. So then it was Mr. Mulvey's turn to say: "Hi! You! Mr. Murbles in the Club?" And Webster said: "Yes, sir. Just gone through, sir." And Mr. Mulvey all but obliterated the same page-boy with his own trappings, and set off hot-foot in pursuit; and detected Mr. Murbles raging down the corridor, and rushed after him; and Mr. Murbles span round, and recognized his enemy, and said: "Ah!"

And Mr. Mulvey also said: "Ah!" and on an impulse which leads all Englishmen to conduct their quarrels so far as possible in private, both members hurled themselves at the door of the lesser writing-room, and passed into it, and the door closed softly, and they were alone.

"Well?" said Mr. Murbles.

"Well?" said Mr. Mulvey.

"Are you going to apologize?" asked Mr. Murbles.

"No," said Mr. Mulvey. "Are you going to beg my pardon?"

"Certainly not," said Mr. Murbles. "And, if I were a younger man——"

"Pah!" interrupted Mr. Mulvey. "If I had a horse-whip——"

"Tchah!" said Mr. Murbles. "You'd better not adopt that tone with me."

"Bah!" said Mr. Mulvey. "I've had enough of you—and your family as well."

"Are you having the insolence," inquired Mr. Murbles, "to refer to my niece?"

" I'm referring," said Mr. Mulvey, " to the young woman who's trying to drag my ward into the gutter."

" Gutter, sir ! " snorted Mr. Murbles. " Let me tell you that if your ward were lucky enough to marry a lady——"

" Piff ! " shouted Mr. Mulvey. " Are you pretending she's too good for him ? Is that what you had the nerve to tell her ? "

" Certainly ! " said Mr. Murbles, passionately and untruthfully.

" Guck ! " said Mr. Mulvey, almost choking with rage. " Then, in that case, let me tell you that he can marry her to-morrow if he's fool enough. Do you think I'd stand in the way of your niece learning what a gentleman's like ? "

" And do you imagine," asked Mr. Murbles, in a paroxysm of choler, " that I'd raise a finger to stop her teaching your ward a few manners if she cares to ? Or are you afraid," asked Mr. Murbles, now shaking with sarcasm, " that if he learns 'em, he'll hardly feel at home in your society ? "

" Afraid ? " roared Mr. Mulvey. " There's only one thing I'm afraid of, and that is that your niece will be cut by the county. Too good for him, indeed ! I'll show you if she's too good for him ! "

He flung himself at the nearest writing-table, seized a pen and a sheet of Club notepaper, and began scribbling like one possessed. Nor was Mr. Murbles backward in following his example, and removing, with similar epistolary emphasis, all his objections to a union which was now, so it seemed, to prove the unquestionable social superiority of his breeding and his clan.

Thus these two elderly members of the Crabapple sat scratching and growling, with their backs to each other ; and presently they rose, glared at each other, and dropped two envelopes into the glass-fronted letter-box. What's posted is posted, and joy was now definitely on its way to Warwickshire. Do you want to hear them wrangling any more after this ? Do you care tuppence when or whether they found out the truth about those cheeses ?

Of course you don't, and no more do we. For that's quite obviously the end of the story.

A. A. MILNE (1882–), *a humorist beloved equally by grown-ups and children, was assistant editor of " Punch " from 1906 until the War. " When we were very Young," in which he introduced his son, Christopher Robin, has become a modern classic of the nursery. " Mr. Pym Passes By " is his most celebrated play, but the Rabbits, which appear in this story, are very popular people indeed.*

WINTER SPORT

I. AN INTRODUCTION

" I HAD better say at once," I announced as I turned over the wine list, " that I have come out here to enjoy myself, and enjoy myself I shall. Myra, what shall we drink ? "

" You had three weeks' honeymoon in October," complained Thomas, " and you're taking another three weeks now. Don't you ever do any work ? "

Myra and I smiled at each other. Coming from Thomas, who spends his busy day leaning up against the wireless installation at the Admiralty, the remark amused us.

" We'll have champagne," said Myra, " because it's our opening night. Archie, after you with the head-waiter."

It was due to Dahlia, really, that the Rabbits were hibernating at the Hôtel des Angéliques, Switzerland (central - heated throughout) ; for she had been ordered abroad, after an illness, to pull herself together a little, and her doctor had agreed with Archie that she might as well do it at a place where her husband could skate. On the point that Peter should come and skate too, however, Archie was firm. While admitting that he loved his infant son, he reminded Dahlia that she couldn't possibly get through Calais and Pontarlier without declaring Peter, and that the duty on this class of goods was remarkably heavy. Peter, therefore, was left behind. He had an army of nurses to look after him, and a stenographer to take down his more important remarks. With a daily bulletin and a record of his table-talk promised her, Dahlia was prepared to be content.

As for Myra and me, we might have hesitated to take another holiday so soon, had it not been for a letter I received one morning at breakfast.

" Simpson is going," I said. " He has purchased a pair of skis."

" That does it," said Myra decisively. And, gurgling happily to herself, she went out and bought a camera.

For Thomas I can find no excuses. At a moment of crisis he left his country's Navy in jeopardy and, the Admiralty yacht being otherwise engaged, booked a first return from Cook's. And so it was that at four o'clock one day we arrived together at the Hôtel des Angéliques, and some three hours later were settling down comfortably to dinner.

" I've had a busy time," said Archie. " I've hired a small bob, a luge, and a pair of skis for myself, a pair of snow-shoes and some skates for Dahlia, a—a tricycle horse for Simpson, and I don't know what else. All in French."

" What *is* the French for a pair of snow-shoes ? " asked Myra.

" I pointed to them in French. The undersized Robert I got at a bargain. The man who hired it last week broke his leg before his fortnight was up, and so there was a reduction of several centimes."

" I've been busy too," I said. " I've been watching Myra unpack, and telling her where not to put my things."

" I packed jolly well—except for the accident."

" An accident to the boot-oil," I explained. " If I get down to my last three shirts you will notice it."

We stopped eating for a moment in order to drink Dahlia's health. It was Dahlia's health which had sent us there.

" Who's your friend, Samuel ? " said Archie, as Simpson caught somebody's eye at another table and nodded.

" A fellow I met in the lift," said Simpson casually.

" Samuel, beware of elevator acquaintances," said Myra in her most solemn manner.

" He's rather a good chap. He was at Peterhouse with a friend of mine. He was telling me quite a good story about a ' wine ' my friend gave there once, when——"

" Did you tell him about your ' ginger-beers ' at Giggleswick ? " I interrupted.

" My dear old chap, he's rather a man to be in with. He knows the President."

" I thought nobody knew the President of the Swiss Republic," said Myra. " Like the Man in the Iron Mask."

" Not *that* President, Myra. The President of the Angéliques Sports Club."

" Never heard of it," we all said.

Simpson polished his glasses and prepared delightedly to give an explanation.

"The Sports Club runs everything here," he began. "It gives you prizes for fancy costumes and skating and so on."

"Introduce me to the President at once," cooed Myra, patting her hair and smoothing down her frock.

"Even if you were the Treasurer's brother," said Archie, "you wouldn't get a prize for skating, Simpson."

"You've never seen him do a rocking seventeen, sideways." Simpson looked at us pityingly.

"There's a lot more in it than that," he said. "The President will introduce you to anybody. One might see—er—somebody one rather liked the look of, and—er—— Well, I mean in an hotel one wants to enter into the hotel life and—er—meet other people."

"Who is she?" said Myra.

"Anybody you want to marry must be submitted to Myra for approval first," I said. "We've told you so several times."

Simpson hastily disclaimed any intention of marrying anybody, and helped himself lavishly to champagne.

It so happened that I was the first of our party to meet the President, an honour which, perhaps, I hardly deserved. While Samuel was seeking tortuous introductions to him through friends of Peterhouse friends of his, the President and I fell into each other's arms in the most natural way.

It occurred like this. There was a dance after dinner; and Myra, not satisfied with my appearance, sent me upstairs to put some gloves on. (It is one of the penalties of marriage that one is always being sent upstairs.) With my hands properly shod I returned to the ball-room, and stood for a moment in a corner while I looked about for her. Suddenly I heard a voice at my side.

"Do you want a partner?" it said.

I turned, and knew that I was face to face with the President.

"Well——" I began.

"You are a new-comer, aren't you? I expect you don't know many people. If there is anybody you would like to dance with——"

I looked round the room. It was too good a chance to miss.

"I wonder," I said. "That girl over there—in the pink frock—just putting up her fan——"

He almost embraced me.

"I congratulate you on your taste," he said. "Excellent! Come with me."

He went over to the girl in the pink dress, I at his heels.

"Er—may I introduce?" he said. "Mr.—er—er—yes,

this is Miss—er—yes. H'r'm." Evidently he didn't know her name.

"Thank you," I said to him. He nodded and left us. I turned to the girl in the pink frock. She was very pretty.

"May I have this dance ? " I asked. "I've got my gloves on," I added.

She looked at me gravely, trying hard not to smile.

"You may," said Myra.

II. THE OPENING RUN

WITH a great effort Simpson strapped his foot securely into a ski and turned doubtfully to Thomas.

"Thomas," he said, "how do you know which foot is which ? "

"It depends whose," said Thomas. He was busy tying a large rucksack of lunch on to himself, and was in no mood for Samuel's ball-room chatter.

"You've got one ski on one foot," I said. "Then the other ski goes on the foot you've got over. I should have thought you would have seen that."

"But I may have put the first one on wrong."

"You ought to know, after all these years, that you are certain to have done so," I said severely. Having had my own hired skis fixed on by the *concierge* I felt rather superior. Simpson, having bought his in London, was regarded darkly by that gentleman, and left to his own devices.

"Are we all ready ? " asked Myra, who had kept us waiting for twenty minutes. "Archie, what about Dahlia ? "

"Dahlia will join us at lunch. She is expecting a letter from Peter by the twelve o'clock post and refuses to start without it. Also she doesn't think she is up to ski-ing just yet. Also she wants to have a heart-to-heart talk with the girl in red, and break it to her that Thomas is engaged to several people in London already."

"Come on," growled Thomas, and he led the way up the hill. We followed him in single file.

It was a day of colour, straight from heaven. On either side the dazzling whiteness of the snow ; above, the deep blue of the sky ; in front of me the glorious apricot of Simpson's winter suiting. London seemed a hundred years away. It was impossible to work up the least interest in the Home Rule Bill, the Billiard Tournament, or the state of St. Paul's Cathedral.

"I feel extremely picturesque," said Archie. "If only we

had a wolf or two after us, the illusion would be complete. The Boy Trappers, or Half-Hours among the Rocky Mountains."

"It is a pleasant thought, Archie," I said, "that in any wolf-trouble the bachelors of the party would have to sacrifice themselves for us. Myra, dear, the loss of Samuel in such circumstances would draw us very close together. There might be a loss of Thomas, too, perhaps—for if there was not enough of Simpson to go round, if there was a hungry wolf left over, would Thomas hesitate?"

"No," said Thomas, "I should run like a hare."

Simpson said nothing. His face I could not see; but his back looked exactly like the back of a man who was trying to look as if he had been brought up on skis from a baby and was now taking a small party of enthusiastic novices out for their first lesson.

"What an awful shock it would be," I said, "if we found that Samuel really did know something about it after all; and, while we were tumbling about anyhow, he sailed gracefully down the steepest slopes. I should go straight back to Cricklewood."

"My dear chap, I've read a *lot* about it."

"Then we're quite safe."

"With all his faults," said Archie, "and they are many—Samuel is a gentleman. He would never take an unfair advantage of us. Hallo, here we are!"

We left the road and made our way across the snow to a little wooden hut which Archie had noticed the day before. Here we were to meet Dahlia for lunch; and here, accordingly, we left the rucksack and such garments as the heat of the sun suggested. Then, at the top of a long snow-slope, steep at first, more gentle later, we stood and wondered.

"Who's going first?" said Archie.

"What do you do?" asked Myra.

"You don't. It does it for you."

"But how do you stop?"

"Don't bother about that, dear," I said. "That will be arranged for you all right. Take two steps to the brink of the hill and pick yourself up at the bottom. Now then, Simpson! Be a man. The lady waits, Samuel. The—— Hallo! Hi! Help!" I cried, as I began to move off slowly. It was too late to do anything about it. "Good-bye," I called. And then things moved more quickly. . . .

Very quickly. . . .

Suddenly there came a moment when I realized that I wasn't keeping up with my feet. . . .

I shouted to my skis to stop. It was no good. They went on. . . .

I decided to stop without them. . . .

The ensuing second went by too swiftly for me to understand rightly what happened. I fancy that, rising from my sitting position and travelling easily on my head, I caught my skis up again and passed them. . . .

Then it was their turn. They overtook me. . . .

But I was not to be beaten. Once more I obtained the lead. This time I took the inside berth, and kept it. . . .

There seemed to be a lot more snow than I really wanted. . . . I struggled bravely with it. . . .

And then the earthquake ceased, and suddenly I was in the outer air. My first ski-run, the most glorious run of modern times, was over.

"Ripping!" I shouted up the hill to them. "But there's rather a nasty bump at the bottom," I added kindly, as I set myself to the impossible business of getting up. . . .

"Jove," said Archie, coming to rest a few yards off, "that's splendid!" He had fallen in a less striking way than myself, and he got to his feet without difficulty. "Why do you pose like that?" he asked, as he picked up his stick.

"I'm a fixture," I announced. "Myra," I said, as she turned a somersault and arrived beaming at my side, "I'm here for some time; you'll have to come out every morning with crumbs for me. In the afternoon you can bring a cheering book and read aloud to your husband. Sometimes I shall dictate little things to you. They will not be my best little things; for this position, with my feet so much higher than my head, is not the one on which inspiration comes to me most readily. The flow of blood to the brain impairs reflection. But no matter."

"Are you really stuck?" asked Myra in some anxiety. "I should hate to have a husband who lived by himself in the snow," she said thoughtfully.

"Let us look on the bright side," said Archie. "The snow will have melted by April, and he will then be able to return to you. Hallo, here's Thomas! Thomas will probably have some clever idea for restoring the family credit."

Thomas got up in a business-like manner and climbed slowly back to us.

"Thomas," I said, "you see the position. Indeed," I added, "it is obvious. None of the people round me seems inclined—or, it may be, able—to help. There is a feeling that

And then the earthquake ceased

if Myra lives in the hotel alone while I remain here—possibly till April—people will talk. You know how ready they are. There is also the fact that I have only hired the skis for three weeks. Also—a minor point, but one that touches me rather—that I shall want my hair cut long before March is out. Thomas, imagine me to be a torpedo-destroyer on the Maplin Sands, and tell me what on earth to do."

" Take your skis off."

" Oh, brilliant ! " said Myra.

" Take my skis off ? " I cried. " Never ! Is it not my duty to be the last to leave my skis ? Can I abandon—— Hallo ! is that Dahlia on the sky-line ? Hooray, lunch ! Archie, take my skis off, there's a good fellow. We mustn't keep Dahlia waiting."

III. A TYPICAL MORNING

" You take lunch out to-day—no ? " said Josef, the head-waiter, in his invariable formula.

Myra and I were alone at breakfast, the first down. I was just putting some honey on to my seventh roll, and was not really in the mood for light conversation with Josef about lunch. By the way, I must say I prefer the good old English breakfast. With eggs and bacon and porridge you do know when you want to stop ; with rolls and honey you hardly notice what you are doing, and there seems no reason why you should not go on for ever. Indeed, once . . . but you would never believe me.

" We take lunch out to-day, *yes*, Josef. Lunch for—let me see——"

" Six ? " suggested Myra.

" What are we all going to do ? Archie said something about skating. I'm off that."

" But whatever we do we must lunch, and it's much nicer outdoors. Six, Josef."

Josef nodded and retired. I took my eighth roll.

" Do let's get off quickly to-day," I said. " There's always so much chat in the morning before we start."

" I've just got one swift letter to write," said Myra, as she got up, " and then I shall be pawing the ground."

Half an hour later I was in the lounge, booted, capped, gloved, and putteed—the complete St. Bernard. The lounge seemed to be entirely full of hot air and entirely empty of any-body I knew. I asked for letters ; and, getting none, went out

17*

and looked at the thermometer. To my surprise I discovered that there were thirty-seven degrees of frost. A little alarmed, I tapped the thing impatiently. "Come, come," I said, "this is not the time for persiflage." However, it insisted on remaining at five degrees below zero. What should I have done about it I cannot say, but at that moment I remembered that it was a Centigrade thermometer with the freezing-point in the wrong place. Slightly disappointed that there were only five degrees of frost (Centigrade) I returned to the lounge.

"Here you are at last," said Archie impatiently. "What are we all going to do?"

"Where's Dahlia?" asked Myra. "Let's wait till she comes and then we can all talk at once."

"Here she is. Dahlia, for Heaven's sake come and tell us the arrangements for the day. Start with the idea fixed in your mind that Myra and I have ordered lunch for six."

Dahlia shepherded us to a quiet corner of the lounge and we all sat down.

"By the way," said Simpson, "are there any letters for me?"

"No; it's your turn to write," said Archie.

"But, my dear chap, there *must* be one, because——"

"But you never acknowledged the bed-socks," I pointed out. "She can't write till you—— I mean, it was rather forward of her to send them at all; and if you haven't even——"

"Well," said Dahlia, "what does anybody want to do?"

Thomas was the first to answer the question. A girl in red came in from the breakfast-room and sat down near us. She looked up in our direction and met Thomas's eye.

"Good morning," said Thomas, with a smile, and he left us and moved across to her.

"That's the girl he danced with all last night," whispered Myra. "I can't think what's come over him. Is this our reserved Thomas—Thomas the taciturn, whom we know and love so well? I don't like the way she does her hair."

"She's a Miss Aylwyn," said Simpson in a loud voice. "I had one dance with her myself."

"The world," said Archie, "is full of people with whom Samuel has had one dance."

"Well, that washes Thomas out, anyway. He'll spend the day teaching her something. What are the rest of us going to do?"

There was a moment's silence.

"Oh, Archie," said Dahlia, "did you get those nails put in my boots?"

I looked at Myra . . . and sighed.

"Sorry, dear," he said. "I'll take them down now. The man will do them in twenty minutes." He walked over to the lift at the same moment that Thomas returned to us.

"I say," began Thomas a little awkwardly, "if you're arranging what to do, don't bother about me. I rather thought of—er—taking it quietly this morning. I think I overdid it a bit yesterday."

"We warned you at the time about the fourth hard-boiled egg," I said.

"I meant the ski-ing. We thought of—I thought of having lunch in the hotel, but, of course, you can have my rucksack to carry yours in. Er—I'll go and put it in for you."

He disappeared rather sheepishly in the direction of the dining-room.

"Now, Samuel," said Myra gently.

"Now what, Myra?"

"It's your turn. If you have a headache, tell us her name."

"My dear Myra, I want to ski to-day. Where shall we go? Let's go to the old slopes and practise the Christiania Turn."

"What you want to practise is the ordinary Hampstead Straight," I said. "A medium performance of yours yesterday, Samuel."

"But, my dear old chap," he said eagerly, "I told you it was the fault of my skis. They would stick to the snow. Oh, I say," he added, "that reminds me. I must go and buy some wax for them."

He dashed off. I looked at Myra . . . and sighed.

"The nail-man won't be long," said Archie to Dahlia, on his return. "I'm to call for them in a quarter of an hour."

"Can't you wear some other boots, Dahlia, or your bedroom slippers or something? It's half-past eleven. We really must get off soon."

"But we haven't settled where we're going yet."

"Then for 'eving's sake let's do it. Myra and I thought we might go up above the wood at the back and explore. We can always ski down. It might be rather exciting."

"Remember," said Dahlia, "I'm not so expert as you are."

"Of course," said Myra, "we're the Oberland mixed champions."

"You know," said Archie, "I was talking to the man who's doing Dahlia's boots and he said the snow would be bad for ski-ing to-day."

"If he talked in French, no doubt you misunderstood him,"

I said, a little annoyed. "He was probably asking you to buy a pair of skates."

"Talking about that," said Archie, "why shouldn't we skate this morning, and have lunch at the hotel, and then get the bob out this afternoon?"

"Here you are," said Thomas, coming up with a heavy rucksack. "Lunch for six, so you'll have an extra one."

"I'd forgotten about lunch," said Archie. "Look here, just talk it over with Dahlia while I go and see about my skates. I don't suppose Josef will mind if we do stay in to lunch after all. What about Simpson?"

I looked at Myra . . . and sighed.

"What about him?" I said.

.   .   .   .

Half an hour later two exhausted people—one of them with lunch for six on his back—began the ascent to the wood, trailing their skis behind them.

"Another moment," said Myra, "and I should have screamed."

IV. THOMAS, AND A TURN

MYRA finished her orange, dried her hands daintily on my handkerchief, and spoke her mind.

"This is the third time," she said, "that Thomas has given us the slip. If he gets engaged to that girl in red I shall cry."

"There are," I said, idly throwing a crust at Simpson and missing him, "engagements and Swiss engagements—just as there are measles and German measles. It is well known that Swiss engagements don't count."

"*We* got engaged in Kent. A bit of luck."

"I have nothing against Miss Aylwyn——" I went on.

"Except the way she does her hair."

"—but she doesn't strike me as being the essential Rabbit. We cannot admit her to the—er—fold."

"The covey," suggested Myra.

"The warren. Anyhow, she—— Simpson, for goodness' sake stop fooling about with your bearded friend and tell us what you think of it all."

We were finishing lunch in the lee of a little chalet, high above the hotel, and Simpson had picked up an acquaintance with a goat, which he was apparently trying to conciliate with a piece of chocolate. The goat, however, seemed to want a piece of Simpson.

" My dear old chap, he won't go away. Here—shoo ! shoo !
I wish I knew what his name was."

" Ernest," said Myra.

" I can't think why you ever got into such a hirsute set,
Simpson. He probably wants your compass. Give it to him
and let him withdraw."

Ernest, having decided that Simpson was not worth knowing,
withdrew, and we resumed our conversation.

" When we elderly married folk have retired," I went on,
" and you gay young bachelors sit up over a last cigar to discuss
your conquests, has not Thomas unbent to you, Samuel, and
told you of his hopes and fears ? "

" He told me last night he was afraid he was going bald,
and he said he hoped he wasn't."

" That's a bad sign," said Myra. " What did you say ? "

" I said I thought he was."

With some difficulty I got up from my seat in the snow and
buckled on my skis.

" Come on, let's forget Thomas for a bit. Samuel is now
going to show us the Christiania Turn."

Simpson, all eagerness, began to prepare himself.

" I said I would, didn't I ? I was doing it quite well yesterday. This is a perfect little slope for it. You understand the
theory of it, don't you ? "

" We hope to after the exhibition."

" Well, the great thing is to lean the opposite way to the way
you think you ought to lean. That's what's so difficult."

" You understand, Myra ? Samuel will lean the opposite
way to what he thinks he ought to lean. Tell Ernest."

" But suppose you think you ought to lean the *proper* way,
the way they do in Christiania," said Myra, " and you lean the
opposite way, then what happens ? "

" That is what Samuel will probably show us," I said.

Simpson was now ready.

" I am going to turn to the left," he said. " Watch carefully. Of course, I may not bring it off the first time."

" I can't help thinking you will," said Myra.

" It depends what you call bringing it off," I said. " We
have every hope of—I mean we don't think our money will
be wasted. Have you got the opera-glasses and the pepper-
mints and the programme, darling ? Then you may begin,
Samuel."

Simpson started down the slope a little unsteadily. For one
moment I feared that there might be an accident before the real

accident, but he recovered himself nobly and sped to the bottom. Then a cloud of snow shot up, and for quite a long time there was no Simpson.

"I knew he wouldn't disappoint us," gurgled Myra.

We slid down to him and helped him up.

"You see the idea," he said. "I'm afraid I spoilt it a little at that end, but——"

"My dear Samuel, you improved it out of all knowledge."

"But that actually *is* the Christiania Turn."

"Oh, *why* don't we live in Christiania?" exclaimed Myra to me. "Couldn't we possibly afford it?"

"It must be a happy town," I agreed. "How the old streets must ring and ring again with jovial laughter."

"Shall I do it once more?"

"*Can* you?" said Myra, clasping her hands eagerly.

"Wait here," said Samuel, "and I'll do it quite close to you."

Myra unstrapped her camera.

Half an hour later, with several excellent films of the scene of the catastrophe, we started for home. It was more than a little steep, but the run down was accomplished without any serious trouble. Simpson went first to discover any hidden ditches (and to his credit be it said that he invariably discovered them); Myra, in the position of safety in the middle, profited by Samuel's frequent object-lessons; while I, at the back, was ready to help Myra up, if need arose, or to repel any avalanche which descended on us from above. On the level snow at the bottom we became more companionable.

"We still haven't settled the great Thomas question," said Myra. "What about to-morrow?"

"Why bother about to-morrow? *Carpe diem.* Latin."

"But the great tailing expedition is for to-morrow. The horses are ordered; everything is prepared. Only one thing remains to settle. Shall we have with us a grumpy but Aylwyn-less Thomas, or shall we let him bring her and spoil the party?"

"She can't spoil the party. I'm here to enjoy myself, and all Thomas's *fiancees* can't stop me. Let's have Thomas happy, anyway."

"She's really quite a nice girl," said Simpson. "I danced with her once."

"Righto, then. I'll tell Dahlia to invite her."

We hurried on to the hotel; but as we passed the rink the President stopped me for a chat. He wanted me to recite at a concert that evening. Basely deserted by Myra and Samuel,

I told him that I did not recite ; and I took the opportunity of adding that personally I didn't think anybody else ought to. I had just persuaded him to my point of view when I noticed Thomas cutting remarkable figures on the ice. He picked himself up and skated to the side.

" Hallo ! " he said. " Had a good day ? "

" Splendid. What have you been doing ? "

" Oh—skating."

" I say, about this tailing expedition to-morrow——"

" Er—yes, I was just going to talk about that."

" Well, it's all right. Myra is getting Dahlia to ask her to come with us."

" Good ! " said Thomas, brightening up.

" You see, we shall only be seven, even with Miss Aylwyn, and——"

" Miss *Aylwyn* ? " said Thomas in a hollow voice.

" Yes, isn't that the name of your friend in red ? "

" Oh, *that* one. Oh, but that's quite—I mean," he went on hurriedly, " Miss Aylwyn is probably booked up for to-morrow. It's Miss Cardew who is so keen on tailing. That girl in green, you know."

For a moment I stared at him blankly. Then I left him and dashed after Myra.

V. A TAILING PARTY

THE procession prepared to start in the following order :

(1) A brace of sinister-looking horses.

(2) Gaspard, the Last of the Bandits ; or " Why cause a lot of talk by pushing your rich uncle over the cliff, when you can have him stabbed quietly for one franc fifty ? " (If ever I were in any vendetta business I should pick Gaspard first.)

(3) A sleigh full of lunch.

(4) A few well-known ladies and gentlemen (being the cream of the Hôtel des Angéliques) on luges ; namely, reading from left to right (which is really the best method—unless you are translating Hebrew), Simpson, Archie, Dahlia, Myra, me, Miss Cardew, and Thomas.

While Gaspard was putting the finishing knots to the luges, I addressed a few remarks to Miss Cardew, fearing that she might be feeling a little lonely amongst us. I said that it was a lovely day, and did she think the snow would hold off till evening ? Also had she ever done this sort of thing before ? I forget what her answers were.

Thomas meanwhile was exchanging badinage on the hotel steps with Miss Aylwyn. There must be something peculiar in the Swiss air, for in England Thomas is quite a respectable man . . . and a godfather.

" I suppose we *have* asked the right one," said Myra doubtfully.

" His young affections are divided. There was a third girl in pink with whom he breakfasted a lot this morning. It is the old tradition of the sea, you know. A sailor—I mean an Admiralty civilian has a wife at every wireless station."

" Take your seats, please," said Archie. " The horses are sick of waiting."

We sat down. Archie took Dahlia's feet on his lap, Myra took mine, Miss Cardew took Thomas's. Simpson, alone in front, nursed a guide-book.

" *En avant !* " cried Simpson in his best French-taught-in-twelve-lessons accent.

Gaspard muttered an oath to his animals. They pulled bravely. The rope snapped—and they trotted gaily down the hill with Gaspard.

We hurried after them with the luges. . . .

" It's a good joke," said Archie, after this had happened three times, " but, personally, I weary of it. Miss Cardew, I'm afraid we've brought you out under false pretences. Thomas didn't explain the thing to you adequately. He gave you to understand that there was more in it than this."

Gaspard, who seemed full of rope, produced a fourth piece and tied a knot that made even Simpson envious.

" Now, Samuel," I begged, " do keep the line taut this time. Why do you suppose we put your apricot suit right in the front ? Is it, do you suppose, for the sunset effects at eleven o'clock in the morning, or is it that you may look after the rope properly ? "

" I'm awfully sorry, Miss Cardew," said Simpson, feeling that somebody ought to apologize for something and knowing that Gaspard wouldn't, " but I expect it will be all right now."

We settled down again. Once more Gaspard cursed his horses, and once more they started off bravely. And this time we went with them.

" The idea all along," I explained to Miss Cardew.

" I rather suspected it," she said. Apparently she has a suspicious mind.

After the little descent at the start, we went uphill slowly for a couple of miles, and then more rapidly over the level. We had driven over the same road in a sleigh, coming from the station, and had been bitterly cold and extremely bored. Why our present position should be so much more enjoyable I didn't quite see.

"It's the expectation of an accident," said Archie. "At any moment somebody may fall off. Good."

"My dear old chap," said Simpson, turning round to take part in the conversation, "why anybody *should* fall off——"

We went suddenly round a corner, and quietly and without any fuss whatever Simpson left his luge and rolled on to the track. Luckily any possibility of a further accident was at once avoided. There was no panic at all. Archie kicked the body temporarily out of the way ; after which Dahlia leant over and pushed it thoughtfully to the side of the road. Myra warded it off with a leg as she neared it ; with both hands I helped it into the deep snow from which it had shown a tendency to emerge ; Miss Cardew put a foot out at it for safety ; and Thomas patted it gently on the head as the end of the " tail " went past. . . .

As soon as we had recovered our powers of speech—all except Miss Cardew, who was in hysterics—we called upon Gaspard to stop. He indicated with the back of his neck that it would be dangerous to stop just then ; and it was not until we were at the bottom of the hill, nearly a mile from the place where Simpson left us, that the procession halted, and gave itself up again to laughter.

"I hope he is not hurt," said Dahlia, wiping the tears from her eyes.

"He wouldn't spoil a good joke like that by getting hurt," said Myra confidently. " He's much too much of a sportsman."

"Why did he do it ? " said Thomas.

"He suddenly remembered he hadn't packed his safety-razor. He's half-way back to the hotel by now."

Miss Cardew remained in hysterics.

Ten minutes later a brilliant sunset was observed approaching from the north. A little later it was seen to be a large dish of apricots and cream.

"He draws near," said Archie. "Now then, let's be stern with him."

At twenty yards' range Simpson began to talk. His trot had heated him slightly.

"I say," he said excitedly. "You——"

Myra shook her head at him.

"Not done, Samuel," she said reproachfully.

"Not what, Myra ? What not——"

" You oughtn't to leave us like that without telling us."

" After all," said Archie, " we are all one party, and we are supposed to keep together. If you prefer to go about by yourself, that's all right ; but if we go to the trouble of arranging something for the whole party——"

" You might have caused a very nasty accident," I pointed out. " If you were in a hurry, you had only to say a word to Gaspard and he would have stopped for you to alight. Now I begin to understand why you kept cutting the rope at the start."

" You have sent Miss Cardew into hysterics by your conduct," said Dahlia.

Miss Cardew gave another peal. Simpson looked at her in dismay.

" I say, Miss Cardew, I'm most awfully sorry. I really didn't—— I say, Dahlia," he went on confidentially, " oughtn't we to do something about this ? Rub her feet with snow or— I mean, I know there's *something* you do when people have hysterics. It's rather serious if they go on. Don't you burn feathers under their nose ? " He began to feel in his pockets. " I wonder if Gaspard's got a feather ? "

With a great effort Miss Cardew pulled herself together. " It's all right, thank you," she said in a stifled voice.

" Then let's get on," said Archie.

We resumed our seats once more. Archie took Dahlia's feet on his lap. Myra took mine. Miss Cardew took Thomas's. Simpson clung tight to his luge with both hands.

" Right ! " cried Archie.

Gaspard swore at his horses. They pulled bravely. The rope snapped—and they trotted gaily up the hill with Gaspard.

We hurried after them with the luges. . . .

VI. A HAPPY ENDING

" FOR our last night they might at least have had a dance," said Myra, " even if there was no public presentation."

" As we had hoped," I admitted.

" What is a gymkhana, anyway ? " asked Thomas.

" A few little competitions," said Archie. " One must cater for the chaperons sometimes. You are all entered for the Hat-making and the Feather-blowing—Dahlia thought it would amuse you."

" At Cambridge," I said reminiscently, " I once blew the feather 119 feet 7 inches. Unfortunately I stepped outside the circle. My official record is 2 feet."

"Did you ever trim a hat at Cambridge?" asked Myra. "Because you've got to do one for me to-night."

I had not expected this. My view of the competition had been that *I* should have to provide the face and that *she* would have to invent some suitable frame for it.

"I'm full of ideas," I lied.

Nine o'clock found a small row of us prepared to blow the feather. The presidential instructions were that we had to race our feather across a chalk-line at the end of the room, anybody touching his feather to be disqualified.

"In the air or on the floor?" asked Simpson earnestly.

"Just as you like," said the President kindly, and came round with the bag.

I selected Percy with care—a dear little feather about half an inch long and of a delicate whity-brown colour. I should have known him again anywhere.

"Go!" said the President. I was rather excited, with the result that my first blow was much too powerful for Percy. He shot up to the ceiling and, in spite of all I could do, seemed inclined to stay there. Anxiously I waited below with my mouth open; he came slowly down at last; and in my eagerness I played my second just a shade too soon. It missed him. My third (when I was ready for it) went harmlessly over his head. A frantic fourth and fifth helped him downwards . . . and in another moment my beautiful Percy was on the floor. I dropped on my knees and played my sixth vigorously. He swirled to the left; I was after him like a shot . . . and crashed into Thomas. We rolled over in a heap.

"Sorry!" we apologized as we got back on to our hands and knees.

Thomas went on blowing.

"Where's my feather?" I said.

Thomas was now two yards ahead, blowing like anything. A terrible suspicion darted through my mind.

"Thomas," I said, "you've got my feather."

He made no answer. I scrambled after him.

"That's Percy," I said. "I should know him anywhere. You're blowing Percy. It's very bad form to blow another man's feather. If it got about, you would be cut by the county. Give me back my feather, Thomas."

"How do you know it's your feather?" he said truculently. "Feathers are just alike."

"How do I know?" I asked in amazement. "A feather that I've brought up from the egg? Of course I know Percy."

I leant down to him. " *P—percy*," I whispered. He darted forward a good six inches. " You see," I said, " he knows his name."

" As a matter of fact," said Thomas, " his name's *P—paul*. Look, I'll show you."

" You needn't bother, Thomas," I said hastily. " This is mere trifling. I *know* that's my feather. I remember his profile distinctly."

" Then where's mine ? "

" How do I know ? You may have swallowed it. Go away and leave Percy and me to ourselves. You're only spoiling the knees of your trousers by staying here."

" Paul and I——" began Thomas.

He was interrupted by a burst of applause. Dahlia had cajoled her feather over the line first. Thomas rose and brushed himself. " You can 'ave him," he said.

" There ! " I said, as I picked Percy up and placed him reverently in my waistcoat pocket. " That shows that he was mine. If he had been your own little Paul you would have loved him even in defeat. Oh, musical chairs now ? Right-o." And at the President's touch I retired from the arena.

We had not entered for musical chairs. Personally I should have liked to, but it was felt that, if none of us did, then it would be more easy to stop Simpson doing so. For at musical chairs Simpson is—I am afraid there is only one word for it ; it is a word that I hesitate to use, but the truth must prevail—Simpson is *rough*. He *lets himself go*. He plays *all he knows*. Whenever I take Simpson out anywhere I always whisper to my hostess, " *Not* musical chairs."

The last event of the evening was the hat-making competition. Each man of us was provided with five large sheets of coloured crinkly paper, a packet of pins, a pair of scissors, and a lady opposite to him.

" Have you any plans at all ? " asked Myra.

" Heaps. Tell me, what sort of hat would you like ? Something for the Park ? " I doubled up a piece of blue paper and looked at it. " You know, if this is a success, Myra, I shall often make your hats for you."

Five minutes later I had what I believe is called a "foundation." Anyhow, it was something for Myra to put her head into.

" Our very latest Bond Street model," said Myra. " Only fifteen guineas—or three-and-ninepence if you buy it at our other establishment in Battersea."

" Now then, I can get going," I said, and I began to cut

out a white feather. " Yes, your ladyship, this is from the genuine bird on our own ostrich farm in the Fulham Road. Plucked while the ingenuous biped had its head in the sand. I shall put that round the brim," and I pinned it round.

" What about a few roses ? " said Myra, fingering the red paper.

" The roses are going there on the right." I pinned them on. " And a humming-bird and some violets next to them. . . . I say, I've got a lot of paper over. What about a nice piece of cabbage . . . there . . . and a bunch of asparagus . . . and some tomatoes and a seagull's wing on the left. The back still looks rather bare—let's have some poppies."

" There's only three minutes more," said Myra, " and you haven't used all the paper yet."

" I've got about one William Allan Richardson and a couple of canaries over," I said, after examining my stock. " Let's put it inside as lining. There, Myra, my dear, I'm proud of you. I always say that in a nice quiet hat nobody looks prettier than you."

" Time ! " said the President.

Anxious matrons prowled round us.

" We don't know any of the judges," I whispered. " This isn't fair."

The matrons conferred with the President. He cleared his throat. " The first prize," he said, " goes to——"

But I had swooned.

.   .   .   .

" Well," said Archie, " the Rabbits return to England with two cups won on the snowfields of Switzerland."

" Nobody need know," said Myra, " which winter-sport they were won at."

" Unless I have ' Ski-ing, First Prize ' engraved on mine," I said, " as I had rather intended."

" Then I shall have ' Figure-Skating ' on mine," said Dahlia.

" Two cups," reflected Archie, " and Thomas engaged to three charming girls. I think it has been worth it, you know."

NEIL MUNRO (1883–1930), *while engaged on the famous " Views and Reviews " column of the Glasgow " Evening News," was building up a second reputation as a humorist of rare attraction under the pseudonym of " Hugh Foulis." The light sketches chronicling the happy adventures of Erchie, Para Handy, and Jimmy Swan were eventually traced to his pen, and appeared in volume form.*

A NEW COOK

THE s.s. *Texa* made a triumphal entry to the harbour by steaming in between two square-rigged schooners, the *Volant* and *Jehu*, of Wick, and slid silently, with the exactitude of long experience, against the piles of Rothesay quay, where Para Handy sat on a log of wood. The throb of her engine, the wash of her propeller, gave place to the strains of a melodeon, which was playing " Stop yer ticklin', Jock," and Para Handy felt some sense of gaiety suffuse him, but business was business, and it was only for a moment he permitted himself to be carried away on the divine wings of music.

" Have you anything for me, McKay ? " he hailed the *Texa's* clerk.

The purser cast a rapid glance over the deck, encumbered with planks, crates, casks of paraffin oil, and herring-boxes, and seeing nothing there that looked like a consignment for the questioner, leaned across the rail, and made a rapid survey of the open hold. It held nothing maritime—only hay-bales, flour-bags, soap-boxes, shrouded mutton carcases, rolls of plumbers' lead, two headstones for Ardrishaig, and the dismantled slates, cushions, and legs of a billiard-table for Strachur.

" Naething the day for you, Peter," said the clerk ; "unless it's yin o' the heid-stanes," and he ran his eyes down the manifest which he held in his hand.

" Ye're aawful smert, McKay," said Para Handy. " If ye wass a rale purser wi' brass buttons and a yellow-and-black strippit tie on your neck, there would be no haadin' ye in ! It's no luggage I'm lookin' for ; it's a kind o' a man I'm expectin'. Maybe he's no' in your depairtment ; he'll be traivellin' saloon. Look behind wan o' them herring-boxes, Lachie, and see if ye canna see a sailor."

His intuition was right ; the *Texa's* only passenger that afternoon was discovered sitting behind the herring-boxes playing a melodeon, and smiling beatifically to himself, with blissful unconsciousness that he had arrived at his destination. He came to himself with a start when the purser asked him if he was going off here ; terminated the melody of his instrument in a melancholy squawk, picked up a carelessly-tied canvas bag that lay at his feet, and hurried over the plank to the quay, shedding from the bag as he went a trail of socks, shoes, collars, penny ballads, and seamen's biscuits, whose exposure in this awkward fashion seemed to cause him no distress of mind, for he only laughed when Para Handy called them to his attention, and left to one of the *Texa's* hands the trouble of collecting them, though he obligingly held the mouth of the sack open himself while the other restored the dunnage. He was a round, short, red-faced, clean-shaven fellow of five-and-twenty, with a thin serge suit, well polished at all the bulgy parts, and a laugh that sprang from a merry heart.

"Are you The Tar's kizzen ? Are you Davie Green ? " asked Para Handy.

"Right-oh ! The very chap," said the stranger. "And you'll be Peter ? Haud my melodeon, will ye, till I draw my breath. Right-oh ! "

"Are ye sure there's no mistake ? " asked Para Handy, as they moved along to the other end of the quay where the *Vital Spark* was lying. "You're the new hand I wass expectin', and your name's Davie ? "

"My name's Davie, richt enough," said the stranger, "but I seldom got it ; when I was on the Cluthas they always ca'd me Sunny Jim."

"Sunny Jum ! " said the Captain. "Man ! I've often heard aboot ye ; you were namely for chumpin' fences ? "

"Not me ! " said Davie. "Catch me jumpin' onything if there was a hole to get through. Is that your vessel ? She's a tipper ! You and me'll get on A1. Wait you till ye see the fun I'll gie ye ! That was the worst o' the Cluthas—awfu' short trips and every noo and then a quay ; ye hadn't a meenute to yerself for a baur at all. Whit sort o' chaps hae ye for a crew ? "

"The very pick ! " said Para Handy, as they came alongside the *Vital Spark*, whose crew, as a matter of fact, were all on deck to see the new hand. "That's Macphail, the chief enchineer, wan of Brutain's hardy sons, wi' the wan gallows ; and the other chap's Dougie, the first mate, a Cowal laad ; you'll see him plainer efter his face iss washed for the tea. Then there's me, mysel', the Captain. Laads, this iss Colin's kizzen, Sunny Jum."

Sunny Jim stood on the edge of the quay, and smiled like a sunset on his future shipmates. "Hoo are yez, chaps?" he cried genially, waving his hand.

"We canna compleen," said Dougie solemnly. "Are ye in good trum yersel'? See's a grup o' your hold-aal, and excuse the gangway."

Sunny Jim jumped on board, throwing his dunnage-bag before him, and his feet had no sooner touched the deck than he indulged in a step or two of the sailor's hornpipe with that proficiency which only years of practice in a close-mouth in Crown Street, S.S., could confer. The Captain looked a little embarrassed; such conduct was hardly business-like, but it was a relief to find that The Tar's nominee and successor was a cheery chap at any rate. Dougie looked on with no disapproval, but Macphail grunted and turned his gaze to sea, disgusted at such free-and-easy informality.

"I hope ye can cook as weel's ye can dance," he remarked coldly.

Sunny Jim stopped immediately. "Am I supposed to cook?" he asked, concealing his surprise as he best could.

"Ye are that!" said Macphail. "Did ye think ye were to be the German band on board, and go roon' liftin' pennies? Cookie's the main thing wi' the second mate o' the *Vital Spark*, and I can tell ye we're gey particular; are we no', Dougie?"

"Aawful!" said Dougie sadly. "Macphail here hass been cookin' since The Tar left; he'll gie ye his receipt for haddies made wi' enchine-oil."

The *Vital Spark* cast off from Rothesay Quay on her way for Bowling, and Sunny Jim was introduced to several pounds of sausages to be fried for dinner, a bag of potatoes, and a jar of salt, with which he was left to juggle as he could, while the others, with expectant appetites, performed their respective duties. Life on the open sea, he found, was likely to be as humdrum as it used to be on the Cluthas, and he determined to initiate a little harmless gaiety. With some difficulty he extracted all the meat from the uncooked sausages, and substituted salt. Then he put them on the frying-pan. They had no sooner heated than they began to dance in the pan with curious little crackling explosions. He started playing his melodeon, and cried on the crew, who hurried to see this unusual phenomenon.

"Well, I'm jeegered," said the Captain; "what in aal the world iss the matter wi' them?"

"It's a waarnin'," said Dougie lugubriously, with wide-staring eyes.

"Warnin' my auntie!" said Sunny Jim, playing a jig-tune. "They started jumpin' like that whenever I begood to play my bonnie wee melodeon."

"I daarsay that," said Para Handy; "for you're a fine, fine player, Jum, but—but it wassna any invitation to a baal I gave them when I paid for them in Ro'sa'."

"I aye said sausages werena meat for sailors," remarked the engineer, with bitterness, for he was very hungry. "Ye'll notice it's an Irish jig they're dancin' to," he added with dark significance.

"I don't see mysel'," said the Captain, "that it maiters whether it iss an Irish jeeg or the Gourock Waltz and Circassian Circle."

"Does it no'?" retorted Macphail. "I suppose ye'll never hae heard o' Irish terrier dugs? I've ett my last sausage ony-wye! Sling us ower that pan-loaf," and seizing the bread for himself he proceeded to make a spartan meal.

Sunny Jim laughed till the tears ran down his jovial countenance. "Chaps," he exclaimed, with firm conviction, "this is the cheeriest ship ever I was on; I'm awful gled I brung my music."

Dougie took a fork and gingerly investigated. "As hard ass whun-stanes!" he proclaimed; "they'll no' be ready by the time we're at the Tail o' the Bank. Did you ever in your mortal life see the like of it?" and he jabbed ferociously with the fork at the bewitched sausages.

"That's richt!" said Macphail. "Put them oot o' pain."

"Stop you!" said Para Handy. "Let us pause and consuder. It iss the first time ever I saw sassages with such a desperate fine ear for music. If they'll no' fry, they'll maybe boil. Put them in a pot, Jum."

"Right-oh!" said Sunny Jim, delighted at the prospect of a second scene to his farce, and the terpsichorean sausages were consigned to the pot of water which had boiled the potatoes. The crew sat round, staving off the acuter pangs of hunger with potatoes and bread.

"You never told us what for they called you Sunny Jum, Davie," remarked the Captain. "Do you think it would be for your complexion?"

"I couldna say," replied the new hand, "but I think mysel' it was because I was aye such a cheery wee chap. The favourite

Clutha on the Clyde, when the Cluthas was rinnin', was the yin
I was on ; hunners o' trips used to come wi' her on the Setturdays
on the aff-chance that I wad maybe gie them a baur. Mony a
pant we had ! I could hae got a job at the Finnieston Ferry
richt enough, chaps, but they wouldna alloo the melodeon,
and I wad sooner want my wages."

" A fine, fine unstrument ! " said Para Handy agreeably.
" Wi' it and Dougie's trump we'll no' be slack in passin' the
time."

" Be happy !—that's my motto," said Sunny Jim, beaming
upon his auditors like one who brings a new and glorious evangel.
" Whatever happens, be happy, and then ye can defy onything.
It's a' in the wye ye look at things. See ? "

" That's what I aalways say mysel' to the wife," said Dougie
in heart-broken tones, and his eye on the pot, which was beginning to boil briskly.

" As shair as daith, chaps, I canna stand the Jock o' Hazel-
dean kind o' thing at a'—folk gaun aboot lettin' the tear doon-fa
a' the time. Gie me a hearty laugh and it's right-oh ! BE
HAPPY !—that's the Golden Text for the day, as we used to say
in the Sunday School."

" I could be happy easy enough if it wassna that I wass so
desperate hungry," said Dougie in melancholy accents, lifting
the lid to look into the pot. He could see no sign of sausages,
and with new forebodings he began to feel for them with a stick.
They had disappeared ! " I said from the very first it wass a
waarnin' ! " he exclaimed, resigning the stick to the incredulous
engineer.

" This boat's haunted," said Macphail, who also failed to
find anything in the pot. " I saw ye puttin' them in wi' my
ain eyes, and noo they're no' there."

Para Handy grabbed the spirtle, and feverishly explored
on his own account, with the same extraordinary results.

" My Chove ! " he exclaimed, " did you ever see the like
of that, and I havena tasted wan drop of stimulants since last
Monday. Laads ! I don't know what you think aboot it, but
it's the church twice for me to-morrow ! "

.   .   .   .

Sunny Jim quite justified his nickname by giving a pleasant
surprise to his shipmates in the shape of a meat-tea later in the
afternoon.

EDITH NESBIT (1858–1924) *was one of the original members of the Fabian Society and among her friends were George Bernard Shaw and H. G. Wells. Her literary career began at eighteen with contributions to the " Weekly Dispatch," but her best work was done after she was forty, when she started writing children's books. Her stories of the Bastable Family display humour and charm that make them as attractive to grown-ups as to children.*

THE CONSCIENCE-PUDDING

IT was Christmas, nearly a year after mother died. I cannot write about mother—but I will just say one thing. If she had only been away for a little while, and not for always, we shouldn't have been so keen on having a Christmas. I didn't understand this then, but I am much older now, and I think it was just because everything was so different and horrid we felt we *must* do something ; and perhaps we were not particular enough *what*. Things make you much more unhappy when you loaf about than when you are doing events.

Father had to go away just about Christmas. He had heard that his wicked partner, who ran away with his money, was in France, and he thought he could catch him, but really he was in Spain, where catching criminals is never practised. We did not know this till afterwards.

Before father went away he took Dora and Oswald into his study, and said :

" I'm awfully sorry I've got to go away, but it is very serious business, and I must go. You'll be good while I'm away, kiddies, won't you ? "

We promised faithfully. Then he said :

" There are reasons—you wouldn't understand if I tried to tell you—but you can't have much of a Christmas this year. But I've told Matilda to make you a good plain pudding. Perhaps next Christmas will be brighter."

(It was ; for the next Christmas saw us the affluent nephews and nieces of an Indian uncle—but that is quite another story, as good old Kipling says.)

When father had been seen off at Lewisham Station with his bags, and a plaid rug in a strap, we came home again, and it was horrid. There were papers and things littered all over his room where he had packed. We tidied the room up—it was the only thing we could do for him. It was Dicky who accidentally broke his shaving-glass, and H. O. made a paper boat out of a letter we found out afterwards father particularly wanted to keep. This took us some time, and when we went into the nursery the fire was black out, and we could not get it alight again, even with the whole *Daily Chronicle*. Matilda, who was our general then, was out, as well as the fire, so we went and sat in the kitchen. There is always a good fire in kitchens. The kitchen hearthrug was not nice to sit on, so we spread newspapers on it.

It was sitting in the kitchen, I think, that brought to our minds my father's parting words—about the pudding, I mean.

Oswald said, " Father said we couldn't have much of a Christmas for secret reasons, and he said he had told Matilda to make us a plain pudding."

The plain pudding instantly cast its shadow over the deepening gloom of our young minds.

" I wonder *how* plain she'll make it ? " Dicky said.

" As plain as plain, you may depend," said Oswald. " A here-am-I-where-are-you pudding—that's her sort."

The others groaned, and we gathered closer round the fire till the newspapers rustled madly.

" I believe I could make a pudding that *wasn't* plain, if I tried," Alice said. " Why shouldn't we ? "

" No chink," said Oswald, with brief sadness.

" How much would it cost ? " Noël asked, and added that Dora had twopence and H. O. had a French halfpenny.

Dora got the cookery-book out of the dresser drawer, where it lay doubled up among clothes-pegs, dirty dusters, scallop shells, string, penny novelettes, and the dining-room corkscrew. The general we had then—it seemed as if she did all the cooking on the cookery-book instead of on the baking-board, there were traces of so many bygone meals upon its pages.

" It doesn't say Christmas pudding at all," said Dora.

" Try plum," the resourceful Oswald instantly counselled.

Dora turned the greasy pages anxiously.

" ' Plum-pudding, 518.

" ' A rich, with flour, 517.

" ' Christmas, 517.

" ' Cold brandy sauce for, 241.'

" We shouldn't care about that, so it's no use looking."

" ' Good without eggs, 518.

" ' Plain, 518.'

" We don't want *that* anyhow, ' Christmas, 517 '—that's the one."

It took her a long time to find the page. Oswald got a shovel of coals and made up the fire. It blazed up like the devouring elephant the *Daily Telegraph* always calls it. Then Dora read : " ' Christmas plum-pudding. Time six hours.' "

" To eat it in ? " said H. O.

" No, silly ! to make it."

" Forge ahead, Dora," Dicky replied.

Dora went on :

" ' 2072. One pound and a half of raisins ; half a pound of currants ; three quarters of a pound of breadcrumbs ; half a pound of flour ; three quarters of a pound of beef suet ; nine eggs ; one wineglassful of brandy ; half a pound of citron and orange peel ; half a nutmeg ; and a little ground ginger.' I wonder *how* little ground ginger."

" A teacupful would be enough, I think," Alice said ; " we must not be extravagant."

" We haven't got anything yet to be extravagant *with*," said Oswald, who had toothache that day. " What would you do with the things if you'd got them ? "

" You'd ' chop the suet as fine as possible '—I wonder how fine that is ? " replied Dora and the book together—" ' and mix it with the breadcrumbs and flour ; add the currants washed and dried.' "

" Not starched, then," said Alice.

" ' The citron and orange peel cut into thin slices '—I wonder what they call thin ? Matilda's thin bread-and-butter is quite different from what I mean by it—' and the raisins stoned and divided.' How many heaps would you divide them into ? "

" Seven, I suppose," said Alice ; " one for each person and one for the pot—I mean pudding."

" ' Mix it all well together with the grated nutmeg and ginger. Then stir in nine eggs well beaten, and the brandy '—we'll leave that out, I think—' and again mix it thoroughly together that every ingredient may be moistened ; put it into a buttered mould, tie over tightly, and boil for six hours. Serve it ornamented with holly and brandy poured over it.' "

" I should think holly and brandy poured over it would be simply beastly," said Dicky.

" I expect the book knows. I dare say holly and water would do as well though. ' This pudding may be made a month before '—it's no use reading about that though, because we've only got four days to Christmas."

"It's no use reading about any of it," said Oswald, with thoughtful repeatedness, "because we haven't got the things, and we haven't got the coin to get them."

"We might get the tin somehow," said Dicky.

"There must be lots of kind people who would subscribe to a Christmas pudding for poor children who hadn't any," Noël said.

"Well I'm going skating at Penn's," said Oswald. "It's no use thinking about puddings. We must put up with it plain."

So he went, and Dicky went with him.

When they returned to their home in the evening the fire had been lighted again in the nursery, and the others were just having tea. We toasted our bread-and-butter on the bare side, and it gets a little warm among the butter. This is called French toast. "I like English better, but it is more expensive." Alice said :

"Matilda is in a frightful rage about your putting those coals on the kitchen fire, Oswald. She says we shan't have enough to last over Christmas as it is. And father gave her a talking to before he went about them—asked her if she ate them, she says— but I don't believe he did. Anyway, she's locked the coal-cellar door, and she's got the key in her pocket. I don't see how we can boil the pudding."

"What pudding ? " said Oswald dreamily. He was thinking of a chap he had seen at Penn's who had cut the date 1899 on the ice with four strokes.

"*The* pudding," Alice said. "Oh, we've had such a time, Oswald ! First Dora and I went to the shops to find out exactly what the pudding would cost—it's only two and elevenpence halfpenny, counting in the holly."

"It's no good," Oswald repeated ; he is very patient and will say the same thing any number of times. "It's no good. You know we've got no tin."

"Ah," said Alice, "but Noël and I went out, and we called at some of the houses in Granville Park and Dartmouth Hill— and we got a lot of sixpences and shillings, besides pennies, and one old gentleman gave us a half-a-crown. He was so nice. Quite bald, with a knitted red and blue waistcoat. We've got eight-and-sevenpence."

Oswald did not feel quite sure father would like us to go asking for shillings and sixpences, or even half-crowns from strangers, but he did not say so. The money had been asked for and got, and it couldn't be helped—and perhaps he wanted the pudding—I am not able to remember exactly why he did not speak up and say, "This is wrong," but anyway he didn't.

Alice and Dora went out and bought the things next morning. They bought double quantities, so that it came to five shillings and elevenpence, and was enough to make a noble pudding. There was a lot of holly left over for decorations. We used very little for the sauce. The money that was left we spent very anxiously in other things to eat, such as dates and figs and toffee.

We did not tell Matilda about it. She was a red-haired girl, and apt to turn shirty at the least thing.

Concealed under our jackets and overcoats we carried the parcels up to the nursery, and hid them in the treasure-chest we had there. It was the bureau drawer. It was locked up afterwards because the treacle got all over the green baize and the little drawers inside it while we were waiting to begin to make the pudding. It was the grocer told us we ought to put treacle in the pudding, and also about not so much ginger as a teacupful.

When Matilda had begun to pretend to scrub the floor (she pretended this three times a week so as to have an excuse not to let us in the kitchen, but I know she used to read novelettes most of the time, because Alice and I had a squint through the window more than once), we barricaded the nursery and set to work. We were very careful to be quite clean. We washed our hands as well as the currants. I have sometimes thought we did not get all the soap off the currants. The pudding smelt like a washing-day when the time came to cut it open. And we washed a corner of the table to chop the suet on. Chopping suet looks easy till you try.

Father's machine he weighs letters with did to weigh out the things. We did this very carefully, in case the grocer had not done so. Everything was right except the raisins. H. O. had carried them home. He was very young then, and there was a hole in the corner of the paper bag and his mouth was sticky.

Lots of people have been hanged to a gibbet in chains on evidence no worse than that, and we told H. O. so till he cried. This was good for him. It was not unkindness to H. O., but part of our duty.

Chopping suet as fine as possible is much harder than any one would think, as I said before. So is crumbling bread— especially if your loaf is new, like ours was. When we had done them the breadcrumbs and the suet were both very large and lumpy, and of a dingy grey colour, something like pale slate pencil.

They looked a better colour when we had mixed them with the flour. The girls had washed the currants with Brown Windsor soap and the sponge. Some of the currants got inside the sponge and kept coming out in the bath for days afterwards. I see now

that this was not quite nice. We cut the candied peel as thin
as we wish people would cut our bread-and-butter. We tried
to take the stones out of the raisins, but they were too sticky, so
we just divided them up in seven lots. Then we mixed the other
things in the wash-hand basin from the spare bedroom that was
always spare. We each put in our own lot of raisins and turned
it all into a pudding-basin, and tied it up in one of Alice's pina-
fores, which was the nearest thing to a proper pudding-cloth we
could find—at any rate clean. What was left sticking to the wash-
hand basin did not taste so bad.

"It's a little bit soapy," Alice said; "but perhaps that will
boil out; like stains in tablecloths."

It was a difficult question how to boil the pudding. Matilda
proved furious when asked to let us, just because some one
happened to knock her hat off the scullery door and Pincher had
got it and done for it. However, part of the embassy nicked a
saucepan while the others were being told what Matilda thought
about the hat, and we got hot water out of the bathroom and
made it boil over our nursery fire. We put the pudding in—it
was now getting on towards the hour of tea—and let it boil.
With some exceptions—owing to the fire going down, and Matilda
not hurrying up with coals—it boiled for an hour and a quarter.
Then Matilda came suddenly in and said, " I'm not going to
have you messing about in here with my saucepans " ; and she
tried to take it off the fire. You will see that we couldn't stand
this ; it was not likely. I do not remember who it was that told
her to mind her own business, and I think I have forgotten who
caught hold of her first to make her chuck it. I am sure no needless violence was used. Anyway, while the struggle progressed,
Alice and Dora took the saucepan away and put it in the boot-
cupboard under the stairs and put the key in their pocket.

This sharp encounter made every one hot and cross. We
got over it before Matilda did, but we brought her round before
bedtime. Quarrels should always be made up before bedtime.
It says so in the Bible. If this simple rule was followed there
would not be so many wars and martyrs and lawsuits and in-
quisitions and bloody deaths at the stake.

All the house was still. The gas was out all over the house
except on the first landing, when several darkly shrouded figures
might have been observed creeping downstairs to the kitchen.

On the way, with superior precaution, we got out our saucepan. The kitchen fire was red, but low; the coal-cellar was
locked, and there was nothing in the scuttle but a little coal-dust
and the piece of brown paper that is put in to keep the coals from

tumbling out through the bottom where the hole is. We put the saucepan on the fire and plied it with fuel—two *Chronicles*, a *Telegraph* and two *Family Herald* novelettes were burned in vain. I am almost sure the pudding did not boil at all that night.

"Never mind," Alice said. "We can each nick a piece of coal every time we go into the kitchen to-morrow."

This daring scheme was faithfully performed, and by night we had nearly half a waste-paper basket of coal, coke, and cinders. And in the depth of night once more we might have been observed, this time with our collier-like waste-paper basket in our guarded hands.

There was more fire left in the grate that night, and we fed it with the fuel we had collected. This time the fire blazed up, and the pudding boiled like mad. This was the time it boiled two hours—at least I think it was about that, but we dropped asleep on the kitchen tables and dresser. You dare not be lowly in the night in the kitchen, because of the beetles. We were aroused by a horrible smell. It was the pudding-cloth burning. All the water had secretly boiled itself away. We filled it up at once with cold, and the saucepan cracked. So we cleaned it and put it back on the shelf and took another and went to bed, You see what a lot of trouble we had over the pudding. Every evening till Christmas, which had now become only the day after to-morrow, we sneaked down in the inky midnight and boiled that pudding for as long as it would.

On Christmas morning we chopped the holly for the sauce, but we put hot water (instead of brandy) and moist sugar. Some of them said it was not so bad. Oswald was not one of these.

Then came the moment when the plain pudding father had ordered smoked upon the board. Matilda brought it in and went away at once. She had a cousin out of Woolwich Arsenal to see her that day, I remember. Those far-off days are quite distinct in memory's recollection still.

Then we got our own pudding from its hiding-place and gave it one last hurried boil—only seven minutes, because of the general impatience which Oswald and Dora could not cope with.

We had found means to secrete a dish, and we now tried to dish the pudding up, but it stuck to the basin, and had to be dislodged with a chisel. The pudding was horribly pale. We poured the holly sauce over it, and Dora took up the knife and was just cutting it when a few simple words from H. O. turned us from happy and triumphing cookery artists to persons in despair.

He said : " How pleased all those kind ladies and gentlemen

would be if they knew *we* were the poor children they gave the shillings and sixpences and things for ! "

We all said, " *What ?* " It was no moment for politeness.

" I say," H. O. said, " they'd be glad if they knew it was us was enjoying the pudding, and not dirty little, really poor children."

" You should say ' you were,' not ' you was,' " said Dora, but it was as in a dream and only from habit.

" Do you mean to say "—Oswald spoke firmly, yet not angrily—" that you and Alice went and begged for money for poor children, and then *kept* it ? "

" We didn't keep it," said H. O., " we spent it."

" We've kept the *things*, you little duffer ! " said Dicky, looking at the pudding sitting alone and uncared for on its dish. " You begged for money for poor children, and then *kept* it. It's stealing, that's what it is. I don't say so much about you— you're only a silly kid—but Alice knew better. Why did you do it ? "

He turned to Alice, but she was now too deep in tears to get a word out.

H. O. looked a bit frightened, but he answered the question. We have taught him this. He said :

" I thought they'd give us more if I said poor children than if I said just us."

" *That's* cheating," said Dicky—" downright beastly, mean, low cheating."

" I'm not," said H. O. ; " and you're another."

Then he began to cry too. I do not know how the others felt, but I understand from Oswald that he felt that now the honour of the House of Bastable had been stamped on in the dust, and it didn't matter what happened. He looked at the beastly holly that had been left over from the sauce and was stuck up over the pictures. It now appeared hollow and disgusting, though it had got quite a lot of berries, and some of it was the varied kind— green and white. The figs and dates and toffee were set out in the doll's dinner service. The very sight of it all made Oswald blush sickly. He owns he would have liked to cuff H. O., and, if he did for a moment wish to shake Alice, the author, for one, can make allowances.

Now Alice choked and spluttered, and wiped her eyes fiercely, and said, " It's no use ragging H. O. It's my fault. I'm older than he is."

H. O. said, " It couldn't be Alice's fault. I don't see as it was wrong."

" That, not as," murmured Dora, putting her arms round the sinner who had brought this degrading blight upon our family tree, but such is girls' undetermined and affectionate silliness. " Tell sister all about it, H. O. dear. Why couldn't it be Alice's fault ? "

H. O. cuddled up to Dora and said snufflingly in his nose :

" Because she hadn't got nothing to do with it. I collected it all. She never went into one of the houses. She didn't want to."

" And then took all the credit of getting the money," said Dicky savagely.

Oswald said, " Not much *credit*," in scornful tones.

" Oh, you are *beastly*, the whole lot of you, except Dora ! " Alice said, stamping her foot in rage and despair. " I tore my frock on a nail going out, and I didn't want to go back, and I got H. O. to go to the houses alone, and I waited for him outside. And I asked him not to say anything because I didn't want Dora to know about the frock—it's my best. And *I* don't know what he said inside. He never told me. But I'll bet anything he didn't *mean* to cheat."

" You said lots of kind people would be ready to give money to get pudding for poor children. So I asked them to."

Oswald, with his strong right hand, waved a wave of passing things over.

" We'll talk about that another time," he said ; " just now we've got weightier things to deal with."

He pointed to the pudding, which had grown cold during the conversation to which I have alluded. H. O. stopped crying, but Alice went on with it. Oswald now said :

" We're a base and outcast family. Until that pudding's out of the house we shan't be able to look any one in the face. We must see that that pudding goes to the poor children—not grisling, grumpy, whiney-piney, pretending poor children—but real poor ones, just as poor as they can stick."

" And the figs too—and the dates," said Noël with regretting tones.

" Every fig," said Dicky sternly. " Oswald is quite right."

This honourable resolution made us feel a bit better. We hastily put on our best things, and washed ourselves a bit, and hurried out to find some really poor people to give the pudding to. We cut it in slices ready, and put it in a basket with the figs and dates and toffee. We would not let H. O. come with us at first because he wanted to. And Alice would not come because of him. So at last we had to let him. The excitement of tearing into your best things heals the hurt that wounded honour feels, as the poetry writer said—or at any rate it makes the hurt feel better.

We went out into the streets. They were pretty quiet—nearly everybody was eating its Christmas dessert. But presently we met a woman in an apron. Oswald said very politely :

" Please, are you a poor person ? " And she told us to get along with us.

The next we met was a shabby man with a hole in his left boot.

Again Oswald said, " Please, are you a poor person, and have you any poor little children ? "

The man told us not to come any of our games with him, or we should laugh on the wrong side of our faces. We went on sadly. We had no heart to stop and explain to him that we had no games to come.

The next was a young man near the Obelisk. Dora tried this time.

She said, " Oh, if you please we've got some Christmas pudding in this basket, and if you're a poor person you can have some."

" Poor as Job," said the young man in a hoarse voice, and he had to come up out of a red comforter to say it.

We gave him a slice of the pudding, and he bit into it without thanks or delay. The next minute he had thrown the pudding slap in Dora's face, and was clutching Dicky by the collar.

" Blime if I don't chuck ye in the river, the whole bloomin' lot of you ! " he exclaimed.

The girls screamed, the boys shouted, and though Oswald threw himself on the insulter of his sister with all his manly vigour, yet but for a friend of Oswald's, who is in the police, passing at that instant, the author shudders to think what might have happened, for he was a strong young man, and Oswald is not yet come to his full strength, and the Quaggy runs all too near.

Our policeman led our assailant aside, and we waited anxiously, as he told us to. After long uncertain moments the young man in the comforter loafed off grumbling, and our policeman turned to us.

" Said you gave him a dollop o' pudding, and it tasted of soap and hair-oil."

I suppose the hair-oil must have been the Brown Windsoriness of the soap coming out. We were sorry, but it was still our duty to get rid of the pudding. The Quaggy was handy, it is true, but when you have collected money to feed poor children and spent it on pudding it is not right to throw that

" Please, are you a poor person ? "

pudding in the river. People do not subscribe shillings and sixpences and half-crowns to feed a hungry flood with Christmas pudding.

Yet we shrank from asking any more people whether they were poor persons, or about their families, and still more from offering the pudding to chance people who might bite into it and taste the soap before we had time to get away.

It was Alice, the most paralysed with disgrace of all of us, who thought of the best idea.

She said, " Let's take it to the workhouse. At any rate they're all poor people there, and they mayn't go out without leave, so they can't run after us to do anything to us after the pudding. No one would give them leave to go out to pursue people who had brought them pudding, and wreck vengeance on them, and at any rate we shall get rid of the conscience-pudding—it's a sort of conscience-money, you know—only it isn't money but pudding."

The workhouse is a good way, but we stuck to it, though very cold, and hungrier than we thought possible when we started, for we had been so agitated that we had not even stayed to eat the plain pudding our good father had so kindly and thoughtfully ordered for our Christmas dinner.

The big bell at the workhouse made a man open the door to us, when we rang it. Oswald said (and he spoke because he is next eldest to Dora, and she had had jolly well enough of saying anything about pudding)—he said :

" Please we've brought some pudding for the poor people."

He looked us up and down, and he looked at our basket, then he said : " You better see the Matron."

We waited in a hall, feeling more and more uncomfy, and less and less like Christmas. We were very cold indeed, especially our hands and our noses. And we felt less and less able to face the Matron if she was horrid, and one of us at least wished he had chosen the Quaggy for the pudding's long home, and made it up to the robbed poor in some other way afterwards.

Just as Alice was saying earnestly in the burning cold ear of Oswald, " Let's put down the basket and make a bolt for it. Oh, Oswald, *let's !* " a lady came along the passage. She was very upright, and she had eyes that went through you like blue gimlets. I should not like to be obliged to thwart that lady if she had any design, and mine was opposite. I am glad this is not likely to occur.

She said, " What's all this about a pudding ? "

H. O. said at once, before we could stop him, " They say I've stolen the pudding, so we've brought it here for the poor people."

"No, we didn't!" "That wasn't why!" "The money was given!" "It was meant for the poor!" "Shut up, H. O.!" said the rest of us all at once.

Then there was an awful silence. The lady gimleted us again one by one with her blue eyes.

Then she said : "Come into my room. You all look frozen."

She took us into a very jolly room with velvet curtains and a big fire, and the gas lighted, because now it was almost dark, even out of doors. She gave us chairs, and Oswald felt as if his was a dock, he felt so criminal, and the lady looked so Judgular.

Then she took the armchair by the fire herself, and said, "Who's the eldest?"

"I am," said Dora, looking more like a frightened white rabbit than I've ever seen her.

"Then tell me all about it."

Dora looked at Alice and began to cry. That slab of pudding in the face had totally unnerved the gentle girl. Alice's eyes were red, and her face was puffy with crying ; but she spoke up for Dora and said :

"Oh, please let Oswald tell. Dora can't. She's tired with the long walk. And a young man threw a piece of it in her face, and——"

The lady nodded, and Oswald began. He told the story from the very beginning, as he has always been taught to, though he hated to lay bare the family honour's wound before a stranger, however judge-like and gimlet-eyed.

He told all—not concealing the pudding-throwing, nor what the young man said about soap.

"So," he ended, "we want to give the conscience-pudding to you. It's like conscience-money—you know what that is, don't you? But if you really think it is soapy and not just the young man's horridness, perhaps you'd better not let them eat it. But the figs and things are all right."

When he had done the lady said, for most of us were crying more or less :

"Come, cheer up! It's Christmas-time, and he's very little —your brother, I mean. And I think the rest of you seem pretty well able to take care of the honour of the family. I'll take the conscience-pudding off your minds. Where are you going now?"

"Home, I suppose," Oswald said. And he thought how nasty and dark and dull it would be. The fire out most likely and father away.

"And your father's not at home, you say," the blue-gimlet

lady went on. " What do you say to having tea with me, and then seeing the entertainment we have got up for our old people ?"

Then the lady smiled and the blue gimlets looked quite merry. The room was so warm and comfortable and the invitation was the last thing we expected. It was jolly of her, I do think.

No one thought quite at first of saying how pleased we should be to accept her kind invitation. Instead we all just said " Oh ! " but in a tone which must have told her we meant " Yes, please," very deeply.

Oswald (this has more than once happened) was the first to restore his manners. He made a proper bow like he has been taught, and said :

" Thank you very much. We should like it very much. It is very much nicer than going home. Thank you very much."

I need not tell the reader that Oswald could have made up a much better speech if he had had more time to make it up in, or if he had not been so filled with mixed flusteredness and furification by the shameful events of the day.

We washed our faces and hands and had a first-rate muffin and crumpet tea, with slices of cold meats, and many nice jams and cakes. A lot of other people were there, most of them people who were giving the entertainment to the aged poor.

After tea it was the entertainment. Songs and conjuring and a play called " Box and Cox," very amusing, and a lot of throwing things about in it—bacon and chops and things—and nigger minstrels. We clapped till our hands were sore.

When it was over we said good-bye. In between the songs and things Oswald had had time to make up a speech of thanks to the lady.

He said :

" We all thank you heartily for your goodness. The entertainment was beautiful. We shall never forget your kindness and hospitableness."

The lady laughed, and said she had been very pleased to have us. A fat gentleman said :

" And your teas ? I hope you enjoyed those—eh ? "

Oswald had not had time to make up an answer to that, so he answered straight from the heart, and said :

" Ra-*ther* ! "

And every one laughed and slapped us boys on the back and kissed the girls, and the gentleman who played the bones in the nigger minstrels saw us home. We ate the cold pudding that night and H. O. dreamed that something came to eat him, like it advises you to in the advertisements on the hoardings. The grown-ups said it was the pudding, but I don't think it could have been that because, as I have said more than once, it was so very plain.

Some of H. O.'s brothers and sisters thought it was a judgment on him for pretending about who the poor children were he was collecting the money for. Oswald does not believe such a little boy as H. O. would have a real judgment made just for him and nobody else, whatever he did.

But it certainly is odd. H. O. was the only one who had bad dreams, and he was also the only one who got any of the things we bought with that ill-gotten money, because, you remember, he picked a hole in the raisin-paper as he was bringing the parcel home. The rest of us had nothing, unless you count the scrapings of the pudding-basin, and those don't really count at all.

BARRY PAIN (1864–1928) *is best known as the author of the delightful " Eliza " books, describing the life at home in the suburbs of a city clerk and his family—although the writer had many interests and produced a great variety of literary work. This story, which is taken from " The Problem Club," displays considerable ingenuity as well as humour.*

THE GIRAFFE PROBLEM

THE general public knows little about the Problem Club. Many are not even aware that it has now been in existence for several years. Nor can it be said that the references to it which have appeared from time to time in the Press have been very enlightening, or even reasonably accurate.

For instance, a paragraph in a recent issue of a society paper (which, it may be admitted, is generally well informed) makes various statements as to the Problem Club. It says that the club has its premises underground in Piccadilly, that a former Premier is a member of it, that all the members are required to swear a most solemn oath to act with scrupulous honour in the monthly competitions, and that high play frequently goes on. The actual truth is that there are no club premises. The famous but old-fashioned restaurant that reserves two rooms on the first floor for the club's monthly meetings is not situated in Piccadilly. No Premier has ever been a member. The story of the solemn oath is even more absurd. After all, the members are gentlemen. They would as soon think of taking a solemn oath not to cheat at cards or at golf. The " scrupulous honour " is taken for granted. Lastly, there is no high play in the accepted sense of the term. The amount that a member can win or lose in the monthly competitions will be stated presently, and any betting on the results is prohibited.

Silly misrepresentations of this kind have caused some annoyance, and it is now thought that a discreet but authorized account of some part of the proceedings of the club would be preferable.

The club consists of twelve members, and the annual subscription is one hundred and thirty-four pounds. Of this sum twenty-four pounds is allotted to the club expenses, including the club dinners which are held on the first Saturday in every month. Each member in turn acts as chairman at one dinner in the year, afterwards adjudicating upon the problem competition for that month ; while at the other eleven meetings he is himself a competitor, the remaining one hundred and ten pounds of his subscription being treated as eleven entrance fees of ten pounds each. The problems are not of a mathematical nature, and were for some time invented and propounded by Leonard, the ingenious head-waiter of the restaurant. The winner receives the whole of the entrance fees, amounting to one hundred and ten pounds ; if there is more than one winner this amount is divided equally between them. Thus for his investment of one hundred and ten pounds it is possible that a member may in one year obtain a return of one thousand two hundred and ten pounds, if he is the sole winner of the eleven competitions for which he is eligible. But the minute-books of the club show that in actual practice this has never happened ; indeed, the record, made by Mr. Pusely-Smythe in 1911, is seven wins, and on two occasions out of the seven he had to share the prize with another successful competitor.

It may be admitted that the club has necessarily been of the nature of a secret society. Some of the problems set have been rather curious, and it has occasionally happened that in the course of their practical solution members have been led to do things which might prejudice them in their domestic or social relations, or even subject them to the penalties of the law.

It is permitted to add an account of some of the pre-War meetings of the club, various natural precautions being taken to prevent the discovery of the identity of members.

It was the forty-third meeting of the Problem Club. Dinner was over, and the members had adjourned to the lofty and comfortable room where the business of the evening was transacted. A side-table was suitably equipped with provision for smokers—all the members were smokers—and for such other refreshments as might be required in the course of the evening. One or two waiters still lingered—removing a coffee-cup, handing a liqueur, or placing an ash-tray and matches conveniently on one of the small tables. A hum of conversation went on through the blue haze of the cigar-smoke. Mr. Pusely-Smythe, with his usual lugubrious manner, was just coming to the end of a screamingly funny story. Any reference to the competition to be settled is by an unwritten law forbidden until the chairman has opened the proceedings, but it was noticeable that Major Byles was once more talking of resigning his membership. He was not taken very seriously. He was an original member, and, though he lived in the country for the greater part of the year, had never been known to miss a single meeting of the club. His continuous bad luck in the competitions had irritated him, but nobody believed in his threat of resignation, and it may be doubted if he quite believed in it himself.

The waiters left the room, and Sir Charles Bunford, an elderly gentleman of distinguished appearance, who was chairman for the evening, took his place at his table and arranged his papers. Among them the club cheque-book showed temptingly. In accordance with the club custom by which the chairman at one meeting acted as secretary at the next, Dr. Alden took his seat beside Sir Charles and prepared to make a note of the proceedings for the club minute-book. Conversation ceased. The other emembers seated themselves informally in a semicircle of easy-chairs. There was, indeed, a marked absence of formality at the Problem Club. There was no order of precedence. The chairman did not rise when he spoke, nor did members rise when they answered him.

" Now, gentlemen," Sir Charles began, " we have before us to-night the Giraffe Problem. I will read it out to you as worded by our esteemed friend Leonard : ' It is required to induce a woman who is unaware of your intention to say to you, " You ought to have been a giraffe." ' Now, of course, I'm not a competitor, but I must say that I'm sorry I'm not. Upon my word, I don't think Leonard has ever given us anything quite so easy."

There were several dissentient voices : " Not a bit of it." " Can't agree with you there, Bunford." " Wish I'd found it so." " Leonard knew what he was doing this time."

" Oh, very well," said Sir Charles, smiling. " I should have thought there were a score of conversational openings to which the inevitable reply would be, ' You ought to have been a giraffe.' I may be wrong, but I still expect that the prize to-night will have to be divided between four or five of you. However, we'll see what luck you've had. I'll begin with you, doctor, and then go on in the direction of the sun and the wine."

Dr. Alden shook his head. He had a strong head, an alert expression, and a bright eye. " No good," he said. " There was too much to do in Harley Street this month for me to be able to give the proper time to it. I made an attempt. It has probably cost me the esteem of an excellent woman ; these excellent women never think you're serious except when you're joking. I gave her the chance to tell me I ought to have been a giraffe, but she never took it. Enough said. Try the next man."

"The next is our only member of Parliament, Mr. Harding Pope."

"Not competing this month," said Mr. Pope rather pompously. "My constituency has made great demands upon me, and I'm unable to defend my entrance fee. Fortunately, the pleasure of the company in which I find myself is worth far more."

"That's all right," said Sir Charles warningly, "but don't get too slack. We've got a long waiting list. What about you, Major Byles ? "

"My usual luck," said the Major. "I worked the whole thing out completely and made all the necessary preparations. I was down at my cottage at the time. I assure you that during the whole of breakfast one morning I talked about practically nothing except giraffes and the way that they can pull down fruit from a tree, thanks to their thundering long necks. My wife, the children's governess, and Mrs. Hebor, who was stopping with us, all heard me, though I can't say that they seemed particularly interested. Afterwards my wife and I were in the garden, and I pointed to a tree full of ripe cherries.

" ' I like fruit,' I said, ' but I hate climbing trees.'

" Now, considering the ground-bait that I had been putting down at breakfast, I consider the betting was ten to one that she would reply that I ought to have been a giraffe. Instead of that, she said that Wilkins would get them for me, and then seemed surprised that I was annoyed. A few minutes later I tried the governess with precisely the same remark, and she asked me if I would like to have a ladder fetched. (I often wonder what I pay that woman her salary for.) Then Mrs. Hebor came out—as dependable a woman as I know in a general way ; you nearly always know what she is going to say before she says it—and I told her that I liked cherries, but hated climbing to get them.

" ' You ought,' she began—and this time I thought I really had got it—' to be able to reach some of those without climbing.'

"After that I gave up. No amount of intelligence can contend against luck like that. Matter of fact, I'm tempted to give up this problem business altogether."

"Oh, don't do that," said Sir Charles soothingly. "It was hard lines, but we shall see you a prize-winner one of these days. Now, Mr. Cunliffe, what have you to tell us ? "

"I failed," said the Rev. Septimus Cunliffe, an elderly cleric who specialized in broadmindedness. " Plausible strategy, but disappointing results. Nothing of interest to report."

" Did you do any better, Mr. Matthews ? "

Mr. Matthews was a man of forty, bald, round-faced, rubicund, and slightly obese. The task of ordering the club dinners and the wines to be drunk therewith was always left in his hands with a confidence which was invariably justified. His knowledge as an epicure was considerable, and it is possible that his intelligence was less considerable, but more than once he had been lucky in a competition. He was the richest man in a club where nobody was very poor, and was good-tempered and popular.

" Well, you know," said Matthews, " I feel as if I ought to have won this. At one time it looked as if I simply had it chucked at me. I was talking to Lady Amelia, who does a lot in the East End and is always nosing round for subscriptions.

" ' Why do you men drink ? ' she asked in her blunt way.

" The question of this competition occurred to me, and it looked like a good chance.

" ' Well,' I said, ' the pleasure begins in the palate, but I fancy that it continues in the throat. I often wish I had a longer throat.'

" You would have hardly thought she could have missed it, but she did. Said that she was sure I was not so bad as I made myself out to be, and milked me of a fiver for some rotten ' good cause.' "

" Look here," said Major Byles, returning from a fruitless visit to the side-table, " I'll ask the chairman for a minute's interval. They've not put out any seltzer, though they must know that I always take seltzer with mine."

" Certainly, Major ; certainly. Would somebody kindly touch the bell ? "

The seltzer-water was brought and business was resumed.

" Your turn next, Jimmy," said Sir Charles.

The Hon. James Feldane, a rather weary young man, said, " Well, I claim to be a winner, but there's a shade of doubt about it, and I'll ask for your ruling. All I can say is that if I don't touch the money my luck's even worse than the Major's. Like him, I was systematic about it. My first step was to buy some of the highest collars that could be got for money—two inches or so too high for me and beastly uncomfortable. I put one of them on, and looked like a bad freak—something out of a back number of *Punch*. My next step was to call on my married sister. She told me to go home and dress myself properly, as I knew she would. So I asked in my innocent way what was wrong, and she said I seemed to have mistaken my neck for the Nelson Column.

" ' Alluding to my collar ? ' I said. ' Well, I like pleytn. I'd wear a collar three feet high if I could.'

" And then my fool of a brother-in-law stuck his oar in, and said, ' You ought to have been a giraffe ' ; and I'm absolutely certain Dora would have said it if he hadn't got in first.

" So there it is—the words were all right, but they were used by a man. Still, for some purposes—bankruptcy and things of that kind—a man and his wife count as one, don't they ? What's the ruling ? "

" My ruling," said Sir Charles, " is that your claim fails. It is required that the words should be used by a woman, and your brother-in-law is not a woman."

" Yes, I was afraid you'd think so," said Jimmy, " but it was worth trying. Anybody want any rotten high collars ? "

" Now, Mr. Pusely-Smythe," said the chairman.

Mr. Pusely-Smythe was a man of middle age, with dark, cavernous eyes and an intellectual forehead. He was pale and thin, and was less solemn than he seemed.

" I claim to have won," he said in a melancholy voice. " My method was not the most obvious or direct, and might easily have failed, but the luck was with me. I must tell you that I happen to know a Mrs. Magsworth, who of late years has given way a good deal to Nature Study. She haunts the Zoo and the Botanical Gardens. She understands about the habitat of the hyena, and if cockroaches devour their young, and which end of the tree the onion grows—all that kind of thing. She is rather severe with people who, as she phrases it, ' show an abysmal ignorance of the simplest facts.' She has got a face like a horse, though that is not germane to the question. I arranged with a kindly hostess to let me take in Mrs. Magsworth to dinner one evening—I gather that there was no particular rush for the job.

" I said : ' I'm so glad to meet you again, Mrs. Magsworth. With your knowledge you will be able to settle a point that has been worrying me for days. My little nephew asked me which was the tallest animal. And, do you know, I couldn't be quite sure.'

" ' Then, Mr. Smythe,' she said, ' you ought to have been. A giraffe is much the tallest of the mammals.'

" So I claim to have won. She, being a woman ignorant of my intention, was induced to say to me the words required in the order required and without the interpolation of any other word."

" But there's the interpolation of a full stop," said Mr.

Harding Pope, and was at once called to order—only the chairman has the right to comment and to adjudicate.

Sir Charles took a few moments to consider his decision, and then gave his ruling as follows :

" My ruling is that Mr. Pusely-Smythe's claim is conditionally allowed. It is true that Mrs. Magsworth used other words both before and after the words required, but that is not precluded by the terms of the problem. The only other possible objection is that there was the interpolation of a full stop. Now, there is no full stop in spoken speech : it is represented by a pause. In this case the pause indicated the end of a sentence. In another case the pause might have indicated that the woman could not for a moment think of the word giraffe. In that case I am sure that no objection would have been raised. Yet there, too, a sign could be used to represent it in print or writing. Leonard requires certain words in a certain order, but he does not forbid a pause to be made between them. Unless some member has induced a woman to use the same words with no pause whatever —which I should rule to be a still better solution—Mr. Pusely-Smythe's claim is allowed."

As no other member had met with any success at all, a cheque for one hundred and ten pounds was drawn to the order of Mr. Pusely-Smythe and handed to him with the congratulations of the chairman.

The chairman's next duty was to open the sealed envelope containing the problem set by the ingenious Leonard for the ensuing month. This was entitled " The Kiss Problem," and when its conditions were read out both Major Byles and the Rev. Septimus Cunliffe objected to it, though on totally different grounds, and urged that Leonard should be asked to substitute something else. However, on a vote being taken, it was agreed by a considerable majority that " The Kiss Problem " should be retained, although, as the chairman pointed out, it looked excessively dangerous.

Mr. Pusely-Smythe was reminded that it was his turn to be chairman at the next meeting. And then, the business of the evening being at an end, the card-tables were brought in, and members addressed themselves to bridge at moderate points.

DOROTHY PARKER (1893–   ), *poet, journalist, and short story writer, has been described as the wittiest woman in America. She is permanently attached to the staff of the " New York Times." Shrewd, sympathetic, with a keen grasp of essentials, her short stories are in the finest de Maupassant tradition. " The Sexes " comes from a group of tales that are fleeting adventures of the heart and mind.*

THE SEXES

THE young man with the scenic cravat glanced nervously down the sofa at the girl in the fringed dress. She was examining her handkerchief; it might have been the first one of its kind she had seen, so deep was her interest in its material, form, and possibilities. The young man cleared his throat, without necessity or success, producing a small, syncopated noise.

" Want a cigarette ? " he said.

" No, thank you," she said. " Thank you ever so much just the same."

" Sorry I've only got these kind," he said. " You got any of your own ? "

" I really don't know," she said. " I probably have, thank you."

" Because if you haven't," he said, " it wouldn't take me a minute to go up to the corner and get you some."

" Oh, thank you, but I wouldn't have you go to all that trouble for anything," she said. " It's awfully sweet of you to think of it. Thank you ever so much."

" Will you for God's sake stop thanking me ? " he said.

" Really," she said, " I didn't know I was saying anything out of the way. I'm awfully sorry if I hurt your feelings. I know what it feels like to get your feelings hurt. I'm sure I didn't realize it was an insult to say ' thank you ' to a person. I'm not exactly in the habit of having people swear at me because I say ' thank you ' to them."

" I did not swear at you ! " he said.

" Oh, you didn't ? " she said. " I see."

" My God," he said, " all I said, I simply asked you if I couldn't go out and get you some cigarettes. Is there anything in that to get up in the air about ? "

562

"Who's up in the air?" she said. "I'm sure I didn't know it was a criminal offence to say I wouldn't dream of giving you all that trouble. I'm afraid I must be awfully stupid, or something."

"Do you want me to go out and get you some cigarettes; or don't you?" he said.

"Goodness," she said, "if you want to go so much, please don't feel you have to stay here. I wouldn't have you feel you had to stay for anything."

"Ah, don't be that way, will you?" he said.

"Be what way?" she said. "I'm not being any way."

"What's the matter?" he said.

"Why, nothing," she said. "Why?"

"You've been funny all evening," he said. "Hardly said a word to me, ever since I came in."

"I'm terribly sorry you haven't been having a good time," she said. "For goodness sake don't feel you have to stay here and be bored. I'm sure there are millions of places you could be having a lot more fun. The only thing, I'm a little bit sorry I didn't know before, that's all. When you said you were coming over to-night, I broke a lot of dates to go to the theatre and everything. But it doesn't make a bit of difference. I'd much rather have you go and have a good time. It isn't very pleasant to sit here and feel you're boring a person to death."

"I'm not bored!" he said. "I don't want to go any place! Ah, honey, won't you tell me what's the matter? Ah, please."

"I haven't the faintest idea what you're talking about," she said. "There isn't a thing on earth the matter. I don't know what you mean."

"Yes, you do," he said. "There's something the trouble. Is it anything I've done, or anything?"

"Goodness," she said, "I'm sure it isn't any of my business, anything you do. I certainly wouldn't feel I had any right to criticize."

"Will you stop talking like that?" he said. "Will you, please?"

"Talking like what?" she said.

"You know," he said. "That's the way you were talking over the telephone to-day, too. You were so snotty when I called you up, I was afraid to talk to you."

"I beg your pardon," she said. "What did you say I was?"

"Well, I'm sorry," he said. "I didn't mean to say that. You get me so balled up."

"You see," she said, "I'm really not in the habit of hearing language like that. I've never had a thing like that said to me in my life."

"I told you I was sorry, didn't I?" he said. "Honest, honey, I didn't mean it. I don't know how I came to say a thing like that. Will you excuse me? Please?"

"Oh, certainly," she said. "Goodness, don't feel you have to apologize to me. It doesn't make any difference at all. It just seems a little bit funny to have somebody you were in the habit of thinking was a gentleman come to your home and use language like that to you, that's all. But it doesn't make the slightest bit of difference."

"I guess nothing I say makes any difference to you," he said. "You seem to be sore at me."

"I'm sore at you?" she said. "I can't understand what put that idea in your head. Why should I be sore at you?"

"That's what I'm asking you," he said. "Won't you tell me what I've done? Have I done something to hurt your feelings, honey? The way you were, over the phone, you had me worried all day. I couldn't do a lick of work."

"I certainly wouldn't like to feel," she said, "that I was interfering with your work. I know there are lots of girls that don't think anything of doing things like that, but I think it's terrible. It certainly isn't very nice to sit here and have some one tell you you interfere with his business."

"I didn't say that!" he said. "I didn't say it!"

"Oh, didn't you?" she said. "Well, that was the impression I got. It must be my stupidity."

"I guess maybe I better go," he said. "I can't get right. Everything I say seems to make you sorer and sorer. Would you rather I'd go?"

"Please do just exactly whatever you like," she said. "I'm sure the last thing I want to do is have you stay here when you'd rather be some place else. Why don't you go some place where you won't be bored? Why don't you go up to Florence Leaming's? I know she'd love to have you."

"I don't want to go up to Florence Leaming's!" he said. "What would I want to go up to Florence Leaming's for? She gives me a pain."

"Oh, really?" she said. "She didn't seem to be giving you so much of a pain at Elsie's party last night, I notice. I notice you couldn't even talk to anybody else, that's how much of a pain she gave you."

"Yeah, and you know why I was talking to her?" he said.

"Why, I suppose you think she's attractive," she said. "I

suppose some people do. It's perfectly natural. Some people think she's quite pretty."

" I don't know whether she's pretty or not," he said. " I wouldn't know her if I saw her again. Why I was talking to her was you wouldn't even give me a tumble, last night. I came up and tried to talk to you, and you just said, ' Oh, how do you do '—just like that, ' Oh, how do you do '—and you turned right away and wouldn't look at me."

" I wouldn't look at you ? " she said. " Oh, that's awfully funny. Oh, that's marvellous. You don't mind if I laugh, do you ? "

" Go ahead and laugh your head off," he said. " But you wouldn't."

" Well, the minute you came in the room," she said, " you started making such a fuss over Florence Leaming I thought you never wanted to see anybody else. You two seemed to be having such a wonderful time together, goodness knows I wouldn't have butted in for anything."

" My God," he said, " this what's-her-name girl came up and began talking to me before I even saw anybody else, and what could I do ? I couldn't sock her in the nose, could I ? "

" I certainly didn't see you try," she said.

" You saw me try to talk to you, didn't you ? " he said. " And what did you do ? ' Oh, how do you do.' Then this what's-her-name came up again, and there I was, stuck. Florence Leaming ! I think she's terrible. Know what I think of her ? I think she's a damn' little fool. That's what I think of her."

" Well, of course," she said, " that's the impression she always gave me, but I don't know. I've heard people say she's pretty. Honestly I have."

" Why, she can't be pretty in the same room with you," he said.

" She has got an awfully funny nose," she said. " I really feel sorry for a girl with a nose like that."

" She's got a terrible nose," he said. " You've got a beautiful nose. Gee, you've got a pretty nose."

" Oh, I have not," she said. " You're crazy."

" And beautiful eyes," he said, " and beautiful hair and a beautiful mouth. And beautiful hands. Let me have one of the little hands. Ah, look atta little hand ! Who's got the prettiest hands in the world ? Who's the sweetest girl in the world ? "

" I don't know," she said. " Who ? "

"You don't know!" he said. "You do so, too, know."

"I do not," she said. "Who? Florence Leaming?"

"Oh, Florence Leaming, my eye!" he said. "Getting sore about Florence Leaming! And me not sleeping all last night and not doing a stroke of work all day because you wouldn't speak to me! A girl like you getting sore about a girl like Florence Leaming!"

"I think you're just perfectly crazy," she said. "I was not sore! What on earth ever made you think I was? You're simply crazy. Ow, my hair-net! Wait a second till I take it off. There!"

GEORGE WILBUR PECK (1840–1916) *was a printer's devil at fifteen, and eventually had his own newspaper and became Governor of Wisconsin. The adventures of the Bad Boy first appeared in his paper, " The Sun," and were an instant success. His most popular book was " Peck's Bad Boy and his Pa," and the story below recounts some of the most mirthful episodes in the career of that incorrigible youth.*

A BAD BOY BEGINS HIS DIARY

I WAS ate years ole yesterday, an' mamma she says to me : " Georgie, wot would you like for a burthday present ? " So I said a " diry," cause all my growed-up sisters keep a diry, an' I thought it would be about the figger. So mamma she got me one. I wanted to begin it all rite, so I stole up to Lily's room, to copy suthin out o' hern ; but she keeps it locked up in her writing-desk, an' I had a offal time getting a key that would fit. At last I found one, an' set down when Lil was out a calling, an' coppied oph a page good as I could.

I've got three sisters what all kepes their dirys an' writes into 'em every night after their hair is took oph an' put in the buro drawer, 'xcept what is put in crimps. So to-nite Mister Wilyem Smith he come to see Lil, like he does most every evening, a big, ugly ole bashlor that my sisters makes fun of behind his back, an' I was in the parlor with my diry in my hand an' he ast me wot I got, an' give me sum candy, an' I showed him my diry, an' he red this out loud to Lil and Bess, which was in the room all fixed up to fits :

" I wish that stupid ole Bill Smith would keep hisself to home. He came agen Sunday night. I never, never, never, never shall like him one bit, but mother says he's wrich an' I must accept him if he offers. Oh, how crewel it is to make me practis such dooplicity ! It seems as if my heart would brake. What awful grate big red hands he's got an' can't talk about nothin' but how many houses he owns, an' his cravats is in retched taste. I wish he'd stay away an' done with it. He tride to kiss me when he was goin' Sunday night, but I'd just as soon have a lobster kiss me. Oh ! he is so different from my sweet, sweet Montague De Jones. Wot a pity Montague is a poor clerk ! I can not bare this misery much longer. Montague

567

is jellus an' reproaches me bitterly. Oh, wot a fraud this life is ! I'm wery of it."

Lil she was a screechin' an' a-tryin' to snatch it all the time, but Mr. Smith he held it up high, an' red it all ; then he sed to me wot made you rite such stuff ? I sed it wasn't stuff — I got it out of my sister Lily's diry, an' I gess she knew enuff to keep one, an' he took his hat an' went, and Bess she sez to me :
" Now you've done it, George Hackett ! "
Lil made a grab at me, but I dodged an' run.

I never see such a boy as I am fur gettin' into scrapes. The hull family is down on me, an' say I've spiled the match an' lost 'em a hundred thousand dollars, but I can't see how I am to blame for jest takin' a few lines out of Lily's diry.

One thing is sure—the rest o' this book will be my own composishun good or bad. I'm disgusted with the fool-stuff in them girls' dirys.

There was such a row to home 'bout it to-day I didn't seem to want any dinner, so I went fishing. It wasn't cloudy, so they wouldn't bite. A man came along an' he sez :
" Got any bites, sonny ? "
I wish folks wouldn't call me sonny—it makes me mad ; so I hollered :
" Confound the fish ! "
And he sez :
" Wot a wicked boy ! "
And I sez :
" Not a tall, the fish is in the dam."
And he scratched his head and went on. Just then suthin' bit, an' I leaned over too far an' fell in. You oughter seen me go over that dam an' shoot into the mill an' go right over the wheel, but it wa'n't until after I got into the shute that I thought I guess they'd be sorry, now they'd never have Georgie to scold no more. I don't know what I thunk wen they got me out, coz I was drowned dead as a door-nale ; but they rolled me on a barel, an' blowed into my inside with a bellows, an' I come to an' ast 'em if they'd saved my fishpole.

I don't know wot made my mama cry wen they brought me home, coz I was all right then, an' I told her so. I was awful glad I fell in, coz they got over bein' mad at me. Lil made me some real good toast an' tea, an' 'bout dark they all went down to supper an' left me rapped up in blankets that I thought I should smother, so I got up an' put on my best sute—my other one was getting dry. I betted they'd scold me for gettin' up, an' I crawled down into the parlor, an' got behind the curtains of the bay winder. I was that tired I fell asleep, an' wen I woken up I heard voices, an' I made out 'twas Susan an' her bow a settin' together on the sofy. Bess she was ratling away at the peano t'other end o' the room. Lil was upstairs, 'cause she knew Mr. Wilyem Smith wouldn't come no more.

"We'll haf to wate," says he, " at leste a year. Old Dockter Bradley wants a younger man to do the ridin', an' he's promised to take me in as pardner this fall. Can you wate for me, my darlin' ? You'll haf to haf lots of pashunts," sez he.

"And so will you," says Sue, and then they laughed.

"We'd better kepe it a profound secret for the present," sez he.

"Yes," sez she, " of course. It's the best policy to kepe long engadgements secret, suthin' mite happen, you know."

And then she jumped up as if she was shot, and run acrost the room, an' set down in a chair jist in time, for some folks come in, and then some more. Everybody wanted to know how poor little Georgie was, an' then mama came in an' said I'd run away—she was awful 'fraid I was dellerious out of my head, my brane might be effected. So I jest gave them curtins a whop, an' jumped right out as if I was a playin' leapfrog, an' the way they hollered would a made you laught.

"Oh, Georgie, Georgie !" groaned poor mama, " you'll be the deth of me, I know you will."

"Were you in the bay-winder all the time ?" ast Sue, a turnin' red an' pale.

"You bet," sez I, an' than I wunk at her an' wunk at him. " I knowed honesty was the best pollicy," I begun ; " but wot makes it the best pollicy not to let on when your engaged, lik you was a talkin' about ?" Then Sue she yerked me out o' the room, an' jis as we got to the door I hollered : " Let go my arm ! I'll go without bein' grabbed. Say Sue, I wonder wot made you hop off the sofy when those folks rung the bell : did Dockter Moore——"

But she put her hand right over my mouth and slammed the door.

"I have as good a mind as ever I had to eat to whip you, Georgie !" she sez, beginning to cry. " You have let the cat out of the bag, you horrid, horrid boy ! "

"Wot cat ?" ast I.

"Docktor Moore will never forgive you," sobbin' as if she'd dropped her only stick o' candy in the well. " We didn't want a sole to dreme of it for the next six months."

"Ime sorry I did it, sis," sez I. " I'll never do it agane if you'll stop blubberin'. What did I do, anyhow? If I'd a knowed he was so easy fritened I wouldn't a jumped out so sudden for the world. I wouldn't marry a feller wots so 'fraid o' things. He might get scart into a fit some time if he saw a white sheet on the close-line in the night. I don't believe in gosts, do you?"

By that mamma she came an' took me up to bed agane, an' tole Betty, the chamber-made, to stay by me till I fell aslepe, an' I got Betty to write this in my diry for me, 'cause I felt so tired and sleepy. Betty's bow's got red hair and a crost eye. I peked through the ary winder onest, and sene him kepe one eye on the cook—that's ill-tempered as she can be—an' one on Betty, an' I wished I had crost eyes, so I could keep one on my book, an' one on Tommy Fuller wen he puts pins in the schollars' seats. Crost eyes would be the convinyuenest things fur boys that have to go to school. Betty yawns like the top of her head would fall off. So I must close.

II

I'VE been 2 sick too write in my diry for most a week. It was gettin' drownded made me ill, an' gettin' out o' bed when I was swetty. Docktor Moore he's been up to see me twist a day. He's been so good to me I'm sorry I fritened him that night. I herd Bess tell Lily this morning she was glad I was sick, 'cause there was some piece in the house now; she hoped I'd stay in bed a month. I wonder wot girls don't like their little brothers for. I'm sure I'm real good to Bess. I go to the post-offis fur her twist a day when I am well. I never lost moren three letters for her. Golly! ain't I glad she don't know 'bout them!

This afternoon I felt so much better I wanted to get up, so when I heard Betty comin' with my supper, I slipped out o' bed an' hid behind the door. I had mamma's shawl around me, an' I jumpted out as she come in, an' barked as like I was a big black dog, an' that careless creture just dropped the server on the floor. Such a mess; the china bowl was broke, the beef-tea spilt on the carpet, an' the hull family rushed up-stairs to hear her scream as if the house was on fire. I didn't know Betty was such a goose. They all blamed me—they always do. I believe when I get well I'll run away, an' be a buf'lo bill, or jine a ship. There never was a boy got such tretement—so unjust.

To-day I was let sit up, tucked up in a quilt in a armchare. I soon got tired o' that, so I ast Betty to get me a glass o' ice-water to squench my thirst, an' when she was gone I cut an' run, an' went into Susan's room to look at all them fotografs of nice young men she's got there in a drawer.

The girls was all down in the parlor, 'cos Miss Watson had come to call. Betty she came a huntin' me, but I hid in the closet behind a ole hoop-skirt. I come out when she went away, an' had a real good time. Some o' them fotografs was written on the back, like this : " Conseated fop ! " " Oh, ain't he sweet ? " " He ast me, but I wouldn't have him." " A perfect darling ! " " What a mouth ! " " Portrait of a donkey ! "

I kep about two dozen o' them I know, to have some fun when I got well. I shut the door so Sue wouldn't notice they was took. I felt as if I could not bare to go to that nasty room, I was so tired of it, an' I thought I'd pass my time a playing I was a young lady. So I put on Sue's old bustle, and a pettycoat with a long tale to it, and Sue's blue silk dress, only it wouldn't be big enuff about the waste. I found a lot o' little curls in the buro, wich I stuck on all around my forehead with a bottle of mewsiledge, and than I seen some red stuff on a sawcer, wich I rubbed onto my cheaks. When I was all fixed up I slid down the bannisters plump againste Miss Watson, wot was sayin' good-by to my sisters. Such a hollerin' as they made.

" My best blue silk, you little imp ! " said Sue.

Miss Watson she turned me to the light, an' sez she, as sweet as pie : " Where did you get them pretty red cheeks, Georgie ? "

Susan she made a sign, but I didn't know it.

" I found some red stuff in Sue's drawer," sez I, and she smiled kind o' hateful, and said :

" Oh ! "

My sister says she is an awful gossip, wich will tell all over town that they paint, wich they don't, 'cause that sawcer was gust to make roses on card-bord, wich is all right.

I stepped on the front of Sue's dress goin' up stares agen, an' tore the front bredth acrost.

She was so mad she boxed my ears.

" Aha, missy ! " sez I to myself, " you don't guess about them fotografs wot I took out o' your drawer ! "

Some folks thinks little boys' ears are made on purpose to be boxed—my sisters do. If they knew wot dark an' desperate thoughts come into little boys' minds, they'd be more careful— it riles 'em up like poking sticks into a mud puddle.

I laid low—but beware to-morrow !

They let me come down to brekfast this mornin'.

I've got those pictures all in my pockets, you bet your life.

"Wot makes your pockets stick out so?" ast Lily, when I was a waiting a chance to slip out unbeknone.

"Oh, things," sez I, an' she laughed.

"I thought mebbe you'd got your books and cloathes packed up in 'em," sez she, "to run away an' be a Injun warryor."

I didn't let on anything, but ansered her :

"I guess I'll go out in the back-yard an' play a spell."

Well, I got off down town, an' had a lot of fun. I called on all the aboriginals of them fotografs.

"Hello, Georgie ! Well agen?" said the first feller I stopped to see.

Oh, my ! when I get big enuff I'll hope my mustaches won't be waxed like his'n ! He's in a store, an' I got him to give me a nice cravat, an' he ast me "Was my sisters well?" so I fished out his fotograf, and gave it to him.

It was the one that had "Conseated Fop !" writ on the back. The girls had drawed his musttaches out twict as long with a pencil, an' made him smile all acrost his face. He got as red as fire, an' then he skowled at me.

"Who did that, you little rascal?"

"I guess the spirits did it," I said, as onest as a owl, an' I went away quick cause he looked as mad as thunder.

The nex plaice I come to was a grocery store, where a nuther young man lived. He had red hair an' freckles, but he seemed to think hisself a beauty. I said :

"Hello, Peters !"

He said :

"The same yourself, Master George. Do you like raisins? Help yourself."

Boys wot has three pretty sisters allers does get treted well, I notiss. I took a big handful of raisins an' a few peanuts, an' sot on the counter eating 'em, till all at oncest, as if I jest thought of it, I took out his fotograf an' squinted at it, an' sez :

"I do declare, it looks like you."

"Let me see it," sez he.

I wouldn't for a long time, then I gave it to him. The girls had made freckles all over it. This was the one they wrote on its back, "He asked me, but I wouldn't have him." They'd painted his hair as red as a rooster's comb. He got quite pale when he seen it clost.

"It's a burning shame," sez I, "for them young ladies to make fun o' their bows."

"Clear out," says Peters.

I grabbed a nuther bunch o' raisins an' quietly disappeared. I tell you he was rathy.

Mister Courtenay he was a lawyer, he's got a offis on the square by the cort-house. I knew him very well, 'cause he comes to our house often. He's a awful queer-lookin' chap, an' so stuck up you'd think he was tryin' to see if the moon was made o' green cheese, like folks sez it is, the way he keeps it in the air. He's got a depe, depe voice way down in his boots. My harte beat when I got in there, I was that fritened ; but I was bound to see the fun out, so I ast him :

" Is the What is It on exabishun to-day ? "

" Wot do you mean ? " sez he, a lookin' down on me.

" Sue said if I would come to Mister Courtenay's offis I would see wot this is the picture of," sez I, giving him his own fotograf inskibed, " The Wonderful What is It."

It's awful funny to see their faces wen they look at their own cards.

In about a minit he up with his foot wich I doged just in time. I herd him muttering suthin' 'bout " suing for scandal." I think myself I oughter arrest her for salt an' battery, boxing my ears. I wishst he would sue Sue, 'twould serve her right.

I'll not get to bed fore midnight if I write enny more. I'm yawning now like a dying fish. So farewell my diry till the next time. I give them cards all back fore dinner-time. There'll be a row I expect. I've laughed myself almost to fits a thinkin' of the feller wot I give " The Portrait of a Donkey " to. He looked so cress fallen. I do believe he cried. They were teazin' ma to let 'em give a party next week wen I got home to dinner. I don't believe one of them young gentlemen will come to it ; the girls have give 'em all away. I don't care wuth a cent. Wot for so they take such libertys with my ears if they want me to be good to 'em.

P.S.—I bet their left ears are burning wass'n ever mine did !

III

O DERE ! Oh, dere ! Wot a world this is ! Little boys are born to trouble as the sparks are to fly upwards. It's over a week sence I've had the harte to rite one word in my diry. Poor diry ! the reckord of a braking harte, I come to the for consultashun ! On this paige will I describe my wose. It hurts me yet to sit down square on my sete, but I will tri to bare it for thi sake.

It all dates from the day I carrid the fellers back their fotografs. As I said, the girls they tezed ma to give 'em a party, wich she promised, so they was in hi fether, an' begun to rite out the list of those they meant to ast, that afternoon. They wur all three as bizy as bees, an' I was bean good, settin' on a chare, a listenin' quietly, coz I was tired, when the bell wrung, an' who do you s'pose it proofed to be but our Aunt Betsey, she that lives to Hoppertown an' comes to see us twicst a yere. My sisters was put out, 'cause they gnu she'd stay a week, an' be here to the party. Lily made a rye face when she herd it.

"Nasty ole thing!" sez she, "she alwis comes at the most unconvynyant times."

"She'll be sure to stay," says Bess, "if she heres about it, and she'l ware that old green silk o' hern, with a yellow heddress, and them lile thred gloves."

"She'll mortify us awfully," sez Sue.

I b'leve Aunt Betsey is wrich, but she's that old-fashuned you'd think she come out o' the ark, with the animals, too an' too, only Aunt Betsey must a come alone, 'cause she is a ole made.

So when I herd 'em say they hoped she wouldn't stay to the party, I hoped she wouldn't too. To tell the truth, I had a gilty conshuns 'bout those fotografs wich I had done for spite. Oh, it is drefful to hav a gilty conshuns, it ways like lead. I wisht I hadn't done it, but thare's no use cryin' for spilt milk, so I resolved I'd do suthin' for my sisters to make up.

When tea was over, I got Aunt Betsey by herself into the hall, and said to her:

"Wood you like to make my sisters happy?"

"What do you mean?" sez she.

"'Cause if you would," sez I, "please go away before the party. They don't want you here that night. I herd 'em say so. Don't let on I tole you, Aunt Betsey, but jus' go home quiet the day before nex' Thursday, an' I'll be obliged to you as ever was."

I don't think it was well-bred o' her to get angry when I spoke to her so polite, do you? It was rele mene to go an' tell when I ast her not to speke about it wich she did so quick as ever she could, an' the nex' morning she up an' went away, sayin' she'd never, never, never, visit us agane.

But that ain't all. It seems my papa had borroed a lot o' money frum her, 'cause the times is hard; she twitted him with that, an' givin' partis on borroed capital. Of coarse the rath of all fell on one poor little ait yere old boy. Suthin' else fell two. I'll not disgrace the, my diry, by sayin' wot—it is enuff to ad they spoiled the child, altho they did not spare the rod. Betty pitied me, an' maid me a rele soft quishion out of a ole pillo. I ain't gone out fur fear the boys would notis thare was suthin' rong ; time passes awful slow. I do not think Ide care to be a Alexander Selkirk. When I grow up an' have a little boy I will not trete him so. I will not punish him fur wot he didn't mean to do, but fede him on spunge-cake three times a day, nor let his older sisters speke to him that rude as if he was a monstir.

All this time my mind was never esy about them photografs. I 'xpected evry hour the cat would be let out the bag wot I had done. Day after day passed by ; the nite of the party came at last. Betty drest me in my best sute, tide on my new cravat, an' put lots o' sent on my hankercher, my sisters lecktured me for half an hour on how to behave at parties or I'd be sent to bed, an' I was aloud to come in the parlor. The house was all lit up, there was bokase everywhere, a man come to play the peano. My mouth wotered to think o' the is-cream an' cake, the orranges an' gelly, the chickun salid, an' the sandwiches wich was in the dinin'-room. The girls looked awful hansome dressed in white, their crimping-pins took out, their eyes brite, flowers in their hair.

The company began to arrive. All the fashionable yung ladys of the villedge wot moved in our set come—the clock struck nine—the only gentleman present was Docktor Moore, the one that's goin' to marry Sue. My sisters began to look trubbled. I was a shaking in my shoes.

The feller at the peany plaid an' plaid. Some of the girls took hold of one anuther an' woltzed around, but they did not seme to enjoy it much. Half-pas nine struck on the clock ! ! !

Oh, how my gilty conshuns wade me down ! I said to myself :

" The trane is lade, the slo-match is applide, now for the jeneral burst-up ! "

The gests bgan to whisper, the girls looked like they would sink thru a augur-hole. Then the bell wrung real loud ; everybuddy brightened up, but it was only Betty brought a card in an' handed it to my sisters. They turned all colors when they seed wot it was. It wasn't " regrets " at all—only a fotograf wich they had writ an' wich used to be in their drawer of their desk. The bell wrung agane—another foto ! Phancy the seen !

That bell wrung twenty times, and every time it was anuther, and anuther, and anuther.

At last two yung men arrived. I knu in a minit how they

happened to come. On their cards was writ : " Oh, you darling felloe ! " an' " Too bright, too butiful to last ! " wich was clerk in a shoe store, but he didn't see the pun.

They got up a set o' lancers, with three gentlemen an' five ladies. Miss Hopkins she giggled a good 'eel of the time ; my sisters most cried. The supper was tip top, but I knu the party was a fizzle. I felt so uneasy I had to give up on my fifth sawcer of ice-cream.

" If I knu who did it," I herd Sue tellin' the doctor, " I'd shoot him ; yes, I would ! A mene, dastardly, practical goke. I hate such gokes ! They're mad at us now. We can never make it up. We'll have to move to some other town to live. I shall never dare to show my face on the strete agane. I wish I could find out who did it ! "

" P'raps George can give you some information," sez the docktor, lookin' me strate in the eye.

" Oh, no ! " sez I, " lest it was Towser. I give him some o' them fotografs to chew on, an' he may a droped 'em on the strete."

" Then you had them ? " sez she, quite awful like.

The cat was out o' the bag. I slipped away an' went to bed. I didn't want to be around when the folks went away. I lay and thunk, and thunk, a long time. I knew I was in for another whipping. I have not yet rekuvered from the effecks o' the tother one. It seemed to me I could not bare the trials wich morning had in store for me. I couldn't sleep a wink. I was detyrmined to run away. There was Aunt Betsey, it was only fifty miles by rale to her house. Ide bin thare oncet. I had two dollars in my bank. The moon was shinin' brite as day. I got up and drest myself, took my bank, krept down stairs as still as a mouse, unlocked the front door and stept out.

I run as fast I could lick it to the depo. It was getting daybrake. A frate train stood on the switch blowing off steme. I wotched my chance, an' krept into a car which was empty.

Pritty soon the bell rung—we wuz off !

" Farewell, my friends," sez I. " You won't be bothered with that bad boy no more. He's goin' to lye lo till the storm blows over."

After that the moshun of the cars made me sleepy, so I thought Ide take a little knap, wich I'll tell you to-morro how I woke up.

" Who's this ? " said a gruff voice.

" It's me, little Georgie, sir," sez I. " I'm, willing to pay my fare. Here's my bank with two dollars in it ; take out what you want."

" How did you get here ? " ast he.

" I run away from home, coz I'm allus in mischief, sir. I was goin' to be whipped for given the young gentlemen fotografs back to 'em which my sisters had written on. Are you the breakman ? "

" You bet ! " sez he, laffing. " Where do you want to stop off ? "

" Hoppertown," sez I, " and I guess I'll stay there till I'm grown up, cause if I don't my sisters'll all die old mades."

IV

I BROKE of ruther abruply las' night 'cause a mouse come out of a hole in my bedroom, so I tride to catch it. I broke my wash-bole throing my shoe at it, but I didn't get the mouse.

Well, the breaksman an' I we had a reel good talk. I tole him 'bout my sisters, an' Aunt Betsey, an' everything. He was sory for me ; he wouldn't take money for my fare ; he said, wen he was my age he used to be whipt evry night reglar, an' I must get use to it and not mind it. " The frog gets used to bein' skinned," sez he, " but don't brake off your sister's matches agane if you can help it, for beaus is scarce this year ; the war in Europe has maid a corner in the market."

Ile love that breaksman till my dyin' day, he was so good to me.

It was about nine a.m. wen we got to the plaice where I was to get off, so we shook hans and said good-by, like we was ole frens. I b'lieve I'll give up bein' a Buflo Bill, and be a breakman wen I gro up. Such a jolly life ! You can ride for nothing all you want to.

Thare were some boys around the depot wich was surprised to see me alite from a frate car. They introduced theirselves, so I thought Ide stop an' play a spell afore I let Aunt Betsy kno Ide come to live with her.

They proofed to be vary wicked, bad boys, wich had no bringing up. They stole my bank, an' tored my new jacket, an' thru mud that I wasn't fit to be seen. I thought wot it said in one o' my books—" Beware of strange dogs."

It was noon when I got to Aunt Betsys. I diden't reelize I was hungry till I smelt those punken pies. She was eating dinner all by herself wen I come in.

" Mersy sakes alive ! George Hackett ! " she screemed lettin' her knife drop on her plate so hard it broke a peace out of the edge. " Whare *did* you come from ? Wot's happened

to your close? Who skratched your face? If I ain't
beat!"

"Aunt Betsy," sez I, "I never told a lie. I've run away."

"Run away!—run away from your buchiful home, your
good papa, your dere mamma, your lovin' sis——"

Thare she stopped as if she'd bin chopped off an' kinder
choked. You sea she rekolected 'bout how they didn't want
her to the party.

"I don't wunder," she ads, "those girls were enuff to
drive ennybuddy a way. Tell me all about it, my poor child."

I explained the hole affare to her. I showed her my bleeding
scars, because Ide made her mad when she was to our house.

Wen I confesed about the fotografs her eyes sparkled, she
was so pleased to think my sisters were in a scrape.

"'Twant rite for you to do that, George," sez she, "but
boys will be boys. Ime glad you cum to me. Go rite in the
kitchen an' wash an' hurry back to dinner fore the chickun gets
cold."

"Will you promise, aunt, not to let 'em kno where I am?"

"If they don't find out till I tell 'em," she sorter snapped,
"you'll stay with me till your groan up."

You sea she had a spite 'ganst our folks 'cause I tole her
they don't want her to stay to the party. She stuffed me that
I couldn't hold no more, I had to leive my third slice o' punken
pie, an' mended my jacket, an' was as good to me as ever was.

Long 'bout four o'clock thare came a telegram from papa:

"Is Georgie thare?"

Aunt telegraffed back:

"What do you mene?"

So of coarse they thought I wasn't.

I forgot to say I brought my diry tide up in a handkerchief
with a clene shirt an' a pare of stockings.

It was Aunt Betsy's wash-bole wich I broke a tryin' to hit
the mouse. It was funny ole blue china—the wash bole not
the mouse—an' aunt felt awful bad. I was afrade she'd send
me home.

I've been here two days now, she kepes me jus to spite my
folks, but O! she makes me wurk like a perfeck slave. I'm
gettin' wery of it. I've had to pick up chips an' even string
benes—a perfeck shame! Cook duz such things at home. She
will not let me play with other boys. Twict I've stolen down to
the depo to look fur my breaksman to take me back. He'll do
it, I am sure. Home-sickness is a fearful thing.

Fore wery, wery days an' nites. How slo time crepes, at

It was Aunt Betsy's washbole which I broke a tryin' to hit the mouse

a snale's pace. Ime desperut, no money, no friends, the breaksman I can never get a chance to sea. To-day I had to pick
twelfe quarts of hukkle berrys, a deggeradation my proud spirut
does not freeze to. Oh ! could I sea my childhood's home
onest more Ide be a moddul boy. Vane are these sad reflec-
shuns ! Stay ! hold on ! I have a thought ! I will not rite
in my diry 'cause I believe Aunt Betsey reads it in my absunce.

Oh, happy boy ! at home onct more ! Teres blind my
eyes wen I think of the seen wen my father brought me home
in triumph ; my mother's sobs, my sisters' kisses, even cook was
blubberin', and Betty's apurn to her eyes. The hull town has
made that fuss over me you'd think I was poor Charley Ross.
Thare was a grate crowd to the depo to meet me ; such a time !
Papa's so angry with my aunt he never spoke to her wen he
come to take me home, 'cause everybuddy said I must be dead
or stolen. The way I got the money to telegraph was this—she
sent me to pick huckel berrys to dry, but I sold 'em an' went to
the depot, and telegrafed.

" Ime at Aunt Bettsy's—plese, plese come and take me home.
Your son, George."

My sisters are awful nice girls. I never, never will do
anything to teaze 'em long as I live. I am furmly resolfed to
take the Father of his Country for my moddul, an' gro up to be
grate an' good.

EDEN PHILLPOTTS (1862–   ), *who was born in India, was a clerk in an Insurance Office for ten years and studied for the stage before finally settling down to a literary career. Between the covers of his books and in his plays he has gathered many convincing characters from the Devon countryside. "The Matchmaker" is a tale of life in a village where private affairs are soon common property.*

THE MATCHMAKER

I BAN'T the sort to offer my opinion till 'tis axed for, an' anybody in this village will tell you the same. A very cautious old woman, an' well I may be, for I've seen an' felt the rough edge of life more'm most people, an' I've met with an amazin' scant share of gratitude for all my well-doing. An' yet, to say it without pride, there's a good few scattered up an' down 'pon Dartymoor as never knowed their happiness till they met me.

Old George Pearn put the case in a nutshell last time he axed me to marry him.

"No," he said, "though you never had no use for holy matrimony yourself, 'tis something wonnerful the folk you've led into it."

"'Tis true," I said, "an', what's more, nine out of ten of 'em bless the day."

"No doubt," he answered me, "an' I wish to God as you'd taste it yourself, for 'tis a cruel thing to see a comely woman like you—as don't look an hour more'n sixty still—biding here all alone wi'out a man."

But George Pearn was a creature of habit, if you understand me, an' one of his habits was to ax me to marry him every autumn. He'd done it since he was a widower, an' that was fifteen years before the matter of young Will Heathman an' Susan Crocker.

I often wondered what George Pearn would have said if I'd up an' taken him. No doubt he'd have felt much surprised an' annoyed about it. But he owed me a something, no doubt, for I married his darter—a very vinegary piece of goods, as weren't for many markets, an' was up home forty year old afore I found the right party for her. A dustman he was, hard of hearing, an' short of an eye—in fact, made for her, you might say. For she

had the pleasure of talking, which was to her what spirits is to
many a female ; an' he had the blessing of not hearing ; so they
never had no trouble to name, an' often said 'twas a good day's
work when they comed to drink tea with me one Lord's Day
an' went to chapel together after.

There was Luke Westley too, an' poor Matthew Yelland as
got killed in the river, an' many others I could tell you about ;
an', to be fair, I might also name that anointed ruffian Joshua
Pike, who knocked his wife's head-bones in, an' would have
knocked in mine if he'd met me that afternoon. He *could* hear ;
an' poor Sarah looked to it that he did hear. But the ugly
truth, morning, noon an' night for five years, got on his nerves
at last ; an' he laid her out wi' a coal-hammer, as many a
nagging woman have been laid out afore her. I could also
mention another man here an' there who had no luck with his
wife ; but 'tis better not to name names.

Though an old maid myself, there ban't much about the men
folk I don't know ; an' having a score of nephews an' nieces,
I'm also pretty well versed in childer an' their ways. In fact,
as Mr. Pearn puts it in his free fashion, I'm a mother in all but
the name an' the pangs. Not that childern like me. To be
candid, they never do. I was asking my sister-in-law the reason
—she being a twin-bearer an' a milky, cow-like soul as dotes
on every babby that comes into Belstone, an' can't keep her
hands off 'em. To see her turn down the flannel off a new-born
babe's face wi' her little fat white hands ! Looks a'most as if
she could eat 'em—goes silly, like a mother cat wi' chets.
But in answer to me she merely said I was too sharp at the
joints.

" 'Tis like running against the edge of the furniture for the
little dears to come to you, Tibby," she said ; an' I couldn't be
vexed wi' her, for there was truth in it. Between me an' her
it's the difference of a scrag o' mutton an' a suet dumpling.

Well, about Will an' Susan. " 'Twas his mother axed me to
have a dish o' tea along wi' her one afternoon ; an' her being a
widow an' well thought upon, an' butt-woman to the church,
I went, knowing of course she wanted something out of me.
Which, sure enough, she did.

" Miss Minifie," she said, " you know my son."

" Him as works to Mr. Arscott's quarry ? " I answered.
An' I pursed up my lips a thought, no doubt.

" I see you do," said the man's poor mother. " His failings
ban't a clever subject for the spinster ear, I allow ; but all the
same, it's not like talking to a girl—you with all your ripe

wisdom an' with your great power at getting people into a marrying spirit."

"Mary Heathman," I answered her, "if you want me to interest myself in William, say so. I know what he is : you can't shock me. His ways are pretty generally understood, for that matter."

"Marriage might be the salvation of him."

"Well, if what they tell be true, he's about it."

"That's what's turning my hair grey," she said, an' in her trouble the bread fell off her fork on the fire an' was spoiled.

"Get them slices toasted first an' tell about William after," I advised her. "You can't do two things at once."

So she minded the tea, an' when we was at it, an' I'd poured my third cup in the saucer, I said :

"You don't want him to marry that girl, Jane Ball ? "

"No, I do not. What mother would ? " she asked. "A touzled, slammocking thing, as spends half her time afore the looking-glass an' t'other half wasting money in Okehampton. Always in other people's shops when she did ought to be behind the counter in her father's."

"She'm too pretty for a working chap's wife," I told Mrs. Heathman.

"That sort trusts to their faces to fetch 'em husbands ; but a beautiful face don't take the place of a well-cooked dinner longer than the honeymoon. How many pretty girls can cook ? "

Of course Mrs. Heathman couldn't think of one.

"If there's to be happiness for that female, she must marry a shopkeeper," I said—"a man of large ideas who'll even keep a servant for her."

"An' the Lord help him," said she, with feeling, "whoever he is."

She told a good deal more against Jane Ball, and I saw things was serious because she was so bitter. Then she named Susan Crocker, an' began to praise her in a way as would be fulsome for a heavenly angel. All the same, I knowed Susie was a very nice young woman, though sly. She belonged to the sort as goes their own way an' keep their mouths shut—a very great art, and commoner among women than men think. Susan was in service to the vicarage. She sang in the choir Sundays an' had her followers ; but they was chaps from Zeal an' Sourton— not Belstone. I knowed all about 'em.

"There's a good few after her," I told Mrs. Heathman, "but nothing's done. It might be brought about, no doubt."

"He'd come into the shadow of the vicarage then, an'

parson would very likely get hold of him," said the poor mother hopefully.

"It might be. I'll do what I can," I promised. Then I axed a question :

"How do they stand to one another ? "

"Very friendly indeed," she told me. If only you can shake him off that yellow-haired toad of a girl, Jane, 'tis just as likely he'll turn to Susan as not."

"Turn somewhere he certainly will," I said, "for he'm built of the sort of mud that can't go far without a woman to moon after."

"Like his father," said Mary Heathman. "My late husband had large ideas, an' would have turned a Turk for certain if he hadn't been a Christian and married to a watchful woman."

So we left it at that, an' I set to work the very next week by axing Mrs. Heathman an' her son to come in an' see some photographs of foreign parts as I'd had from a sailor nephew. An' I got Susan Crocker too, though I had to make a favour of it. Girls was shy of me owing to my reputation. Not but what a homely maiden or two have comed to me on the quiet before now for the very same reason. But never a penny did I make in my life by it, except the five-pound note Saul Barkell left me sarcastic in his will, for shortening his miserable life by marrying him to Charity Grepe, an' making him cease to have any fear of death, but a great longing to go instead. He didn't mean it kindly ; but five pound is five pound, whether 'tis left in a proper or an improper spirit ; an' 'twas as useful as any other five I've ever come by.

Mary Heathman arrived first, an' said that William was on the way. Presently in comed my gentleman, strolling along as if time was eternity. He'd got his Sunday black on, an' must needs begin playing my harmonium, which not a hand had touched for years, being a gift to me when Mrs. Morris died and having no knowledge of it myself.

"Don't you do that, Will," I said, "for 'tis a kicklish thing an' rough fingers may put the works out of order."

"They be out of order," he said. " 'Tis more like a roaring hoss than a musical instrument."

With that he played " Rock of Ages," an' the bellows broke, an' it ended in a cloud of dust an' a noise like a pig being sticked.

I was vexed about it through remembering poor Mrs. Morris, as had thought the world of it ; but in justice to the young man, he weren't to blame, for we found that 'twas a hot-bed of vermin and the wood bored through an' through by worms.

19*

We was clearing up, an' Will had just offered to get a wheelbarrow an' carry the thing out 'pon the village dustheap, when Susan Crocker arrived in all her Sunday finery—a black-eyed girl with very little to say to company, but no difficulty when alone with one of the male sex. Red she wore—brick-colour with a touch of yellow an' some wonnerful imitation cherries in her hat you could most have eaten, being the very daps of real ones. A neat-built girl, as put me in mind of myself at her age.

I set 'em down together an' gived 'em my nephew's roll of photographs, an' kept the tail of my eye on 'em while I talked to Mary Heathman.

Nought happed for a long while ; then Will set up a great laugh an' 'peared to be much amused—why for I couldn't think, because though pictures of palm trees an' the heathen an such like be very instructive to home-dwellers, there'd naught to raise a laugh in 'em.

" What's the fun ? " I asks William, and he says :

" This here photograph of your nephew, Sam Minifie, miss."

" There ain't no photograph of Sam among 'em," I answered.

" Oh yes, there is," he said. " I mind Sam very well. We was friends afore he runned away to sea. Put on your glasses an' have a look."

I marked that Susie Crocker had gone a trifle red, though I thought 'twas only along of so much laughing.

Well, there was a picture, sure enough, that I had missed altogether, owing to it having got stuck to another of a missionary church, though a very different subject. 'Twas my favourite nephew, my own brother's boy, sitting between two ink-black females wi' an arm around each of their waists ! All three was grinning an' showing enough teeth to set up a dentist's shop.

" Do make me wish I was a sailor-man myself," said that 'dashus Will Heathman.

For my part I felt the blood of shame burn my cheek, and I gasped.

" He never meant to send that," I said. " It got stuck to the missionary picture—an' time there was missionaries there by the look of it ! "

With that I tore the disgraceful thing in half an' put it on the fire.

" All the same, it do make me wish to go for a sailor," said that dissolute young youth.

An' then Susie spoke—in her sly, dreamy way, as if she was only thinking to herself out aloud :

" I suppose English girls have got waists too, if it comes to that."

An' her from the vicarage !

Of course 'twas the man who answered.

" Yes, they have," he said, " but you can't put your arms around two of 'em to once. That's the beauty of the tropics seemingly."

An' then I changed the conversation.

In five or six minutes the tea ended, for I'd forgotten the young man's appetite, an' the crumpets was gone afore me an' his mother had settled to the table.

'Twas my plan to let him an' Mrs. Heathman take their leave first. Then I had a talk with Susan, an' found her to be a very sensible girl an' not flighty at heart. In fact, she knowed which side her bread was buttered very well and wanted to be married as soon as might be.

I said :

" Have you ever thought of Will Heathman ? "

An' she said :

" Just as often as he've thought of me."

And I asked how often that might be ; and she said :

" Not once."

Then I beginned my work an' told her that in my judgment he was the right sort an' a good wage-earner, an' only wanted a sensible wife to find himself foreman at Arscott's quarry and a rising man.

An' she said :

" There's others, however."

" If you mean they Zeal fellows," I answered, " an' especially Maddaford or Charlie Cousins, you'll be wise to think twice. It don't do for Belstone girls to marry foreigners, as I've always said."

" Charlie Cousins be getting three-an'-twenty shillings a week, whether or no," she answered. " I've not heard that Heathman makes more'n a pound."

But I explained how Charlie, who was a gardener, might lose his job or have to take less any day, especially as his master, a retired Army gentleman, was known to be saddled with a lot of grandchildren, owing to his only daughter's husband dying uninsured in India.

" He could get as good a job again," she said.

" Don't do nothing in a hurry, my dear," I told her ; an' then she went off.

I saw her twice after that, an' the man once. Him I met

alone coming up through the valley from Okehampton. He overtook me an' carried my parcels for me, as a young man should. But not till I'd axed him to do it. He was down in the mouth about the yellow-haired girl, Jane Ball, an' said 'twas a hell of a world, an' other violent, one-sided things. But I let him run on, an' agreed with him where I could, an' got in a few words about Susie Crocker.

"There's only one woman in the world for me, an' I'll make her father give her to me afore I've done," he said.

So that's how it stood at starting. Not a promising case exactly; but I'd had harder ones in my time, an' comed very well out of 'em. So, like the old fool I was, I went on with it.

A lot of thought I gave to the subject, but somehow there weren't any getting forwarder with 'em. He was always growling about Jane Ball, an' even went so far as to fight a man outside the White Hart Inn because the man said as Jane's teeth had begun life in another mouth. 'Twas an insult that Heathman couldn't put up with, an' he knocked the chap down (both being market-merry at the time) and left him in the kennel till his friends came an' took him home.

Jane got to hear about it, an' it warmed her heart to Heathman, so he seemed further off t'other girl than ever; an' I met Susie Crocker with her gardener twice on her evenings out. Altogether it looked as if they young people was going to have their own way against me.

I wish I'd taken it so and let 'em alone; but I'm the sort that hates to be bested, an' it seemed a silly thing for a couple scarcely counted twenty year apiece, to be cleverer than a woman of my years an' experience. So I took a rash step an' done what I'd done once afore in a similar case. It worked very well that time; an' I was hopeful it would again.

I spoke to the girl first when we comed out of church elbow to elbow one Sunday evening.

"Have'e seen anything of Will Heathman lately?" I axed.

"Only in the distance," she said.

"He's going out of his mind, I'm afeared," I said, "an' you'm the reason. No cause to shake your head. He'll make a hole in the river, my dear, an' the fault will be yours."

"Never!" cried Susan.

"'Tis so," I told her. "The least you can do is to hear him an' give him a little hope. If you'd but meet him part of the way—such a modest, hang-back soul as him."

"Hadn't heard he was that sort," she said.

" Well, let him see you, an' be gentle an' helpful. He's the very man for you. Meet him half way, I ax no more."

Luckily she'd had a bit of a tiff with Charlie Cousins at the time, and made no objection to meeting Will.

" Remember the goodness and the prospects of the man," I said ; an' the very same night I went to the Heathmans' an' telled a bit there, an' then axed Will to see me back-along to the village, because their cottage was down past the Old Rectory Farm, in a lonesome part half a mile an' more from Belstone.

Of course he comed, and I spoke about Susie Crocker.

" She'll do what she said, sure as death be death," I said, an' sighed very sorrowfully.

" An' what might that be ? " he axed.

" Make an end of herself, poor maiden," I answered him. But he shook his head.

" Only her cunning. She's after Charlie Cousins. She don't care a farden damn for me," he answered.

" Into the water she'll go for you," I told him, "an' as a man, it becomes you to save her life an' take her. There's a good wife going begging in her," I said. " She've got a lofty nature, an' cooks so well as a professed cook, an' regular at church as parson's self, an' saved a bit of money too."

" How much ? " he axed, waking up a trifle ; but I told him I didn't know.

He said naught for a while, and I heard afterwards that the day before he'd had a proper row with Jane because she catched him beside the river with one of the girls from the laundry.

" I don't want nobody to make away with herself on my account, God knows," said young Heathman. All the same, he looked rather pleased about it—such is the conceit of men.

" Take her," I said ; " a better wife no chap ever yet had. Propose, an' if she's too flustered to say ' yes,' *make* her say it."

" As to that, I must think upon it. Anyway I'll see the poor woman," he promised.

Then I left him. 'Twas a clear going from the truth and doing evil that good might come, no doubt. I didn't feel too easy about it, for I've got a conscience. But this same trick had worked so amazing well in the case of just such another pair of young people two years earlier, that I believed myself justified.

Not that I was happy. In fact, I had a fore-token of evil by a dream the very same night. An' inside a week the dream comed true. Nobody was ever punished for wrongdoing

quicker'n me. 'Twas a sorry come-along-o't for a woman of
my years, an' many a tear scalded my cheeks in secret after.

The tragedy falled out in a very coorious way indeed, for the
last thing likely was that I should hear with my own ears the
result of my bit o' work ; but I did. In fact, I sat within three
yards of them two souls when they comed together full of what
I'd told 'em ; an' though I've met with a deal of conversation
in my life an' listened to love talk, like any other woman, in my
springtime, never did I hear anything like Susan and William
a-telling upon Belstone Tor.

For there, on a day in late August, the thing comed to its
horrid conclusion. I was up-along wi' a party or two " hurting,"
as we call it ; that is, gathering the whortleberries that grow
abundant 'pon the west of they rocks. An' as I picked an'
picked, an' reckoned I'd made very near a shilling an' sixpence
by my work, who should I see passing along but young Heathman
an' Susie Crocker ? He was just away from the quarry, an' she
had evidently met him by appointment out 'pon the Moor.
They headed straight for me, an' first I thought as they'd actually
seed me an' was coming along for that reason. Then I went
aquatt, like a hare in her form, hoping as they'd pass wi'out
seeing me. But, instead, if they didn't pitch ten feet off on a
gert slab of granite ! I ought to have got up an' bade 'em good
evening an' gone on my way ; but I didn't. Curiosity never
dies in a woman. For my dear life I couldn't move. And, of
course, after I'd listened two minutes, 'twas too late. She
beginned it in her honey-soft voice :

" 'Twas kind of you to meet me, William."

" Not at all—very pleased, I'm sure," he said. " I'd do
anything for you—in reason."

" An' I for you—in reason—William."

" That's as it should be."

Then they hanged fire a lot, for each thought the other was
sore smitten, an' neither knowed exactly how to start.

" Of course there's as good fish in the sea as ever comed out
of it, you must know, Susan," said young William suddenly.

" I'm very glad 'tis so, and that you know it," she answered.
" Certainly there be—an' no maiden's so good but you can't find
a better."

" 'Tis hard when a chap—I mean when a girl—when
anybody, in fact—be very much set on any other body. 'Tis
dreadful hard—but still there's many quite as good men as me
in the world, Susan, an' many would make a better husband
than what I should."

Susie Crocker seemed a thought surprised at this. 'Twasn't what she expected from a man as meant to drown hisself for her.

For my part I was sorry that Will had taken that line. Something told me I'd failed.

" Not but what you're a very good man and would make any woman happy," said Susan cautiously.

" No, I wouldn't," he said. " You mustn't think that, Susan. You mustn't think I'm half the man you suppose. I'll be frank with you—for my peace of mind as well as yours. I never have looked much at dark women. I can't help it, but I never have. My nature don't yearn to 'em."

" An' 'tis a coorious thing, William," she said quick as lightning, " that I've always had a sort of bias against fair men. They don't fill my eye."

He started at that, being as smooth and sandy-headed a soul as ever waited and hoped against hope for a beard. He gave a sniff of wonder, and then another silence falled between them. For my part, I began to wish myself further. Then Will went off again :

" 'Tis strange, Susan, that being against a fair face, you feel so kind to me. But you must fight it, because if you have that feeling against my sort o' colour, you'd never be happy with me for long."

" My stars, you do astonish one ! " she burst out. " Why, my good man, do'e call this courting ? Who on earth would think now that you cared a brass farthing for me ? "

" You mustn't say that. I like you very well and I want to see you happy an' married."

" So I want to see myself."

" But, in sober honesty, Susie, you must try an' understand that I'm not the man for you. 'Twould be cruel kindness to pretend different."

" Since when did you find that out ? " she axed with a voice full o' wonder.

" It have always been my opinion," he answered.

" Well, in sober honesty—though, if I didn't know, I should think ' sober ' weren't the word—in sober honesty, I never thought you was the man."

" The dowl you didn't ! Then why for——? "

He broke off, an' though the day was warm, I went gooseflesh down the spine. 'Twas one of my failures, no doubt, an' I'd have given a golden sovereign to be ten mile off at that moment.

" Did the feeling against me come over your mind sudden ? " he axed her.

" I haven't got no feeling against you, Will. I'm just neither one way nor t'other toward you—except the general dislike of your pink and white."

" 'Tis just the same here ! As for being in love with you, Susie, to say it polite, I never was—not a twinkle. Jane Ball——" He stopped an' sighed, like a cow breathing.

" This is very wonnerful," she said. " I begin to see how things are. An' as a self-respecting woman, William, I must tell you that while I thought you a very nice young man, I never hankered after you as—as you seem to think."

" I didn't think it," he said, " I was told it."

The stones an' berry-bushes got dancing in my old eyes then. I felt my bones give under me, an' if I could have crawled in a rabbit-hole, I would have done so.

" An' me too," she answered him. " They said that if I didn't have you, you'd make a hole in the river ! "

" The things that happen ! " he cried.

" 'Twas Tibby Minifie told me."

" An' what d'you think she told me ? " he axed, an' answered himself in a breath. " She said you was dying for me, an' that if I didn't take you, you'd drown yourself without a doubt."

" Oh, the wickedness ! " cried Susie Crocker.

" She've over-reached herself this journey—bad old baggage. Ban't for nothing she'm called ' the matchmaker.' "

" 'Tis a great weight off my mind," the girl said.

" An' mine," he admitted. " We shouldn't have suited each other at all."

" Not a bit in the world. You'll make a very good husband— for Jane Ball ; but not for me."

" Exactly so," he answered. " 'Tis my one hope an' prayer to get her father round. An' as for you, the sense you've got be something amazing for a woman. An' I do hope you'll be happy along with Charles Cousins. He's a very good fellow in his way, an' known to me ; an' he's a saving man an' a Bible Christian from his youth up, if he tells truth. I ban't any of these vartuous things."

" I'm glad you like him," she said ; " an', for that matter, I like Jane Ball."

" Do you know her father ? "

" Yes ; the vicarage deals there."

" Fancy that ! Well, if you can say a word for me——"

" I will next time the old man serves me. He's friendly to me— old Ball is. I'll tell him what a good, hard-working chap you are."

" An' tell him I keep my mother."

" Yes, I will."

" An' that I'd sign the pledge to-morrow if 'twould give him any satisfaction."

" I will do so."

" I can't help you no ways ? "

" No, thank you, Will. As a matter of fact, me an' Cousins be tokened. Don't you mention it ; but if he gets his rise come Easter, we'm going to be married."

" Lucky devil—I mean him," said young Heathman.

" There's nothing more to be said, then—except the name of Tibby Minifie ? "

The man would have forgiven me, I do believe ; but evidently the woman didn't mean to.

" Her ought to be ducked in the pond," said William. " Dang the old witch—for she's no better."

" She ought to be proclaimed," said Susan with a horrid cold tone of voice. " Come what may, she shall hear what I think of it."

" Better drop the old liar. She ban't fit company for truth-telling folk," he said.

" Twas almost too much. Humped up though I was, an' aching in the joints, an' swimming in the head, I felt my temper rise.

" Upon the whole," he said, " you'd better leave her to me. She wants a man to talk to her."

" If you do, I hope you'll let her have it straight, then," cried that indecent girl. " She's made fools of us—or tried to."

" 'Twas done to please my mother," he answered ; " an' that being so, one can't say very much to her. Besides, I never would use language to a woman ; I've got my pride like other people. I shall call her a damned old meddlesome cat, as ought to be shot an' nailed up on a barn door—not a word beyond that. 'Twill shame her a sight more if I be quiet an' dignified like."

Susan seemed disappointed, but for my part, even in my indignation, I couldn't help wondering what the man called " language."

Anyway, I done a bold thing, for I couldn't hold in no more, so up I jumped, an' faced 'em both, an' said :

" A meddlesome cat be I ? an' that's all the thanks you graceless hard-hearted brats give me for striving an' plotting to bring happiness into your lives ! You ought to blush to your boots, both of you, to dare to talk of an old woman in that beastly way ! I'm 'shamed of 'e, an' I've a good mind to tell the countryside what a pair you be ! "

" That's all jolly fine," he said. " But how about your lies ? "

" Lies or no lies," I told him, " I haven't got to answer for 'em to you. I meant well by the pair of you. I thought you'd make a couple so happy as you be handsome ; my sole thought was to bring you together in a marrying spirit, an' though I may have failed to do it, owing to you both being set elsewhere, that's no fault of mine, an' to call me a meddlesome cat, ban't right or fair. So now then ! "

" Us certainly didn't look at it like that," said Will, who was a weak man behind his bluster.

" An' whether or no, 'twas a very dangerous step to take," declared Susan. " I'm sure you know that, Miss Minifie."

" Ban't I punished enough ? " I asked. " Ban't it bad enough for me to find I've failed, without making this set against me ? You should judge me by my good feelings an' high intentions an' wishes for your happiness here and hereafter. You ought to go on your knees and ax my pardon for such cowardly cruelty to an old woman as don't feel nought to you but kindness."

" Of course, if you put it like that——" beginned the man, with repentance coming over him.

" There's no other way to put it," I said.

Then I talked to 'em pretty strong, an' at last they both caved in, an' saw that I'd meant terrible well to 'em, an' ended by begging my pardon an' carrying my basket home.

Then having conquered 'em, I stretched a point myself.

" Least said, soonest mended," I told 'em. " There ban't no good telling the parish about this. I meant well, but I was wrong to try and influence two clever people like what you be. I ought to have knowed you was both wise enough to get married without any help from me, an' I'm sorry I took you in hand. Nobody can say more than that."

So there it ended, though the man's mother, of course, blamed me bitterly, as mothers will if you try to do them a turn with their offspring an' fail. But when Jane Ball did take Heathman, an' her father died, an' young Heathman actually rose to the shop, an' became a grocer, an' got four childern, an' she turned out as good a mother as any woman need desire to be—then Mrs. Heathman grudgingly forgived me ; an' declared that 'twas better after all to trust to Providence. In a nasty tone of voice she put it, being as much to say that I'd tried to take over Providence's work an' messed it up.

Susie took her gardener also ; an' that strangely enough turned out well too, as far as one could see. 'Twas the very uncommon case of four young people having their own way an' not coming to grief as a consequence. At least, so George Pearn said, last time he axed me to take him.

J. B. PRIESTLEY (1894–   ), *son of a Bradford schoolmaster, captured the imagination of the public in 1929 with his novel, " The Good Companions," which became equally popular as a play and a film. He had already written a life of George Meredith and much literary criticism. The sturdy independence, good heartedness, and good humour of Yorkshire breathe through the pages of his stories.*

THE TAXI AND THE STAR

MR. HEBBLETHWAITE, buyer for the Luddenstall Cooperative Society, was in a desperate hurry, so desperate a hurry that he decided to take a taxi. When a man from Luddenstall, or from any similar place from the West Riding, is willing to take a taxi, though not encumbered with any luggage or on his way to catch a train, you may be sure that desperation has set in, for Luddenstall looks queerly at any man who is ready to take taxis as if they were buses or trams. Heads are shaken over such men, and afterwards, when the inevitable crash arrives, it is pointed out that, " they couldn't carry corn." Now Mr. Hebblethwaite, as anybody in Luddenstall would admit, was a man who *could* carry corn. If he demanded a taxi, then you may be sure that the situation urgently demanded a taxi too. And so it did, for Mr. Hebblethwaite had only eight minutes in which to catch Mr. Greenbaum, of Huskins and Greenbaum, wholesale millinery. Mr. Greenbaum was to be found in Aldersgate Street, whereas Mr. Hebblethwaite was standing in the upper part of Shaftesbury Avenue.

It was one of those miserable, wet afternoons when nearly all the London taxi-drivers, who wait and wait for custom on fine days, seem to sneak off home to their startled wives. For a minute or two there was not a single empty taxi to be seen. Mr. Hebblethwaite, standing at the kerb, shouted to two or three, but they were all engaged ; and there is something even more humiliating about making advances to engaged taxis than there is about making advances to engaged girls. As they went splashing past, these taxis seemed to sneer. Mr. Hebblethwaite, who felt that he had shown great enterprise by deciding to take a taxi at all, was annoyed. Where, now, were all those waiting cabs he noticed every time he came to London ?

At last one came crawling along, looking hungry. Mr. Hebblethwaite shouted to it and waved his hand. It heard him and saw him, and approached. But when it was just slowing up, a shortish man, with a large head and a hat too small for him, popped up from nowhere and promptly stepped in front of Mr. Hebblethwaite.

"That's right," he said to the driver. "Here you are."

"Here, half a minute," said Mr. Hebblethwaite. "This taxi came for me, not you."

"Oh no ! Oh no ! My taxi," the man replied, with an autocratic wave of his hand. He seemed to be quite an autocratic little man. Now he addressed the driver. "You came for me, didn't you ? You know me—Victor Cranton—don't you ? Course you do. I waved to you first."

"That's right, sir," said the driver, with a grin, and held the door open for him. And before Mr. Hebblethwaite could do anything beyond making preliminary noises of protest, this Victor Cranton had shouted the address he wanted, slipped into the cab, and had departed, leaving Mr. Hebblethwaite still waiting in the rain, very angry.

He considered that a very dirty little trick had been played upon him, and though the taxi-driver was partly responsible, the real instigator of it was Mr. Victor Cranton, shortish, with a large head, and a hat too small for him. The name seemed vaguely familiar. Mr. Hebblethwaite, belatedly on his way to Huskins and Greenbaum, brooded over this name, its owner, and the trick he had been served. "An' if ivver I've a chance, lad," he told a mental image of Mr. Cranton, "I'll get one back on you."

Such a chance appeared to be very remote, yet, so curiously twisted are the strands of this life, an opportunity arrived during Mr. Hebblethwaite's very next visit to London. On the very first night of his visit he left his modest little hotel in Bloomsbury for a magnificent and horribly expensive service flat in Mayfair. The owner of this flat was a colossal celebrity, a woman whose name and face were known throughout England and the Eastern States of America. And yet, when Mr. Hebblethwaite walked in, this delicious and famous creature immediately rushed up to him and at once imprinted a large and luscious kiss on his cheek, a kiss that he received quite calmly.

However much we may prefer short and dramatic methods, it is obvious that we must depart from them for a moment here. That visit and that kiss demand an immediate explanation. The fact is that Mr. Hebblethwaite was only incidentally visiting Miss Allie Marsden, the famous music-hall and revue star. The

" Oh no !   Oh no !   My taxi," the man replied

person he was really visiting was Alice Marsden, who was Mrs. Hebblethwaite's cousin and a Luddenstall lass. Alice Marsden went on the stage and became Allie Marsden, and, after a few years of very hard work and very little money, suddenly caught the fancy of West-end audiences with the very same tricks of voice and gesture that had made Luddensdall laugh years before. After that, Allie worked up a tremendous career for herself, on the halls, in revue, and in films. She was not pretty, and her rather short, square figure could not be called beautiful ; but she had a stage personality as vivid as a flash of lightning, any amount of charm when she wanted it, a little trick of pathos, and a whole Pennine range of North-country humour. She never received less than four hundred pounds for a week's work, and there was not a box-office manager in London or New York who would have denied that she was worth every penny of it. Actually, she was now neither Alice Marsden of Luddenstall nor Miss Allie Marsden of the bills, but Mrs. Richard Haycroft, wife of a stalwart and good-looking stockbroker.

" Well, Tom, lad," cried this famous person, dropping back again into the Luddenstall tongue, " it's nice to see you. Get yourself a drink. Dick'll be in, in a minute. How's Rose ? " Rose was her cousin, now Mrs. Hebblethwaite.

" She's champion," said Mr. Hebblethwaite. " And so's the family."

" That's grand. I'd like to see 'em again. Why don't you bring 'em all up to see me, Tom ? "

" Why don't you come an' see us, Allie ? " Mr. Hebblethwaite retorted. " It's easier. There's fewer of you, and more brass to do it on."

In Luddenstall, the rule in conversation is candour, and the great Allie was not at all offended by these remarks.

" I've been thinking," she said seriously, " I'd like to have a look at t'owd shop again, Tom. But I don't know how I can manage it. I've just came back from America specially for this new show here, *Ducks and Drakes.*"

" I know that, lass," said Mr. Hebblethwaite. " We read all about it i' t'paper. We can't pick up a paper without there's summat about you. We're getting fair sick and tired o' hearing tell of you, Allie. I met owd Joe Holmes t'other day—you remember him ? "

" Think I do ! " cried the celebrity, her face lighting up. " He once chased me out of his shop."

" Well, an' I'll bet you asked for it an' all. You wor a cheeky kid. But I met owd Joe t'other day, an' he says, ' They mun be fast what to put in t'paper these days when they can print so much silly stuff about Jack Marsden's lass. You might think she wor t'Queen o' England, t'way they go on abaht her.' So you see, Allie."

She laughed at this. "I must see old Joe again, Tom. Perhaps if I put my tongue out at him, he'd chase me out of his shop again. You know, Tom, I work very hard nowadays and I've a lot of responsibility, but I have a good time——"

"An' I should think an' all. If you don't, who does?"

"I'll tell you one who does, Tom. That's Rose. Oh yes, I know what you're going to say. But Rose has got all she wants—she's got you and those three grand little kids—and she's happy. I know that. And I'm glad. But what I was going to say was this : I have a good time, in spite of the hard work and the responsibility and the nerves and the palaver—but I often think I'd like to be a kid again, walking down Moor Lane with a dirty little red tam-o'-shanter at the back of my head and a big hole in my stocking. That's when you have the fun, lad. It's not the same when you get older, they can say what they like. Perhaps it'ud be different if I'd some kids of my own, just to watch them."

"Aye, it makes a difference," said Mr. Hebblethwaite awkwardly, not at his ease with her in this rare sentimental mood.

"But as I was saying," she continued more, briskly, " I can't manage a trip up North. I've been hard at it rehearsing ever since I came back. I only just knocked off an hour ago. They're still at it now, but I said, ' Here, I've had enough for to-day,' and walked out. I'm tired lad, I can tell you. Talk about the Luddenstall Co-op. It's just a picnic compared to my job."

"And paid accordingly," said Mr. Hebblethwaite, dryly. " Hello, here's Dick."

"Hello, Tom ! What about a little drink ? Had one, Allie ?' Dick Haycroft helped himself, then beamed upcn the other two. "What's the news from Luddenstall, Tom ? Hoʍ's trade ? "

" Well, it's a bit better than it was," said Mr. Hebblethwaite, cautiously. And for the next five minutes he and Dick discussed trade in general.

" How did the *Ducks and Drakes* go to-day, Allie ? " asked her husband. " I saw your musical chap—what's his name ?—Akeley—at the club to-night, for a minute, and he said they were all quacking in pretty good style."

" I was just telling Tom," said Allie, " I walked out on 'em about an hour ago. I'd had enough for one day."

" Quite right."

" I'm getting a bit fed up with Victor," Allie continued.

" His head's swelling. And just because I know how difficult it all is and try to play fair and don't give him the temperamental star stuff, he's beginning to think I'll eat out of his hand. He's done so well lately that it's going to be hard for him to get his head down Shaftesbury Avenue. They'll have to widen it for him."

" And who's this Victor when he's at home ? " Mr. Hebblethwaite inquired. His acquaintance with the theatrical world was limited to Allie.

" That's a good one, Allie," cried her husband. " We ought to tell Victor that one. That'll larn him. Who is he ? Ha, ha ! "

" I'll bet anything he comes round to-night," said Allie, screwing up her delightful features in a manner familiar to so many audiences " Just for two minutes, my dear—only two-oo-oo minutes. Busiest man in London, my dear. "

" Victor to the life ! " And Dick applauded.

" Must run away after two-oo-oo minutes. Haven't had a moment to myself, my dear, since last July. The great Victor Cranton."

" Is that his name ? " cried Mr. Hebblethwaite.

" Of course it is, Tom lad. And don't start pretending you've never heard of it before. I don't mind you doing so to him—it'll do him good—but don't try it on with me. Victor Cranton's one of our biggest men in the theatre now, and he's recently engaged me—which was very sensible of him—to play in his new show, *Ducks and Drakes*."

" She's the chief Doock," said Dick, having a shot—for the millionth time—at a north-country accent, and missing it.

" I've heard of him all right," said Mr. Hebblethwaite grimly. " But I didn't know what he was. Here—is he a shortish chap with a big head and a hat too small for him ? "

" Sounds like him," Allie replied. " I don't suppose he could get a hat big enough for him now ; they wouldn't sell one big enough for the new head he's getting. But I'm tired of Victor. Let's talk about something else. What's happening at the Moor Lane Congregational Chapel these days? "

Her husband laughed.

" Don't laugh, yer gurt nowt," cried Allie. " I used to go to the Moor Lane Congs., didn't I, Tom ? When I was sixteen, I tried to get into the choir—as a so-prano—do, mee, so, der-ho— but old Halstead wouldn't have me in. Tom was in, among the basses—weren't you, Tom ? But Tom was grown up then, with a moustache too. He was rather good looking then—don't blush, Tom ; you were, but that's a long time since—and we used to make eyes at him and gather round him at the bazaars, but our Rose got in first, because she was the nicest and prettiest. D'you remember, Tom ? Dick, shut up. We want to have a serious Luddenstall conversation, don't we, Tom ? If you don't keep quiet, Dick, I'll go to Luddenstall to-morrow morning."

Mr. Victor Cranton did visit them that night. He arrived about an hour later, and, as Allie had prophesied, he announced at once that he could only stay for two minutes. On being introduced to Mr. Hebblethwaite, he gave him a nod and then took no further notice of him. With Dick he exchanged about ten words, and accepted a drink from his hands. Then he addressed himself to Allie : " My dear, I can't stay. Only came round for two minutes. I've left Robertson working with the chorus and Jimmy Dudley. But what made you cut away ? Of course, it's all right, it's perfectly all right. Only I like to be asked. It's a rule I've made. Everybody at rehearsals, and nobody to leave without my permission—and everybody includes the stars, even *you*, my dear. It's the only way to do it. You remember I signed up Stella Fragerson for my last show, *The Golden Garter*—and then she never appeared ? Well, my dear Allie, I'll tell you what happened—in confidence, of course. She wouldn't work my way. I told her—I told her straight. She said, ' I'm Stella Fragerson.' I said, ' And I'm Victor Cranton, and this is a Victor Cranton production. Now what about it, Stella ? ' She threatened to walk out. I called her bluff. She walked. Well, of course, my dear, you're *not* Stella Fragerson——"

" Thank Heaven ! " murmured Dick.

" But that's my way. The public wants a big Victor Cranton show—they're ready to eat it—and the only way I can give it to them is to have everybody, *everybody*, working to my plan. And you know what the results are ? Wonderful, my dear, wonderful—you know that. And now I must run. No, no, old man, no more—I only slipped in for two minutes, just to have a word with Allie. Well, see you at eleven to-morrow morning, my dear."

" You might," said Allie, smiling mysteriously.

He wagged a forefinger at her. " Now, now, Allie. No teasing. And remember, I may be a bit of an autocrat, but I do get results. There's no bungling, no mess. Well, I'll run."

" How's that for a head ? " Allie asked, when he had gone.

" That's him," Mr. Hebblethwaite announced emphatically. " No mistake about it. That's him."

"Hello, Tom!" cried Allie. "You sound as if you've met Victor before. He didn't seem to recognize you."

"He didn't. But I recognized him all right. Last time I was here, that chap played a dirty little trick on me—at least, I call it a dirty trick. I'll tell you." And he told them the story of the taxi.

"Now, that's just like him," cried Allie, when the story was told. "I feel like paying him out for that."

"I've felt that way for some time," said Mr. Hebblethwaite.

"Listen." And Allie put a hand on each man's coat, and immediately all three of them had a conspiratorial air. "Can't we do something? Wait a minute. What about this?"

We now present Mr. Victor Cranton on the telephone next day. "Yes, yes, that's Mrs. Haycroft's house, isn't it? Can I speak to her? Mr. Cranton, Mr. Victor Cranton. It's very urgent. *Ur-gent*, I said. She *must* speak to me. Yes, of course. I'll wait. But hurry up. I say—*hurry up*. Hello! Hel-*lo!* No, I haven't finished. Leave us alone. Hello! Oh, is that you, Allie? Look here, my dear, what *is* the idea? You're going to—*what?* But you can't. You're crazy, my dear. Look here, have a rest to-day and to-morrow. I understand— you're tired, that's what it is, Allie. You want a rest. I've been working you too hard. What's that? You *can't* do that. Oh, you know what I mean. Of course you can if you want to, but look what it means. You'll ruin the whole show. Oh no, Allie, you wouldn't do that. You're joking, my dear. You can't mean it. Look here, I'm coming round to see you. You *must* see me. Just two-oo-oo minutes."

A further scene, very short and dramatic, showing a distracted Mr. Victor Cranton arriving at the flat of Miss Allie Marsden, and being told very firmly by a maid that she cannot be seen, and told not once but half a dozen times. Exit Mr. Cranton, in smoke and flame.

We now present Mr. Victor Cranton once more on the telephone. It is the day following that on which he made his unsuccessful attempt to see his leading lady. This time he is speaking to her husband. "Look here, Haycroft, old man, I had to ring you. About Allie. Yes, about Allie. I can't get a word out of her, can't see her, can't speak to her. What does it mean? *Wha-a-at?* To where? Luddenstall? What's she want to go there for? Oh, but she's crazy. We're opening next week. I say—*we're opening*. She'll ruin me. She'll ruin herself. She'll ruin all of us. It's suicide. It's murder. But I tell you, something *must* be done. Can't you persuade her?

Come along, old man. I'm sure you can. You can't ? Who ?
Who's he ? Her cousin ? I see. She's going to stay there.
What's the name ? Spell it. H-e-b-b-l-e-t-h-w-a-i-t-e. Yes,
I've got it. Where's he staying ? I see. All right, old man, I'll
get hold of him. Good Lord, yes !—I'll work it somehow.
Thanks for the tip."

A very obscure provincial person called Hebblethwaite,
staying in a rather cheap Bloomsbury hotel, now suddenly
became the most important person in London to the great Victor
Cranton. This Hebblethwaite was telephoned to, but could not
be found. A letter was sent through the post, and then another
letter was sent by messenger. Finally, Mr. Cranton himself
descended upon the Bloomsbury hotel and insisted upon seeing
Mr. Hebblethwaite.   The interview took place, at Mr. Hebblethwaite's request, in a very small and very cold bedroom, the
kind of place Mr. Cranton had not seen for years. Mr. Hebblethwaite was a very difficult man, for he would not go out and have
a meal, or even a drink, with Mr. Cranton, He insisted upon
staying in his cold little bedroom. Victor Cranton found it hard
to be charming, faced with such a man and such an apartment,
but he did his best.

" I don't think you quite realize, Mr. Hebblethwaite," he
said earnestly, " what this means to me and to the people who are
backing me. Miss Allie Marsden, as you know, is our star. I
don't say she's the whole show, by any means ; but she's a
good part of it, and we can't get on without her. We can't even re-
hearse properly without her. As for opening without her, it's
unthinkable. And every night we delay the opening means a
a dead loss of several hundred pounds. You're a business man
yourself, and you can see what it means."

Mr. Hebblethwaite nodded, but said nothing. He would
never have admitted it for the world, but actually this mixture of
charm and earnestness was having its effect on him.

" If Miss Marsden was ill, it would be different," Mr. Cranton
continued, mournfully now. " We'd have to disappoint the
public. There'd be no help for it. But she isn't. It's just a
whim. And I didn't expect to be treated like this by Allie
Marsden. She's got a name for playing up to her managers and
the public, not like some of the stars. She's a Yorkshire girl
and she's always kept her word. Now, look here, Mr. Hebblethwaite. Dick Haycroft tells me she's going away like this
because she wants to stay with you and Mrs. Hebblethwaite at—
er—Luddenstall. Very nice. We all like to see the old places

again. But you can see yourself that this isn't the time to go away. It's not playing the game. It's taking a holiday not at your own expense but at other people's. Dick Haycroft said you could persuade her to stay on in town. Well, what about it, Mr. Hebblethwaite ? "

" Aye, what about it ? " the other repeated, his face without expression.

" Well, if you'd do that, you'd find Victor Cranton very grateful," that gentleman continued persuasively. " Look here, you do that for me, Mr. Hebblethwaite, and you can have a whole row of stalls for the first night of *Ducks and Drakes*. I don't know how the devil I'll manage it—because, let me tell you, Victor Cranton's first nights are big events in this city—but I'll manage it. A whole row of stalls, if you want 'em."

A certain self-assertivenes that had crept back into Mr. Cranton's voice made Mr. Hebblethwaite look grim again. " Nay, you can keep your stalls and first nights. This show o' yours is nowt to me. I wouldn't be paid to see it—t'first night or onny other night."

" What ? " Mr. Cranton was genuinely horrified.

" Why should I ? Allie Marsden's been making me laugh for twenty year, long afore you ever set eyes on her, so there's nowt new about her, and as for t'rest of it, you can keep it."

Mr. Cranton stared at this barbarian in despair. " Well," he said, finally trying to smile, " perhaps there's something else I can do for you. Er—let me see——"

" I'll tell you summat," said Mr. Hebblethwaite grimly. " I come up here on business, and I find it a bother getting about. T'last time I were up, when it were raining hard nearly all time, I were in a hurry one afternoon and I couldn't get a taxi. But I found one at finish, and I were just getting into it when a chap slipped in front of me and said it were his, and 'cos t'driver knew this chap's name and knew he were well off, this chap got taxi all right and left me stranded." And Mr. Hebblethwaite stared so hard at his companion when he said this that there could be no doubt who the taxi-stealing chap was.

" My dear fellow, d'you mean to say I did that ? I'd no idea. I'm terribly sorry, terribly sorry."

" An' so were I at time," said Mr. Hebblethwaite.

" Look here, Mr. Hebblethwaite, I'd not the least idea I'd offended you in this way. Did you tell Allie this ? Ah, you did. Now I begin to see daylight. Mr. Hebblethwaite, I don't know how long you're staying in London, but I promise you shall have a car at your disposal for the rest of the time you're here."

"But I don't want a car at my disposal," said Mr. Hebblethwaite. "It were a taxi you robbed me of, so we'll stick to taxis."

"A taxi, then."

"Nay, not one taxi. You can be diddled out o' one taxi so easy. I've seen that. I'll have five taxis, thank you."

"Five taxis! But what you're going to do with them? You can't ride in five taxis."

Mr. Hebblethwaite grinned. "I'll ride i' t'middle one, and have two in front an' two at back. An' if you see I've got five taxis in t'morning, Mr. Cranton, an' mak' arrangements for me to use 'em as long as I'm here, I promise you'll not have any more bother wi' Miss Allie Marsden."

Mr. Cranton clapped his hands. "Done. It's a bargain. You'll have five taxis in the morning. Mr. Hebblethwaite. They'll be waiting outside this hotel at—er—what time shall we say?—ten o'clock, eh? Right. And now what about getting hold of Allie?"

"Come downstairs and I'll ring her up now an' settle it for you," said Mr. Hebblethwaite, with more than a shade of patronage in his tone. He went first, and he did not see the smile that had now found its way to Mr. Cranton's broad and very intelligent face. If he had seen that smile, he might have felt less triumphant.

After the short and successful telephone conversation with the star, Mr. Hebblethwaite and Mr. Cranton shook hands. "Five taxis, eh?" said the latter chuckling. "An amusing idea, that. I congratulate you. Well, I must run. I've got an idea, too. Look out for the five taxis in the morning. They'll be outside here."

They were. Mr. Cranton kept his word, and, being a born showman, had turned that word to good account. The publicity agent of *Ducks and Drakes* had had a very busy time since that little talk between Messrs. Hebblethwaite and Cranton. Many strings came easily into that agent's hands, and he had been pulling them hard. That obscure Bloomsbury hotel favoured by Mr. Hebblethwaite had been suddenly put on the map.

Mr. Hebblethwaite came down to find the five taxis awaiting him and great deal else too. There were six reporters in the hall, all waiting for his "story." There were four ordinary Press photographers and two men with film cameras, all waiting for him to climb into the middle taxi and order the cavalcade to start. There were about two hundred idle sightseers waiting too,

attracted by the spectacle of the taxis and the camera-men.
There were three policemen and a sergeant, keeping the crowd
from blocking up the entrance to the hotel. The man from
Luddenstall was given a hint as to what the word " publicity "
meant in London.

He pushed his way through the little swarm of reporters,
who were all asking him questions that he did not answer, and
glared at the array of cabs, cameras, policemen, and spectators
outside the front door.

" Mr. 'Ebblethwaite, that right ? " said a husky voice. It
came from the leader or the five taxi-drivers.

" That's right," said Mr. Hebblethwaite. " And I don't
want you, any of you. Who d'you think I am ? Mary Pick-
ford ? I'm not goin to mak' a show o' myself. Go on, clear off.
I don't want you."

They went, but not before the cameras had clicked and the
reporters had made a few mental notes. If Mr. Hebblethwaite
imagined that by not using even one of the five taxis he would
escape publicity, he was sadly mistaken. Wheels had been set
in motion that he could not stop. The camera-men had been
sent out to take pictures, and they took them. The reporters
had been sent out to get a "story," and they got it. They got
little from Mr. Hebblethwaite himself, but they had Victor
Cranton's publicity man to fall back upon, and they fell back
upon him. Mr. Hebblethwaite was in two of the evening papers
that night, and in three of the morning papers the next day, and
there were photographs, too. The story the Press told was an
amusing one, but Victor Cranton seemed to be the hero of it.
Mr. Hebblethwaite, the man who had refused to give the journalists the information they required, appeared to play a rather
foolish part in it.

" And I don't see," said Mr. Hebblethwaite to Miss Allie
Marsden, " that I did get even wi' yond chap Cranton. He'd got
t'laugh at me at finish."

" Well, I will say that for Victor," replied the star. " He's
bossy, but he's clever. But if I do come to Luddenstall, Tom, I
won't say nowt about it."

" Nay lass, it doesn't matter," said Mr. Hebblethwaite, who
knew his Luddenstall.

" You can bet your boots they know now."

W. PETT RIDGE (1860–1930), *author of* " *Mord Em'ly*," " *'Erb*," *and* " *The Wickhamses*," *among other delightful and sympathetic studies of the humbler folk of London, had a deep and sensitive understanding of life as lived by everyday people. He found in their problems material for a rich and kindly humour, and his mastery of the short story allows a happy example of his style to be included here.*

RETIRING INSPECTOR

INSPECTOR RICHARDS mentioned to several of the staff that, whilst he had often taken part in the presentation of testimonials, he specially wished that no tribute of a valuable nature should be paid to him on his retirement, and the men, after private consideration, took him at his word. The night of his departure was the occasion, nevertheless, for many touching incidents. Inspector Richards made a point of shaking hands with all those inferior to him in position ; a compliment they accepted shyly, after rubbing the palm down the side of trousers.

" Always been my desire," he said benevolently, " to treat every one alike, and I trust I've succeeded."

" You've done it, sir. No mistake about that."

" I hope I have never shown anything in the shape of favouritism."

" There again, sir, you're right."

" I am anxious to express the desire that nothing but what I may call kindly thoughts will be entertained concerning me when I leave the duties I have so long carried out," said Inspector Richards elaborately, " and there's no objection to you mentioning it, as freely as you like, that I shall be glad to see old friends at any hour, and any time, from half-past eight in the morning till eleven o'clock o' night at three-two-seven, Hampstead Road."

A few of the junior members were under the impression that the words suggested liberal and cheerful hospitality ; those who knew Mr. Richards better warned them not to expect too much from old T. R. T. R., they said, had never yet given away a ha'porth of anything, and acquaintance with human nature induced them to believe that he, at his age, was not likely to begin. The one person who had known T. R. the longest found herself swiftly disillusioned. Harriet was to live with her father over the shop in Hampstead Road, and to keep house for him ; her wedding was to take place when Mr. Richards found it possible to make other arrangements, and not until then.

" I shall look after the shop," he said commandingly. " That's my part of the work. All you've got to do is to see to the cooking, and the cleaning up, the washing on Mondays, the ironing later on, the boots, the garden at the back, and so on and so forth. You sweep out the shop first thing in the morning, but apart from that, you're not to show your face there. Understand ? "

" Yes, father."

" Don't give me the trouble of speaking twice," he went on in his official manner. " I've been used to managing much bigger affairs, without any trouble, and this will be mere child's play. I look on it more as a hobby than anything else. Worst thing that can happen to a man of my industrious nature is to have nothing to occupy his mind. Go in now, and don't you ever dare come out 'less I call you."

The shop opened promptly on the first morning, Mr. Richards wearing a silk hat as he took down the shutters, to indicate that shirt-sleeves did not mean inferiority. He nodded distantly to his neighbours, and when they asked him a question concerning the weather of the day shook his head reservedly to convey the idea that he had not yet decided the point. Inside, he arranged the cash-drawer neatly and prepared change, blew a speck of dust from the counter, and, replacing the silk hat with a grey tweed cap, lighted a pipe and waited for the rush of custom. A drawback of official life had consisted in the fact that one could not be seen smoking within a certain distance of the terminus ; it had been his duty on many occasions to reprove the staff for indulging in a pipe at the wrong moment, or at the inappropriate place ; the match which he struck on the sole of his slippers made a bright, flaming signal of the inauguration of liberty. During the morning Mr. Richards struck many matches and smoked several pipes, so that at one o'clock when his daughter called out respectfully, " Dinner's ready, father ! " his appetite was not so good as, at this hour, it should have been.

" What sort of a morning has it been, father ? " asked Harriet, with deference.

" Mind your own business," he retorted. " And pull the muslin curtain aside so that I can see when any one comes in. I've told you before the shop's nothing to do with you."

"There's a lad rapping at the counter," she remarked, disregarding his orders.

Mr. Richards upset his chair in the anxiety to attend to his first customer, and hurried in, wiping his mouth with the back of his hand.

"How do?" said the lad familiarly. "How you getting on at your new job? Settling down all right?"

"What can I do for you, Jenkinson?" Richards rested the tips of his fingers on the counter and beamed across. "Tobacco or cigarettes?"

"Last time me and you held conversation together," remarked the lad—"I'm speaking now of a matter of six weeks ago, or it might be a couple of months—you distinctly told me, as far as I remember, that smoking at my time of life was playing the deuce with my health."

"Everything's good if taken in moderation."

"And, furthermore, you said that if you caught me with a fag again, you'd report me to headquarters."

"My humour is what they call dry," urged Richards. "You have to go below the surface to see what I'm really driving at. How are they managing at the old place? What's the new inspector like? Some of you will find a difference, if I'm not greatly mistaken."

"We have!"

"Ah!"

"General opinion," said the lad, with marked emphasis, "seems to be that this one is a gentleman."

Mr. Richards eyed him across the counter; the other, almost quailing, asked whether the establishment included matches amongst its stores. A box being produced, he inquired how many it contained. Mr. Richards said he did not know. The lad, opening the box, remarked that it appeared to have been tampered with, and expressed a desire not to be swindled. The proprietor imperatively ordered him to go out of the shop, and went back to his meal. This had become cold; the circumstance that he himself was considerably heated did not compensate.

"There's another!" mentioned Harriet.

A lamp-boy, bearing on his features evidence of occupation, wished to make an inquiry, and, accepting the reply, stayed to argue that tin-tacks were a necessity to many people at many times and should therefore be kept by those who desired to serve the public; he went on to give a brief lecture on the laws of supply and demand, and, this finished, seemed unwilling to leave without confessing something in the way of patronage, and Mr. Richards found himself called upon to give two half-pennies in exchange for a penny and to say " Thank you " to an individual whom he had not, in official days, condescended to notice.

" You must put some brains into it," counselled the boy, before going out of the doorway. " That's your only chance. Competition's very keen at the present time. And don't forget civility. Civility goes a long way with a lot of people."

" Take your hand away from that new paint ! I don't want to identify customers by finger-marks."

" You won't have any if you don't treat 'em properly."

" Go back to the station," roared Mr. Richards, " and give them features of yours a good wash ! "

" Used soap and water just before I came away."

" Then get them to turn the hose on you."

The boy tried to think of a retort, but none came. He made a face and went.

That evening, at half-past six, saw the real start of business. In less than five minutes the shop filled with customers, all talking loudly, all demanding to be served at once, but, in spite of this, making no attempt to leave quickly. More than once in the flurry and bustle of taking money—it was the night of pay-day, and much change therefore required—he called up-stairs to inquire whether Harriet's young man had arrived ; the last answer received was to the effect that the youth in question had been told not to come round that evening.

" Who told you to say that ? "

" I thought it best, father."

He made an appeal to the customers for sympathy on the grounds that he had a fool for a daughter. They asked what else he had a right to expect.

It was satisfactory to see the shop crowded, but he wished the deportment had been of a more careful nature. Some called him Richards, quite shortly ; a porter, for whom it had been his painful duty to obtain three days' suspension, referred to him more familiarly ; and the retired inspector found, as many have discovered, that few of us in London, however important, escape a nickname. A few in sportive mood en-deavoured to confuse him over the coins tendered, and when he had to beg one to go out and obtain some small silver for a sovereign, the messenger prolonged absence to such an extent that Mr. Richards became seriously alarmed, refusing to con-sider the bets offered concerning the possibility of the man never being heard of again. Temper was exhibited when the messenger returned with eighty threepenny-pieces, obtained from a friend connected with a chapel ; and when it was pointed out that folk had a prejudice against accepting these, prompt answer came to the effect that in future Richards had better run errands for himself. A mouth-organ started a tune in a corner, and a porter solicited the favour of a labeller's hand for a dance.

"I'm not going to have that noise." They explained that it was not noise, but music. "Whatever it is, I'm not going to have it. Put a stop to it at once ! "

"Look here, old man, you're out of uniform now. None of your gold-braid behaviour, if you please. That's gone and done with. All change is the motto."

"But," he pleaded, "I don't want to be a nuisance to my neighbours."

"You always have been."

They gave up, with reluctance, the idea of frivolous entertainment, and went on to the discussion of political matters. Richards had prided himself on the definite nature of his opinions concerning affairs of the nation, and even intimate colleagues rarely ventured to disagree ; he reminded himself now that a shopkeeper had to be extremely careful to show impartiality, and to be cautious not to give offence. Consequently he found that many cherished views had to go ; appealed to when the debate became warm, he said there was a good deal to be said on both sides ; you found good and bad in everybody ; seemed to him you might say in general of politicians that they were six of one and half-dozen of the other. In preparing to go, the customers declared they would not give a brass button for a man who was unable to make up his mind.

"Look in again soon," he said, with a determined effort at cordiality. "Come to-morrow evening, if you're doing nothing else. Always glad to see you. No friends like the old ones."

He relaxed the usual attitude towards his daughter, and said that if she felt certain hers was a case of genuine affection, and not a mere idle fancy, he had no objection to the young man looking in any evening, every evening in fact, at about half-past six. Harriet promised to convey the permission, although she could not be sure that Arthur would take advantage of it.

"Tell him he can stay on to supper," recommended her father.

"That might influence him," admitted Harriet. "Would

you like me to give a hand with the shop when you're so busy as you were to-night ? "

" How many more times am I to tell you that I can manage the business myself ? Besides, I don't want a set of young men coming in just for the sake of chatting and talking with you. What do you think your poor mother would have said to such an idea ? "

The young man on arriving the next night found a hearty handshake awaiting him, and an American cigarette. He was ordered to sit inside the counter and to have a good look around. Mr. Richards gave something like a lesson in geography, pointing out that Log Cabin was bordered on the east by Navy Cut, on the west by Honey Dew ; that twopenny cigars were situated on a peninsula, and wax matches formed a range of mountains. Proceeding to the cash drawers, Arthur was instructed to observe that four separate lakes existed, each with its own duty, and one was not on any account to be confused with the rest. When he exhibited a desire to go in and see Harriet, Mr. Richards upbraided him for want of attention, and mentioned that all knowledge was worth acquiring, in that you never knew when it might prove useful ; to retain him until the rush of business came many reminiscent anecdotes were told of railway life, incidents of difficulty faced by Inspector Richards at various periods, and always triumphantly overcome. Coming to more recent occurrences, a complaint was made that Harriet that morning going out to shop in High Street had been absent for no less than three-quarters of an hour.

" Don't go in there ! " said a voice at the doorway. " That's old T. R.'s show. Let's go on higher up. He'll only try to boss it over us."

When Harriet sang out an announcement concerning the meal, the proprietor of the tobacconist's shop remarked brusquely that there was probably enough for two, but not sufficient for three, and in these circumstances he would not trouble Arthur to stay.

Mr. Richards was still watching the roadway, and wondering how it was possible for so many folk to pass by an attractive shop-window without stopping to give it the compliment of a glance, when he caught sight of one of his fellow-inspectors on the opposite side. Anxious for congenial company, he gave an invitation with a wave of the hand, and the other, after a moment of thought, crossed over. Harriet made another deferential announcement.

"Just in time!" he cried genially. "Come along inside, Wilkinson, and share pot-luck."

"What do you call pot-luck?" inquired Wilkinson, with caution. Mr. Richards recited the brief menu, and the inspector decided to enter.

"Brought a friend," said Richards to his daughter in the back parlour .

"Then we shall want a fourth chair, father."

"No, we shan't. Wilkinson, sit you down and make yourself thoroughly at home. How are you muddling on without me?"

"Do you want the truth?"

"Let's hear the worst."

"We're getting on first class," announced Wilkinson, his eyes on Harriet, but his words addressed to her father. "Some of them were saying only this evening that it just proved how much could be done by kindness. There hasn't been a cross word since you left, and not a single member of the staff has had to be reported."

"You'll all have a nice job later on," he prophesied. "Let them get slack and out of control, and it'll take you months to get 'em well in hand again."

"How do you like the change, Miss?" asked Wilkinson, accepting the offer of lettuce. "How does business life suit you, may I ask?"

"Nothing to do with her!" interrupted her father sharply. "All she's responsible for is household duties. I believe in women keeping to their proper sphere. Once they come out of it——"

"The change hasn't improved your temper, old man."

He stopped in the act of helping himself to mustard, and stared at his late colleague. "Me?" he said, in a dazed way. "Me, got a temper? Well, upon my word, we live and learn. This is news!"

"Pretty stale to other people."

"I venture to challenge that statement," said Richards hotly. "I should like to have a decision on the point by some independent authority."

"Ask her!"

Harriet, appealed to and ordered to speak without fear or favour, said she wanted to know why Arthur was sent away. The answer was to the effect if she had finished gorging herself with food, she could go upstairs and leave her father and his friend to discuss matters which her youth and sex prevented her from understanding. Harriet had not completed her share of the meal, but she obeyed at once.

"That's the way to bring up a child," said Richards, with a jerk of the head. "I've only got to give her a hint. Wonderful control I exercise. I give my orders ; she carries 'em out."

"You don't seem overwhelmed with customers," remarked the visitor, looking through the glass portion of the door.

"They either come with a run," he explained, "or not at all."

"I only go," went on Wilkinson, "by what I've heard at the station. They came here once for the lark of the thing, but the notion seems to be that once is plenty."

"And that," ejaculated the ex-inspector bitterly, "that, I suppose, is what they call *esprit de corps*."

"That's what they call getting their own back. And I don't want to discourage you, and I should like you to believe that I'm saying it only for your own good, but it's pretty clear to my mind that, in regard to this tobacconist's business, you're going to lose your little all. The savings of a lifetime are going to vanish like smoke, or rather not like smoke, but into thin air. Unless," added Wilkinson impressively—"unless you act wisely."

"Don't I always act wisely ? "

Wilkinson shook his head. "The best of us are liable to make mistakes," he said diplomatically, "and consequently you're more liable than most."

Mr. Richards failed in the attempt to make a knife balance on a fork, and sighed deeply.

"I've been here now for—how long ?—and there hasn't been a single, solitary ring of the bell," went on Wilkinson. "You've got to look the facts squarely in the face."

"If the worst comes to the worst," announced the other grimly, "I shall sell the business and the goodwill and stock and everything, and embark on something entirely fresh—something where I shan't be dependent on the kindness of old friends."

"You'll get a big price for the goodwill," mentioned the visitor, with sarcasm. "And I suppose you've taken the premises on a lease ? "

"Let me fetch you a cigar," suggested Mr. Richards desperately, "and then you give me the best advice that lays in your power."

"Pick out one that I can smoke."

Wilkinson's counsel, given after he had submitted the cigar to a sufficient test, was this. Competition, brisk and determined, existed in the trade on the part of large firms who opened shops all over the place.　Small establishments could only exist by the possession of something in the shape of what Wilkinson called a magnet—a magnet to draw the people in.

"You mean a gramophone?"

Wilkinson meant nothing of the kind.　What you had to bear in mind was, first, that all your possible customers belonged to what was known as the male persuasion; second, that by an old-established arrangement, which you might argue against but you had to accept, the male was always attracted by the female.　Wilkinson added that in his opinion the daughter upstairs was a dashed good-looking girl, and, the cigar being near to its end, suggested that another might be presented to bear him company on the way home.　And went.

"Harriet, my girl," said Mr. Richards, "I've thought of an idea that I may as well mention at once before I forget it. No doubt you've heard the remark about Satan and idle hands. And as there's no good reason why I should work my fingers to the bone, I shall want you to come into the shop of an afternoon and evening, and serve customers, and smile at 'em, and make yourself generally useful."

"Afraid you're too late, father," she said.　"If you had let Arthur stay to supper, we were not going to tell you anything about it.　As it is, you've got to be told that we were married this morning at the registrar's, and that I'm going to leave you now."

.　　.　　.　　.　　.　　.　　.　　.

The shop is doing very well, and when you happen to pass that way, you might step in and buy something.　You will find Harriet at the counter serving goods of excellent quality at current prices; in the evening her husband is also there. Glancing through the windowed door of the shop parlour, you may catch sight of ex-Inspector Richards, looking after the baby.

"SAKI" (1870–1916) *is the pseudonym which was chosen from "The Rubaiyat of Omar Khayyam" by H. H. Munro, who was killed in action during the Great War. Amongst the great variety of his stories and sketches can be found elements of almost every type of humour. One of the best collections of his tales is "The Chronicles of Clovis" from which this most unusual hunting story is taken.*

ESMÉ

"ALL hunting stories are the same," said Clovis; "just as all Turf stories are the same, and all——"

"My hunting story isn't a bit like any you've ever heard," said the Baroness. "It happened quite a while ago, when I was about twenty-three. I wasn't living apart from my husband then; you see, neither of us could afford to make the other a separate allowance. In spite of everything that proverbs may say, poverty keeps together more homes than it breaks up. But we always hunted with different packs. All this has nothing to do with the story."

"We haven't arrived at the meet yet. I suppose there was a meet," said Clovis.

"Of course there was a meet," said the Baroness; "all the usual crowd were there, especially Constance Broddle. Constance is one of those strapping florid girls that go so well with autumn scenery or Christmas decorations in church. ' I feel a presentiment that something dreadful is going to happen,' she said to me; ' am I looking pale? '

"She was looking about as pale as a beetroot that has suddenly heard bad news.

" ' You're looking nicer than usual,' I said, ' but that's so easy for you.' Before she had got the right bearings of this remark we had settled down to business; hounds had found a fox lying out in some gorse-bushes."

"I knew it," said Clovis; "in every fox-hunting story that I've ever heard there's been a fox and some gorse-bushes."

"Constance and I were well mounted," continued the Baroness serenely, "and we had no difficulty in keeping ourselves in the first flight, though it was a fairly stiff run. Towards the finish, however, we must have held rather too independent

617   20*

a line, for we lost the hounds, and found ourselves plodding aimlessly along miles away from anywhere. It was fairly exasperating, and my temper was beginning to let itself go by inches, when on pushing our way through an accommodating hedge we were gladdened by the sight of hounds in full cry in a hollow just beneath us.

" ' There they go,' cried Constance, and then added in a gasp, ' In Heaven's name, what are they hunting ? '

" It was certainly no mortal fox. It stood more than twice as high, had a short, ugly head, and an enormous thick neck.

" ' It's a hyæna,' I cried ; ' it must have escaped from Lord Pabham's Park.'

" At that moment the hunted beast turned and faced its pursuers, and the hounds (there were only about six couple of them) stood round in a half-circle and looked foolish. Evidently they had broken away from the rest of the pack on the trail of this alien scent, and were not quite sure how to treat their quarry now they had got him.

" The hyæna hailed our approach with unmistakable relief and demonstrations of friendliness. It had probably been accustomed to uniform kindness from humans, while its first experience of a pack of hounds had left a bad impression. The hounds looked more than ever embarrassed as their quarry paraded its sudden intimacy with us, and the faint toot of a horn in the distance was seized on as a welcome signal for unobtrusive departure. Constance and I and the hyæna were left alone in the gathering twilight.

" ' What are we to do ? ' asked Constance.

" ' What a person you are for questions,' I said.

" ' Well, we can't stay here all night with a hyæna,' she retorted.

" ' I don't know what your ideas of comfort are,' I said ; ' but I shouldn't think of staying here all night even without a hyæna. My home may be an unhappy one, but at least it has hot and cold water laid on, and domestic service, and other conveniences which we shouldn't find here. We had better make for that ridge of trees to the right ; I imagine the Crowley road is just beyond.'

" We trotted off slowly along a faintly marked cart-track, with the beast following cheerfully at our heels.

" ' What on earth are we to do with the hyæna ? ' came the inevitable question.

" ' What does one generally do with hyænas ? ' I asked crossly.

" ' I've never had anything to do with one before,' said Constance.

" ' Well, neither have I. If we even knew its sex we might give it a name. Perhaps we might call it Esmé. That would do in either case.'

" There was still sufficient daylight for us to distinguish wayside objects, and our listless spirits gave an upward perk as we came upon a small half-naked gipsy brat picking blackberries from a low-growing bush. The sudden apparition of two horsewomen and a hyæna set it off crying, and in any case we should scarcely have gleaned any useful geographical information from that source ; but there was a probability that we might strike a gipsy encampment somewhere along our route. We rode on hopefully but uneventfully for another mile or so.

" ' I wonder what that child was doing there,' said Constance presently.

" ' Picking blackberries. Obviously.'

" ' I don't like the way it cried,' pursued Constance ; ' somehow its wail keeps ringing in my ears.'

" I did not chide Constance for her morbid fancies ; as a matter of fact the same sensation, of being pursued by a persistent fretful wail, had been forcing itself on my rather overtired nerves. For company's sake I hulloed to Esmé, who had lagged somewhat behind. With a few springy bounds he drew up level, and then shot past us.

" The wailing accompaniment was explained. The gipsy child was firmly, and I expect painfully, held in his jaws.

" ' Merciful Heaven ! ' screamed Constance, ' what on earth shall we do ? What are we to do ? '

" I am perfectly certain that at the Last Judgment Constance will ask more questions than any of the examining Seraphs.

" ' Can't we do something ? ' she persisted tearfully, as Esmé cantered easily along in front of our tired horses.

" Personally I was doing everything that occurred to me at the moment. I stormed and scolded and coaxed in English and French and gamekeeper language ; I made absurd, ineffectual cuts in the air with my thongless hunting-crop ; I hurled my sandwich case at the brute ; in fact, I really don't know what more I could have done. And still we lumbered on through the deepening dusk, with that dark uncouth shape lumbering ahead of us, and a drone of lugubrious music floating in our ears. Suddenly Esmé bounded aside into some thick bushes, where we could not follow ; the wail rose to a shriek and then stopped altogether. This part of the story I always hurry over, because it is really rather horrible. When the beast joined us again, after an absence of a few minutes, there was an air of patient understanding about him, as though he knew that he had done something of which we disapproved, but which he felt to be thoroughly justifiable.

"'How can you let that ravening beast trot by your side?' asked Constance. She was looking more than ever like an albino beetroot.

"'In the first place, I can't prevent it,' I said; 'and in the second place, whatever else he may be, I doubt if he's ravening at the present moment.'

"Constance shuddered. 'Do you think the poor little thing suffered much?' came another of her futile questions.

"'The indications were all that way,' I said; 'on the other hand, of course, it may have been crying from sheer temper. Children sometimes do.'

"It was nearly pitch-dark when we emerged suddenly into the high road. A flash of lights and the whir of a motor went past us at the same moment at uncomfortably close quarters. A thud and a sharp screeching yell followed a second later. The car drew up, and when I had ridden back to the spot I found a young man bending over a dark motionless mass lying by the roadside.

"'You have killed my Esmé,' I exclaimed bitterly.

"'I'm so awfully sorry,' said the young man; 'I keep dogs myself, so I know what you must feel about it. I'll do anything I can in reparation.'

"'Please bury him at once,' I said; 'that much I think I may ask of you.'

"'Bring the spade, William,' he called to the chauffeur. Evidently hasty roadside interments were contingencies that had been provided against.

"The digging of a sufficiently large grave took some little time. 'I say, what a magnificent fellow,' said the motorist as the corpse was rolled over into the trench. 'I'm afraid he must have been rather a valuable animal.'

"'He took second in the puppy class at Birmingham last year,' I said resolutely.

"Constance snorted loudly.

"'Don't cry, dear,' I said brokenly; 'it was all over in a moment. He couldn't have suffered much.'

"'Look here,' said the young fellow desperately, 'you simply must let me do something by way of reparation.'

" I refused sweetly, but as he persisted I let him have my address.

" Of course, we kept our own counsel as to the earlier episodes of the evening. Lord Pabham never advertised the loss of his hyæna; when a strictly fruit-eating animal strayed from his park a year or two previously he was called upon to give compensation in eleven cases of sheep-worrying and practically to re-stock his neighbours' poultry-yards, and an escaped hyæna would have mounted up to something on the scale of a Government grant. The gipsies were equally unobtrusive over their missing offspring; I don't suppose in large encampments they really know to a child or two how many they've got."

The Baroness paused reflectively, and then continued :

" There was a sequel to the adventure, though. I got through the post a charming little diamond brooch, with the name Esmé set in a sprig of rosemary. Incidentally, too, I lost the friendship of Constance Broddle. You see, when I sold the brooch I quite properly refused to give her any share of the proceeds. I pointed out that the Esmé part of the affair was my own invention, and the hyæna part of it belonged to Lord Pabham, if it really was his hyæna, of which, of course, I've no proof."

RICHARD BRINSLEY SHERIDAN (1751–1816), *dramatist, politician, and orator, had his play, " The Rivals " produced when he was twenty-four. He married at twenty-two, after fighting two duels for his bride. His speech in the trial of Warren Hastings has gone down in the history of oratory. His keen sense of the ridiculous is shown in this scene from " The Critic," which satirizes the popular drama and dramatic criticism of his day.*

THE REHEARSAL

ACT II. Scene I.—*The Theatre before the Curtain.*

Enter Dangle, Puff, *and* Sneer.

Puff. No, no, sir ; what Shakspeare says of actors may be better applied to the purpose of plays ; they ought to be *the abstract and brief chronicles of the time.* Therefore when history, and particularly the history of our own country, furnishes anything like a case in point, to the time in which an author writes, if he knows his own interest, he will take advantage of it ; so, sir, I call my tragedy *The Spanish Armada* ; and have laid the scene before Tilbury Fort.

Sneer. A most happy thought, certainly !

Dang. Egad it was—I told you so. But pray now, I don't understand how you have contrived to introduce any love into it.

Puff. Love ! oh, nothing so easy ! for it is a received point among poets, that where history gives you a good heroic outline for a play, you may fill up with a little love at your own discretion : in doing which, nine times out of ten, you only make up a deficiency in the private history of the times. Now, I rather think I have done this with some success.

Sneer. No scandal about Queen Elizabeth, I hope ?

Puff. O Lud ! no, no ;—I only suppose the governor of Tilbury Fort's daughter to be in love with the son of the Spanish admiral.

Sneer. Oh, is that all !

Dang. Excellent, i'faith ! I see at once. But won't this appear rather improbable ?

Puff. To be sure it will—but what the plague ! a play is

622

not to show occurrences that happen every day, but things just so strange, that though they never did, they might happen.

Sneer. Certainly nothing is unnatural, that is not physically impossible.

Puff. Very true—and for that matter Don Ferolo Whiskerandos, for that's the lover's name, might have been over here in the train of the Spanish ambassador, or Tilburina, for that is the lady's name, might have been in love with him, from having heard his character, or seen his picture ; or from knowing that he was the last man in the world she ought to be in love with—or for any other good female reason.—However, sir, the fact is, that though she is but a knight's daughter, egad ! she is in love like any princess !

Dang. Poor young lady ! I feel for her already ! for I can conceive how great the conflict must be between her passion and her duty ; her love for her country, and her love for Don Ferolo Whiskerandos !

Puff. Oh, amazing !—her poor susceptible heart is swayed to and fro by contending passions like——

Enter UNDER PROMPTER.

Und. Promp. Sir, the scene is set, and everything is ready to begin, if you please.

Puff. Egad, then we'll lose no time.

Und. Promp. Though, I believe, sir, you will find it very short, for all the performers have profited by the kind permission you granted them.

Puff. Hey ! what ?

Und. Promp. You know, sir, you gave them leave to cut out or omit whatever they found heavy or unnecessary to the plot, and I must own they have taken very liberal advantage of your indulgence.

Puff. Well, well.—They are in general very good judges, and I know I am luxuriant.—Now, Mr. Hopkins, as soon as you please.

Und. Promp. [*To the* Orchestra.] Gentlemen, will you play a few bars of something, just to——

Puff. Ay, that's right ; for as we have the scenes and dresses, egad, we'll go to't, as if it was the first night's performance ;—but you need not mind stopping between the acts—[*Exit* UNDER PROMPTER.—Orchestra *play—then the bell rings.*] Soh ! stand clear, gentlemen. Now you know there will be a cry of down ! down !—Hats off !—Silence !—Then up curtain, and let us see what our painters have done for us. [*Curtain rises.*

SCENE II.—*Tilbury Fort*

" *Two* SENTINELS *discovered asleep.*"

Dang. Tilbury Fort !—very fine indeed !

Puff. Now, what do you think I open with ?

Sneer. Faith, I can't guess——

Puff. A clock.—Hark !—[*Clock strikes.*] I open with a clock striking, to beget an awful attention in the audience : it also marks the time, which is four o'clock in the morning, and saves a description of the rising sun, and a great deal about gilding the eastern hemisphere.

Dang. But pray, are the sentinels to be asleep ?

Puff. Fast as watchmen.

Sneer. Isn't that odd though at such an alarming crisis ?

Puff. To be sure it is,—but smaller things must give way to a striking scene at the opening ; that's a rule. And the case is, that two great men are coming to this very spot to begin the piece ; now it is not to be supposed they would open their lips, if these fellows were watching them ; so, egad, I must either have sent them off their posts, or set them asleep.

Sneer. Oh, that accounts for it. But tell us, who are these coming ?

Puff. These are they—Sir Walter Raleigh, and Sir Christopher Hatton. You'll know Sir Christopher by his turning out his toes—famous, you know, for his dancing. I like to preserve all the little traits of character.—Now attend.

" *Enter* SIR WALTER RALEIGH *and* SIR CHRISTOPHER HATTON.
Sir Christ. True, gallant Raleigh ! "

Dang. What, they had been talking before ?

Puff. Oh yes ; all the way as they came along.—[*To the* actors.] I beg pardon, gentlemen, but these are particular friends of mine, whose remarks may be of great service to us.—[*To* SNEER *and* DANGLE.] Don't mind interrupting them whenever anything strikes you.

" *Sir Christ.* True, gallant Raleigh !
But oh, thou champion of thy country's fame,
There is a question which I yet must ask :
A question which I never ask'd before—
What mean these mighty armaments ?
This general muster ? and this throng of chiefs ? "

Sneer. Pray, Mr. Puff, how came Sir Christopher Hatton never to ask that question before ?

Puff. What before the play began ?—how the plague could he ?
Dang. That's true, i'faith !
Puff. But you will hear what he thinks of the matter.

" *Sir Christ.*   Alas ! my noble friend, when I behold
                 Yon tented plains in martial symmetry
                 Array'd ; when I count o'er yon glittering lines
                 Of crested warriors, where the proud steeds' neigh,
                 And valour-breathing trumpet's shrill appeal,
                 Responsive vibrate on my listening ear ;
                 When virgin majesty herself I view,
                 Like her protecting Pallas, veil'd in steel,
                 With graceful confidence exhort to arms !
                 When, briefly, all I hear or see bears stamp
                 Of martial vigilance and stern defence,
                 I cannot but surmise—forgive, my friend,
                 If the conjecture's rash—I cannot but
                 Surmise the state some danger apprehends ! "

Sneer. A very cautious conjecture that.
Puff. Yes, that's his character ; not to give an opinion but
on secure grounds.—Now then.

" *Sir Walt.*   O most accomplish'd Christopher ! "——

Puff. He calls him by his Christian name, to show that they
are on the most familiar terms.

" *Sir Walt.*   O most accomplish'd Christopher ! I find
                 Thy staunch sagacity still tracks the future,
                 In the fresh print of the o'ertaken past."

Puff. Figurative !

" *Sir Walt.*   Thy fears are just.
  Sir Christ. But where ? whence ? when ? and what
                 The danger is,—methinks I fain would learn.
  Sir Walt.   You know, my friend, scarce two revolving suns,
                 And three revolving moons, have closed their course
                 Since haughty Philip, in despite of peace,
                 With hostile hand hath struck at England's trade.
  Sir Christ. I know it well.
  Sir Walt.   Philip, you know, is proud Iberia's king !
  Sir Christ. He is.
  Sir Walt.   His subjects in base bigotry
                 And Catholic oppression held ;—while we,
                 You know, the Protestant persuasion hold.
  Sir Christ. We do.
  Sir Walt.   You know, beside, his boasted armament,
                 The famed Armada, by the Pope baptized,
                 With purpose to invade these realms——
  Sir Christ.   Is sailed,
                 Our last advices so report.
  Sir Walt.   While the Iberian admiral's chief hope,
                 His darling son——

Sir Christ.   Ferolo Whiskerandos hight—
Sir Walt.   The same—by chance a prisoner hath been ta'en,
                And in this fort of Tilbury——
Sir Christ.   Is now
                Confined—'tis true, and oft from yon tall turret's top
                I've mark'd the youthful Spaniard's haughty mien—
                Unconquer'd, though in chains.
Sir Walt.   You also know "——

Dang. Mr. Puff, as he knows all this, why does Sir Walter
go on telling him ?

Puff. But the audience are not supposed to know anything
of the matter, are they ?

Sneer. True ; but I think you manage ill : for there certainly
appears no reason why Sir Walter should be so communicative.

Puff. 'Fore Gad, now, that is one of the most ungrateful
observations I ever heard !—for the less inducement he has to
tell all this, the more, I think, you ought to be obliged to him ;
for I am sure you'd know nothing of the matter without it.

Dang. That's very true, upon my word.

Puff. But you will find he was not going on.

"*Sir Christ.* Enough, enough—'tis plain—and I no more
                Am in amazement lost ! "——

Puff. Here, now you see, Sir Christopher did not in fact ask
any one question for his own information.

Sneer. No, indeed : his has been a most disinterested curiosity !

Dang. Really, I find that we are very much obliged to them
both.

Puff. To be sure you are. Now then for the commander-in-
chief, the Earl of Leicester, who, you know, was no favourite
but of the queen's.—We left off—*in amazement lost* !

"*Sir Christ.*   Am in amazement lost.
                But, see where noble Leicester comes ! supreme
                In honours and command.
Sir Walt.   And yet, methinks,
                At such a time, so perilous, so fear'd,
                That staff might well become an abler grasp.
Sir Christ.   And so, by Heaven ! think I ; but soft, he's here ! "

Puff. Ay, they envy him !

Sneer. But who are these with him ?

Puff. Oh ! very valiant knights : one is the governor of the
fort, the other the master of the horse. And now, I think, you
shall hear some better language : I was obliged to be plain and
intelligible in the first scene, because there was so much matter

of fact in it ; but now, i'faith, you have trope, figure, and metaphor, as plenty as noun-substantives.

> " *Enter* EARL OF LEICESTER, GOVERNOR, MASTER OF THE HORSE, KNIGHTS, ETC.

Leic.   How's this, my friends ! is't thus your new-fledged zeal,
And plumed valour moulds in roosted sloth ?
Why dimly glimmers that heroic flame,
Whose reddening blaze, by patriot spirit fed,
Should be the beacon of a kindling realm ?
Can the quick current of a patriot heart
Thus stagnate in a cold and weedy converse,
Or freeze in tideless inactivity ?
No ! rather let the fountain of your valour
Spring through each stream of enterprise,
Each petty channel of conducive daring,
Till the full torrent of your foaming wrath
O'erwhelm the flats of sunk hostility ! "

Puff. There it is—followed up !

" *Sir Walt.*   No more !—the freshening breath of thy rebuke
Hath fill'd the swelling canvas of our souls !
And thus, though fate should cut the cable of
                                                    [*All take hands.*
Our topmost hopes, in friendship's closing line
We'll grapple with despair, and if we fall,
We'll fall in glory's wake !
Leic.   There spoke old England's genius !
Then, are we all resolved ?
All.   We are—all resolved.
Leic.   To conquer—or be free ?
All.   To conquer, or be free.
Leic.   All ?
All.   All."

Dang. Nem. con. egad !

Puff. Oh yes !—where they do agree on the stage, their unanimity is wonderful !

" *Leic.*   Then let's embrace—and now——   [*Kneels.*"

Sneer. What the plague, is he going to pray ?

Puff. Yes ; hush !—in great emergencies, there is nothing like a prayer.

" *Leic.*   O mighty Mars ! "

Dang. But why should he pray to Mars ?
Puff. Hush !

" *Leic.*   If in thy homage bred,
Each point of discipline I've still observed ;
Nor but by due promotion, and the right
Of service, to the rank of major-general
Have risen ; assist thy votary now !

Gov.	Yet do not rise—hear me !	[*Kneels.*
Mast.	And me !	[*Kneels.*
Knight.	And me !	[*Kneels.*
Sir Walt.	And me !	[*Kneels.*
Sir Christ.	And me !	[*Kneels.*"

Puff. Now pray altogether.

" *All.*   Behold thy votaries submissive beg,
That thou wilt deign to grant them all they ask ;
Assist them to accomplish all their ends,
And sanctify whatever means they use
To gain them ! "

Sneer. A very orthodox quintetto !

Puff. Vastly well, gentlemen !—Is that well managed or not ? Have you such a prayer as that on the stage ?

Sneer. Not exactly.

Leic. [*To* Puff.] But, sir, you haven't settled how we are to get off here.

Puff. You could not go off kneeling, could you ?

Sir Walt. [*To* Puff.] Oh no, sir ; impossible !

Puff. It would have a good effect, i'faith, if you could exeunt praying !—Yes, and would vary the established mode of springing off with a glance at the pit.

Sneer. Oh, never mind, so as you get them off !—I'll answer for it, the audience won't care how.

Puff. Well, then, repeat the last line standing, and go off the old way.

" *All.*   And sanctify whatever means we use
To gain them.   [*Exeunt.*"

Dang. Bravo ! a fine exit.

Sneer. Well, really, Mr. Puff——

Puff. Stay a moment !

" *The* Sentinels *get up.*

1 *Sent.*	All this shall to Lord Burleigh's ear.	
2 *Sent.*	'Tis meet it should.	[*Exeunt.*'

Dang. Hey !—why, I thought those fellows had been asleep ?

Puff. Only a pretence ; there's the art of it : they were spies of Lord Burleigh's.

Sneer. But isn't it odd they never were taken notice of, not even by the commander-in-chief ?

Puff. O Lud, sir ! if people who want to listen, or overhear, were not always connived at in a tragedy, there would be no carrying on any plot in the world.

Dang. That's certain.

Puff. But take care, my dear Dangle ! the morning gun is going to fire.   [*Cannon fires.*

Dang. Well, that will have a fine effect !

Puff. I think so, and helps to realize the scene.—[*Cannon twice.*] What the plague ! three morning guns ! there never is but one !—Ay, this is always the way at the theatre : give these fellows a good thing, and they never know when to have done with it.—You have no more cannon to fire ?

Und. Promp. [*Within.*] No, sir.

Puff. Now, then, for soft music.

Sneer. Pray, what's that for ?

Puff. It shows that Tilburina is coming !—nothing introduces you a heroine like soft music. Here she comes !

Dang. And her confidant, I suppose ?

Puff. To be sure ! Here they are—inconsolable to the minuet in Ariadne !   [*Soft music.*

" *Enter* TILBURINA *and* CONFIDANT.

Tilb.   Now has the whispering breath of gentle morn
         Bid Nature's voice and Nature's beauty rise ;
         While orient Phœbus, with unborrow'd hues,
         Clothes the waked loveliness which all night slept
         In heavenly drapery ! Darkness is fled.
         Now flowers unfold their beauties to the sun,
         And, blushing, kiss the beam he sends to wake them—
         The striped carnation, and the guarded rose,
         The vulgar wallflower, and smart gillyflower,
         The polyanthus mean—the dapper daisy,
         Sweet-william, and sweet marjoram—and all
         The tribe of single and of double pinks !
         Now, too, the feather'd warblers tune their notes
         Around, and charm the listening grove. The lark !
         The linnet ! chaffinch ! bullfinch ! goldfinch ! green-
             finch !
         But O, to me no joy can they afford !
         Nor rose, nor wallflower, nor smart gillyflower,
         Nor polyanthus mean, nor dapper daisy,
         Nor William sweet, nor marjoram—nor lark,
         Linnet, nor all the finches of the grove ! "

Puff. Your white handkerchief, madam !——

Tilb. I thought, sir, I wasn't to use that till *heart-rending woe.*

Puff. Oh yes, madam, at *the finches of the grove*, if you please.

" *Tilb.*   Nor lark,
         Linnet, nor all the finches of the grove !   [*Weeps.*"

Puff. Vastly well, madam !

Dang. Vastly well, indeed !

" *Tilb.*   For, O, too sure, heart-rending woe is now
         The lot of wretched Tilburina ! "

Dang. Oh !—it's too much.

Sneer. Oh !—it is indeed.

" *Con.*   Be comforted, sweet lady ; for who knows,
             But Heaven has yet some milk-white day in store ?

Tilb.   Alas ! my gentle Nora,
             Thy tender youth as yet hath never mourn'd
             Love's fatal dart. Else wouldst thou know, that when
             The soul is sunk in comfortless despair,
             It cannot taste of merriment."

Dang. That's certain.

" *Con.*   But see where your stern father comes :
             It is not meet that he should find you thus."

Puff. Hey, what the plague !—what a cut is here ! Why, what is become of the description of her first meeting with Don Whiskerandos—his gallant behaviour in the sea-fight—and the simile of the canary-bird ?

Tilb. Indeed, sir, you'll find they will not be missed.

Puff. Very well, very well !

Tilb. [*To* CONFIDANT.] The cue, ma'am, if you please.

" *Con.*   It is not meet that he should find you thus.

Tilb.   Thou counsel'st right ; but 'tis no easy task
             for barefaced grief to wear a mask of joy.

Enter GOVERNOR.

Gov.   How's this !—in tears ?—O Tilburina, shame !
             Is this a time for maudling tenderness,
             And Cupid's baby woes ?—Hast thou not heard
             That haughty Spain's pope-consecrated fleet
             Advances to our shores, while England's fate,
             Like a clipp'd guinea, trembles in the scale ?

Tilb.   Then is the crisis of my fate at hand !
             I see the fleets approach—I see——"

Puff. Now, pray, gentlemen, mind. This is one of the most useful figures we tragedy writers have, by which a hero or heroine, in consideration of their being often obliged to overlook things that are on the stage, is allowed to hear and see a number of things that are not.

Sneer. Yes ; a kind of poetical second-sight !

Puff. Yes.—Now then, madam.

" *Tilb.*   I see their decks
             Are clear'd !—I see the signal made !
             The line is form'd !—a cable's length asunder !
             I see the frigates station'd in the rear ;
             And now, I hear the thunder of the guns !
             I hear the victor's shouts—I also hear

> The vanquish'd groan !—and now 'tis smoke—and now
> I see the loose sails shiver in the wind !
> I see—I see—what soon you'll see——
>
> *Gov.* Hold, daughter ! peace ! this love hath turn'd thy brain ;
> The Spanish fleet thou canst not see—because
> —It is not yet in sight ! "

Dang. Egad, though, the governor seems to make no allowance for this poetical figure you talk of.

Puff. No, a plain, matter-of-fact man ;—that's his character.

> " *Tilb.* But will you then refuse his offer ?
> *Gov.* I must—I will—I can—I ought—I do.
> *Tilb.* Think what a noble price.
> *Gov.* No more—you urge in vain.
> *Tilb.* His liberty is all he asks."

Sneer. All who asks, Mr. Puff ? Who is——

Puff. Egad, sir, I can't tell ! Here has been such cutting and slashing, I don't know where they have got to myself.

Tilb. Indeed, sir, you will find it will connect very well.

> " —And your reward secure."

Puff. Oh, if they hadn't been so devilish free with their cutting here, you would have found that Don Whiskerandos has been tampering for his liberty, and has persuaded Tilburina to make this proposal to her father. And now, pray observe the conciseness with which the argument is conducted. Egad, the *pro* and *con* goes as smart as hits in a fencing match. It is indeed a sort of small-sword-logic, which we have borrowed from the French.

> " *Tilb.* A retreat in Spain !
> *Gov.* Outlawry here !
> *Tilb.* Your daughter's prayer !
> *Gov.* Your father's oath !
> *Tilb.* My lover !
> *Gov.* My country !
> *Tilb.* Tilburina !
> *Gov.* England !
> *Tilb.* A title !
> *Gov.* Honour !
> *Tilb.* A pension !
> *Gov.* Conscience !
> *Tilb.* A thousand pounds !
> *Gov.* Ha ! thou hast touch'd me nearly ! "

Puff. There you see—she threw in *Tilburina*. Quick, parry carte with *England* ! Ha ! thrust in tierce *a title* !—parried by *honour*. Ha ! *a pension* over the arm !—put by by *conscience*.

Then flankonade with *a thousand pounds*—and a palpable hit, egad !

> " *Tilb.* Canst thou—
> Reject the suppliant, and the daughter too ?
> *Gov.* No more ; I would not hear thee plead in vain :
> The father softens—but the governor
> Is fix'd ! *[Exit.*"

Dang. Ay, that antithesis of persons is a most established figure.

> " *Tilb.* 'Tis well,—hence then, fond hopes,—fond passion hence;
> Duty, behold I am all over thine——
> *Whisk.* [*Without.*] Where is my love—my——
> *Tilb.* Ha !

Enter Don Ferolo Whiskerandos.

> *Whisk.* My beauteous enemy !——"

Puff. Oh dear, ma'am, you must start a great deal more than that ! Consider, you had just determined in favour of duty—when, in a moment, the sound of his voice revives your passion—overthrows your resolution—destroys your obedience. If you don't express all that in your start, you do nothing at all.

Tilb. Well, we'll try again.

Dang. Speaking from within has always a fine effect.

Sneer. Very.

> " *Whisk.* My conquering Tilburina ! How ! is't thus
> We meet ? why are thy looks averse ? what means
> That falling tear—that frown of boding woe ?
> Ha ! now indeed I am a prisoner !
> Yes, now I feel the galling weight of these
> Disgraceful chains—which, cruel Tilburina !
> Thy doting captive gloried in before.—
> But thou art false, and Whiskerandos is undone !
> *Tilb.* O no ! how little dost thou know thy Tilburina !
> *Whisk.* Art thou then true ?—Begone cares, doubts, and fears,
> I make you all a present to the winds ;
> And if the winds reject you—try the waves."

Puff. The wind, you know, is the established receiver of all stolen sighs, and cast-off griefs and apprehensions.

> " *Tilb.* Yet must we part !—stern duty seals our doom :
> Though here I call yon conscious clouds to witness,
> Could I pursue the bias of my soul,
> All friends, all right of parents, I'd disclaim,
> And thou, my Whiskerandos, shouldst be father
> And mother, brother, cousin, uncle, aunt,
> And friend to me !
> *Whisk.* Oh, matchless excellence ! and must we part ?
> Well, if—we must—we must—and in that case
> The less is said the better."

" What means that falling tear—that frown of boding woe ? "

Puff. Heyday ! here's a cut !—What, are all the mutual protestations out ?

Tilb. Now, pray, sir, don't interrupt us just here : you ruin our feelings.

Puff. Your feelings !—but, zounds, my feelings, ma'am !

Sneer. No, pray don't interrupt them.

" *Whisk.* One last embrace.
Tilb. Now,—farewell, for ever.
Whisk. For ever !
Tilb. Ay, for ever !   [*Going.*"

Puff. 'Sdeath and fury !—Gad's life !—sir ! madam ! if you go out without the parting look, you might as well dance out. Here, here !

Con. But pray, sir, how am I to get off here ?

Puff. You ! pshaw ! what the devil signifies how you get off ! edge away at the top, or where you will—[*Pushes the* CONFIDANT *off.*] Now, ma'am, you see——

Tilb. We understand you, sir.

" Ay, for ever.
Both.   Oh !   [*Turning back, and exeunt.—Scene closes.*"

Dang. Oh, charming !

Puff. Hey !—'tis pretty well, I believe : you see I don't attempt to strike out anything new—but I take it I improve on the established modes.

Sneer. You do, indeed ! But pray is not Queen Elizabeth to appear ?

Puff. No, not once—but she is to be talked of for ever ; so that, egad, you'll think a hundred times that she is on the point of coming in.

Sneer. Hang it, I think it's a pity to keep her in the green-room all the night.

Puff. Oh no, that always has a fine effect—it keeps up expectation.

Dang. But are we not to have a battle ?

Puff. Yes, yes, you will have a battle at last : but, egad, it's not to be by land, but by sea—and that is the only quite new thing in the piece.

Dang. What, Drake at the Armada, hey ?

Puff. Yes, i'faith—fire-ships and all ; then we shall end with the procession. Hey, that will do, I think ?

Sneer. No doubt on't.

Puff. Come, we must not lose time ; so now for the underplot.

Sneer. What the plague, have you another plot ?

Puff. O Lord, yes ; ever while you live have two plots to

your tragedy. The grand point in managing them is only to let your under-plot have as little connection with your main-plot as possible.—I flatter myself nothing can be more distinct than mine ; for as in my chief plot the characters are all great people, I have laid my under-plot in low life, and as the former is to end in deep distress, I make the other end as happy as a farce.—Now, Mr. Hopkins, as soon as you please.

Enter UNDER PROMPTER.

Under Promp. Sir, the carpenter says it is impossible you can go to the park scene yet.

Puff. The park scene ! no ! I mean the description scene here, in the wood.

Under Promp. Sir, the performers have cut it out.

Puff. Cut it out !

Under Promp. Yes, sir.

Puff. What ! the whole account of Queen Elizabeth ?

Under Promp. Yes, sir.

Puff. And the description of her horse and side-saddle ?

Under Promp. Yes, sir.

Puff. So, so ; this is very fine indeed !—Mr. Hopkins, how the plague could you suffer this ?

Mr. Hop. [*Within.*] Sir, indeed the pruning-knife——

Puff. The pruning-knife—zounds !—the axe ! Why, here has been such lopping and topping, I shan't have the bare trunk of my play left presently !—Very well, sir—the performers must do as they please ; but, upon my soul, I'll print it every word.

Sneer. That I would, indeed.

Puff. Very well, sir ; then we must go on.—Zounds ! I would not have parted with the description of the horse !—Well, sir, go on.—Sir, it was one of the finest and most laboured things.—Very well, sir ; let them go on.—There you had him and his accoutrements, from the bit to the crupper.—Very well, sir ; we must go to the park scene.

Under Promp. Sir, there is the point : the carpenters say, that unless there is some business put in here before the drop, they shan't have time to clear away the fort, or sink Gravesend and the river.

Puff. So ! this is a pretty dilemma, truly !—Gentlemen, you must excuse me—these fellows will never be ready, unless I go and look after them myself.

Sneer. Oh dear, sir, these little things will happen.

Puff. To cut out this scene !—but I'll print it—egad, I'll print it every word ! [*Exeunt.*

E. Œ. SOMERVILLE AND M. ROSS
(1862–1915), *whose real name was Violet
Martin, were cousins. They were born in
and lived in Ireland. Together they wrote
a number of fine studies of Irish life, both
serious and humorous. "Some Experiences
of an Irish R.M.," among which this story
appeared, was the first collection, and
quickly established the authors' reputation.*

OCCASIONAL LICENSES

"IT's out of the question," I said, looking forbiddingly at
Mrs. Moloney through the spokes of the bicycle that I
was pumping up outside the grocer's in Skebawn.

"Well, indeed, Major Yeates," said Mrs. Moloney, advancing
excitedly, and placing on the nickel plating a hand that I had
good and recent cause to know was warm, "sure I know well
that if th' angel Gabriel came down from heaven looking for a
license for the races, your honour wouldn't give it to him
without a charackther, but as for Michael! Sure, the world
knows what Michael is!"

I had been waiting for Philippa for already nearly half an
hour, and my temper was not at its best.

"Character or no character, Mrs. Moloney," said I with
asperity, "the magistrates have settled to give no occasional
licenses, and if Michael were as sober as——"

"Is it sober! God help us!" exclaimed Mrs. Moloney
with an upward rolling of her eye to the Recording Angel;
"I'll tell your honour the truth. I'm his wife, now, fifteen
years, and I never seen the sign of dhrink on Michael only once,
and that was when he went out o' good-nature helping Timsy
Ryan to whitewash his house, and Timsy and himself had a
couple o' pots o' porther, and look, he was as little used to it
that his head got light, and he walked away out to dhrive in the
cows and it no more than eleven o'clock in the day! And the
cows, the craytures, as much surprised, goin' hither and over
the four corners of the road from him! Faith, ye'd have to
laugh. 'Michael,' says I to him, 'ye're dhrunk!' 'I am,'
says he, and the tears rained from his eyes. I turned the cows
from him. 'Go home,' I says, 'and lie down on Willy Tom's
bed——'"

At this affecting point my wife came out of the grocer's with a large parcel to be strapped to my handlebar, and the history of Mr. Moloney's solitary lapse from sobriety got no further than Willy Tom's bed.

" You see," I said to Philippa, as we bicycled quietly home through the hot June afternoon, " we've settled we'll give no licenses for the sports. Why even young Sheehy, who owns three pubs in Skebawn, came to me and said he hoped the magistrates would be firm about it, as these one-day licenses were quite unnecessary, and only led to drunkenness and fighting, and every man on the Bench has joined in promising not to grant any."

" How nice, dear ! " said Philippa absently. " Do you know Mrs. McDonnell can only let me have three dozen cups and saucers ; I wonder if that will be enough ? "

" Do you mean to say you expect three dozen people ? " said I.

" Oh, it's always well to be prepared," replied my wife evasively.

During the next few days I realized the true inwardness of what it was to be prepared for an entertainment of this kind. Games were not at a high level in my district. Football, of a wild, guerilla species, was waged intermittently, blended in some inextricable way with Home Rule and a brass band, and on Sundays gatherings of young men rolled a heavy round stone along the roads, a rudimentary form of sport, whose fascination lay primarily in the fact that it was illegal, and, in lesser degree, in betting on the length of each roll. I had had a period of enthusiasm, during which I thought I was going to be the apostle of cricket in the neighbourhood, but my mission dwindled to single wicket with Peter Cadogan, who was indulgent but bored, and I swiped the ball through the dining-room window, and some one took one of the stumps to poke the laundry fire. Once a year, however, on that festival of the Roman Catholic Church which is familiarly known as " Pether and Paul's day," the district was wont to make a spasmodic effort at athletic sports, which were duly patronized by the gentry and promoted by the publicans, and this year the honour of a steward's green rosette was conferred upon me. Philippa's genius for hospitality here saw its chance, and broke forth into unbridled tea-party in connection with the sports, even involving me in the hire of a tent, the conveyance of chairs and tables, and other large operations.

It chanced that Flurry Knox had on this occasion lent the fields for the sports, with the proviso that horse-races and a tug-of-war were to be added to the usual programme ; Flurry's participation in events of this kind seldom failed to be of an inflaming character. As he and I planted larch spars for the high jump, and stuck furze-bushes into hurdles (locally known as " hurrls "), and skirmished hourly with people who wanted to sell drink on the course, I thought that my next summer leave would singularly coincide with the festival consecrated to St. Peter and St. Paul. We made a grand stand of quite four feet high, out of old fish-boxes, which smelt worse and worse as the day wore on, but was, none the less, as sought after by those for whom it was not intended, as is the Royal enclosure at Ascot ; we broke gaps in all the fences to allow carriages on to the ground, we armed a gang of the worst blackguards in Skebawn with cart-whips, to keep the course, and felt that organization could go no further.

The momentous day of Pether and Paul opened badly, with heavy clouds and every indication of rain, but after a few thunder showers things brightened, and it seemed within the bounds of possibility that the weather might hold up. When I got down to the course on the day of the sports the first thing I saw was a tent of that peculiar filthy grey that usually enshrines the sale of porter, with an array of barrels in a crate beside it ; I bore down upon it in all the indignant majesty of the law, and in so doing came upon Flurry Knox, who was engaged in flogging boys off the Grand Stand

" Sheehy's gone one better than you ! " he said, without taking any trouble to conceal the fact that he was amused.

" Sheehy ! " I said ; " why, Sheehy was the man who went to every magistrate in the country to ask them to refuse a license for the sports."

" Yes, he took some trouble to prevent any one else having a look in," replied Flurry ; " he asked every magistrate but one, and that was the one that gave him the license."

" You don't mean to say that it was you ? " I demanded in high wrath and supicion, remembering that Sheehy bred horses, and that my friend Mr. Knox was a person of infinite resource in the matter of a deal.

" Well, well," said Flurry, rearranging a disordered fish-box, " and me that's a churchwarden, and sprained my ankle a month ago with running downstairs at my grandmother's to be in time for prayers ! Where's the use of a good character in this country ? "

" Not much when you keep it eating its head off for want of exercise," I retorted ; " but if it wasn't you, who was it ? "

" Do you remember old Moriarty out at Castle Ire ? "

I remembered him extremely well as one of those representatives of the people with whom a paternal Government had leavened the effete ranks of the Irish magistracy.

" Well," resumed Flurry, " that license was as good as a five-pound note in his pocket."

I permitted myself a comment on Mr. Moriarty suitable to the occasion.

" Oh, that's nothing," said Flurry easily ; " he told me one day when he was half screwed that his Commission of the Peace was worth a hundred and fifty a year to him in turkeys and whisky, and he was telling the truth for once."

At this point Flurry's eye wandered, and following its direction I saw Lady Knox's smart 'bus cleaving its way through the throng of country people, lurching over the ups and downs of the field like a ship in a sea. I was too blind to make out the component parts of the white froth that crowned it on top, and seethed forth from it when it had taken up a position near the tent in which Philippa was even now propping the legs of the tea-table, but from the fact that Flurry addressed himself to the door, I argued that Miss Sally had gone inside.

Lady Knox's manner had something more than its usual bleakness. She had brought, as she promised, a large contingent, but from the way that the strangers within her gates melted impalpably and left me to deal with her single-handed, I drew the further deduction that all was not well.

" Did you ever in your life see such a gang of women as I have brought with me ? " she began with her wonted directness, as I piloted her to the Grand Stand, and placed her on the stoutest looking of the fish-boxes. " I have no patience with men who yacht ! Bernard Shute has gone off to the Clyde, and I had counted on his being a man at my dance next week. I suppose you'll tell me you're going away too."

I assured Lady Knox that I would be a man to the best of my ability.

" This is the last dance I shall give," went on her ladyship, unappeased ; " the men in this country consist of children and cads."

I admitted that we were but a poor lot, " but," I said, " Miss Sally told me——"

" Sally's a fool ! " said Lady Knox, with a falcon eye at her daughter, who happened to be talking to her distant kinsman, Mr. Flurry of that ilk.

The races had by this time begun with a competition known

as the " Hop, Step, and Lep " ; this, judging by the yells, was a highly interesting display, but as it was conducted between two impervious rows of onlookers, the aristocracy on the fish-boxes saw nothing save the occasionaly purple face of a competitor, starting into view above the wall of backs like a jack-in-the-box. For me, however, the odorous sanctuary of the fish-boxes was not to be. I left it guarded by Slipper with a cart-whip of flail-like dimensions, as disreputable an object as could be seen out of low comedy, with some one's old white cords on his bandy legs, butcher-boots three sizes too big for him, and a black eye. The small boys fled before him ; in the glory of his office he would have flailed his own mother off the fish-boxes had occasion served.

I had an afternoon of decidedly mixed enjoyment. My stewardship blossomed forth like Aaron's rod, and added to itself the duties of starter, handicapper, general referee, and chucker-out, besides which I from time to time strove with emissaries who came from Philippa with messages about water and kettles. Flurry and I had to deal single-handed with the foot-races (our brothers in office being otherwise engaged at Mr. Sheehy's), a task of many difficulties, chiefest being that the spectators all swept forward at the word " Go ! " and ran the race with the competitors, yelling curses, blessings, and advice upon them, taking short cuts over anything and everybody, and mingling inextricably with the finish. By fervent applications of the whips, the course was to some extent purged for the quarter-mile, and it would, I believe, have been a triumph of handicapping had not an unforeseen disaster overtaken the favourite—old Mrs. Knox's bath-chair boy. Whether, as was alleged, his braces had or had not been tampered with by a rival was a matter that the referee had subsequently to deal with in the thick of a free fight ; but the painful fact remained that in the course of the first lap what were described as " his galluses " abruptly severed their connection with the garments for whose safety they were responsible, and the favourite was obliged to seek seclusion in the crowd.

The tug-of-war followed close on this *contretemps*, and had the excellent effect of drawing away, like a blister, the inflam-mation set up by the grievances of the bath-chair boy. I cannot at this moment remember of how many men each team con-sisted ; my sole aim was to keep the numbers even, and to baffle the volunteers who, in an ecstasy of sympathy, attached themselves to the tail of the rope at moments when their champions weakened. The rival forces dug their heels in and

tugged, in an uproar that drew forth the innermost line of
customers from Mr. Sheehy's porter tent, and even attracted
" the quality " from the haven of the fish-boxes, Slipper, in the
capacity of Squire of Dames, pioneering Lady Knox through
the crowd with the cart-whip, and with language whose nature
was providentially veiled, for the most part, by the din. The
tug-of-war continued unabated. One team was getting the
worst of it, but hung doggedly on, sinking lower and lower till
they gradually sat down ; nothing short of the trump of judgment
could have conveyed to them that they were breaking rules, and
both teams settled down by slow degrees on to their sides, with the
rope under them, and their heels still planted in the ground,
bringing about complete deadlock. I do not know the record
duration for a tug-of-war, but I can certify that the Cullinagh
and Knockranny teams lay on the ground at full tension for half
an hour, like men in apoplectic fits, each man with his respective
adherents howling over him, blessing him, and adjuring him to
continue.

With my own nauseated eyes I saw a bearded countryman,
obviously one of Mr. Sheehy's best customers, fling himself on
his knees beside one of the combatants, and kiss his crimson
and streaming face in a rapture of encouragement. As he
shoved unsteadily past me on his return journey to Mr. Sheehy's,
I heard him informing a friend that " he cried a handful over
Danny Mulloy, when he seen the poor brave boy so shtubborn,
and, indeed, he couldn't stay why he cried."

" For good nature ye'd cry," suggested the friend.

" Well, just that, I suppose," returned Danny Mulloy's
admirer resignedly ; " indeed, if it was only two cocks ye seen
fightin' on the road, yer heart'd take part with one o' them ! "

I had begun to realize that I might as well abandon the tug-
of-war and occupy myself elsewhere, when my wife's much
harassed messenger brought me the portentous tidings that
Mrs. Yeates wanted me at the tent at once. When I arrived I
found the tent literally bulging with Philippa's guests ; Lady
Knox, seated on a hamper, was taking off her gloves, and loudly
announcing her desire for tea, and Philippa, with a flushed face
and a crooked hat, breathed into my ear the awful news that
both the cream and the milk had been forgotten.

" But Flurry Knox says he can get me some," she went on ;
" he's gone to send people to milk a cow that lives near here.
Go out and see if he's coming."

I went out and found, in the first instance, Mrs. Cadogan,
who greeted me with the prayer that the divil might roast Julia

McCarthy, that legged it away to the races like a wild goose, and left the cream afther her on the servants' hall table. " Sure, Misther Flurry's gone looking for a cow, and what cow would there be in a backwards place like this ? And look at me shtriving to keep the kettle simpering on the fire, and not as much coals undher it as'd redden a pipe ! "

" Where's Mr. Knox ? " I asked.

" Himself and Slipper's galloping the counthry like the deer. I believe it's to the house above they went, sir."

I followed up a rocky hill to the house above, and there found Flurry and Slipper engaged in the patriarchal task of driving two brace of coupled and spancelled goats into a shed.

" It's the best we can do," said Flurry briefly ; " there isn't a cow to be found, and the people are all down at the sports. Be d——d to you, Slipper, don't let them go from you ! " as the goats charged and doubled like football players.

" But goat's milk ! " I said, paralysed by horrible memories of what tea used to taste like at Gib.

" They'll never know it ! " said Flurry, cornering a venerable nanny ; " here, hold this divil, and hold her tight ! "

I have no time to dwell upon the pastoral scene that followed. Suffice it to say, that at the end of ten minutes of scorching profanity from Slipper, and incessant warfare with the goats, the latter had reluctantly yielded two small jugfuls, and the dairymaids had exhibited a nerve and skill in their trade that won my lasting respect.

" I knew I could trust *you*, Mr. Knox ! " said Philippa, with shining eyes, as we presented her with the two foaming beakers. I suppose a man is never a hero to his wife, but if she could have realized the bruises on my legs, I think she would have reserved a blessing for me also.

What was thought of the goats' milk I gathered symptomatically from a certain fixity of expression that accompanied the first sip of the tea, and from observing that comparatively few ventured on second cups. I also noted that after a brief conversation with Flurry, Miss Sally poured hers secretly on to the grass. Lady Knox had throughout the day preserved an aspect so threatening that no change was perceptible in her demeanour. In the throng of hungry guests I did not for some time notice that Mr. Knox had withdrawn until something in Miss Sally's eye summoned me to her, and she told me she had a message from him for me.

" Couldn't we come outside ? " she said.

Outside the tent, within less than six yards of her mother, Miss

Sally confided to me a scheme that made my hair stand on end. Summarized, it amounted to this : That, first, she was in the primary stage of a deal with Sheehy for a four-year-old chestnut colt, for which Sheehy was asking double its value on the assumption that it had no rival in the country ; that, secondly, they had just heard it was going to run in the first race ; and, thirdly and lastly, that as there was no other horse available, Flurry was going to take old Sultan out of the 'bus and ride him in the race ; and that Mrs. Yeates had promised to keep mamma safe in the tent, while the race was going on, and " you know, Major Yeates, it would be delightful to beat Sheehy after his getting the better of you all about the license ! "

With this base appeal to my professional feelings, Miss Knox paused and looked at me insinuatingly. Her eyes were greeny-grey, and very beguiling.

" Come on," she said ; " they want you to start them ! "

Pursued by visions of the just wrath of Lady Knox, I weakly followed Miss Sally to the farther end of the second field, from which point the race was to start. The course was not a serious one : two or three natural banks, a stone wall, and a couple of " hurrls." There were but four riders, including Flurry, who was seated composedly on Sultan, smoking a cigarette and talking confidentially to Slipper. Sultan, although something stricken in years and touched in the wind, was a brown horse who in his day had been a hunter of no mean repute ; even now he occasionally carried Lady Knox in a sedate and gentlemanly manner, but it struck me that it was trying him rather high to take him from the pole of the 'bus after twelve miles on a hilly road, and hustle him over a country against a four-year-old. My acutest anxiety, however, was to start the race as quickly as possible, and to get back to the tent in time to establish an *alibi* ; therefore I repressed my private sentiments, and, tying my handkerchief to a stick, determined that no time should be fashionably frittered away in false starts.

They got away somehow ; I believe Sheehy's colt was facing the wrong way at the moment when I dropped the flag, but a friend turned him with a stick, and, with a cordial and timely whack, speeded him on his way on sufficiently level terms, and then somehow, instead of returning to the tent, I found myself with Miss Sally on the top of a tall narrow bank, in a precarious line of other spectators, with whom we toppled and swayed, and, in moments of acuter emotion, held on to each other in unaffected comradeship.

Flurry started well, and from our commanding position we

could see him methodically riding at the first fence at a smart hunting canter, closely attended by James Canty's brother on a young black mare, and by an unknown youth on a big white horse. The hope of Sheehy's stable, a leggy chestnut, ridden by a cadet of the house of Sheehy, went away from the friend's stick like a rocket, and had already refused the first bank twice before old Sultan decorously changed feet on it and dropped down into the next field with tranquil precision. The white horse scrambled over it on his stomach, but landed safely, despite the fact that his rider clasped him round the neck during the process ; the black mare and the chestnut shouldered one another over at the hole the white horse had left, and the whole party went away in a bunch and jumped the ensuing hurdle without disaster. Flurry continued to ride at the same steady hunting pace, accompanied respectfully by the white horse and by Jerry Canty on the black mare. Sheehy's colt had clearly the legs of the party, and did some showy galloping between the jumps, but as he refused to face the banks without a lead, the end of the first round found the field still a sociable party personally conducted by Mr. Knox.

"That's a dam nice horse," said one of my hangers-on, looking approvingly at Sultan as he passed us at the beginning of the second round, making a good deal of noise but apparently going at his ease ; "you might depind your life on him, and he have the crabbedest jock in the globe of Ireland on him this minute."

"Canty's mare's very sour," said another ; "look at her now, baulking the bank ! she's as cross as a bag of weasels."

"Begob, I wouldn't say but she's a little sign lame," resumed the first : "she was going light on one leg on the road a while ago."

"I tell you what it is," said Miss Sally, very seriously, in my ear, "that chestnut of Sheehy's is settling down. I'm afraid he'll gallop away from Sultan at the finish, and the wall won't stop him. Flurry can't get another inch out of Sultan. He's riding him well," she ended in a critical voice, which yet was not quite like her own. Perhaps I should not have noticed it but for the fact that the hand that held my arm was trembling. As for me, I thought of Lady Knox, and trembled too.

There now remained but one bank, the trampled remnant of the furze hurdle, and the stone wall. The pace was beginning to improve, and the other horses drew away from Sultan ; they charged the bank at full gallop, the black mare and the chestnut flying it perilously, with a windmill flourish of legs and arms from their riders, the white horse racing up to it with a gallantry that deserted him at the critical moment, with the result that his rider turned a somersault over his head and landed, amidst the roars of the onlookers, sitting on the fence facing his horse's nose. With creditable presence of mind he remained on the bank, towed the horse over, scrambled on to his back again and started afresh. Sultan, thirty yards to the bad, pounded doggedly on, and Flurry's cane and heels remained idle ; the old horse, obviously blown, slowed cautiously coming in at the jump. Sally's grip tightened on my arm, and the crowd yelled as Sultan, answering to a hint from the spurs and a touch at his mouth, heaved himself on to the bank. Nothing but sheer riding on Flurry's part got him safe off it, and saved him from the consequences of a bad peck on landing ; none the less, he pulled himself together and went away down the hill for the stone wall as stoutly as ever. The high road skirted the last two fields, and there was a gate in the roadside fence beside the place where the stone wall met it at right angles. I had noticed this gate, because during the first round Slipper had been sitting on it, demonstrating with his usual fervour. Sheehy's colt was leading, with his nose in the air, his rider's hands going like a circular saw, and his temper, as a bystander remarked, " up on end " ; the black mare, half mad from spurring, was going hard at his heels, completely out of hand ; the white horse was steering steadily for the wrong side of the flag, and Flurry, by dint of cutting corners and of saving every yard of ground, was close enough to keep his antagonists' heads over their shoulders, while their right arms rose and fell in unceasing flagellation.

" There'll be a smash when they come to the wall ! If one falls they'll all go ! " panted Sally. " Oh !—— Now ! Flurry ! Flurry !——"

What had happened was that the chestnut colt had suddenly perceived that the gate at right angles to the wall was standing wide open, and, swinging away from the jump, he had bolted headlong out on to the road, and along it at top speed for his home. After him fled Canty's black mare, and with her, carried away by the spirit of stampede, went the white horse.

Flurry stood up in his stirrups and gave a view-halloa as he cantered down to the wall. Sultan came at it with the send of the hill behind him, and jumped it with a skill that intensified, if that were possible, the volume of laughter and yells around us. By the time the black mare and the white horse had returned and ignominiously bundled over the wall to finish as best they might, Flurry was leading Sultan towards us.

" That blackguard, Slipper ! " he said, grinning ; " every one'll say I told him to open the gate ! But look here, I'm afraid we're in for trouble. Sultan's given himself a bad over-reach ; you could never drive him home to-night. And I've just seen Norris lying blind drunk under a wall ! "

Now Norris was Lady Knox's coachman. We stood aghast at this " horror on horror's head," the blood trickled down Sultan's heel, and the lather lay in flecks on his dripping, heaving sides, in irrefutable witness to the iniquity of Lady Knox's only daughter. Then Flurry said :

" Thank the Lord, here's the rain ! "

At the moment I admit that I failed to see any cause for gratitude in this occurrence, but later on I appreciated Flurry's grasp of circumstances.

That appreciation was, I think, at its highest development about half an hour afterwards, when I, an unwilling conspirator (a part with which my acquaintance with Mr. Knox had rendered me but too familiar) unfurled Mrs. Cadogan's umbrella over Lady Knox's head, and hurried her through the rain from the tent to the 'bus, keeping it and my own person well between her and the horses. I got her in, with the rest of her bedraggled and exhausted party, and slammed the door.

" Remember, Major Yeates," she said through the window, " you are the *only* person here in whom I have any confidence. I don't wish *any* one else to touch the reins ! " this with a glance towards Flurry, who was standing near.

" I'm afraid I'm only a moderate whip," I said.

" My dear man," replied Lady Knox testily, " those horses could drive themselves ! "

I slunk round to the front of the 'bus. Two horses, carefully rugged, were in it, with the inevitable Slipper at their heads.

" Slipper's going with you," whispered Flurry, stepping up to me ; " she won't have me at any price. He'll throw the rugs over them when you get to the house, and if you hold the umbrella well over her she'll never see. I'll manage to get Sultan over somehow, when Norris is sober. That will be all right."

I climbed to the box without answering, my soul being bitter within me, as is the soul of a man who has been persuaded by womankind against his judgment.

" Never again ! " I said to myself, picking up the reins ; " let her marry him or Bernard Shute, or both of them if she likes, but I won't be roped into this kind of business again ! "

Slipper drew the rugs from the horses, revealing on the near side Lady Knox's majestic carriage horse, and on the off, a thick-set brown mare of about fifteen hands.

" What brute is this ? " said I to Slipper, as he swarmed up beside me.

" I don't rightly know where Misther Flurry got her," said Slipper, with one of his hiccoughing crows of laughter ; " give her the whip, Major, and "—here he broke into song :

> " *Howld to the shteel,*
> *Honamaundhiaoul ; she'll run off like an eel !* "

" If you don't shut your mouth," said I, with pent-up ferocity, " I'll chuck you off the 'bus."

Slipper was but slightly drunk, and, taking this delicate re-buke in good part, he relapsed into silence.

Wherever the brown mare came from, I can certify that it was not out of double harness. Though humble and anxious to oblige, she pulled away from the pole as if it were red hot, and at critical moments had a tendency to sit down. However, we squeezed without misadventure among the donkey carts and between the groups of people, and bumped at length in safety out on to the high road.

Here I thought it no harm to take Slipper's advice, and I applied the whip to the brown mare, who seemed inclined to turn round. She immediately fell into an uncertain canter that no effort of mine could frustrate ; I could only hope that Miss Sally would foster conversation inside the 'bus and create a dis-traction ; but judging from my last view of the party, and of Lady Knox in particular, I thought she was not likely to be successful. Fortunately the rain was heavy and thick, and a rising west wind gave every promise of its continuance. I had little doubt but that I should catch cold, but I took it to my bosom with gratitude as I reflected how it was drumming on the roof of the 'bus and blurring the windows.

We had reached the foot of a hill, about a quarter of a mile from the racecourse ; the Castle Knox horse addressed himself to it with dignified determination, but the mare showed a sudden and alarming tendency to jib.

" Belt her, Major ! " vociferated Slipper, as she hung back from the pole chain, with the collar half-way up her ewe neck, " and give it to the horse, too ! He'll dhrag her ! "

I was in the act of " belting," when a squealing whinny struck upon my ear, accompanied by a light pattering gallop on the road behind us ; there was an answering roar from the brown mare, a roar, as I realized with a sudden drop of the heart, of outraged maternal feeling, and in another instant a pale, yellow foal sprinted up beside us, with shrill whickerings of joy. Had there at this moment been a boghole handy, I should have turned the bus into it without hesitation ; as there was no accommodation of the kind, I laid the whip severely into everything I could reach, including the foal. The result was that we topped the hill at a gallop, three abreast, like a Russian troitska ; it was like my usual luck that at this identical moment we should meet the police patrol, who saluted respectfully.

" That the divil may blisther Michael Moloney ! " ejaculated Slipper, holding on to the rail ; " didn't I give him the foaleen and a halther on him to keep him ! I'll howld you a pint 'twas the wife let him go, for she being vexed about the license ! Sure that one's a March foal, an' he'd run from here to Cork ! "

There was no sign from my inside passengers, and I held on at a round pace, the mother and child galloping absurdly, the carriage horse pulling hard, but behaving like a gentleman. I wildly revolved plans of how I would make Slipper turn the foal in at the first gate we came to, of what I should say to Lady Knox supposing the worst happened and the foal accompanied us to her hall door, and of how I would have Flurry's blood at the earliest possible opportunity, and here the fateful sound of galloping behind us was again heard.

" It's impossible ! " I said to myself ; " she can't have twins ! "

The galloping came nearer, and Slipper looked back.

" Murdher alive ! " he said in a stage whisper ; " Tom Sheehy's afther us on the butcher's pony ! "

" What's that to me ? " I said, dragging my team aside to let him pass ; " I suppose he's drunk, like every one else ! "

Then the voice of Tom Sheehy made itself heard.

" Shtop ! Shtop thief ! " he was bawling ; " give up my mare ! How will I get me porther home ! "

That was the closest shave I have ever had, and nothing could have saved the position but the torrential nature of the rain and the fact that Lady Knox had on a new bonnet. I explained to her at the door of the 'bus that Sheehy was drunk (which was the one unassailable feature of the case), and had come after his foal, which, with the fatuity of its kind, had escaped from a field and followed us. I did not mention to Lady Knox that when Mr. Sheehy retreated, apologetically, dragging the foal after him in a halter belonging to one of her own carriage horses, he had a sovereign of mine in his pocket,

21*

and during the narration I avoided Miss Sally's eye as carefully as she avoided mine.

The only comments on the day's events that are worthy of record were that Philippa said to me that she had not been able to understand what the curious taste in the tea had been till Sally told her it was turf-smoke, and that Mrs. Cadogan said to Philippa that night that " the Major was that dhrinched that if he had a shirt between his skin and himself he could have wrung it," and that Lady Knox said to a mutual friend that though Major Yeates had been extremely kind and obliging, he was an uncommonly bad whip.

WILLIAM TAPPAN THOMPSON
(1812–1882) *began his career with the " Philadelphia Chronicle," and later established himself as a humorist of insight and originality. He contributed to a Miscellany column which he conducted some letters chronicling the adventures of Major Jones, who speedily became famous. One of the most important episodes in the Major's career is recounted here.*

HOW MAJOR JONES PROPOSED

PINEVILLE, *December* 27, 1842.

TO MR. THOMPSON. DEAR SIR—Crismus is over, and the thing is done did ! You know I told you in my last letter I was gwine to bring Miss Mary up to the chalk on Crismus. Well, I done it, slick as a whistle, though it come mighty nigh bein a serious bisness. But I'll tell you all about the whole circumstance.

The fact is, I's made my mind up more'n twenty times to jest go and come right out with the whole bisness ; but whenever I got whar she was, and whenever she looked at me with her witchin eyes, and kind o' blushed at me, I always felt sort 'o' skeered and fainty, and all what I made up to tell her was forgot, so I couldn't think of it to save me. But you's a married man, Mr. Thompson, so I couldn't tell you nothin about poppin the question, as they call it. It's a mighty grate favour to ax of a pretty gall ; and to people what ain't used to it, it goes monstrous hard, don't it. They say widders don't mind it no more'n nothing. But I'm makin a transgression, as the preacher ses.

Crismus eve I put on my new suit and shaved my face as slick as a smoothin iron, and after tea went over to old Miss Stallinses. As soon as I went into the parler whar they was all settin round the fire, Miss Carline and Miss Kesiah both laughed right out.

" There ! there ! " ses they, " I told you so ! I know'd it would be Joseph."

" What's I done, Miss Carline ? " ses I.

" You come under little sister's chicken bone, and I do believe she know'd you was comin when she put it over the dore."

" No, I didn't—I didn't no such thing, now," ses Miss Mary, and her face blushed red all over.

" Oh, you needn't deny it," ses Miss Kesiah ; " you belong to Joseph now jest as sure as ther's any charm in chicken bones."

I know'd that was a first-rate chance to say somethin, but the dear little creeter looked so sorry and kep blushin so, I couldn't say nothin zactly to the pint ! So I tuck a chair, and reached up and tuck down the bone and put it in my pocket.

" What are you gwine to do with that old chicken bone now, Majer ? " ses Miss Mary.

" I'm gwine to keep it as long as I live," ses I, " as a Crismus present from the handsomest gall in Georgia."

When I sed that she blushed worse and worse.

" Ain't you shamed, Majer ? " ses she.

" Now you ought to give her a Crismus gift, Joseph, to keep all her life," sed Miss Carline.

" Ah," ses old Miss Stallins, " when I was a gall we used to hang up our stockins——"

" Why, mother ! " ses all of 'em, " to say stockins right before——"

Then I felt a little streaked, too, cause they was all blushin as hard as they could.

" Highty-tity ! " ses the old lady, " what monstrous 'finement, to be shore ! I'd like to know what harm ther is in stockins. People nowadays is gittin so mealy-mouthed they can't call nothin by its right name, and I don't see as they's any better than the old-time people was. When I was a gall like you, child, I use to hang up my stockins and git 'em full of presents."

The galls kep laughin and blushin.

" Never mind," ses Miss Mary, " Majer's got to give me a Crismus gift—won't you, Majer ? "

" Oh yes," ses I ; " you know I promised you one."

" But I didn't mean that," ses she.

" I've got one for you, what I want you to keep all your life, but it would take a two-bushel bag to hold it," ses I.

" Oh, that's the kind," ses she.

" But will you promise to keep it as long as you live ? " ses I.

" Certainly I will, Majer."

" Monstrous 'finement nowadays—old people don't know nothin about perliteness," said old Miss Stallins, jest gwine to sleep with her nittin in her lap.

" Now you hear that, Miss Carline," ses I. " She ses she'll keep it all her life."

" Yes, I will," ses Miss Mary ; " but what is it ? "

" Never mind," ses I ; " you hang up a bag big enough to

hold it, and you'll find out what it is when you see it in the mornin."

Miss Carline winked at Miss Kesiah, and then whispered to her ; then they both laughed and looked at me as mischievous as they could. They 'spicioned something.

" You'll be shore to give it to me now, if I hang up a bag ? " ses Miss Mary.

" And promise to keep it," ses I.

" Well, I will, cause I know that you wouldn't give me nothin that wasn't worth keepin."

They all agreed they would hang up a bag for me to put Miss Mary's Crismus present in, on the back porch, and about ten o'clock I told 'em good evenin and went home.

I sot up till midnight, and when they was all gone to bed I went softly into the back gate and went up to the porch, and thar, shore enough, was a great big meal-bag hangin to the jice. It was monstrous unhandy to git to it, but I was termined not to back out. So I sot some chairs on top of a bench, and got hold of the rope, and let myself down into the bag ; but jest as I was gittin in, it swung gain the chairs, and down they went with a terrible racket ; but nobody didn't wake up but Miss Stallinses old cur dog, and here he come rippin and tearin through the yard like rath, and round and round he went, tryin to find what was the matter. I scrooch'd down in the bag and didn't breathe louder nor a kitten, for fear he'd find me out, and after a while he quit barkin.

The wind begun to blow bominable cold, and the old bag kep turnin round and swingin so it made me seasick as the mischief. I was afraid to move for fear the rope would break and let me fall, and thar I sot with my teeth rattlin like I had a ager. It seemed like it would never come daylight, and I do believe if I didn't love Miss Mary so powerful I would froze to death, for my heart was the only spot that felt warm, and it didn't beat more'n two licks a minit, only when I thought how she would be surprised in the mornin, and then it went in a canter. Bimeby the cussed old dog come up on the porch and begun to smell about the bag, and then he barked like he thought he'd treed somethin.

" Bow ! wow ! wow ! " ses he. Then he'd smell agin, and try to git up to the bag. " Git out ! " ses I, very low, for fear the galls mought hear me. " Bow ! wow ! " ses he. " Be gone ! you bominable fool ! " ses I, and I felt all over in spots, for I spected every minit he'd nip me, and what made it worse, I didn't know wharabouts he'd take hold. " Bow ! wow ! wow ! "

Then I tried coaxin. "Come here, good feller," ses I, and whistled a little to him, but it wasn't no use. Thar he stood and kep up his everlastin whinin and barkin all night. I couldn't tell when daylight was breakin, only by the chickens crowin, and I was monstrous glad to hear 'em, for if I'd had to stay thar one hour more I don't believe I'd ever got out of that bag alive.

Old Miss Stallins come out fust, and as soon as she seed the bag ses she :

"What upon yeath has Joseph went and put in that bag for Mary ? I'll lay it's a yearlin or some live animal, or Bruin wouldn't bark at it so."

She went in to call the galls, and I sot thar, shiverin all over so I couldn't hardly speak if I tried to—but I didn't say nothin. Bimeby they all come runnin out on the porch.

"My goodness ! what is it ? " ses Miss Mary.

"Oh, it's alive ! " ses Miss Kesiah. "I seed it move."

"Call Cato, and make him cut the rope," ses Miss Carline, "and let's see what it is. Come here, Cato, and git this bag down."

"Don't hurt it for the world," ses Miss Mary.

Cato untied the rope that was round the jice and let the bag down easy on the floor, and I tumbled out, all covered with corn-meal from head to foot.

"Goodness gracious ! " ses Miss Mary, "if it ain't the Majer himself ! "

"Yes," ses I, "and you know you promised to keep my Crismus present as long as you lived."

The galls laughed themselves almost to death, and went to brushin off the meal as fast as they could, sayin they were gwine to hang that bag up every Crismus till they got husbands too. Miss Mary—bless her bright eyes !—she blushed as beautiful as a mornin-glory, and sed she'd stick to her word. She was right out of bed, and her hair wasn't komed, and her dress wasn't fix'd at all, but the way she looked pretty was real distractin. I do believe, if I was froze stiff, one look at her sweet face, as she stood thar lookin down to the floor with her roguish eyes, and her bright curls fallin all over her snowy neck, would have fotched me too. I tell you what, it was worth hangin in a meal bag from one Crismus to another to feel as happy as I have ever sense.

I went home after we had the laugh out, and sot by the fire till I got thawed. In the forenoon all the Stallinses come over to our house, and we had one of the greatest Crismus dinners that ever was seed in Georgia, and I don't believe a happier company ever sot down to the same table. Old Miss Stallins and mother settled the match and talked over everything that ever happened in ther families, and laughed at me and Mary, and cried about ther dead husbands, cause they wasn't alive to see ther children married.

It's all settled now, 'cept we hain't sot the weddin day. I'd like to have it all over at once, but young galls always like to be engaged a while, you know, so I spose I must wait a month or so. Mary (she ses I mustn't call her Miss Mary now) has been a good deal of trouble and botheration to me, but if you could see her you wouldn't think I ought to grudge a little sufferin to get sich a sweet little wife.

You must come to the weddin if you possibly kin. I'll let you know when. No more from—Your friend, till death,

Jos Jones.

MARK TWAIN (1835–1910), *whose real name was Samuel Langhorne Clemens, was for some years a pilot on a boat in the Mississippi, and adopted as his pseudonym the leadsman's call with which he had thus become familiar. In his boyhood he was apprenticed to a printer. "Jim Smiley and his Jumping Frog" brought him into literary prominence, and "Tom Sawyer" and "Huckleberry Finn" have become immortal among humorous masterpieces.*

THE STOLEN WHITE ELEPHANT *

THE following curious history was related to me by a chance railway acquaintance. He was a gentleman more than seventy years of age, and his thoroughly good and gentle face and earnest and sincere manner imprinted the unmistakable stamp of truth upon every statement which fell from his lips. He said :

You know in what reverence the royal white elephant of Siam is held by the people of that country. You know it is sacred to kings, only kings may possess it, and that it is indeed in a measure even superior to kings, since it receives not merely honour but worship. Very well ; five years ago, when the troubles concerning the frontier line arose between Great Britain and Siam, it was presently manifest that Siam had been in the wrong. Therefore every reparation was quickly made, and the British representative stated that he was satisfied and the past should be forgotten. This greatly relieved the King of Siam, and partly as a token of gratitude, but partly also, perhaps, to wipe out any little remaining vestige of unpleasantness which England might feel toward him, he wished to send the Queen a present—the sole sure way of propitiating an enemy, according to Oriental ideas. This present ought not only to be a royal one, but transcendently royal. Wherefore, what offering could be so meet as that of a white elephant ? My position in the Indian civil service was such that I was deemed peculiarly worthy the honour of conveying the present to Her Majesty. A ship was fitted out for me and my servants and the officers

* Left out of *A Tramp Abroad*, because it was feared that some of the particulars had been exaggerated, and that others were not true. Before these suspicions had been proven groundless, the book had gone to press.—M. T.

656

and attendants of the elephant, and in due time I arrived in New York harbour and placed my royal charge in admirable quarters in Jersey City. It was necessary to remain awhile in order to recruit the animal's health before resuming the voyage.

All went well during a fortnight—then my calamities began. The white elephant was stolen ; I was called up at dead of night and informed of this fearful misfortune. For some moments I was beside myself with terror and anxiety ; I was helpless. Then I grew calmer and collected my faculties. I soon saw my course—for indeed there was but the one course for an intelligent man to pursue. Late as it was, I flew to New York and got a policeman to conduct me to the headquarters of the detective force. Fortunately I arrived in time, though the chief of the force, the celebrated Inspector Blunt, was just on the point of leaving for his home. He was a man of middle size and compact frame, and when he was thinking deeply he had a way of knitting his brows and tapping his forehead reflectively with his finger, which impressed you at once with the conviction that you stood in the presence of a person of no common order. The very sight of him gave me confidence and made me hopeful. I stated my errand. It did not flurry him in the least ; it had no more visible effect upon his iron self-possession than if I had told him somebody had stolen my dog. He motioned me to a seat, and said calmly :

" Allow me to think a moment, please."

So saying, he sat down at his office table and leaned his head upon his hand. Several clerks were at work at the other end of the room ; the scratching of their pens was all the sound I heard during the next six or seven minutes. Meantime the inspector sat there buried in thought. Finally he raised his head, and there was that in the firm lines of his face which showed me that his brain had done its work and his plan was made. Said he—and his voice was low and impressive :

" This is no ordinary case. Every step must be warily taken ; each step must be made sure before the next is ventured. And secrecy must be observed—secrecy profound and absolute. Speak to no one about the matter, not even the reporters. I will take care of *them* ; I will see that they get only what it may suit my ends to let them know." He touched a bell ; a youth appeared. " Alaric, tell the reporters to remain for the present." The boy retired. " Now let us proceed to business— and systematically. Nothing can be accomplished in this trade of mine without strict and minute method."

He took a pen and some paper. " Now—name of the elephant ? "

" Hassan Ben Ali Ben Selim Abdallah Mohammed Moisé Alhammal Jamsetjejeebhoy Dhuleep Sultan Ebu Bhudpoor."

" Very well.   Given name ? "

" Jumbo."

" Very well.   Place of birth ? "

" The capital city of Siam."

" Parents living ? "

" No—dead."

" Had they any other issue besides this one ? "

" None—he was an only child."

" Very well.   These matters are sufficient under that head. Now please describe the elephant, and leave out no particular, however insignificant—that is, insignificant from *your* point of view.   To men in my profession there *are* no insignificant particulars ; they do not exist."

I described ; he wrote.   When I was done, he said :

" Now listen.   If I have made any mistakes, correct me."

He read as follows :

" Height, 19 feet ; length, from apex of forehead to insertion of tail, 26 feet ; length of trunk, 16 feet ; length of tail, 6 feet ; total length, including trunk and tail, 48 feet ; length of tusks, 9½ feet ; ears in keeping with these dimensions ; footprint resembles the mark when one up-ends a barrel in the snow ; colour of the elephant, a dull white ; has a hole the size of a plate in each ear for the insertion of jewellery, and possesses the habit in a remarkable degree of squirting water upon spectators and of maltreating with his trunk not only such persons as he is acquainted with, but even entire strangers ; limps slightly with his right hind leg, and has a small scar in his left armpit caused by a former boil ; had on, when stolen, a castle containing seats for fifteen persons, and a gold-cloth saddle-blanket the size of an ordinary carpet."

There were no mistakes.   The inspector touched the bell, handed the description to Alaric, and said :

" Have fifty thousand copies of this printed at once and mailed to every detective office and pawnbroker's shop on the Continent."   Alaric retired.   " There—so far, so good.   Next, I must have a photograph of the property."

I gave him one.   He examined it critically, and said :

" It must do, since we can do no better ; but he has his trunk curled up and tucked into his mouth.   That is unfortunate, and is calculated to mislead, for of course he does not usually have it in that position." He touched his bell.

" Alaric, have fifty thousand copies of this photograph made, the first thing in the morning, and mail them with the descriptive circulars."

Alaric retired to execute his orders. The inspector said :

" It will be necessary to offer a reward, of course. Now as to the amount ? "

" What sum would you suggest ? "

" To *begin* with, I should say—well, twenty-five thousand dollars. It is an intricate and difficult business ; there are a thousand avenues of escape and opportunities of concealment. These thieves have friends and pals everywhere——"

" Bless me, do you know who they are ? "

The wary face, practised in concealing the thoughts and feelings within, gave me no token, nor yet the replying words, so quietly uttered :

" Never mind about that. I may, and I may not. We generally gather a pretty shrewd inkling of who our man is by the manner of his work and the size of the game he goes after. We are not dealing with a pickpocket or a hall thief, now, make up your mind to that. This property was not ' lifted ' by a novice. But, as I was saying, considering the amount of travel which will have to be done, and the diligence with which the thieves will cover up their traces as they move along, twenty-five thousand may be too small a sum to offer, yet I think it worth while to start with that."

So we determined upon that figure, as a beginning. Then this man, whom nothing escaped which could by any possibility be made to serve as a clue, said :

" There are cases in detective history to show that criminals have been detected through peculiarities in their appetites. Now, what does this elephant eat, and how much ? "

" Well, as to *what* he eats—he will eat *anything*. He will eat a man, he will eat a Bible—he will eat anything *between* a man and a Bible."

" Good—very good indeed, but too general. Details are necessary—details are the only valuable things in our trade. Very well—as to men. At one meal—or, if you prefer, during one day—how many men will he eat, if fresh ? "

" He would not care whether they were fresh or not ; at a single meal he would eat five ordinary men."

" Very good ; five men ; we will put that down. What nationalities would he prefer ? "

" He is indifferent about nationalities. He prefers acquaintances, but is not prejudiced against strangers."

" Very good. Now as to Bibles. How many Bibles would he eat at a meal ? "

" He would eat an entire edition."

" It is hardly succinct enough. Do you mean the ordinary octavo, or the family illustrated ? "

" I think he would be indifferent to illustrations ; that is, I think he would not value illustrations above simple letterpress."

" No, you do not get my idea. I refer to bulk. The ordinary octavo Bible weighs about two pounds and a half, while the great quarto with the illustrations weighs ten or twelve. How many Doré Bibles would he eat at a meal ? "

" If you knew this elephant, you could not ask. He would take what they had."

" Well, put it in dollars and cents, then. We must get at it somehow. The Doré costs a hundred dollars a copy, Russia leather, bevelled."

" He would require about fifty thousand dollars' worth— say an edition of five hundred copies."

" Now, that is more exact. I will put that down. Very well ; he likes men and Bibles ; so far, so good. What else will he eat ? I want particulars."

" He will leave Bibles to eat bricks, he will leave bricks to eat bottles, he will leave bottles to eat clothing, he will leave clothing to eat cats, he will leave cats to eat oysters, he will leave oysters to eat ham, he will leave ham to eat sugar, he will leave sugar to eat pie, he will leave pie to eat potatoes, he will leave potatoes to eat bran, he will leave bran to eat hay, he will leave hay to eat oats, he will leave oats to eat rice, for he was mainly raised on it. There is nothing whatever that he will not eat but European butter, and he would eat that if he could taste it."

" Very good. General quantity at a meal—say about——"

" Well, anywhere from a quarter to half a ton."

" And he drinks——"

" Everything that is fluid. Milk, water, whisky, molasses, castor oil, camphene, carbolic acid—it is no use to go into particulars ; whatever fluid occurs to you set it down. He will drink anything that is fluid, except European coffee."

" Very good. As to quantity ? "

" Put it down five to fifteen barrels—his thirst varies ; his other appetites do not."

" These things are unusual. They ought to furnish quite good clues toward tracing him."

He touched the bell.

" Alaric, summon Captain Burns."

Burns appeared. Inspector Blunt unfolded the whole matter to him, detail by detail. Then he said in the clear, decisive tones of a man whose plans are clearly defined in his head, and who is accustomed to command :

" Captain Burns, detail Detectives Jones, Davis, Halsey, Bates, and Hackett to shadow the elephant."

" Yes, sir."

" Detail Detectives Moses, Dakin, Murphy, Rogers, Tupper, Higgins, and Bartholomew to shadow the thieves."

" Yes, sir."

" Place a strong guard—a guard of thirty picked men, with a relief of thirty—over the place from whence the elephant was stolen, to keep strict watch there night and day, and allow none to approach—except reporters—without written authority from me."

" Yes, sir."

" Place detectives in plain clothes in the railway, steamship, and ferry depots, and upon all roadways leading out of Jersey City, with orders to search all suspicious persons."

" Yes, sir."

" Furnish all these men with photograph and accompanying description of the elephant, and instruct them to search all trains and outgoing ferryboats and other vessels."

" Yes, sir."

" If the elephant should be found, let him be seized, and the information forwarded to me by telegraph."

" Yes, sir."

" Let me be informed at once if any clues should be found— footprints of the animal, or anything of that kind."

" Yes, sir."

" Get an order commanding the harbour police to patrol the frontages vigilantly."

" Yes, sir."

" Dispatch detectives in plain clothes over all the railways, north as far as Canada, west as far as Ohio, south as far as Washington."

" Yes, sir."

" Place experts in all the telegraph offices to listen to all messages ; and let them require that all cipher dispatches be interpreted to them."

" Yes, sir."

" Let all these things be done with the utmost secrecy—mind, the most impenetrable secrecy."

" Yes, sir."

" Report to me promptly at the usual hour."

" Yes, sir."

" Go ! "

" Yes, sir."

He was gone.

Inspector Blunt was silent and thoughtful a moment, while the fire in his eye cooled down and faded out. Then he turned to me and said in a placid voice :

" I am not given to boasting, it is not my habit ; but—we shall find the elephant."

I shook him warmly by the hand and thanked him ; and I *felt* my thanks, too. The more I had seen of the man the more I liked him, and the more I admired and marvelled over the mysterious wonders of his profession. Then we parted for the night, and I went home with a far happier heart than I had carried with me to his office.

II

NEXT morning it was all in the newspapers, in the minutest detail. It even had additions—consisting of Detective This, Detective That, and Detective The Other's " Theory " as to how the robbery was done, who the robbers were, and whither they had flown with their booty. There were eleven of these theories, and they covered all the possibilities ; and this single fact shows what independent thinkers detectives are. No two theories were alike, or even much resembled each other, save in one striking particular, and in that one all the eleven theories were absolutely agreed. That was, that although the rear of my building was torn out and the only door remained locked, the elephant had not been removed through the rent, but by some other (undiscovered) outlet. All agreed that the robbers had made that rent only to mislead the detectives. That never would have occurred to me or to any other layman, perhaps, but it had not deceived the detectives for a moment. Thus, what I had supposed was the only thing that had no mystery about it was in fact the very thing I had gone farthest astray in. The eleven theories all named the supposed robbers, but no two named the same robbers ; the total number of suspected persons was thirty-seven. The various newspaper accounts all closed with the most important opinion of all—that of Chief Inspector Blunt. A portion of this statement read as follows :

THE STOLEN WHITE ELEPHANT

" The chief knows who the two principals are, namely, 'Brick' Duffy and 'Red' McFadden. Ten days before the robbery was achieved he was already aware that it was to be attempted, and had quietly proceeded to shadow these two noted villains ; but unfortunately on the night in question their track was lost, and before it could be found again the bird was flown—that is, the elephant.

" Duffy and McFadden are the boldest scoundrels in the profession ; the chief has reason for believing that they are the men who stole the stove out of the detective headquarters on a bitter night last winter—in consequence of which the chief and every detective were in the hands of the physicians before morning, some with frozen feet, others with frozen fingers, ears, and other members."

When I read the first half of that I was more astonished than ever at the wonderful sagacity of this strange man. He not only saw everything in the present with a clear eye, but even the future could not be hidden from him. I was soon at his office, and said I could not help wishing he had had those men arrested, and so prevented the trouble and loss ; but his reply was simple and unanswerable :

" It is not our province to prevent crime, but to punish it. We cannot punish it until it is committed."

I remarked that the secrecy with which we had begun had been marred by the newspapers ; not only all our facts but all our plans and purposes had been revealed ; even all the suspected persons had been named ; these would doubtless disguise themselves now, or go into hiding.

" Let them. They will find that when I am ready for them, my hand will descend upon them, in their secret places, as unerringly as the hand of fate. As to the newspapers, we *must* keep in with them. Fame, reputation, constant public mention —these are the detective's bread and butter. He must publish his facts, else he will be supposed to have none ; he must publish his theory, for nothing is so strange or striking as a detective's theory, or brings him so much wondering respect ; we must publish our plans, for these the journals insist upon having, and we could not deny them without offending. We must constantly show the public what we are doing, or they will believe we are doing nothing. It is much pleasanter to have a newspaper say, ' Inspector Blunt's ingenious and extraordinary theory is as follows,' than to have it say some harsh thing, or, worse still, some sarcastic one."

" I see the force of what you say. But I noticed that in one part of your remarks in the papers this morning, you refused to reveal your opinion upon a certain minor point."

"Yes, we always do that ; it has a good effect. Besides, I had not formed any opinion on that point, any way."

I deposited a considerable sum of money with the inspector, to meet current expenses, and sat down to wait for news. We were expecting the telegrams to begin to arrive at any moment now. Meantime I re-read the newspapers and also our descriptive circular, and observed that our $25,000 reward seemed to be offered only to detectives. I said I thought it ought to be offered to anybody who would catch the elephant. The inspector said :

"It is the detectives who will find the elephant, hence the reward will go to the right place. If other people found the animal, it would only be by watching the detectives and taking advantage of clues and indications stolen from them, and that would entitle the detectives to the reward, after all. The proper office of a reward is to stimulate the men who deliver up their time and their trained sagacities to this sort of work, and not to confer benefits upon chance citizens who stumble upon a capture without having earned the benefits by their own merits and labours."

This was reasonable enough, certainly. Now the telegraphic machine in the corner began to click, and the following dispatch was the result :

"FLOWER STATION, N.Y. : 7.30 a.m.

"*Have got a clue. Found a succession of deep tracks across a farm near here. Followed them two miles east without result ; think elephant went west. Shall now shadow him in that direction.*

"DARLEY, *Detective.*"

"Darley's one of the best men on the force," said the inspector. "We shall hear from him again before long."

Telegram No. 2 came :

"BARKER'S, N.J. : 7.40 a.m.

"*Just arrived. Glass factory broken open here during night and eight hundred bottles taken. Only water in large quantity near here is five miles distant. Shall strike for there. Elephant will be thirsty. Bottles were empty.*

"BAKER, *Detective.*"

" That promises well, too," said the inspector.   " I told you the creature's appetites would not be bad clues."

Telegram No. 3 :

" TAYLORVILLE, L.I. : 8.15 a.m.

" *A haystack near here disappeared during night.   Probably eaten.   Have got a clue, and am off.*

" HUBBARD, *Detective.*"

" How he does move around ! " said the inspector.   " I knew we had a difficult job on hand, but we shall catch him yet."

" FLOWER STATION, N.Y. : 9. a.m.

" *Shadowed the tracks three miles westward.   Large, deep, and ragged.   Have just met a farmer who says they are not elephant tracks.   Says they are holes where he dug up saplings for shade-trees when ground was frozen last winter.   Give me orders how to proceed.*

" DARLEY, *Detective.*"

" Aha ! a confederate of the thieves ! The thing grows warm," said the inspector.

He dictated the following telegram to Darley :

" *Arrest the man and force him to name his pals.   Continue to follow the tracks—to the Pacific, if necessary.*

" *Chief* BLUNT."

Next telegram :

" CONEY POINT, PA. : 8.45 a.m.

" *Gas office broken here during night and three months' unpaid gas bills taken.   Have got a clue and am away.*

" MURPHY, *Detective.*"

" Heavens ! " said the inspector, " would he eat gas bills ? "

" Through ignorance—yes ; but they cannot support life. At least, unassisted."

Now came this exciting telegram :

" IRONVILLE, N.Y. : 9.30 a.m.

" *Just arrived.   This village in consternation.   Elephant passed through here at five this morning.   Some say he went east, some say west, some north, some south—but all say they did not wait to notice particularly. He killed a horse ; have secured a piece of it for a clue. Killed it with his trunk ; from style of blow, think he struck it left-handed. From position in which horse lies, think elephant travelled northward along line of Berkley railway. Has four and a half hours' start ; but I move on his track at once.*

" HAWES, *Detective."*

I uttered exclamations of joy. The inspector was as self-contained as a graven image. He calmly touched his bell.

" Alaric, send Captain Burns here."

Burns appeared.

" How many men are ready for instant orders ? "

" Ninety-six, sir."

" Send them north at once. Let them concentrate along the line of the Berkley road north of Ironville."

" Yes, sir."

" Let them conduct their movements with the utmost secrecy. As fast as others are at liberty, hold them for orders."

" Yes, sir."

" Go ! "

" Yes, sir."

Presently came another telegram :

"SAGE CORNERS, N.Y. : 10.30.

" Just arrived. Elephant passed through here at 8.15. All escaped from the town but a policeman. Apparently elephant did not strike at policeman, but at the lamp-post. Got both. I have secured a portion of the policeman as clue.

" STUMM, *Detective."*

" So the elephant has turned westward," said the inspector " However, he will not escape, for my men are scattered all over that region."

The next telegram said :

"GLOVER'S, 11.15.

" Just arrived. Village deserted, except sick and aged. Elephant passed through three-quarters of an hour ago. The anti-temperance mass meeting was in session ; he put his trunk in at a window and washed it out with water from cistern. Some swallowed it—since dead ; several drowned. Detectives Cross and O'Shaughnessy were passing through town, but going south, so missed elephant. Whole region for many miles around in

terror—people flying from their homes. Wherever they turn they meet elephant, and many are killed.

"BRANT, *Detective.*"

I could have shed tears, this havoc so distressed me. But the inspector only said :

"You see—we are closing in on him. He feels our presence ; he has turned eastward again."

Yet further troublous news was in store for us. The telegraph brought this :

"HOGANPORT, 12.19.

"*Just arrived. Elephant passed through half an hour ago, creating wildest fright and excitement. Elephant raged around streets ; two plumbers going by, killed one—other escaped. Regret general.*

"O'FLAHERTY, *Detective.*"

"Now he is right in the midst of my men," said the inspector. "Nothing can save him."

A succession of telegrams came from detectives who were scattered through New Jersey and Pennsylvania, and who were following clues consisting of ravaged barns, factories, and Sunday-school libraries, with high hopes—hopes amounting to certainties, indeed. The inspector said :

"I wish I could communicate with them and order them north, but that is impossible. A detective only visits a telegraph office to send his report ; then he is off again, and you don't know where to put your hand on him."

Now came this dispatch :

"BRIDGEPORT, CT. : 12.15.

"*Barnum offers rate of $4000 a year for exclusive privilege of using elephant as travelling advertising medium from now till detectives find him. Wants to paste circus-posters on him. Desires immediate answer.*

"BOGGS, *Detective.*"

"That is perfectly absurd !" I exclaimed.

"Of course it is," said the inspector. "Evidently Mr. Barnum, who thinks he is so sharp, does not know me—but I know him."

Then he dictated this answer to the dispatch :

"*Mr. Barnum's offer declined. Make it $7000 or nothing.*

"*Chief* BLUNT."

" There. We shall not have to wait long for an answer, Mr. Barnum is not at home ; he is in the telegraph office—it is his way when he has business on hand. Inside of three——"

"DONE—P. T. BARNUM."

So interrupted the clicking telegraphic instrument. Before I could make a comment upon this extraordinary episode, the following dispatch carried my thoughts into another and very distressing channel :

"BOLIVIA, N.Y. : 12.50.

" *Elephant arrived here from south and passed through toward the forest at 11.50, dispersing a funeral on the way, and diminishing the mourners by two. Citizens fired some small cannon-balls into him, and then fled. Detective Burke and I arrived ten minutes later, from the north, but mistook some excavations for footprints, and so lost a good deal of time ; but at last we struck the right trail and followed it to the woods. We then got down on our hands and knees and continued to keep a sharp eye on the track, and so shadowed it into the brush. Burke was in advance. Unfortunately the animal had stopped to rest ; therefore, Burke having his head down, intent upon the track, butted up against the elephant's hind legs before he was aware of his vicinity. Burke instantly rose to his feet, seized the tail, and exclaimed joyfully, ' I claim the re——' but got no further, for a single blow of the huge trunk laid the brave fellow's fragments low in death. I fled rearward, and the elephant turned and shadowed me to the edge of the wood, making tremendous speed, and I should inevitably have been lost, but that the remains of the funeral providentially intervened again and diverted his attention. I have just learned that nothing of that funeral is now left ; but this is no loss, for there is an abundance of material for another. Meantime the elephant has disappeared again.*

"MULROONEY, *Detective.*"

We heard no news except from the diligent and confident detectives scattered about New Jersey, Pennsylvania, Delaware, and Virginia—who were all following fresh and encouraging clues—until shortly after 2 p.m., when this telegram came :

"BAXTER CENTRE, 2.15.

" *Elephant been here, plastered over with circus-bills, and broke up a revival, striking down and damaging many who were on the point of entering upon a better life. Citizens penned him*

Burke . . . seized the tail, and exclaimed joyfully, " I claim the re——"
but got no further

*up, and established a guard. When Detective Brown and I
arrived, some time after, we entered enclosure and proceeded to
identify elephant by photograph and description. All marks
tallied exactly except one, which we could not see—the boil-scar
under armpit. To make sure, Brown crept under to look, and
was immediately brained—that is, head crushed and destroyed,
though nothing issued from débris. All fled ; so did elephant,
striking right and left with much effect. Has escaped, but left
bold blood-track from cannon-wounds. Rediscovery certain.
He broke southward through a dense forest.*

"BRENT, *Detective.*"

That was the last telegram. At nightfall a fog shut down
which was so dense that objects but three feet away could not be
discerned. This lasted all night. The ferry-boats and even the
omnibuses had to stop running.

III

NEXT morning the papers were as full of detective theories as
before ; they had all our tragic facts in detail also, and a
great many more which they had received from their telegraphic correspondents. Column after column was occupied,
a third of its way down, with glaring headlines, which it made
my heart sick to read. Their general tone was like this :

"THE WHITE ELEPHANT AT LARGE ! HE MOVES UPON HIS
FATAL MARCH ! WHOLE VILLAGES DESERTED BY THEIR FRIGHT-
STRICKEN OCCUPANTS ! PALE TERROR GOES BEFORE HIM,
DEATH AND DEVASTATION FOLLOW AFTER ! AFTER THESE, THE
DETECTIVES. BARNS DESTROYED, FACTORIES GUTTED, HARVESTS
DEVOURED, PUBLIC ASSEMBLAGES DISPERSED, ACCOMPANIED BY
SCENES OF CARNAGE IMPOSSIBLE TO DESCRIBE ! THEORIES OF
THIRTY-FOUR OF THE MOST DISTINGUISHED DETECTIVES ON THE
FORCE ! THEORY OF CHIEF BLUNT ! "

"There ! " said Inspector Blunt, almost betrayed into excitement, " this is magnificent ! This is the greatest windfall
that any detective organization ever had. The fame of it will
travel to the ends of the earth, and endure to the end of time,
and my name with it."

But there was no joy for me. I felt as if I had committed
all those red crimes, and that the elephant was only my irresponsible agent. And how the list had grown ! In one place

he had " interfered with an election and killed five repeaters."
He had followed this act with the destruction of two poor fellows,
named O'Donohue and McFlannigan, who had " found a refuge
in the home of the oppressed of all lands only the day before,
and were in the act of exercising for the first time the noble right
of American citizens at the polls, when stricken down by the
relentless hand of the Scourge of Siam."   In another, he had
" found a crazy sensation-preacher preparing his next season's
heroic attacks on the dance, the theatre, and other things which
can't strike back, and had stepped on him."   And in still another place he had " killed a lightning-rod agent."   And so the
list went on, growing redder and redder, and more and more
heartbreaking.   Sixty persons had been killed, and two hundred
and forty wounded.   All the accounts bore just testimony to the
activity and devotion of the detectives, and all closed with the
remark that " three hundred thousand citizens and four
detectives saw the dread creature, and two of the latter he
destroyed."

I dreaded to hear the telegraphic instrument begin to click
again.   By and by the messages began to pour in, but I was
happily disappointed in their nature.   It was soon apparent
that all trace of the elephant was lost.   The fog had enabled him
to search out a good hiding-place unobserved.   Telegrams from
the most absurdly distant points reported that a dim vast mass
had been glimpsed there through the fog at such and such an
hour, and was " undoubtedly the elephant."   This dim vast
mass had been glimpsed in New Haven, in New Jersey, in
Pennsylvania, in interior New York, in Brooklyn, and even in the
city of New York itself !   But in all cases the dim vast mass had
vanished quickly and left no trace.   Every detective of the large
force scattered over this huge extent of country sent his hourly
report, and each and every one of them had a clue, and was
shadowing something, and was hot upon the heels of it.

But the day passed without other result.

The next day the same.

The next day just the same.

The newspaper reports began to grow monotonous with facts
that amounted to nothing, clues which led to nothing, and
theories which had nearly exhausted the elements which surprise
and delight and dazzle.

By advice of the inspector I doubled the reward.

Four more dull days followed.   Then came a bitter blow
to the poor, hard-working detectives—the journalists declined to
print their theories, and coldly said, " Give us a rest."

Two weeks after the elephant's disappearance I raised the reward to $75,000 by the inspector's advice. It was a great sum, but I felt that I would rather sacrifice my whole private fortune than lose my credit with my Government. Now that the detectives were in adversity, the newspapers turned upon them, and began to fling the most stinging sarcasms at them. This gave the minstrels an idea, and they dressed themselves as detectives and hunted the elephant on the stage in the most extravagant way. The caricaturists made pictures of detectives scanning the country with spy-glasses, while the elephant, at their backs, stole apples out of their pockets. And they made all sorts of ridiculous pictures of the detective badge—you have seen that badge printed in gold on the back of detective novels, no doubt—it is a wide-staring eye, with the legend, " WE NEVER SLEEP." When detectives called for a drink, the would-be facetious bar-keeper resurrected an obsolete form of expression, and said, " Will you have an eye-opener ? " All the air was thick with sarcasms.

But there was one man who moved calm, untouched, unaffected through it all. It was that heart of oak, the Chief Inspector. His brave eye never drooped, his serene confidence never wavered. He always said :

" Let them rail on ; he laughs best who laughs last."

My admiration for the man grew into a species of worship. I was at his side always. His office had become an unpleasant place to me, and now became daily more and more so. Yet, if he could endure it, I meant to do so also ; at least, as long as I could. So I came regularly, and stayed—the only outsider who seemed to be capable of it. Everybody wondered how I could ; and often it seemed to me that I must desert, but at such times I looked into that calm and apparently unconscious face, and held my ground.

About three weeks after the elephant's disappearance I was about to say, one morning, that I should *have* to strike my colours and retire, when the great detective arrested the thought by proposing one more superb and masterly move.

This was to compromise with the robbers. The fertility of this man's invention exceeded anything I have ever seen, and I have had a wide intercourse with the world's finest minds. He said he was confident he could compromise for $100,000 and recover the elephant. I said I believed I could scrape the amount together ; but what would become of the poor detectives who had worked so faithfully ? He said :

" In compromises they always get half."

GBH   22

This removed my only objection. So the inspector wrote two notes, in this form :

> " *Dear Madam,—Your husband can make a large sum of money (and be entirely protected from the law) by making an immediate appointment with me.*
>
> " *Chief* BLUNT."

He sent one of these by his confidential messenger to the " reputed wife " of Brick Duffy, and the other to the reputed wife of Red McFadden.

Within the hour these offensive answers came :

> " *Ye Owld fool : brick McDuffys bin ded 2 yere.*
>
> " BRIDGET MAHONEY."

> " *Chief Bat,—Red McFadden is hung and in heving 18 month. Any Ass but a detective knose that.*
>
> " MARY O'HOOLIGAN."

" I had long suspected these facts," said the inspector ; " this testimony proves the unerring accuracy of my instinct."

The moment one resource failed him he was ready with another. He immediately wrote an advertisement for the morning papers, and I kept a copy of it :

> " *A.—xwblv. 242 N. Tjnd—fz328wmlg. Ozpo,—; 2 m ! ogw. Mum.*"

He said that if the thief was alive this would bring him to the usual rendezvous. He further explained that the usual rendezvous was a place where all business affairs between detectives and criminals were conducted. This meeting would take place at twelve the next night.

We could do nothing till then, and I lost no time in getting out of the office, and was grateful indeed for the privilege.

At eleven the next night I brought $100,000 in bank-notes and put them into the chief's hands, and shortly afterward he took his leave, with the brave old undimmed confidence in his eye. An almost intolerable hour dragged to a close : then I heard his welcome tread, and rose gasping and tottered to meet him. How his fine eyes flamed with triumph ! He said :

" We've compromised ! The jokers will sing a different tune to-morrow ! Follow me ! "

He took a lighted candle and strode down into the vast vaulted basement where sixty detectives always slept, and where a score were now playing cards to while the time. I followed close after him. He walked swiftly down to the dim remote end of the place, and just as I succumbed to the pangs of suffocation and was swooning away he stumbled and fell over the outlying members of a mighty object, and I heard him exclaim as he went down :

"Our noble profession is vindicated. Here is your elephant ! "

I was carried to the office above and restored with carbolic acid. The whole detective force swarmed in, and such another season of triumphant rejoicing ensued as I had never witnessed before. The reporters were called, baskets of champagne were opened, toasts were drunk, the handshakings and congratulations were continuous and enthusiastic. Naturally the chief was the hero of the hour, and his happiness was so complete and had been so patiently and worthily and bravely won that it made me happy to see it, though I stood there a homeless beggar, my priceless charge dead, and my position in my country's service lost to me through what would always seem my fatally careless execution of a great trust. Many an eloquent eye testified its deep admiration for the chief, and many a detective's voice murmured, " Look at him—just the king of the profession—only give him a clue, it's all he wants, and there ain't anything hid that he can't find." The dividing of the $50,000 made great pleasure ; when it was finished the chief made a little speech while he put his share in his pocket, in which he said, " Enjoy it, boys, for you've earned it ; and more than that—you've earned for the detective profession undying fame."

A telegram arrived, which read :

" MONROE, MICH. : 10 p.m.

" *First time I've struck a telegraph office in over three weeks. Have followed those footprints, horseback, through the woods, a thousand miles to here, and they get stronger and bigger and fresher every day. Don't worry—inside of another week I'll have the elephant. This is dead sure.*

" DARLEY, *Detective.*"

The chief ordered three cheers for " Darley, one of the finest minds on the force," and then commanded that he be telegraphed to come home and receive his share of the reward.

So ended that marvellous episode of the stolen elephant.

The newspapers were pleasant with praises once more, the next day, with one contemptible exception.   This sheet said, " Great is the detective !   He may be a little slow in finding a little thing like a mislaid elephant—he may hunt him all day and sleep with his rotting carcass all night for three weeks, but he will find him at last—if he can get the man who mislaid him to show him the place ! "

Poor Hassan was lost to me for ever.   The cannon-shots had wounded him fatally.   He had crept to that unfriendly place in the fog ; and there, surrounded by his enemies and in constant danger of detection, he had wasted away with hunger and suffering till death gave him peace.

The compromise cost me $100,000 ; my detective expenses were $42,000 more ; I never applied for a place again under my Government ; I am a ruined man and a wanderer in the earth —but my admiration for that man, whom I believe to be the greatest detective the world has ever produced, remains undimmed to this day, and will so remain unto the end.

EDGAR WALLACE (1875–1932) *was a soldier serving in South Africa when he started his journalistic and literary career. He became a war correspondent and helped to found the Johannesburg " Daily Mail." Of the famous characters he has created in his enormous output of novels, short stories, plays, and scenarios, that delightful little Cockney, Educated Evans, who appears here, is among the most popular.*

A SOUVENIR

THROUGH his uncurtained window Mr. Evans could see the young lady in grey.. She occupied the rooms immediately opposite his own and on the other side of the mews. Her uncle was a musher and drove a taxi which he and his brother George had purchased on the " never, never " system. You pay £80 down and more than you can afford for the rest of your life. Her aunt was genteel and wore eyeglasses. They lived in a large suite of rooms which extended over two garages, in one of which the cab was cleaned : it never stayed there for any appreciable time. The uncle drove it by day, and another uncle, whose name was George, by night, or *vice versa*. The taxi-cab never complained about this perpetual motion because it was inarticulate.

Mr. Evans was not interested in the cab, or the uncle, who always seemed to have boils on his neck, or Uncle George, who was a thin, acidulated man who talked to himself all the time. Nor did he look twice at the aunt. But the niece in grey, with her black hair and her saucy way of putting her hand on her hip, and her shining silk stockings—this young woman was, and had been since she first nodded to him brightly and said " Morning," an object of profound speculation and delight. Sometimes she nursed a baby prettily. He discovered in subsequent conversations that it was her sister's.

Mr. Evans was not old. On the other hand, he was not young. And anyway, scholars have no age : they are youthful or ancient according to the measure of their erudition.

" I'll bet she wonders who I am," said Mr. Evans with a quiet, sad smile. " Few people know me outside of the profession. I'll bet she says, ' I wonder who that lonely man is ? He looks as if he's had a lot of trouble—an' what an interestin' face he's got, mother or auntie, as the case may be ! ' ''

Thus Evans communed with himself before the mirror, not knowing at that time the exact relationship of the lady with the driver of cabs.

One evening he leaned over the balustrade of the landing outside his door. She came out, looked, and nodded.

" Evening," she said. " It's a nice evening."

" Not so good as Palermo in the south of France, or dear old India," said Evans. " Give me Egyp' for nice evenin's an' a half-hour's row down the Nile Canal."

She looked at him awe-stricken, red lips parted, violet eyes wide open.

" Have you been there ? " she asked.

" Lots of times," said Evans carelessly ; " *and* China, which is the most highly populized country in the world. That's where we get china from, an' Chinese lanterns."

She leaned over her landing too. There was twelve feet of space between them. Down below a dazed horse-keeper stopped work to listen.

" It must be wonderful going abroad."

Evans shrugged so violently that one of his brace buttons came off and fell with a musical tinkle on the cobble-stones below.

" You get used to it if you're a racehorse owner," he said. " I've won the Calcutta Cup once but gave away the ticket to a footman at my club—couldn't be bothered. The Melbourne Cup—that's a wonderful race ! Down in Orstralia."

She drew a long, sighing breath ; her eyes were bright. He had, he saw, assumed a new interest in her eyes. The glow of it made his flannel undershirt feel prickly.

" Fancy . . . you own race-horses ! Do they ever win ? " Evans smiled tiredly.

" Now and again. I don't like winnin' too often. The other members of the Jockey Club get that jealous there's no holdin' 'em ! "

" But how mean ! "

Mr. Evans started to shrug again but remembered in time. Down below in the mews, the horse-keeper swooned against the wall.

" You can't please everybody," said Educated Evans. " Even Queen Elizabeth couldn't do that—that's why she got her napp —her head cut off by B—— Mary the celebrated Queen of Scotch. That led to the Diet of Worms an' the rise an' fall of the far-famed Oliver Cromwell, fourteen hundred and seventy-six," he added.

She was stricken speechless for a moment, and Educated Evans proceeded.

"That brings us to the question of Astronomy. Very few people know that the eclipse of the sun is caused by the earth in its revolutions comin' between the moon an' the sun, thus causin' many ignorant people to think that the whole thing's wrong, when, as a matter of fact, it's an act of nature."

He was now speaking fluently, swinging his hat with the same easy carelessness as a sailor swings the lead. And when he dropped the hat into a puddle immediately below him, he just smiled. He was that much careless.

"Take the law," he said. "There's a good many people don't understand the law. Many a time I've stood up in court and said to the other lawyers——"

"Are you a lawyer too!"

Below, the horse-keeper tried to say that Mr. Evans was less of a lawyer than a something liar, but his lips would not frame the words.

"Bit of everything," said Mr. Evans modestly. "Scientific—take sidlitz powders——"

The beautiful girl in grey was spared the need. Her aunt appeared in the open doorway, a mass of undigested knitting in her hands, and called her in.

"Come in, Clara, do!"

"Yes, auntie," said the girl meekly.

"What on earth do you want to talk to that old man for?" demanded the aunt, too audibly : the rest was undistinguishable.

Mr. Evans sneered at her. Old! What a nerve! Still, he had impressed her : he could see that. He went down the wooden steps, retrieved his hat and his button, and returned to the privacy of his " den " to dry the one and sew the other. She knew him now for what he was. An educated man. She was probably talking to her aunt about it at that moment, chiding her parent for her uncharity.

"No, auntie, you are wrong. I won't allow you to say that. He is *not* old—and what is age? One loves a man's mind ; his breadth—his education."

That's what he imagined her saying. What she actually said was :

"Who *is* that funny old geezer, aunt?"

"God knows," said her aunt, a pious woman. "I think he's something to do with dogs."

But Clara Develle was honestly and sincerely interested in Educated Evans and wondered about him. For example, she often wondered if he was right in his head. And she wondered who gave him his plaid trousers, and she wondered if he was a burglar, but decided that he was too tender on his feet for that nippy profession. And as her wonderment grew, there came to her a realization that there really were possibilities about the educated man.

" Never mind about *him*," said her aunt sharply, when she approached the subject. " Your uncle Alf says things can't go on as they're going. You've got to find something to do. He can't keep you in idleness, because we're poor people, and if we wasn't we wouldn't."

Miss Clara said nothing.

" Your uncle's a man of the world—so is your uncle George," her aunt went on. " There's some things we don't know and don't *want* to know. Certain things have been remarked, but the least said soonest mended. Only it seems *funny* ! "

Her niece was evidently in agreement with these cryptic sentiments, hints, and innuendos, for she sighed sadly. Mr. Evans did not see her again that night, but he did notice, as he had noticed before, a young man going up the steps after dark.

Dark suspicions gathered in Mr. Evans' mind. Could this young man be a Fellow ? Was he a Chap ? The thing was preposterous . . . such a child . . . the aunt would never allow it. Not if she was a Good Woman. . . .

Occasionally The Miller drifted down Bayham Mews. Generally it was a matter of duty which brought him to this place of silence, but sometimes he mounted the wooden steps that led to the habitation of one who was called, for excellent reason, Educated Evans, in search of social relaxation—for even a detective-sergeant has a human side to his character.

On this chilly night in March The Miller came up the steps and knocked at the door.

" Hullo, Mr. Challoner ! " said Educated Evans graciously. " Kindly step inside and take the chair."

" Have you got a meeting, Evans ? " asked The Miller good-humouredly.

" No—but I've only got one chair," said Evans.

He wore his overcoat, for the night was cold and the fire that burnt in the grate was so small as to be almost invisible. The Miller glanced at the table, where a paraffin lamp shed its rays upon a litter of paper.

"Just writing to a few of my clients," said Evans, rubbing his long nose. "They don't deserve it, but I've got to do it—Cold Feet for the Hurst Park Hurdle. He's been kept special for it. Not a yard at Lingfield—but this time his head's loose."

"Old Sam says——" began The Miller, but the look of pain, reproach, contempt, and acid amusement in Evans' face cancelled his communique. Old Sam had been a propper of boozers, a holder of horses, an opener of cab doors. As lowly as a slave to Educated Evans, who had given him money and orders. And in the protracted absence of Mr. Evans in the country, Old Sam, traitor, ingrate, and saturated beer-hound, had blossomed forth as a tipster.

"I'm sorry I mentioned your rival," said The Miller.

The pain in Mr. Evans' face grew more acute.

If The Miller had any reason for his call he did not state it. Evans was almost glad to see him go. Great was his fortune when later, slipping out to get a quick one, he met the grey girl at the end of the mews. He had an impression that she had just seen somebody off—a brief, blurred glimpse of a figure vanishing in the darkness. Should he speak to her or pass with a stately bow.

"Good-evening, Mr. Evans."

She knew his name.

"Good-evening, Miss—— ? "

"Miss Develle," she said. "Just been seeing a friend off," she went on. "Not exactly a friend, but a gentleman who is always running after me."

"What a cheek ! " said Evans hotly. "I never heard such a thing in my life. It's preposterous ! "

They lingered awhile. Her eyes shone hotly out of the dark ; the dusk of night was in her hair. Evans grew agitated. It was within five minutes of closing time.

"I'd like to have a chat with you, Mr. Evans," she said earnestly. "You're such a Man of the World, or Gentleman of the World as one might say. I'll be going to the Rialto pictures at eight to-morrow night. Please don't mention it to auntie."

She was gone before he realized ; her black hair and violet eyes were swallowed in the void. Educated Evans reeled to the nearest house of refreshment and drank heavily, for him.

They met in the ornate vestibule of the Rialto. Harold Lloyd favoured them with a celluloid smile as they slipped into the dark interior.

". . . Yes, my aunt. My papa married beneath him—he

was a Colonel in the army . . . that little baby's my sister Annie's. . . . Oh, I'm so glad to have a chat with you, Mr. Evans! I'm in such trouble. I must get some kind of work—I really must. It's hateful depending on relations or even relatives. . . ."

She told him of her struggles; of the weary round she went from aunt to aunt—

" There's a cashier wanted at Lammer's. That's my work . . . if only I knew somebody who knew somebody else who knew Mr. Lammer."

Honestly she was not aware that Mr. Lammer was an acquaintance of his. When he explained that he had only to crook his finger for Mr. Lammer to skip like an intoxicated lamb, she thought he was swanking. The most she had expected of her new-found friend was a novel angle which would help her.

When the lights went up he saw (for her hat was removed) that she was a little older than he had thought. This pleased him. He paid for a light fish supper out of his last half-crown and went to bed full of noble resolves.

Mr. Evans, of Sansovino House, Bayham Mews, was not without influence. There were people in Camden Town who never heard his name mentioned without employing the most regrettable expressions to describe The World's Premier Racing Prophet and Turf Adviser; but there were others who through thick and thin were loyalty personified.

Mr. Lammer, the High-Class Draper and Ladies' Outfitter, for example, never ceased to sound the praises of one who, at a critical moment in his history, when every other man who came into his office carried a writ of summons in his inside left-hand pocket, had imparted to Mr. Lammer the exclusive information that Braxted could fall down, have a fit and *then* win the Stewards' Cup.

The distracted Mr. Lammer had in his possession at the time the sum of four hundred pounds, which he had put aside for the rainy day when he would be obliged (in the language of Camden Town) to do a guy. This sum, withheld from his creditors, he invested on Braxted at 25–1. And Braxted won. Twenty-five times £400 is exactly £10,000, and with this sum Mr. Lammer paid his debts, extended his premises, and entered upon a newer and brighter life.

He was not a cultured man, being one of those who admitted responsibility for his own success, and he admired the erudition of his humble friend beyond words.

"Certainly, Mr. Evans," he said, as the educated man sat on the edge of a chair in his office and made his request, "I'll do anything I can for you. I've given up backin' 'orses, but if you're ever short of a few pound, step in and ask for what you want. You say that this young lady is All Right?"

Evans drew a long breath.

"She's the daughter of a colonel in the Army," he explained fervently, "and a perfect lady : owin' to a bank failure the family's ruined. She's like the celebrated Dick Whittin'ton an' don't know the way to turn. And she reminds me of the well-known an' highly respected wife of Julius Cæsar, the far-famed Italian—she's above the position."

So it was arranged that Clara Develle should go into Lammer's store as junior cashier at a reasonable salary, and Evans purred his way back to Bayham Mews, where the young aristocrat was in residence, and waited for the friendly dark to tell her the good news.

"I must say it's awfully good of you, Mr. Evans," she said rapidly—she was rather a quick talker. "What a bit of luck for me that I met you as I did ! I'm sure my poor pa would have died with shame if he knew I was going into business—as a matter of fact he died from eppoplexity during the air-raids, him being a general and naturally brave."

Educated Evans scarcely noticed her parent's promotion.

"Has that feller been worrying you again?" he asked with a sub-tone of ferocity.

On the previous night they had discussed the furtive young man who came and went in the dark. Mr. Evans had recognized him.

"Mr. Erman? Oh, dear, no," she protested. "I'd never dream of looking twice at him. Saucy monkey if ever there was one."

"I saw him talking to you in the mews to-night——" began Evans.

"Merely passing the time of day. One has to be civil in my position. I mean to say, you've got to be polite if you're a lady," she said breathlessly.

Evans, the loyalest of men, felt she should know the worst.

"He's a crook, a hook, and a twister," said Evans. "He's done time for burglary and he owes me two pun' ten over Charley's Mount, what I put him on to. Remember, miss, if there's any trouble, I'm around ! "

She said she would remember : she said this rather vaguely, as though she were thinking of something else.

"You've been simply marvellous to me," said the General's daughter with a sigh, "and when I get working I'm going to give you a little souvenir."

"A bit of ribbon," said Educated Evans sentimentally, "a stay lace—anything to remind me of you—nothing expensive."

Things were not going well with Evans. He might have paraphrased a Mr. Browning and said, "Never the chance and the girl and the money all together."

A week later Educated Evans watched the stream of life passing along Hampstead Road, and mused a little sorrowfully upon the unattainable value of things. Every motor-omnibus that flew by was worth a thousand pounds ; not a cyclist plodded across the field of his vision that was not supported by a couple of pounds' worth of old iron and rubber.

The landlord of his suite in Bayham Mews had that morning demanded (with a certain significant reference to the number of people who were begging and praying for the accommodation usurped by Mr. Evans) that the four weeks' arrears of rent should be paid by twelve noon on the following day, failing which——

Detective-Sergeant Challoner stood by his side in as earnest a contemplation of the pageant of life. A keen wind blew down High Street, though the sun shone overhead in a blue and white sky. It was spring. Outside the White Hart the red-nosed Lolly Marks stood behind a big basket banked high with daffodils and narcissi—the placards bore the magic slogan "Lincolnshire Favourite Coughing"—the vernal equinox had swung to Camden Town.

"If people would act honourable," said Mr. Evans, "this would be a grand world to live in. As William Shakespeare, the well-known and highly popular poet, says, 'What a game it is !' and he was right."

"Broke ?" asked The Miller, with a certain hard sympathy.

Yet he did not look broke. Mr. Evans for once was dressed up to his position. His moustache was trimmed, his collar was clean, and only an expert could see where he had scissored the frayed edges. A ready-made cravat was embellished by a jewel that might have been a ruby worth a couple of thousand pounds, but probably wasn't.

"To pieces," said Educated Evans, and shrugged his hock-bottle shoulders. "When you re'lize that I sent out the winner of the Newbury Hurdle to three thousan' nine hundred and forty clients, and that all I had back for my trouble was twelve bob and a 'slush' ten-shillin' note that I nearly got penal servitude for passin', you understand why men like the celebrated Sir Francis Columbus went an' lived in America."

" Why don't you see Lammer—he's a pal of yours ? "

Evans screwed up his face in contempt.

" I never ' touch ' a client," he said, and spoke the amazing truth.

" Why are you waiting here ? " asked The Miller after a long silence. " Lookin' for anybody ? By the way, you haven't seen Nosey Erman about, have you ? "

" No, I haven't," said Evans, " that feller's less than the dust to me, to use a well-known expression."

" I wonder why he's turned up in Camden Town ? " The Miller mused. " He's got some game on, I'll bet."

Well Mr. Evans knew the game of the wanderer. He had returned to filch the heart of an innocent girl—the sharp eyes of the educated man had detected the amorous Nosey. His exposure was accomplished.

The Miller pulled at his long nose, and then :

" Come round to my lodgings this afternoon and I'll hand you a pound," he said as he prepared to go. " But don't come if you can tap anybody else."

Between gratitude and sardonic mirth at the prospect of tapping anybody Mr. Evans was slightly incoherent.

Long after The Miller had gone he waited, and presently his vigil was rewarded. A slim, neatly dressed girl walked quickly up Bayham Street and turned towards the High Street. In an instant Educated Evans was flying across the roadway, and at the sound of his voice the girl turned with a smile.

" Why, Mr. Evans," she said, " I thought you were at Cheltenham ! "

" My car broke down," said Mr. Evans mendaciously. " The carburetter keeps on back-firing : for two pins I'd send it back to old Rolls and give him a bit of me mind ! "

He fell in by her side, and for two minutes fifty-five seconds and a few fifths he trod on air, and his heart sang comic songs.

Just short of Lammer's Corner she stopped and held out her hand with a sigh.

" You are lucky, Mr. Evans," she said enviously. " It must be wonderful to be your own master : to go where you like and how you like. I wish I had a lot of money."

Evans wished the same thing as fervently, but he did not say so.

She sighed.

"I wish I knew what was going to win that big race at Cheltenham," she said.

"Benny's Hope," replied Evans promptly. "I had it from the owner, who's a personal friend of mine. That horse could fall down, get up, turn round to see what was going to be last, and then win."

"Benny's Hope," she said thoughtfully, and then : "I've got that souvenir for you, Mr. Evans," she said. "You wouldn't think I was fast if I brought it round to your flat one night, would you ? "

And before he realized it, she had disappeared through the ornamental portals of Lammer's High-Class Drapers and Ladies' Outfitters.

Evans walked thoughtfully back to his apartment, planning matrimony.

.   .   .   .

Educated Evans got out of bed and slipped on his dressing-gown, which was also his overcoat, an extra blanket, and on occasions a mackintosh. The hour was seven ; outside in the dark mews rain was falling steadily.

It was not an hour at which one might expect the most enthusiastic of clients would call upon the World's Champion. In truth, of late, Evans had found his erstwhile clientele somewhat sceptical of his information even when he sought them out.

He lit the oil lamp and opened the door. There was nobody in sight, and then he heard a sound, and, stooping, lifted the long basket that stood on the landing and carried it into the room.

"Good Gawd ! " said Evans.

He heard the wail before he opened the lid and saw the solemn eyes staring up from the interior of the basket.

"Good Gawd ! " said Evans again.

He picked up the baby and laid it on the bed, and with a flutter of eyelids the tiny mortal went instantly into a sound sleep.

Evans examined the basket. It bore the label of a local fishmonger and smelt strongly of the sea. The World's Champion ran his fingers through his hair and strove to recover his composure. And then he heard a heavy step upon the stairs, and the door opened to reveal a figure in a shiny mackintosh.

"Hullo, Mr. Challoner—come in."

The straw between The Miller's teeth was soddened with rain, and as he stood in the room near the door, tiny rivulets of water dripped hurriedly to the floor.

Without any preliminary :

" Do you know Mrs. Erman—a pasty-faced girl with goggly eyes ? "

" I don't——" began Evans.

" You got her a job at Lammer's," said The Miller sharply. " I knew she was staying here with her aunt, and I came down to make sure the other night, but I never dreamt she'd plant herself on you. She was hanging round here for something, but I couldn't guess what it was."

Evans was pale, his mouth wide open.

" Wha's—wha's happened ? " he croaked, and The Miller laughed unpleasantly.

" To-night they cleared Lammer's safe and made a get-away. We'll be able to pick them up because she's got a baby."

Educated Evans opened his mouth again and tried to speak, blinked impotently and tried again.

" Miss Develle. . . ."

" Mrs. Erman," corrected The Miller, and his eyes fell upon the little slumberer. " Yours ? " he asked, and Educated Evans shook his head, speechless.

The Miller walked across the room and examined the child. He saw what Evans in his agitation had failed to see. A card tied to the baby's wrist by a piece of pink ribbon, and the card was inscribed :

A little sooveneer.

Mrs. Erman was good at figures, but her spelling left much to be desired.

H. G. WELLS (1866–   ), *scholar, social satirist, and master of fantasy and imagination, is also one of our most attractive humorists and as capable in the short story as in the novel. While his " Outline of History " and his phantasies and prophecies, such as " The Sleeper Awakes," are challenges to thought and stimulants of the imagination, novels like " Kipps " and " The History of Mr. Polly " are delightful studies of character and humour.*

A DEAL IN OSTRICHES

"Talking of the prices of birds, I've seen an ostrich that cost three hundred pounds," said the Taxidermist, recalling his youth of travel. " Three hundred pounds ! "
He looked at me over his spectacles. " I've seen another that was refused at four.

" No," he said, " it wasn't any fancy points. They was just plain ostriches. A little off-colour, too—owing to dietary. And there wasn't any particular restriction of the demand either. You'd have thought five ostriches would have ruled cheap on an East Indiaman. But the point was, one of 'em had swallowed a diamond.

" The chap it got it off was Sir Mohini Padishah, a tremendous swell, a Piccadilly swell you might say up to the neck of him, and then an ugly black head and a whopping turban, with this diamond in it. The blessed bird pecked suddenly and had it, and when the chap made a fuss it realized it had done wrong, I suppose, and went and mixed itself with the others to preserve its *incog.* It all happened in a minute. I was among the first to arrive, and there was this heathen going over his gods, and two sailors and the man who had charge of the birds laughing fit to split. It was a rummy way of losing a jewel, come to think of it. The man in charge hadn't been about just at the moment, so that he didn't know which bird it was. Clean lost, you see. I didn't feel half sorry, to tell you the truth. The beggar had been swaggering over his blessed diamond ever since he came aboard.

" A thing like that goes from stem to stern of a ship in no time. Every one was talking about it. Padishah went below to hide his feelings. At dinner—he pigged at a table by himself, him and two other Hindoos—the captain kind of jeered at him about it, and he got very excited. He turned round and talked into my ear. He would not buy the birds ; he would have his diamond. He demanded his rights as a British subject. His diamond must be found. He was firm upon that. He would appeal to the House of Lords. The man in charge of the birds was one of those wooden-headed chaps you can't get a new idea into anyhow. He refused any proposal to interfere with the birds by way of medicine. His instructions were to feed them so-and-so and treat them so-and-so, and it was as much as his place was worth not to feed them so-and-so and treat them so-and-so. Padishah had wanted a stomach-pump— though you can't do that to a bird, you know. This Padishah was full of bad law, like most of these blessed Bengalis, and talked of having a lien on the birds, and so forth. But an old boy, who said his son was a London barrister, argued that what a bird swallowed became *ipso facto* part of the bird, and that Padishah's only remedy lay in an action for damages, and even then it might be possible to show contributory negligence. He hadn't any right of way about an ostrich that didn't belong to him. That upset Padishah extremely, the more so as most of us expressed an opinion that that was the reasonable view. There wasn't any lawyer aboard to settle the matter, so we all talked pretty free. At last, after Aden, it appears that he came round to the general opinion, and went privately to the man in charge and made an offer for all five ostriches.

" The next morning there was a fine shindy at breakfast. The man hadn't any authority to deal with the birds, and nothing on earth would induce him to sell ; but it seems he told Padishah that a Eurasian named Potter had already made him an offer, and on that Padishah denounced Potter before us all. But I think the most of us thought it rather smart of Potter, and I know that when Potter said that he'd wired at Aden to London to buy the birds, and would have an answer at Suez, I cursed pretty richly at a lost opportunity.

" At Suez, Padishah gave way to tears—actual wet tears— when Potter became the owner of the birds, and offered him two hundred and fifty right off for the five, being more than two hundred per cent., on what Potter had given. Potter said he'd be hanged if he parted with a feather of them—that he meant to kill them off one by one and find the diamond ; but afterwards, thinking it over, he relented a little. He was a gambling hound, was this Potter, a little queer at cards, and this kind of prize-packet business must have suited him down to the ground. Anyhow, he offered, for a lark, to sell the birds separately to separate people by auction at a starting price of eighty pound for a bird. But one of them, he said, he meant to keep for luck.

" You must understand this diamond was a valuable one—a little Jew chap, a diamond merchant, who was with us, had put it at three or four thousand when Padishah had shown it to him—and this idea of an ostrich gamble caught on. Now it happened that I'd been having a few talks on general subjects with the man who looked after these ostriches, and quite incidentally he'd said one of the birds was ailing, and he fancied it had indigestion. It had one feather in its tail almost all white, by which I knew it, and so when, next day, the auction started with it, I capped Padishah's eighty-five by ninety. I fancy I was a bit too sure and eager with my bid, and some of the others spotted the fact that I was in the know. And Padishah went for that particular bird like an irresponsible lunatic. At last the Jew diamond merchant got it for £175, and Padishah said £180 just after the hammer came down—so Potter declared. At any rate the Jew merchant secured it, and there and then he got a gun and shot it. Potter made a Hades of a fuss because he said it would injure the sale of the other three, and Padishah, of course, behaved like an idiot ; but all of us were very much excited. I can tell you I was precious glad when that dissection was over, and no diamond had turned up— precious glad. I'd gone to one-forty on that particular bird myself.

" The little Jew was like most Jews—he didn't make any great fuss over bad luck ; but Potter declined to go on with the auction until it was understood that the goods could not be delivered until the sale was over. The little Jew wanted to argue that the case was exceptional, and as the discussion ran pretty even, the thing was postponed until the next morning. We had a lively dinner-table that evening, I can tell you, but in the end Potter got his way, since it would stand to reason he would be safer if he stuck to all the birds, and that we owed him some consideration for his sportsmanlike behaviour. And the old gentleman whose son was a lawyer said he'd been thinking the thing over and that it was very doubtful if, when a bird had been opened and the diamond recovered, it ought not to be handed back to the proper owner. I remember I suggested it came under the laws of treasure-trove—which was really the truth of the matter. There was a hot argument, and we settled it was certainly foolish to kill the bird on board the ship. Then the old gentleman, going at large through his legal talk, tried to make out the sale was a lottery and illegal, and appealed to the captain ; but Potter said he sold the birds *as* ostriches.

He didn't want to sell any diamonds, he said, and didn't offer that as an inducement. The three birds he put up, to the best of his knowledge and belief, did *not* contain a diamond. It was in the one he kept—so he hoped.

" Prices ruled high next day all the same. The fact that now there were four chances instead of five of course caused a rise. The blessed birds averaged 227, and, oddly enough, this Padishah didn't secure one of 'em—not one. He made too much shindy, and when he ought to have been bidding he was talking about liens, and, besides, Potter was a bit down on him. One fell to a quiet little officer chap, another to the little Jew, and the third was syndicated by the engineers. And then Potter seemed suddenly sorry for having sold them, and said he'd flung away a clear thousand pounds, and that very likely he'd draw a blank and that he always had been a fool, but when I went and had a bit of a talk to him, with the idea of getting him to hedge on his last chance, I found he'd already sold the bird he'd reserved to a political chap that was on board, a chap who'd been studying Indian morals and social questions in his vacation. That last was the three hundred pounds bird. Well, they landed three of the blessed creatures at Brindisi— though the old gentleman said it was a breach of the Customs regulations—and Potter and Padishah landed too. The Hindoo seemed half-mad as he saw his blessed diamond going this way and that, so to speak. He kept on saying he'd get an injunction —he had injunction on the brain—and giving his name and address to the chaps who'd bought the birds, so that they'd know where to send the diamond. None of them wanted his name and address, and none of them would give their own. It was a fine row I can tell you—on the platform. They all went off by different trains. I came on to Southampton, and there I saw the last of the birds, as I came ashore ; it was the one the engineers bought, and it was standing up near the bridge, in a kind of crate, and looking as leggy and silly a setting for a valuable diamond as ever you saw—if it *was* a setting for a valuable diamond.

" *How did it end?* Oh ! like that. Well—perhaps. Yes, there's one more thing that may throw light on it. A week or so after landing I was down Regent Street doing a bit of shop-ping, and who should I see arm-in-arm and having a purple time of it but Padishah and Potter. If you come to think of it——

" Yes. *I've* thought that. Only, you see, there's no doubt the diamond was real. And Padishah was an eminent Hindoo. I've seen his name in the papers—often. But whether the bird swallowed the diamond certainly is another matter, as you say."

OSCAR WILDE (1856–1900), *a brilliant wit with an exuberant fancy and a deep sense of beauty, left a variety of lovely works in prose and poetry. His most famous poem was "The Ballad of Reading Gaol." Of his plays, with their sparkling dialogue and deftly managed situations, "The Importance of Being Earnest" is considered the most amusing.*

THE IMPORTANCE OF BEING EARNEST

THE PERSONS OF THE PLAY

JOHN WORTHING, J.P.
ALGERNON MONCRIEFF
REV. CANON CHASUBLE, D.D.
MERRIMAN, Butler
LANE, Manservant

LADY BRACKNELL
HON. GWENDOLEN FAIRFAX
CECILY CARDEW
MISS PRISM, Governess

THE SCENES OF THE PLAY

ACT I. *Algernon Moncrieff's Flat in Half-Moon Street, W.*
ACT II. *The Garden at the Manor House, Woolton.*
ACT III. *Drawing-room at the Manor House, Woolton.*
TIME : *The Present.*

FIRST ACT

SCENE.—*Morning-room in Algernon's flat in Half-Moon Street. The room is luxuriously and artistically furnished. The sound of a piano is heard in the adjoining room.*

LANE *is arranging afternoon tea on the table, and after the music has ceased,* ALGERNON *enters.*

Algernon : Did you hear what I was playing, Lane ?
Lane : I didn't think it polite to listen, sir.
Algernon : I'm sorry for that, for your sake. I don't play accurately—any one can play accurately—but I play with wonderful expression. As far as the piano is concerned, sentiment is my forte. I keep science for Life.
Lane : Yes, sir.

692

Algernon : And, speaking of the science of Life, have you got the cucumber sandwiches cut for Lady Bracknell ?

Lane : Yes, sir. (*Hands them on a salver.*)

Algernon (*inspects them, takes two, and sits down on the sofa*) : Oh ! . . . by the way, Lane, I see from your book that on Thursday night, when Lord Shoreman and Mr. Worthing were dining with me, eight bottles of champagne are entered as having been consumed.

Lane : Yes, sir ; eight bottles and a pint.

Algernon : Why is it that at a bachelor's establishment the servants invariably drink the champagne ? I ask merely for information.

Lane : I attribute it to the superior quality of the wine, sir. I have often observed that in married households the champagne is rarely of a first-rate brand.

Algernon : Good heavens ! Is marriage so demoralizing as that ?

Lane : I believe it *is* a very pleasant state, sir. I have had very little experience of it myself up to the present. I have only been married once. That was in consequence of a misunderstanding between myself and a young person.

Algernon (*languidly*) : I don't know that I am much interested in your family life, Lane.

Lane : No, sir ; it is not a very interesting subject. I never think of it myself.

Algernon : Very natural, I am sure. That will do, Lane, thank you.

Lane : Thank you, sir.

    LANE *goes out.*

Algernon : Lane's views on marriage seem somewhat lax. Really, if the lower orders don't set us a good example, what on earth is the use of them ? They seem, as a class, to have absolutely no sense of moral responsibility.

    Enter LANE.

Lane : Mr. Ernest Worthing.

    Enter JACK. LANE *goes out.*

Algernon : How are you, my dear Ernest ? What brings you up to town ?

Jack : Oh, pleasure, pleasure ! What else should bring one anywhere ? Eating as usual, I see, Algy !

Algernon (*stiffly*) : I believe it is customary in good society to take some slight refreshment at five o'clock. Where have you been since last Thursday ?

Jack (smiling down on the sofa) : In the country.

Algernon : What on earth do you do there?

Jack (pulling off his gloves) : When one is in town one amuses oneself. When one is in the country one amuses other people. It is excessively boring.

Algernon : And who are the people you amuse?

Jack (airily) : Oh, neighbours, neighbours.

Algernon : Got nice neighbours, in your part of Shropshire?

Jack : Perfectly horrid! Never speak to one of them.

Algernon : How immensely you must amuse them! (*Goes over and takes sandwich.*) By the way, Shropshire is your county, is it not?

Jack : Eh? Shropshire? Yes, of course. Hallo! Why all these cups? Why cucumber sandwiches? Why such reckless extravagance in one so young? Who is coming to tea?

Algernon : Oh! merely Aunt Augusta and Gwendolen.

Jack : How perfectly delightful!

Algernon : Yes, that is all very well; but I am afraid Aunt Augusta won't quite approve of your being here.

Jack : May I ask why?

Algernon : My dear fellow, the way you flirt with Gwendolen is perfectly disgraceful. It is almost as bad as the way Gwendolen flirts with you.

Jack : I am in love with Gwendolen. I have come up to town expressly to propose to her.

Algernon : I thought you had come up for pleasure? . . . I call that business.

Jack : How utterly unromantic you are!

Algernon : I really don't see anything romantic in proposing. It is very romantic to be in love. But there is nothing romantic about a definite proposal. Why, one may be accepted. One usually is, I believe. Then the excitement is all over. The very essence of romance is uncertainty. If ever I get married, I'll certainly try to forget the fact.

Jack : I have no doubt about that, dear Algy. The Divorce Court was specially invented for people whose memories are so curiously constituted.

Algernon : Oh! there is no use speculating on that subject. Divorces are made in Heaven—— (JACK *puts out his hand to take a sandwich.* ALGERNON *at once interferes.*) Please don't touch the cucumber sandwiches. They are ordered specially for Aunt Augusta. (*Takes one and eats it.*)

Jack : Well, you have been eating them all the time.

Algernon : That is quite a different matter. She is my aunt.

(*Takes plate from below.*) Have some bread and butter. The bread and butter is for Gwendolen. Gwendolen is devoted to bread and butter.

Jack (*advancing to table and helping himself*) : And very good bread and butter it is too.

Algernon : Well, my dear fellow, you need not eat as if you were going to eat it all. You behave as if you were married to her already. You are not married to her already, and I don't think you ever will be.

Jack : Why on earth do you say that?

Algernon : Well, in the first place, girls never marry the men they flirt with. Girls don't think it right.

Jack : Oh, that is nonsense!

Algernon : It isn't. It is a great truth. It accounts for the extraordinary number of bachelors that one sees all over the place. In the second place, I don't give my consent.

Jack : Your consent!

Algernon : My dear fellow, Gwendolen is my first cousin. And before I allow you to marry her, you will have to clear up the whole question of Cecily. (*Rings bell.*)

Jack : Cecily! What on earth do you mean? What do you mean, Algy, by Cecily! I don't know any one of the name of Cecily.

Enter LANE.

Algernon : Bring me that cigarette case Mr. Worthing left in the smoking-room the last time he dined here.

Lane : Yes, sir.

LANE *goes out.*

Jack : Do you mean to say you have had my cigarette case all this time? I wish to goodness you had let me know. I have been writing frantic letters to Scotland Yard about it. I was very nearly offering a large reward.

Algernon : Well, I wish you would offer one. I happen to be more than usually hard up.

Jack : There is no good offering a large reward now that the thing is found.

Enter LANE *with the cigarette case on a salver.* ALGERNON *takes it at once.* LANE *goes out.*

Algernon : I think that is rather mean of you, Ernest, I must say. (*Opens case and examines it.*) However, it makes no matter, for, now that I look at the inscription inside, I find that the thing isn't yours after all.

Jack : Of course it's mine. (*Moving to him.*) You have seen me with it a hundred times, and you have no right whatsoever to read what is written inside. It is a very ungentlemanly thing to read a private cigarette case.

Algernon : Oh! it is absurd to have a hard and fast rule about what one should read and what one shouldn't. More than half of modern culture depends on what one shouldn't read.

Jack : I am quite aware of the fact, and I don't propose to discuss modern culture. It isn't the sort of thing one should talk of in private. I simply want my cigarette case back.

Algernon : Yes ; but this isn't your cigarette case. This cigarette case is a present from some one of the name of Cecily, and you said you didn't know any one of that name.

Jack : Well, if you want to know, Cecily happens to be my aunt.

Algernon : Your aunt !

Jack : Yes. Charming old lady she is, too. Lives at Tunbridge Wells. Just give it back to me, Algy.

Algernon (retreating to back of sofa) : But why does she call herself little Cecily if she is your aunt and lives at Tunbridge Wells ? (*Reading.*) " From little Cecily with her fondest love."

Jack (moving to sofa and kneeling upon it) : My dear fellow, what on earth is there in that ? Some aunts are tall, some aunts are not tall. That is a matter that surely an aunt may be allowed to decide for herself. You seem to think that every aunt should be exactly like your aunt ! That is absurd ! For Heaven's sake give me back my cigarette case. (*Follows* ERNEST *round the room.*)

Algernon : Yes. But why does your aunt call you her uncle ? " From little Cecily, with her fondest love to her dear Uncle Jack." There is no objection, I admit, to an aunt being a small aunt, but why an aunt, no matter what her size may be, should call her own nephew her uncle, I can't quite make out. Besides, your name isn't Jack at all ; it is Ernest.

Jack : It isn't Ernest ; it's Jack.

Algernon : You have always told me it was Ernest. I have introduced you to every one as Ernest. You answer to the name of Ernest. You look as if your name was Ernest. You are the most earnest-looking person I ever saw in my life. It is perfectly absurd your saying that your name isn't Ernest. It's on your cards. Here is one of them. (*Taking it from case.*) " Mr. Ernest Worthing, B.4, The Albany." I'll keep this as a proof that your name is Ernest if ever you attempt to deny it to me, or to Gwendolen, or to any one else. (*Puts the card in his pocket.*)

Jack : Well, my name is Ernest in town and Jack in the country, and the cigarette case was given to me in the country.

Algernon : Yes, but that does not account for the fact that your small Aunt Cecily, who lives at Tunbridge Wells, calls you her dear uncle. Come, old boy, you had much better have the thing out at once.

Jack : My dear Algy, you talk exactly as if you were a dentist. It is very vulgar to talk like a dentist when one isn't a dentist. It produces a false impression.

Algernon : Well, that is exactly what dentists always do. Now, go on ! Tell me the whole thing. I may mention that I have always suspected you of being a confirmed and secret Bunburyist ; and I am quite sure of it now.

Jack : Bunburyist ? What on earth do you mean by a Bunburyist ?

Algernon : I'll reveal to you the meaning of that incomparable expression as soon as you are kind enough to inform me why you are Ernest in town and Jack in the country.

Jack : Well, produce my cigarette case first.

Algernon : Here it is. (*Hands cigarette case.*) Now produce your explanation, and pray make it improbable. (*Sits on sofa.*)

Jack : My dear fellow, there is nothing improbable about my explanation at all. In fact, it's perfectly ordinary. Old Mr. Thomas Cardew, who adopted me when I was a little boy, made me in his will guardian to his granddaughter, Miss Cecily Cardew. Cecily, who addresses me as her uncle from motives of respect that you could not possibly appreciate, lives at my place in the country under the charge of her admirable governess, Miss Prism.

Algernon : Where is that place in the country, by the way ?

Jack : That is nothing to you, dear boy. You are not going to be invited. . . . I may tell you candidly that the place is not in Shropshire.

Algernon : I suspected that, my dear fellow ! I have Bunburyed all over Shropshire on two separate occasions. Now, go on. Why are you Ernest in town and Jack in the country ?

Jack : My dear Algy, I don't know whether you will be able to understand my real motives. You are hardly serious enough. When one is placed in the position of guardian, one has to adopt a very high moral tone on all subjects. It's one's duty to do so. And as a high moral tone can hardly be said to conduce very much to either one's health or one's happiness, in order to get up to town I have always pretended to have a younger brother of the name of Ernest, who lives in the Albany, and gets into the most dreadful scrapes. That, my dear Algy, is the whole truth pure and simple.

Algernon : The truth is rarely pure and never simple. Modern life would be very tedious if it were either, and modern literature a complete impossibility !

Jack : That wouldn't be at all a bad thing.

Algernon : Literary criticism is not your forte, my dear fellow. Don't try it. You should leave that to people who haven't been at a University. They do it so well in the daily papers. What you really are is a Bunburyist. I was quite right in saying you were a Bunburyist. You are one of the most advanced Bunburyists I know.

Jack : What on earth do you mean ?

Algernon : You have invented a very useful younger brother called Ernest, in order that you may be able to come up to town as often as you like. I have invented an invaluable permanent invalid called Bunbury, in order that I may be able to go down into the country whenever I choose. Bunbury is perfectly invaluable. If it wasn't for Bunbury's extraordinary bad health, for instance, I wouldn't be able to dine with you at Willis's to-night, for I have been really engaged to Aunt Augusta for more than a week.

Jack : I haven't asked you to dine with me anywhere to-night.

Algernon : I know. You are absurdly careless about sending out invitations. It is very foolish of you. Nothing annoys people so much as not receiving invitations.

Jack : You had much better dine with your Aunt Augusta.

Algernon : I haven't the smallest intention of doing anything of the kind. To begin with, I dined there on Monday, and once a week is quite enough to dine with one's own relations. In the second place, whenever I do dine there I am always treated as a member of the family, and sent down with either no woman at all, or two. In the third place, I know perfectly well whom she will place me next to to-night. She will place me next Mary Farquhar, who always flirts with her own husband across the dinner-table. That is not very pleasant. Indeed, it is not even decent . . . and that sort of thing is enormously on the increase. The amount of women in London who flirt with their own husbands is perfectly scandalous. It looks so bad. It is simply washing one's clean linen in public. Besides, now that I know you to be a confirmed Bunburyist I naturally want to talk to you about Bunburying. I want to tell you the rules.

Jack : I'm not a Bunburyist at all. If Gwendolen accepts me, I am going to kill my brother, indeed I think I'll kill him in any case. Cecily is a little too much interested in him. It is rather a bore. So I am going to get rid of Ernest. And I strongly advise you to do the same with Mr. . . . with your invalid friend who has the absurd name.

Algernon : Nothing will induce me to part with Bunbury, and if you ever get married, which seems to me extremely problematic, you will be very glad to know Bunbury. A man who marries without knowing Bunbury has a very tedious time of it.

Jack : That is nonsense. If I marry a charming girl like Gwendolen, and she is the only girl I ever saw in my life that I would marry, I certainly won't want to know Bunbury.

Algernon : Then your wife will. You don't seem to realize that in married life three is company and two is none.

Jack (sententiously) : That, my dear young friend, is the theory that the corrupt French Drama has been propounding for the last fifty years.

Algernon : Yes ; and that the happy English home has proved in half the time.

Jack : For Heaven's sake, don't try to be cynical. It's perfectly easy to be cynical.

Algernon : My dear fellow, it isn't easy to be anything nowadays. There's such a lot of beastly competition about. (*The sound of an electric bell is heard.*) Ah ! that must be Aunt Augusta. Only relatives, or creditors, ever ring in that Wagnerian manner. Now, if I get her out of the way for ten minutes, so that you can have an opportunity for proposing to Gwendolen, may I dine with you to-night at Willis's ?

Jack : I suppose so, if you want to.

Algernon : Yes, but you must be serious about it. I hate people who are not serious about meals. It is so shallow of them.

> *Enter* LANE.

Lane : Lady Bracknell and Miss Fairfax.

> ALGERNON *goes forward to meet them.* Enter LADY BRACK-
> NELL *and* GWENDOLEN.

Lady Bracknell : Good afternoon, dear Algernon, I hope you are behaving very well.

Algernon : I'm feeling very well, Aunt Augusta.

Lady Bracknell : That's not quite the same thing. In fact the two things rarely go together. (*Sees* JACK *and bows to him with icy coldness.*)

Algernon (*to* GWENDOLEN) : Dear me, you are smart !

Gwendolen : I am always smart ! Am I not, Mr. Worthing ?

Jack : You're quite perfect, Miss Fairfax.

Gwendolen : Oh ! I hope I am not that. It would leave no room for developments, and I intend to develop in many directions. (GWENDOLEN *and* JACK *sit down together in the corner*.)

Lady Bracknell : I'm sorry if we are a little late, Algernon, but I was obliged to call on dear Lady Harbury. I hadn't been there since her poor husband's death. I never saw a woman so altered ; she looks quite twenty years younger. And now I'll have a cup of tea, and one of those nice cucumber sandwiches you promised me.

Algernon : Certainly, Aunt Augusta. (*Goes over to tea-table*.)

Lady Bracknell : Won't you come and sit here, Gwendolen ?

Gwendolen : Thanks, mamma, I'm quite comfortable where I am.

Algernon (*picking up empty plate in horror*) : Good heavens ! Lane ! Why are there no cucumber sandwiches ? I ordered them specially.

Lane (*gravely*) : There were no cucumbers in the market this morning, sir. I went down twice.

Algernon : No cucumbers !

Lane : No, sir. Not even for ready money.

Algernon : That will do, Lane, thank you.

Lane : Thank you, sir. (*Goes out*.)

Algernon : I am greatly distressed, Aunt Augusta, about there being no cucumbers, not even for ready money.

Lady Bracknell : It really makes no matter, Algernon. I had some crumpets with Lady Harbury, who seems to me to be living entirely for pleasure now.

Algernon : I hear her hair has turned quite gold from grief.

Lady Bracknell : It certainly has changed its colour. From what cause I, of course, cannot say. (ALGERNON *crosses and hands tea*.) Thank you. I've quite a treat for you to-night, Algernon. I am going to send you down with Mary Farquhar. She is such a nice woman, and so attentive to her husband. It's delightful to watch them.

Algernon : I am afraid, Aunt Augusta, I shall have to give up the pleasure of dining with you to-night after all.

Lady Bracknell (*frowning*) : I hope not, Algernon. It would put my table completely out. Your uncle would have to dine upstairs. Fortunately he is accustomed to that.

Algernon : It is a great bore, and, I need hardly say, a terrible disappointment to me, but the fact is I have just had a telegram to say that my poor friend Bunbury is very ill again. (*Exchanges glances with* JACK.) They seem to think I should be with him.

Lady Bracknell : It is very strange. This Mr. Bunbury seems to suffer from curiously bad health.

Algernon : Yes ; poor Bunbury is a dreadful invalid.

Lady Bracknell : Well, I must say, Algernon, that I think it is high time that Mr. Bunbury made up his mind whether he was going to live or to die. This shilly-shallying with the question is absurd. Nor do I in any way approve of the modern sympathy with invalids. I consider it morbid. Illness of any kind is hardly a thing to be encouraged in others. Health is the primary duty of life. I am always telling that to your poor uncle, but he never seems to take much notice . . . as far as any improvement in his ailment goes. I should be much obliged if you would ask Mr. Bunbury, from me, to be kind enough not to have a relapse on Saturday, for I rely on you to arrange my music for me. It is my last reception, and one wants something that will encourage conversation, particularly at the end of the season when every one has practically said whatever they had to say, which, in most cases, was probably not much.

Algernon : I'll speak to Bunbury, Aunt Augusta, if he is still conscious, and I think I can promise you he'll be all right by Saturday. Of course the music is a great difficulty. You see, if one plays good music, people don't listen, and if one plays bad music people don't talk. But I'll run over the programme I've drawn out, if you will kindly come into the next room for a moment.

Lady Bracknell : Thank you, Algernon. It is very thoughtful of you. (*Rising, and following* ALGERNON.) I'm sure the programme will be delightful, after a few expurgations. French songs I cannot possibly allow. People always seem to think that they are improper, and either look shocked, which is vulgar, or laugh, which is worse. But German sounds a thoroughly respectable language, and indeed, I believe is so. Gwendolen, you will accompany me.

Gwendolen : Certainly, mamma.

LADY BRACKNELL *and* ALGERNON *go into the music-room,* GWENDOLEN *remains behind.*

Jack : Charming day it has been, Miss Fairfax.

Gwendolen : Pray don't talk to me about the weather, Mr. Worthing. Whenever people talk to me about the weather, I always feel quite certain that they mean something else. And that makes me so nervous.

Jack : I do mean something else.

Gwendolen : I thought so. In fact, I am never wrong.

Jack : And I would like to be allowed to take advantage of Lady Bracknell's temporary absence . . .

Gwendolen : I would certainly advise you to do so. Mamma has a way of coming back suddenly into a room that I have often had to speak to her about.

Jack (nervously) : Miss Fairfax, ever since I met you I have admired you more than any girl . . . I have ever met since . . . I met you.

Gwendolen : Yes, I am quite well aware of the fact. And I often wish that in public, at any rate, you had been more demonstrative. For me you have always had an irresistible fascination. Even before I met you I was far from indifferent to you. (JACK *looks at her in amazement.*) We live, as I hope you know, Mr. Worthing, in an age of ideals. The fact is constantly mentioned in the more expensive monthly magazines, and has reached the provincial pulpits, I am told ; and my ideal has always been to love some one of the name of Ernest. There is something in that name that inspires absolute confidence. The moment Algernon first mentioned to me that he had a friend called Ernest, I knew I was destined to love you.

Jack : You really love me, Gwendolen ?

Gwendolen : Passionately !

Jack : Darling ! You don't know how happy you've made me.

Gwendolen : My own Ernest !

Jack : But you don't really mean to say that you couldn't love me if my name wasn't Ernest ?

Gwendolen : But your name is Ernest.

Jack : Yes, I know it is. But supposing it was something else ? Do you mean to say you couldn't love me then ?

Gwendolen (glibly) : Ah ! that is clearly a metaphysical speculation, and like most metaphysical speculations has very little reference at all to the actual facts of real life, as we know them.

Jack : Personally, darling, to speak quite candidly, I don't much care about the name of Ernest. . . . I don't think the name suits me at all.

Gwendolen : It suits you perfectly. It is a divine name. It has a music of its own. It produces vibrations.

Jack : Well, really, Gwendolen, I must say that I think there are lots of other much nicer names. I think Jack, for instance, a charming name.

Gwendolen : Jack ? . . . No, there is very little music in the name Jack, if any at all, indeed. It does not thrill. It produces absolutely no vibrations. . . . I have known several Jacks, and they all, without exception, were more than usually plain. Besides, Jack is a notorious domesticity for John ! And I pity any woman who is married to a man called John. She would probably never be allowed to know the entrancing pleasure of a single moment's solitude. The only really safe name is Ernest.

Jack : Gwendolen, I must get christened at once—I mean we must get married at once. There is no time to be lost.

Gwendolen : Married, Mr. Worthing ?

Jack (astounded) : Well . . . surely. You know that I love you, and you led me to believe, Miss Fairfax, that you were not absolutely indifferent to me.

Gwendolen : I adore you. But you haven't proposed to me yet. Nothing has been said at all about marriage. The subject has not even been touched on.

Jack : Well . . . may I propose to you now ?

Gwendolen : I think it would be an admirable opportunity. And to spare you any possible disappointment, Mr. Worthing, I think it only fair to tell you quite frankly beforehand that I am fully determined to accept you.

Jack : Gwendolen !

Gwendolen : Yes, Mr. Worthing, what have you got to say to me ?

Jack : You know what I have got to say to you.

Gwendolen : Yes, but you don't say it.

Jack : Gwendolen, will you marry me ? *(Goes on his knees.)*

Gwendolen : Of course I will, darling. How long you have been about it ! I am afraid you have had very little experience in how to propose.

Jack : My own one, I have never loved any one in the world but you.

Gwendolen : Yes, but men often propose for practice. I know my brother Gerald does. All my girl-friends tell me so. What wonderfully blue eyes you have, Ernest ! They are quite, quite blue. I hope you will always look at me just like that, especially when there are other people present.

Enter LADY BRACKNELL.

Lady Bracknell : Mr. Worthing ! Rise, sir, from this semi-recumbent posture. It is most indecorous.

Gwendolen : Mamma ! *(He tries to rise ; she restrains him.)* I must beg you to retire. This is no place for you. Besides, Mr. Worthing has not quite finished yet.

Lady Bracknell : Finished what, may I ask ?

Gwendolen : I am engaged to Mr. Worthing, mamma. (*They rise together.*)

Lady Bracknell : Pardon me, you are not engaged to any one. When you do become engaged to some one, I, or your father, should his health permit him, will inform you of the fact. An engagement should come on a young girl as a surprise, pleasant or unpleasant, as the case may be. It is hardly a matter that she could be allowed to arrange for herself. . . . And now I have a few questions to put to you, Mr. Worthing. While I am making these inquiries, you, Gwendolen, will wait for me below in the carriage.

Gwendolen (reproachfully) : Mamma !

Lady Bracknell : In the carriage, Gwendolen !

> GWENDOLEN *goes to the door.* She and JACK *blow kisses to each other behind* LADY BRACKNELL's *back.* LADY BRACK-NELL *looks vaguely about as if she could not understand what the noise was. Finally turns round.*

Gwendolen, the carriage !

Gwendolen : Yes, mamma. (*Goes out, looking back at* JACK.)

Lady Bracknell (sitting down) : You can take a seat, Mr. Worthing.

> *Looks in her pocket for notebook and pencil.*

Jack : Thank you, Lady Bracknell, I prefer standing.

Lady Bracknell (pencil and notebook in hand) : I feel bound to tell you that you are not down on my list of eligible young men, although I have the same list as the dear Duchess of Bolton has. We work together, in fact. However, I am quite ready to enter your name, should your answers be what a really affectionate mother requires. Do you smoke ?

Jack : Well, yes, I must admit I smoke.

Lady Bracknell : I am glad to hear it. A man should always have an occupation of some kind. There are far too many idle men in London as it is. How old are you ?

Jack : Twenty-nine.

Lady Bracknell : A very good age to be married at. I have always been of opinion that a man who desires to get married should know either everything or nothing. Which do you know ?

Jack (after some hesitation) : I know nothing, Lady Bracknell.

Lady Bracknell : I am pleased to hear it. I do not approve of anything that tampers with natural ignorance. Ignorance is like a delicate exotic fruit ; touch it and the bloom is gone. The whole theory of modern education is radically unsound. Fortunately in England, at any rate, education produces no effect whatsoever. If it did, it would prove a serious danger to the upper classes, and probably lead to acts of violence in Grosvenor Square. What is your income ?

Jack : Between seven and eight thousand a year.

Lady Bracknell (*makes a note in her book*) *:* In land, or in investments ?

Jack : In investments, chiefly.

Lady Bracknell : That is satisfactory. What between the duties expected of one during one's lifetime, and the duties exacted from one after one's death, land has ceased to be either a profit or a pleasure. It gives one position, and prevents one from keeping it up. That's all that can be said about land.

Jack : I have a country house with some land, of course, attached to it, about fifteen hundred acres, I believe ; but I don't depend on that for my real income. In fact, as far as I can make out, the poachers are the only people who make anything out of it.

Lady Bracknell : A country house ! How many bedrooms ? Well, that point can be cleared up afterwards. You have a town house, I hope ? A girl with a simple, unspoiled nature, like Gwendolen, could hardly be expected to reside in the country.

Jack : Well, I own a house in Belgrave Square, but it is let by the year to Lady Bloxham. Of course, I can get it back whenever I like, at six months' notice.

Lady Bracknell : Lady Bloxham ? I don't know her.

Jack : Oh, she goes about very little. She is a lady considerably advanced in years.

Lady Bracknell : Ah, nowadays that is no guarantee of respectability of character. What number in Belgrave Square ?

Jack : 149.

Lady Bracknell (*shaking her head*) *:* The unfashionable side. I thought there was something. However, that could easily be altered.

Jack : Do you mean the fashion, or the side ?

Lady Bracknell (*sternly*) *:* Both, if necessary, I presume. What are your politics ?

Jack : Well, I am afraid I really have none. I am a Liberal Unionist.

Lady Bracknell : Oh, they count as Tories. They dine with us. Or come in the evening, at any rate. Now to minor matters. Are your parents living ?

Jack : I have lost both my parents.

Lady Bracknell : Both ? . . . That seems like carelessness. Who was your father ? He was evidently a man of some wealth.

GBH   23

Was he born in what the Radical papers call the purple of commerce, or did he rise from the ranks of the aristocracy ?

Jack : I am afraid I really don't know. The fact is, Lady Bracknell, I said I had lost my parents. It would be nearer the truth to say that my parents seem to have lost me. . . . I don't actually know who I am by birth. I was . . . well, I was found.

Lady Bracknell : Found !

Jack : The late Mr. Thomas Cardew, an old gentleman of a very charitable and kindly disposition, found me, and gave me the name of Worthing, because he happened to have a first-class ticket for Worthing in his pocket at the time. Worthing is a place in Sussex. It is a seaside resort.

Lady Bracknell : Where did the charitable gentleman who had a first-class ticket for this seaside resort find you ?

Jack (gravely) : In a hand-bag.

Lady Bracknell : A hand-bag ?

Jack (very seriously) : Yes, Lady Bracknell. I was in a hand-bag—a somewhat large, black leather hand-bag, with handles to it—an ordinary hand-bag in fact.

Lady Bracknell : In what locality did this Mr. James, or Thomas, Cardew come across this ordinary hand-bag ?

Jack : In the cloak-room at Victoria Station. It was given to him in mistake for his own.

Lady Bracknell : The cloak-room at Victoria Station ?

Jack : Yes. The Brighton line.

Lady Bracknell : The line is immaterial. Mr. Worthing, I confess I feel somewhat bewildered by what you have just told me. To be born, or at any rate bred, in a hand-bag, whether it had handles or not, seems to me to display a contempt for the ordinary decencies of family life that reminds one of the worst excesses of the French Revolution. And I presume you know what that unfortunate movement led to ? As for the particular locality in which the hand-bag was found, a cloak-room at a railway station might serve to conceal a social indiscretion— has probably, indeed, been used for that purpose before now— but it could hardly be regarded as an assured basis for a recognized position in good society.

Jack : May I ask you then what you would advise me to do ? I need hardly say I would do anything in the world to ensure Gwendolen's happiness.

Lady Bracknell : I would strongly advise you, Mr. Worthing, to try and acquire some relations as soon as possible, and to make a definite effort to produce at any rate one parent, of either sex, before the season is quite over.

Jack : Well, I don't see how I could possibly manage to do that. I can produce the hand-bag at any moment. It is in my dressing-room at home. I really think that should satisfy you, Lady Bracknell.

Lady Bracknell : Me, sir ! What has it to do with me ? You can hardly imagine that I and Lord Bracknell would dream of allowing our only daughter—a girl brought up with the utmost care—to marry into a cloak-room, and form an alliance with a parcel. Good-morning, Mr. Worthing !

LADY BRACKNELL *sweeps out in majestic indignation.*

Jack : Good-morning ! (ALGERNON, *from the other room, strikes up the Wedding March.* JACK *looks perfectly furious, and goes to the door.*) For goodness' sake don't play that ghastly tune, Algy ! How idiotic you are !

The music stops and ALGERNON *enters cheerily.*

Algernon : Didn't it go off all right, old boy ? You don't mean to say Gwendolen refused you ? I know it is a way she has. She is always refusing people. I think it is most ill-natured of her.

Jack : Oh, Gwendolen is as right as a trivet. As far as she is concerned, we are engaged. Her mother is perfectly unbearable. Never met such a Gorgon. . . . I don't really know what a Gorgon is like, but I am quite sure that Lady Bracknell is one. In any case, she is a monster, without being a myth, which is rather unfair. . . . I beg your pardon, Algy, I suppose I shouldn't talk about your own aunt in that way before you.

Algernon : My dear boy, I love hearing my relations abused. It is the only thing that makes me put up with them at all. Relations are simply a tedious pack of people, who haven't got the remotest knowledge of how to live, nor the smallest instinct about when to die.

Jack : Oh, that is nonsense !

Algernon : It isn't !

Jack : Well, I won't argue about the matter. You always want to argue about things.

Algernon: That is exactly what things were originally made for.

Jack : Upon my word, if I thought that, I'd shoot myself. . . . (*A pause.*) You don't think there is any chance of Gwendolen becoming like her mother in about a hundred and fifty years, do you, Algy ?

Algernon : All women become like their mothers. That is their tragedy. No man does. That's his.

Jack : Is that clever ?

Algernon : It is perfectly phrased ! And quite as true as any observation in civilized life should be.

Jack : I am sick to death of cleverness. Everybody is clever nowadays. You can't go anywhere without meeting clever people. The thing has become an absolute public nuisance. I wish to goodness we had a few fools left.

Algernon : We have.

Jack : I should extremely like to meet them. What do they talk about ?

Algernon : The fools ? Oh ! about the clever people of course.

Jack : What fools.

Algernon : By the way, did you tell Gwendolen the truth about your being Ernest in town, and Jack in the country ?

Jack (in a very patronising manner) : My dear fellow, the truth isn't quite the sort of thing one tells to a nice, sweet, refined girl. What extraordinary ideas you have about the way to behave to a woman !

Algernon : The only way to behave to a woman is to make love to her, if she is pretty, and to some one else, if she is plain.

Jack : Oh, that is nonsense.

Algernon : What about your brother ? What about the profligate Ernest ?

Jack : Oh, before the end of the week I shall have got rid of him. I'll say he died in Paris of apoplexy. Lots of people die of apoplexy, quite suddenly, don't they ?

Algernon : Yes, but it's hereditary, my dear fellow. It's a sort of thing that runs in families. You had much better say a severe chill.

Jack : You are sure a severe chill isn't hereditary, or anything of that kind ?

Algernon : Of course it isn't !

Jack : Very well, then. My poor brother Ernest is carried off suddenly, in Paris, by a severe chill. That gets rid of him.

Algernon : But I thought you said that . . . Miss Cardew was a little too much interested in your poor brother Ernest ? Won't she feel his loss a good deal ?

Jack : Oh, that is all right . Cecily is not a silly romantic girl, I am glad to say. She has got a capital appetite, goes long walks, and pays no attention at all to her lessons.

Algernon : I would rather like to see Cecily.

Jack : I will take very good care you never do. She is excessively pretty, and she is only just eighteen.

Algernon : Have you told Gwendolen yet that you have an excessively pretty ward who is only just eighteen ?

Jack : Oh! one doesn't blurt these things out to people. Cecily and Gwendolen are perfectly certain to be extremely great friends. I'll bet you anything you like that half an hour after they have met they will be calling each other sister.

Algernon : Women only do that when they have called each other a lot of other things first. Now, my dear boy, if we want to get a good table at Willis's, we really must go and dress. Do you know it is nearly seven?

Jack (irritably) : Oh! it always is nearly seven.

Algernon : Well, I'm hungry.

Jack : I never knew you when you weren't. . . .

Algernon : What shall we do after dinner? Go to a theatre?

Jack : Oh no! I loathe listening.

Algernon : Well, let us go to the Club?

Jack : Oh, no! I hate talking.

Algernon : Well, we might trot round to the Empire at ten?

Jack : Oh, no! I can't bear looking at things. It is so silly.

Algernon : Well, what shall we do?

Jack : Nothing!

Algernon : It is awfully hard work doing nothing. However, I don't mind hard work where there is no definite object of any kind.

> *Enter* LANE.

Lane : Miss Fairfax.

> *Enter* GWENDOLEN. LANE *goes out.*

Algernon : Gwendolen, upon my word!

Gwendolen : Algy, kindly turn your back. I have something very particular to say to Mr. Worthing.

Algernon : Really, Gwendolen, I don't think I can allow this at all.

Gwendolen : Algy, you always adopt a strictly immoral attitude towards life. You are not quite old enough to do that. (ALGERNON *retires to the fireplace.*)

Jack : My own darling!

Gwendolen : Ernest, we may never be married. From the expression on mamma's face I fear we never shall. Few parents nowadays pay any regard to what their children say to them. The old-fashioned respect for the young is fast dying out. Whatever influence I ever had over mamma I lost at the age of three. But although she may prevent us from becoming man and wife, and I may marry some one else, and marry often, nothing that she can possibly do can alter my eternal devotion to you.

Jack : Dear Gwendolen!

Gwendolen : The story of your romantic origin, as related to me by mamma, with unpleasing comments, has naturally stirred the deeper fibres of my nature. Your Christian name has an irresistible fascination. The simplicity of your character makes you exquisitely incomprehensible to me. Your town address at the Albany I have. What is your address in the country?

Jack : The Manor House, Woolton, Hertfordshire.

> ALGERNON, *who has been carefully listening, smiles to himself, and writes the address on his shirt-cuff. Then picks up the Railway Guide.*

Gwendolen : There is a good postal service, I suppose? It may be necessary to do something desperate. That, of course, will require serious consideration. I will communicate with you daily.

Jack : My own one !

Gwendolen : How long do you remain in town?

Jack : Till Monday.

Gwendolen : Good ! Algy, you may turn round now.

Algernon : Thanks, I've turned round already.

Gwendolen : You may also ring the bell.

Jack : You will let me see you to your carriage, my own darling?

Gwendolen : Certainly.

Jack (to LANE, *who now enters) :* I will see Miss Fairfax out.

Lane : Yes, sir.

> JACK *and* GWENDOLEN *go off.*

> LANE *presents several letters on a salver to* ALGERNON. *It is to be surmised that they are bills, as* ALGERNON, *after looking at the envelopes, tears them up.*

Algernon : A glass of sherry, Lane.

Lane : Yes, sir.

Algernon : To-morrow, Lane, I'm going Bunburying.

Lane : Yes, sir.

Algernon : I shall probably not be back till Monday. You can put up my dress clothes, my smoking jacket, and all the Bunbury suits . . .

Lane : Yes, sir. (*Handing sherry.*)

Algernon : I hope to-morrow will be a fine day, Lane.

Lane : It never is, sir.

Algernon : Lane, you're a perfect pessimist.

Lane : I do my best to give satisfaction, sir.

> *Enter* JACK. LANE *goes off.*

Jack : There's a sensible, intellectual girl ! the only girl I ever cared for in my life. (ALGERNON *is laughing immoderately.*) What on earth are you so amused at ?

Algernon : Oh, I'm a little anxious about poor Bunbury, that is all.

Jack : If you don't take care, your friend Bunbury will get you into a serious scrape some day.

Algernon : I love scrapes. They are the only things that are never serious.

Jack : Oh, that's nonsense, Algy. You never talk anything but nonsense.

Algernon : Nobody ever does.

JACK *looks indignantly at him, and leaves the room.* ALGERNON *lights a cigarette, reads his shirt-cuff, and smiles.*

ACT DROP.

SECOND ACT

SCENE.—*Garden at the Manor House. A flight of grey stone steps leads up to the house. The garden, an old-fashioned one, full of roses. Time of year, July. Basket chairs, and a table covered with books, are set under a large yew-tree.*

MISS PRISM *discovered seated at the table.* CECILY *is at the back watering flowers.*

Miss Prism (calling) : Cecily, Cecily ! Surely such a utilitarian occupation as the watering of flowers is rather Moulton's duty than yours ? Especially at a moment when intellectual pleasures await you. Your German grammar is on the table. Pray open it at page fifteen. We will repeat yesterday's lesson.

Cecily (coming over very slowly) : But I don't like German. It isn't at all a becoming language. I know perfectly well that I look quite plain after my German lesson.

Miss Prism : Child, you know how anxious your guardian is that you should improve yourself in every way. He laid particular stress on your German as he was leaving for town yesterday. Indeed, he always lays stress on your German when he is leaving for town.

Cecily : Dear Uncle Jack is so very serious ! Sometimes he is so serious that I think he cannot be quite well.

Miss Prism (drawing herself up) : Your guardian enjoys the best of health, and his gravity of demeanour is especially to be commended in one so comparatively young as he is. I know no one who has a higher sense of duty and responsibility.

Cecily : I suppose that is why he often looks a little bored when we three are together.

Miss Prism : Cecily ! I am surprised at you. Mr. Worthing has many troubles in his life. Idle merriment and triviality would be out of place in his conversation. You must remember his constant anxiety about that unfortunate young man, his brother.

Cecily : I wish Uncle Jack would allow that unfortunate young man, his brother, to come down here sometimes. We might have a good influence over him, Miss Prism. I am sure you certainly would. You know German, and geology, and things of that kind influence a man very much.

CECILY *begins to write in her diary.*

Miss Prism (shaking her head) : I do not think that even I could produce any effect on a character that according to his own brother's admission is irretrievably weak and vacillating. Indeed I am not sure that I would desire to reclaim him. I am not in favour of this modern mania for turning bad people into good people at a moment's notice. As a man sows so let him reap. You must put away your diary, Cecily. I really don't see why you should keep a diary at all.

Cecily : I keep a diary in order to enter the wonderful secrets of my life. If I didn't write them down, I should probably forget all about them.

Miss Prism : Memory, my dear Cecily, is the diary that we all carry about with us.

Cecily : Yes, but it usually chronicles the things that have never happened, and couldn't possibly have happened. I believe that Memory is responsible for nearly all the three-volume novels that Mudie sends us.

Miss Prism : Do not speak slightingly of the three-volume novel, Cecily. I wrote one myself in earlier days.

Cecily : Did you really, Miss Prism ? How wonderfully clever you are ! I hope it did not end happily ? I don't like novels that end happily. They depress me so much.

Miss Prism : The good ended happily, and the bad unhappily. That is what Fiction means.

Cecily : I suppose so. But it seems very unfair. And was your novel ever published ?

Miss Prism : Alas ! no. The manuscript unfortunately was abandoned. (CECILY *starts.*) I use the word in the sense of lost or mislaid. To your work, child, these speculations are profitless.

Cecily (smiling) : But I see dear Dr. Chasuble coming up through the garden.

Miss Prism (rising and advancing) : Dr. Chasuble ! This is indeed a pleasure.

Enter CANON CHASUBLE.

Chasuble : And how are we this morning ? Miss Prism, you are, I trust, well ?

Cecily : Miss Prism has just been complaining of a slight headache. I think it would do her so much good to have a short stroll with you in the Park, Dr. Chasuble.

Miss Prism : Cecily, I have not mentioned anything about a headache.

Cecily : No, dear Miss Prism, I know that, but I felt in-stinctively that you had a headache. Indeed I was thinking about that, and not about my German lesson, when the Rector came in.

Chasuble : I hope, Cecily, you are not inattentive.

Cecily : Oh, I am afraid I am.

Chasuble : That is strange. Were I fortunate enough to be Miss Prism's pupil, I would hang upon her lips. (MISS PRISM *glares.*) I spoke metaphorically.—My metaphor was drawn from bees. Ahem ! Mr. Worthing, I suppose, has not returned from town yet ?

Miss Prism : We do not expect him till Monday afternoon.

Chasuble : Ah yes, he usually likes to spend his Sunday in London. He is not one of those whose sole aim is enjoyment, as, by all accounts, that unfortunate young man his brother seems to be. But I must not disturb Egeria and her pupil any longer.

Miss Prism : Egeria ? My name is Lætitia, Doctor.

Chasuble (bowing) : A classical allusion merely, drawn from the Pagan authors. I shall see you both no doubt at Evensong ?

Miss Prism : I think, dear Doctor, I will have a stroll with you. I find I have a headache after all, and a walk might do it good.

Chasuble : With pleasure, Miss Prism, with pleasure. We might go as far as the schools and back.

Miss Prism : That would be delightful. Cecily, you will read your Political Economy in my absence. The chapter on the Fall of the Rupee you may omit. It is somewhat too sen-sational. Even these metallic problems have their melodramatic side.

Goes down the garden with DR. CHASUBLE.

Cecily (picks up books and throws them back on table) : Horrid

23*

Political Economy ! Horrid Geography ! Horrid, horrid German !

Enter MERRIMAN *with a card on a salver.*

Merriman : Mr. Ernest Worthing has just driven over from the station. He has brought his luggage with him.

Cecily (takes the card and reads it) : " Mr. Ernest Worthing, B.4, The Albany, W." Uncle Jack's brother ! Did you tell him Mr. Worthing was in town ?

Merriman : Yes, Miss. He seemed very much disappointed. I mentioned that you and Miss Prism were in the garden. He said he was anxious to speak to you privately for a moment.

Cecily : Ask Mr. Ernest Worthing to come here. I suppose you had better talk to the housekeeper about a room for him.

Merriman : Yes, Miss.

MERRIMAN *goes off.*

Cecily : I have never met any really wicked person before. I feel rather frightened. I am so afraid he will look just like every one else.

Enter ALGERNON, *very gay and debonair.*

He does !

Algernon (raising his hat) : You are my little cousin Cecily, I'm sure.

Cecily : You are under some strange mistake. I am not little. In fact, I believe I am more than usually tall for my age. (ALGERNON *is rather taken aback.*) But I am your cousin, Cecily. You, I see from your card, are Uncle Jack's brother, my cousin Ernest, my wicked cousin Ernest.

Algernon : Oh ! I am not really wicked at all, cousin Cecily. You mustn't think that I am wicked.

Cecily : If you are not, then you have certainly been deceiving us all in a very inexcusable manner. I hope you have not been leading a double life, pretending to be wicked and being really good all the time. That would be hypocrisy.

Algernon (looks at her in amazement) : Oh ! Of course I have been rather reckless.

Cecily : I am glad to hear it.

Algernon : In fact, now you mention the subject, I have been very bad in my own small way.

Cecily : I don't think you should be so proud of that, though I am sure it must have been very pleasant.

Algernon : It is much pleasanter being here with you.

Cecily : I can't understand how you are here at all. Uncle Jack won't be back till Monday afternoon.

Algernon : That is a great disappointment. I am obliged to go up by the first train on Monday morning. I have a business appointment that I am anxious . . . to miss !

Cecily : Couldn't you miss it anywhere but in London ?

Algernon : No ; the appointment is in London.

Cecily : Well, I know, of course, how important it is not to keep a business engagement, if one wants to retain any sense of the beauty of life, but still I think you had better wait till Uncle Jack arrives. I know he wants to speak to you about your emigrating.

Algernon : About my what ?

Cecily : Your emigrating. He has gone up to buy your outfit.

Algernon : I certainly wouldn't let Jack buy my outfit. He has no taste in neckties at all.

Cecily : I don't think you will require neckties. Uncle Jack is sending you to Australia.

Algernon : Australia ! I'd sooner die.

Cecily : Well, he said at dinner on Wednesday night, that you would have to choose between this world, the next world, and Australia.

Algernon : Oh, well ! The accounts I have received of Australia and the next world are not particularly encouraging. This world is good enough for me, cousin Cecily.

Cecily : Yes, but are you good enough for it ?

Algernon : I'm afraid I'm not that. That is why I want you to reform me. You might make that your mission, if you don't mind, cousin Cecily.

Cecily : I'm afraid I've no time, this afternoon.

Algernon : Well, would you mind my reforming myself this afternoon ?

Cecily : It is rather Quixotic of you. But I think you should try.

Algernon : I will. I feel better already.

Cecily : You are looking a little worse.

Algernon : That is because I am hungry.

Cecily : How thoughtless of me. I should have remembered that when one is going to lead an entirely new life, one requires regular and wholesome meals. Won't you come in ?

Algernon : Thank you. Might I have a buttonhole first ? I never have any appetite unless I have a buttonhole first.

Cecily : A Maréchal Niel ? (*Picks up scissors.*)

Algernon : No, I'd sooner have a pink rose.

Cecily : Why ? (*cuts a flower.*)

Algernon : Because you are like a pink rose, cousin Cecily.

Cecily : I don't think it can be right for you to talk to me like that. Miss Prism never says such things to me.

Algernon : Then Miss Prism is a short-sighted old lady. (CECILY *puts the rose in his buttonhole.*) You are the prettiest girl I ever saw.

Cecily : Miss Prism says that all good looks are a snare.

Algernon : They are a snare that every sensible man would like to be caught in.

Cecily : Oh, I don't think I would care to catch a sensible man. I shouldn't know what to talk to him about.

> *They pass into the house.* MISS PRISM *and* DR. CHASUBLE *return.*

Miss Prism : You are too much alone, dear Dr. Chasuble. You should get married. A misanthrope I can understand—a womanthrope, never !

Chasuble (*with a scholar's shudder*) *:* Believe me, I do not deserve so neologistic a phrase. The precept as well as the practice of the Primitive Church was distinctly against matrimony.

Miss Prism (*sententiously*) *:* That is obviously the reason why the Primitive Church has not lasted up to the present day. And you do not seem to realize, dear Doctor, that by persistently remaining single, a man converts himself into a permanent public temptation. Men should be more careful ; this very celibacy leads weaker vessels astray.

Chasuble : But is a man not equally attractive when married ?

Miss Prism : No married man is ever attractive except to his wife.

Chasuble : And often, I've been told, not even to her.

Miss Prism : That depends on the intellectual sympathies of the woman. Maturity can always be depended on. Ripeness can be trusted. Young women are green. (DR. CHASUBLE *starts.*) I spoke horticulturally. My metaphor was drawn from fruits. But where is Cecily ?

Chasuble : Perhaps she followed us to the schools.

> *Enter* JACK *slowly from the back of the garden. He is dressed in the deepest mourning, with crêpe hatband and black gloves.*

Miss Prism : Mr. Worthing !

Chasuble : Mr. Worthing ?

Miss Prism : This is indeed a surprise. We did not look for you till Monday afternoon.

Jack (*shakes* MISS PRISM'S *hand in a tragic manner*) *:* I have returned sooner than I expected. Dr. Chasuble, I hope you are well ?

Chasuble : Dear Mr. Worthing, I trust this garb of woe does not betoken some terrible calamity ?

Jack : My brother.

Miss Prism : More shameful debts and extravagance ?

Chasuble : Still leading his life of pleasure ?

Jack (shaking his head) : Dead !

Chasuble : Your brother Ernest dead ?

Jack : Quite dead.

Miss Prism : What a lesson for him ! I trust he will profit by it.

Chasuble : Mr. Worthing, I offer you my sincere condolence. You have at least the consolation of knowing that you were always the most generous and forgiving of brothers.

Jack : Poor Ernest ! He had many faults, but it is a sad, sad blow.

Chasuble : Very sad indeed. Were you with him at the end ?

Jack : No. He died abroad ; in Paris, in fact. I had a telegram last night from the manager of the Grand Hotel.

Chasuble : Was the cause of death mentioned ?

Jack : A severe chill, it seems.

Miss Prism : As a man sows, so shall he reap.

Chasuble (raising his hand) : Charity, dear Miss Prism, charity ! None of us are perfect. I myself am peculiarly susceptible to draughts. Will the interment take place here ?

Jack : No. He seems to have expressed a desire to be buried in Paris.

Chasuble : In Paris ! (*Shakes his head.*) I fear that hardly points to any very serious state of mind at the last. You would no doubt wish me to make some slight allusion to this tragic domestic affliction next Sunday. (JACK *presses his hand convulsively.*) My sermon on the meaning of the manna in the wilderness can be adapted to almost any occasion, joyful, or, as in the present case, distressing. (*All sigh.*) I have preached it at harvest celebrations, christenings, confirmations, on days of humiliation, and festal days. The last time I delivered it was in the Cathedral, as a charity sermon on behalf of the Society for the Prevention of Discontent among the Upper Orders. The Bishop, who was present, was much struck by some of the analogies I drew.

Jack : Ah ! that reminds me, you mentioned christenings, I think, Dr. Chasuble ? I suppose you know how to christen all right ? (DR. CHASUBLE *looks astounded.*) I mean, of course, you are continually christening, aren't you ?

Miss Prism : It is, I regret to say, one of the Rector's most constant duties in this parish. I have often spoken to the poorer classes on the subject. But they don't seem to know what thrift is.

Chasuble : But is there any particular infant in whom you are interested, Mr. Worthing? Your brother was, I believe, unmarried, was he not?

Jack : Oh, yes.

Miss Prism (bitterly) : People who live entirely for pleasure usually are.

Jack : But it is not for any child, dear Doctor. I am very fond of children. No! the fact is, I would like to be christened myself, this afternoon, if you have nothing better to do.

Chasuble : But surely, Mr. Worthing, you have been christened already?

Jack : I don't remember anything about it.

Chasuble : But have you any grave doubts on the subject?

Jack : I certainly intend to have. Of course I don't know if the thing would bother you in any way, or if you think I am a little too old now.

Chasuble : Not at all. The sprinkling, and, indeed, the immersion of adults is a perfectly canonical practice.

Jack : Immersion!

Chasuble : You need have no apprehensions. Sprinkling is all that is necessary, or indeed I think advisable. Our weather is so changeable. At what hour would you wish the ceremony performed?

Jack : Oh, I might trot round about five if that would suit you.

Chasuble : Perfectly, perfectly! In fact, I have two similar ceremonies to perform at that time. A case of twins that occurred recently in one of the outlying cottages on your own estate. Poor Jenkins, the carter, a most hard-working man.

Jack : Oh! I don't see much fun in being christened along with other babies. It would be childish. Would half-past five do?

Chasuble : Admirably! Admirably! *(Takes out watch.)* And now, dear Mr. Worthing, I will not intrude any longer into a house of sorrow. I would merely beg you not to be too much bowed down by grief. What seem to us bitter trials are often blessings in disguise.

Miss Prism : This seems to me a blessing of an extremely obvious kind.

Enter CECILY *from the house.*

Cecily : Uncle Jack! Oh, I am pleased to see you back.

But what horrid clothes you have got on ! Do go and change them.

Miss Prism : Cecily !

Chasuble : My child ! my child !

> CECILY *goes towards* JACK *; he kisses her brow in a melancholy manner.*

Cecily : What is the matter, Uncle Jack ? Do look happy ! You look as if you had toothache, and I have got such a surprise for you. Who do you think is in the dining-room ? Your brother !

Jack : Who ?

Cecily : Your brother Ernest. He arrived about half an hour ago.

Jack : What nonsense ! I haven't got a brother.

Cecily : Oh, don't say that. However badly he may have behaved to you in the past he is still your brother. You couldn't be so heartless as to disown him. I'll tell him to come out. And you will shake hands with him, won't you, Uncle Jack ? (*Runs back into the house.*)

Chasuble : These are very joyful tidings.

Miss Prism : After we had all been resigned to his loss, his sudden return seems to me peculiarly distressing.

Jack : My brother is in the dining-room ? I don't know what it all means. I think it is perfectly absurd.

> *Enter* ALGERNON *and* CECILY *hand in hand. They come slowly up to* JACK.

Jack : Good heavens ! (*Motions* ALGERNON *away.*)

Algernon : Brother John, I have come down from town to tell you that I am very sorry for all the trouble I have given you, and that I intend to lead a better life in the future. (JACK *glares at him and does not take his hand.*)

Cecily : Uncle Jack, you are not going to refuse your own brother's hand ?

Jack : Nothing will induce me to take his hand. I think his coming down here disgraceful. He knows perfectly well why.

Cecily : Uncle Jack, do be nice. There is some good in every one. Ernest has just been telling me about his poor invalid friend Mr. Bunbury whom he goes to visit so often. And surely there must be much good in one who is kind to an invalid, and leaves the pleasures of London to sit by a bed of pain.

Jack : Oh ! he has been talking about Bunbury, has he ?

Cecily : Yes, he has told me all about poor Mr. Bunbury, and his terrible state of health.

Jack : Bunbury ! Well, I won't have him talk to you about Bunbury or about anything else. It is enough to drive one perfectly frantic.

Algernon : Of course I admit that the faults were all on my side. But I must say that I think that Brother John's coldness to me is peculiarly painful. I expected a more enthusiastic welcome, especially considering it is the first time I have come here.

Cecily : Uncle Jack, if you don't shake hands with Ernest I will never forgive you.

Jack : Never forgive me ?

Cecily : Never, never, never !

Jack : Well, this is the last time I shall ever do it. (*Shakes hands with* ALGERNON *and glares.*)

Chasuble : It's pleasant, is it not, to see so perfect a reconciliation ? I think we might leave the two brothers together.

Miss Prism : Cecily, you will come with us.

Cecily : Certainly, Miss Prism. My little task of reconciliation is over.

Chasuble : You have done a beautiful action to-day, dear child.

Miss Prism : We must not be premature in our judgments.

Cecily : I feel very happy.

> *They all go off except* JACK *and* ALGERNON.

Jack : You young scoundrel, Algy, you must get out of this place as soon as possible. I don't allow any Bunburying here.

> *Enter* MERRIMAN.

Merriman : I have put Mr. Ernest's things in the room next to yours, sir. I suppose that is all right ?

Jack : What ?

Merriman : Mr. Ernest's luggage, sir. I have unpacked it and put it in the room next to your own.

Jack : His luggage ?

Merriman : Yes, sir. Three portmanteaus, a dressing-case, two hat-boxes, and a large luncheon-basket.

Algernon : I am afraid I can't stay more than a week this time.

Jack : Merriman, order the dog-cart at once. Mr. Ernest has been suddenly called back to town.

Merriman : Yes, sir. (*Goes back to the house.*)

Algernon : What a fearful liar you are, Jack. I have not been called back to town at all.

Jack : Yes, you have.

Algernon : I haven't heard any one call me.

Jack : Your duty as a gentleman calls you back.

Algernon : My duty as a gentleman has never interfered with my pleasures in the smallest degree.

Jack : I can quite understand that.

Algernon : Well, Cecily is a darling.

Jack : You are not to talk of Miss Cardew like that. I don't like it.

Algernon : Well, I don't like your clothes. You look perfectly ridiculous in them. Why on earth don't you go up and change ? It is perfectly childish to be in deep mourning for a man who is actually staying for a whole week with you in your house as a guest. I call it grotesque.

Jack : You are certainly not staying with me for a whole week as a guest or anything else. You have got to leave . . . by the four-five train.

Algernon : I certainly won't leave you so long as you are in mourning. It would be most unfriendly. If I were in mourning you would stay with me, I suppose. I should think it very unkind if you didn't.

Jack : Well, will you go if I change my clothes ?

Algernon : Yes, if you are not too long. I never saw anybody take so long to dress, and with such little result.

Jack : Well, at any rate, that is better than being always over-dressed as you are.

Algernon : If I am occasionally a little over-dressed, I make up for it by being always immensely over-educated.

Jack : Your vanity is ridiculous, your conduct an outrage, and your presence in my garden utterly absurd. However, you have got to catch the four-five, and I hope you will have a pleasant journey back to town. This Bunburying, as you call it, has not been a great success for you. (*Goes into the house.*)

Algernon : I think it has been a great success. I'm in love with Cecily, and that is everything.

> *Enter* CECILY *at the back of the garden. She picks up the can and begins to water the flowers.*

But I must see her before I go, and make arrangements for another Bunbury. Ah, there she is.

Cecily : Oh, I merely came back to water the roses. I thought you were with Uncle Jack.

Algernon : He's gone to order the dog-cart for me.

Cecily : Oh, is he going to take you for a nice drive ?

Algernon : He's going to send me away.

Cecily : Then have we got to part ?

Algernon : I am afraid so. It's a very painful parting.

Cecily : It is always painful to part from people whom one has known for a very brief space of time. The absence of old friends one can endure with equanimity. But even a momentary separation from any one to whom one has just been introduced is almost unbearable.

Algernon : Thank you.

Enter MERRIMAN.

Merriman : The dog-cart is at the door, sir.

ALGERNON *looks appealing at* CECILY.

Cecily : It can wait, Merriman, for five minutes.

Merriman : Yes, Miss.

Exit MERRIMAN.

Algernon : I hope, Cecily, I shall not offend you if I state quite frankly and openly that you seem to me to be in every way the visible personification of absolute perfection.

Cecily : I think your frankness does you great credit, Ernest. If you will allow me, I will copy your remarks into my diary. (*Goes over to table and begins writing in diary.*)

Algernon : Do you really keep a diary? I'd give anything to look at it. May I ?

Cecily : Oh, no. (*Puts her hand over it.*) You see, it is simply a very young girl's record of her own thoughts and impressions, and consequently meant for publication. When it appears in volume form I hope you will order a copy. But pray, Ernest, don't stop. I delight in taking down from dictation. I have reached " absolute perfection." You can go on. I am quite ready for more.

Algernon (somewhat taken aback) : Ahem ! Ahem !

Cecily : Oh, don't cough, Ernest. When one is dictating one should speak fluently and not cough. Besides, I don't know how to spell a cough. (*Writes as* ALGERNON *speaks.*)

Algernon (speaking very rapidly) : Cecily, ever since I first looked upon your wonderful and incomparable beauty, I have dared to love you wildly, passionately, devotedly, hopelessly.

Cecily : I don't think that you should tell me that you love me wildly, passionately, devotedly, hopelessly. Hopelessly doesn't seem to make much sense, does it ?

Algernon : Cecily !

Enter MERRIMAN.

Merriman : The dog-cart is waiting, sir.

Algernon : Tell it to come round next week, at the same hour.

Merriman (looks at CECILY, *who makes no sign) :* Yes, sir.

MERRIMAN *retires.*

Cecily : Uncle Jack would be very much annoyed if he knew you were staying on till next week, at the same hour.

Algernon : Oh, I don't care about Jack. I don't care for anybody in the whole world but you. I love you, Cecily. You will marry me, won't you ?

Cecily : You silly boy ! Of course. Why, we have been engaged for the last three months.

Algernon : For the last three months ?

Cecily : Yes, it will be exactly three months on Thursday.

Algernon : But how did we become engaged ?

Cecily : Well, ever since dear Uncle Jack first confessed to us that he had a younger brother who was very wicked and bad, you, of course, have formed the chief topic of conversation between myself and Miss Prism. And, of course, a man who is much talked about is always very attractive. One feels there must be something in him, after all. I dare say it was foolish of me, but I fell in love with you, Ernest.

Algernon : Darling. And when was the engagement actually settled ?

Cecily : On the 14th of February last. Worn out by your entire ignorance of my existence, I determined to end the matter one way or the other, and after a long struggle with myself I accepted you under this dear old tree here. The next day I bought this little ring in your name, and this is the little bangle with the true lover's knot I promised you always to wear.

Algernon : Did I give you this ? It's very pretty, isn't it ?

Cecily : Yes, you've wonderfully good taste, Ernest. It's the excuse I've always given for your leading such a bad life. And this is the box in which I keep all your dear letters. (*Kneels at table, opens box, and produces letters tied up with blue ribbon.*)

Algernon : My letters ! But, my own sweet Cecily, I have never written you any letters.

Cecily : You need hardly remind me of that, Ernest. I remember only too well that I was forced to write your letters for you. I wrote always three times a week, and sometimes oftener.

Algernon : Oh, do let me read them, Cecily ?

Cecily : Oh, I couldn't possibly. They would make you far too conceited. (*Replaces box.*) The three you wrote me after I had broken off the engagement are so beautiful, and so badly spelled, that even now I can hardly read them without crying a little.

Algernon : But was our engagement ever broken off?

Cecily : Of course it was. On the 22nd of last March. You can see the entry if you like. *(Shows diary.)* "To-day I broke off my engagement with Ernest. I feel it is better to do so. The weather still continues charming."

Algernon : But why on earth did you break it off? What had I done? I had done nothing at all. Cecily, I am very much hurt indeed to hear you broke it off. Particularly when the weather was so charming.

Cecily : It would hardly have been a really serious engagement if it hadn't been broken off at least once. But I forgave you before the week was out.

Algernon (crossing to her, and kneeling) : What a perfect angel you are, Cecily.

Cecily : You dear romantic boy. *(He kisses her, she puts her fingers through his hair.)* I hope your hair curls naturally, does it?

Algernon : Yes, darling, with a little help from others.

Cecily : I am so glad.

Algernon : You'll never break off our engagement again, Cecily?

Cecily : I don't think I could break it off now that I have actually met you. Besides, of course, there is the question of your name.

Algernon : Yes, of course. *(Nervously.)*

Cecily : You must not laugh at me, darling, but it had always been a girlish dream of mine to love some one whose name was Ernest.

ALGERNON *rises,* CECILY *also.*

There is something in that name that seems to inspire absolute confidence. I pity any poor married woman whose husband is not called Ernest.

Algernon : But, my dear child, do you mean to say you could not love me if I had some other name?

Cecily : But what name?

Algernon : Oh, any name you like—Algernon—for instance . . .

Cecily : But I don't like the name of Algernon.

Algernon : Well, my own dear, sweet, loving little darling, I really can't see why you should object to the name of Algernon. It is not at all a bad name. In fact, it is rather an aristocratic name. Half of the chaps who get into the Bankruptcy Court are called Algernon. But seriously, Cecily—(*moving to her*)—if my name was Algy, couldn't you love me ?

Cecily (*rising*) : I might respect you, Ernest, I might admire your character, but I fear that I should not be able to give you my undivided attention.

Algernon : Ahem ! Cecily ! (*Picking up hat.*) Your Rector here is, I suppose, thoroughly experienced in the practice of all the rites and ceremonials of the Church ?

Cecily : Oh, yes. Dr. Chasuble is a most learned man. He has never written a single book, so you can imagine how much he knows.

Algernon : I must see him at once on a most important christening—I mean on most important business.

Cecily : Oh !

Algernon : I shan't be away more than half an hour.

Cecily : Considering that we have been engaged since February the 14th, and that I only met you to-day for the first time, I think it is rather hard that you should leave me for so long a period as half an hour. Couldn't you make it twenty minutes ?

Algernon : I'll be back in no time. (*Kisses her and rushes down the garden.*)

Cecily : What an impetuous boy he is ! I like his hair so much. I must enter his proposal in my diary.

Enter MERRIMAN.

Merriman : A Miss Fairfax has just called to see Mr. Worthing. On very important business, Miss Fairfax states.

Cecily : Isn't Mr. Worthing in his library ?

Merriman : Mr. Worthing went over in the direction of the Rectory some time ago.

Cecily : Pray ask the lady to come out here ; Mr. Worthing. is sure to be back soon. And you can bring tea.

Merriman : Yes, Miss. (*Goes out.*)

Cecily : Miss Fairfax ! I suppose one of the many good elderly women who are associated with Uncle Jack in some of his philanthropic work in London. I don't quite like women who are interested in philanthropic work. I think it is so forward of them.

Enter MERRIMAN.

Merriman : Miss Fairfax.

Enter GWENDOLEN. *Exit* MERRIMAN.

Cecily (*advancing to meet her*) : Pray let me introduce myself to you. My name is Cecily Cardew.

Gwendolen : Cecily Cardew ? (*Moving to her and shaking hands.*) What a very sweet name ! Something tells me that we are going to be great friends. I like you already more than I can say. My first impressions of people are never wrong.

Cecily : How nice of you to like me so much after we have known each other such a comparatively short time. Pray sit down.

Gwendolen (*still standing up*) : I may call you Cecily, may I not ?

Cecily : With pleasure !

Gwendolen : And you will always call me Gwendolen, won't you ?

Cecily : If you wish.

Gwendolen : Then that is all quite settled, is it not ?

Cecily : I hope so.

A pause. They both sit down together.

Gwendolen : Perhaps this might be a favourable opportunity for my mentioning who I am. My father is Lord Bracknell. You have never heard of papa, I suppose ?

Cecily : I don't think so.

Gwendolen : Outside the family circle, papa, I am glad to say, is entirely unknown. I think that is quite as it should be. The home seems to me to be the proper sphere for the man. And certainly once a man begins to neglect his domestic duties he becomes painfully effeminate, does he not ? And I don't like that. It makes men so very attractive. Cecily, mamma, whose views on education are remarkably strict, has brought me up to be extremely short-sighted ; it is part of her system ; so do you mind my looking at you through my glasses ?

Cecily : Oh ! not at all, Gwendolen. I am very fond of being looked at.

Gwendolen (*after examining* CECILY *carefully through a lorgnette*) : You are here on a short visit, I suppose.

Cecily : Oh no ! I live here.

Gwendolen (*severely*) : Really ? Your mother, no doubt, or some female relative of advanced years resides here also ?

Cecily : Oh no ! I have no mother, nor, in fact, any relations.

Gwendolen : Indeed ?

Cecily : My dear guardian, with the assistance of Miss Prism, has the arduous task of looking after me.

Gwendolen : Your guardian ?

Cecily : Yes, I am Mr. Worthing's ward.

Gwendolen : Oh ! It is strange he never mentioned to me that he had a ward. How secretive of him ! He grows more interesting hourly. I am not sure, however, that the news inspires me with feelings of unmixed delight. (*Rising and going to her.*) I am very fond of you, Cecily ; I have liked you ever since I met you ! But I am bound to state that now that I know that you are Mr. Worthing's ward, I cannot help expressing a wish you were—well, just a little older than you seem to be— and not quite so very alluring in appearance. In fact, if I may speak candidly——

Cecily : Pray do ! I think that whenever one has anything unpleasant to say, one should always be quite candid.

Gwendolen : Well, to speak with perfect candour, Cecily, I wish that you were fully forty-two, and more than usually plain for your age. Ernest has a strong upright nature. He is the very soul of truth and honour. Disloyalty would be as impossible to him as deception. But even men of the noblest possible moral character are extremely susceptible to the influence of the physical charms of others. Modern, no less than Ancient History, supplies us with many most painful examples of what I refer to. If it were not so, indeed, History would be quite unreadable.

Cecily : I beg your pardon, Gwendolen, did you say Ernest ?

Gwendolen : Yes.

Cecily : Oh, but it is not Mr. Ernest Worthing who is my guardian. It is his brother—his elder brother.

Gwendolen (*sitting down again*) *:* Ernest never mentioned to me that he had a brother.

Cecily : I am sorry to say they have not been on good terms for a long time.

Gwendolen : Ah ! that accounts for it. And now that I think of it I have never heard any man mention his brother. The subject seems distasteful to most men. Cecily, you have lifted a load from my mind. I was growing almost anxious. It would have been terrible if any cloud had come across a friendship like ours, would it not ? Of course you are quite, quite sure that it is not Mr. Ernest Worhing who is your guardian ?

Cecily : Quite sure. (*A pause.*) In fact, I am going to be his.

Gwendolen (*inquiringly*) *:* I beg your pardon ?

Cecily (*rather shy and confidingly*) *:* Dearest Gwendolen, there is no reason why I should make a secret of it to you. Our little county newspaper is sure to chronicle the fact next week. Mr. Ernest Worthing and I are engaged to be married.

Gwendolen (quite politely, rising) : My darling Cecily, I think there must be some slight error. Mr. Ernest Worthing is engaged to me. The announcement will appear in the *Morning Post* on Saturday at the latest.

Cecily (very politely, rising) : I am afraid you must be under some misconception. Ernest proposed to me exactly ten minutes ago. *(Shows diary.)*

Gwendolen (examines diary through her lorgnette carefully) : It is certainly very curious, for he asked me to be his wife yesterday afternoon at 5.30. If you would care to verify the incident, pray do so. *(Produces diary of her own.)* I never travel without my diary. One should always have something sensational to read in the train. I am so sorry, dear Cecily, if it is any disappointment to you, but I am afraid I have the prior claim.

Cecily : It would distress me more than I can tell you, dear Gwendolen, if it caused you any mental or physical anguish, but I feel bound to point out that since Ernest proposed to you he clearly has changed his mind.

Gwendolen (meditatively) : If the poor fellow has been entrapped into any foolish promise I shall consider it my duty to rescue him at once, and with a firm hand.

Cecily (thoughtfully and sadly) : Whatever unfortunate entanglement my dear boy may have got into, I will never reproach him with it after we are married.

Gwendolen : Do you allude to me, Miss Cardew, as an entanglement? You are presumptuous. On an occasion of this kind it becomes more than a moral duty to speak one's mind. It becomes a pleasure.

Cecily : Do you suggest, Miss Fairfax, that I entrapped Ernest into an engagement? How dare you? This is no time for wearing the shallow mask of manners. When I see a spade I call it a spade.

Gwendolen (satirically) : I am glad to say that I have never seen a spade. It is obvious that our social spheres have been widely different.

Enter MERRIMAN, *followed by the footman. He carries a salver, tablecloth, and plate stand.* CECILY *is about to retort. The presence of the servants exercises a restraining influence, under which both girls chafe.*

Merriman : Shall I lay tea here as usual, Miss?
Cecily (sternly, in a calm voice) : Yes, as usual.

MERRIMAN *begins to clear table and lay cloth. A long pause.* CECILY *and* GWENDOLEN *glare at each other.*

Gwendolen : Are there many interesting walks in the vicinity, Miss Cardew ?

Cecily : Oh yes ! a great many. From the top of one of the hills quite close one can see five counties.

Gwendolen : Five counties ! I don't think I should like that ; I hate crowds.

Cecily (sweetly) : I suppose that is why you live in town ?

> GWENDOLEN *bites her lip, and beats her foot nervously with her parasol.*

Gwendolen (looking round) : Quite a well-kept garden this is, Miss Cardew.

Cecily : So glad you like it, Miss Fairfax.

Gwendolen : I had no idea there were any flowers in the country.

Cecily : Oh, flowers are as common here, Miss Fairfax, as people are in London.

Gwendolen : Personally I cannot understand how anybody manages to exist in the country, if anybody who is anybody does. The country always bores me to death.

Cecily : Ah ! This is what the newspapers call agricultural depression, is it not ? I believe the aristocracy are suffering very much from it just at present. It is almost an epidemic amongst them, I have been told. May I offer you some tea, Miss Fairfax ?

Gwendolen (with elaborate politeness) : Thank you. *(Aside) :* Detestable girl ! But I require tea !

Cecily (sweetly) : Sugar ?

Gwendolen (superciliously) : No, thank you. Sugar is not fashionable any more.

> CECILY *looks angrily at her, takes up the tongs and puts four lumps of sugar into the cup.*

Cecily (severely) : Cake or bread and butter ?

Gwendolen (in a bored manner) : Bread and butter, please. Cake is rarely seen at the best houses nowadays.

Cecily (cuts a very large slice of cake and puts it on the tray) : Hand that to Miss Fairfax.

> MERRIMAN *does so, and goes out with footman.* GWENDOLEN *drinks the tea and makes a grimace. Puts down cup at once, reaches out her hand to the bread and butter, looks at it, and finds it is cake. Rises in indignation.*

Gwendolen : You have filled my tea with lumps of sugar, and though I asked most distinctly for bread and butter, you have given me cake. I am known for the gentleness of my disposition, and the extraordinary sweetness of my nature, but I warn you, Miss Cardew, you may go too far.

Cecily (rising): To save my poor, innocent, trusting boy from the machinations of any other girl there are no lengths to which I would not go.

Gwendolen : From the moment I saw you I distrusted you. I felt that you were false and deceitful. I am never deceived in such matters. My first impressions of people are invariably right.

Cecily : It seems to me, Miss Fairfax, that I am trespassing on your valuable time. No doubt you have many other calls of a similar character to make in the neighbourhood.

    Enter JACK.

Gwendolen (catching sight of him) : Ernest ! My own Ernest !

Jack : Gwendolen ! Darling ! (*Offers to kiss her.*)

Gwendolen (drawing back) : A moment ! May I ask if you are engaged to be married to this young lady ? (*Points to* CECILY.)

Jack (laughing) : To dear little Cecily ! Of course not ! What could have put such an idea into your pretty little head ?

Gwendolen : Thank you. You may ! (*Offers her cheek.*)

Cecily (very sweetly) : I knew there must be some misunderstanding, Miss Fairfax. The gentleman whose arm is at present round your waist is my guardian, Mr. John Worthing.

Gwendolen : I beg your pardon ?

Cecily : This is Uncle Jack.

Gwendolen (receding) : Jack ! Oh !

    Enter ALGERNON.

Cecily : Here is Ernest.

Algernon (goes straight over to CECILY *without noticing any one else) :* My own love ! (*Offers to kiss her.*)

Cecily (drawing back) : A moment, Ernest ! May I ask you— are you engaged to be married to this young lady ?

Algernon (looking round) : To what young lady ? Good heavens ! Gwendolen !

Cecily : Yes ! to good heavens, Gwendolen, I mean to Gwendolen.

Algernon (laughing) : Of course not ! What could have put such an idea into your pretty little head ?

Cecily : Thank you. (*Presenting her cheek to be kissed.*) You may. (ALGERNON *kisses her.*)

Gwendolen : I felt there was some slight error, Miss Cardew. The gentleman who is now embracing you is my cousin, Mr. Algernon Moncrieff.

Cecily (breaking away from ALGERNON*) :* Algernon Moncrieff ! Oh !

> *The two girls move towards each other and put their arms round each other's waists as if for protection.*

Cecily : Are you called Algernon ?

Algernon : I cannot deny it.

Cecily : Oh !

Gwendolen : Is your name really John ?

Jack (standing rather proudly) : I could deny it if I liked. I could deny anything if I liked. But my name certainly is John. It has been John for years.

Cecily (to GWENDOLEN*) :* A gross deception has been practised on both of us.

Gwendolen : My poor wounded Cecily !

Cecily : My sweet wronged Gwendolen !

Gwendolen (slowly and seriously) : You will call me sister, will you not ?

> *They embrace.* JACK *and* ALGERNON *groan and walk up and down.*

Cecily (rather brightly) : There is just one question I would like to be allowed to ask my guardian.

Gwendolen : An admirable idea ! Mr. Worthing, there is just one question I would like to be permitted to put to you. Where is your brother Ernest ? We are both engaged to be married to your brother Ernest, so it is a matter of some importance to us to know where your brother Ernest is at present.

Jack (slowly and hesitatingly) : Gwendolen—Cecily—it is very painful for me to be forced to speak the truth. It is the first time in my life that I have ever been reduced to such a painful position, and I am really quite inexperienced in doing anything of the kind. However, I will tell you quite frankly that I have no brother Ernest. I have no brother at all. I never had a brother in my life, and I certainly have not the smallest intention of ever having one in the future.

Cecily (surprised) : No brother at all ?

Jack (cheerily) : None !

Gwendolen (severely) : Had you never a brother of any kind ?

Jack (pleasantly) : Never. Not even of any kind.

Gwendolen : I am afraid it is quite clear, Cecily, that neither of us is engaged to be married to any one.

Cecily : It is not a very pleasant position for a young girl suddenly to find herself in. Is it ?

Gwendolen : Let us go into the house. They will hardly venture to come after us there.

Cecily : No, men are so cowardly, aren't they ?

They retire into the house with scornful looks.

Jack : This ghastly state of things is what you call Bunbury-ing, I suppose ?

Algernon : Yes, and a perfectly wonderful Bunbury it is. The most wonderful Bunbury I have ever had in my life.

Jack : Well, you've no right whatsoever to Bunbury here.

Algernon : That is absurd. One has a right to Bunbury anywhere one chooses. Every serious Bunburyist knows that.

Jack : Serious Bunburyist ! Good heavens !

Algernon : Well, one must be serious about something, if one wants to have any amusement in life. I happen to be serious about Bunburying. What on earth you are serious about I haven't got the remotest idea. About everything, I should fancy. You have such an absolutely trivial nature.

Jack : Well, the only small satisfaction I have in the whole of this wretched business is that your friend Bunbury is quite exploded. You won't be able to run down to the country quite so often as you used to do, dear Algy. And a very good thing too.

Algernon : Your brother is a little off colour, isn't he, dear Jack ? You won't be able to disappear to London quite so frequently as your wicked custom was. And not a bad thing either.

Jack : As for your conduct towards Miss Cardew, I must say that your taking in a sweet, simple, innocent girl like that is quite inexcusable. To say nothing of the fact that she is my ward.

Algernon : I can see no possible defence at all for your deceiving a brilliant, clever, thoroughly experienced young lady like Miss Fairfax. To say nothing of the fact that she is my cousin.

Jack : I wanted to be engaged to Gwendolen, that is all. I love her.

Algernon : Well, I simply wanted to be engaged to Cecily. I adore her.

Jack : There is certainly no chance of your marrying Miss Cardew.

Algernon : I don't think there is much likelihood, Jack, of you and Miss Fairfax being united.

Jack : Well, that is no business of yours.

Algernon : If it was my business, I wouldn't talk about it. (*Begins to eat muffins.*) It is very vulgar to talk about one's business. Only people like stockbrokers do that, and then merely at dinner-parties.

Jack : How can you sit there, calmly eating muffins when we are in this horrible trouble, I can't make out. You seem to me to be perfectly heartless.

Algernon : Well, I can't eat muffins in an agitated manner. The butter would probably get on my cuffs. One should always eat muffins quite calmly. It is the only way to eat them.

Jack : I say it's perfectly heartless your eating muffins at all, under the circumstances.

Algernon : When I am in trouble, eating is the only thing that consoles me. Indeed, when I am in really great trouble, as any one who knows me intimately will tell you, I refuse everything except food and drink. At the present moment I am eating muffins because I am unhappy. Besides, I am particularly fond of muffins. (*Rising.*)

Jack (rising) : Well, that is no reason why you should eat them all in that greedy way. (*Takes muffins from* ALGERNON.)

Algernon (offering tea-cake) : I wish you would have tea-cake instead. I don't like tea-cake.

Jack : Good heavens ! I suppose a man may eat his own muffins in his own garden.

Algernon : But you have just said it was perfectly heartless to eat muffins.

Jack : I said it was perfectly heartless of you, under the circumstances. That is a very different thing.

Algernon : That may be. But the muffins are the same. (*He seizes the muffin-dish from* JACK.)

Jack : Algy, I wish to goodness you would go.

Algernon : You can't possibly ask me to go without having some dinner. It's absurd. I never go without my dinner. No one ever does, except vegetarians and people like that. Besides, I have just made arrangements with Dr. Chasuble to be christened at a quarter to six under the name of Ernest.

Jack : My dear fellow, the sooner you give up that nonsense the better. I made arrangements this morning with Dr. Chasuble to be christened myself at 5.30, and I naturally will take the name of Ernest. Gwendolen would wish it. We can't both be christened Ernest. It's absurd. Besides, I have a perfect right to be christened if I like. There is no evidence at all that I have ever been christened by anybody. I should think it extremely probable I never was, and so does Dr. Chasuble.

It is entirely different in your case. You have been christened already.

Algernon : Yes, but I have not been christened for years.

Jack : Yes, but you have been christened. That is the important thing.

Algernon : Quite so. So I know my constitution can stand it. If you are not quite sure about your ever having been christened, I must say I think it rather dangerous your venturing on it now. It might make you very unwell. You can hardly have forgotten that some one very closely connected with you was very nearly carried off this week in Paris by a severe chill.

Jack : Yes, but you said yourself that a severe chill was not hereditary.

Algernon : It usen't to be, I know—but I dare say it is now. Science is always making wonderful improvements in things.

Jack (picking up the muffin-dish) : Oh, that is nonsense ; you are always talking nonsense.

Algernon : Jack, you are at the muffins again ! I wish you wouldn't. There are only two left. (*Takes them.*) I told you I was particularly fond of muffins.

Jack : But I hate tea-cake.

Algernon : Why on earth then do you allow tea-cake to be served up for your guests ? What ideas you have of hospitality !

Jack : Algernon ! I have already told you to go. I don't want you here. Why don't you go !

Algernon : I haven't quite finished my tea yet ! and there is still one muffin left.

> JACK *groans, and sinks into a chair.* ALGERNON *still continues eating.*

ACT DROP.

THIRD ACT

SCENE.—*Morning-room at the Manor House.*

GWENDOLEN and CECILY *are at the window, looking out into the garden.*

Gwendolen : The fact that they did not follow us at once nto the house, as any one else would have done, seems to me to show that they have some sense of shame left.

Cecily : They have been eating muffins. That looks like repentance.

Gwendolen (after a pause) : They don't seem to notice us at all. Couldn't you cough ?

Cecily : But I haven't got a cough.

Gwendolen : They're looking at us. What effrontery !

Cecily : They're approaching. That's very forward of them.

Gwendolen : Let us preserve a dignified silence.

Cecily : Certainly. It's the only thing to do now.

Enter JACK *followed by* ALGERNON. *They whistle some dreadful popular air from a British Opera.*

Gwendolen : This dignified silence seems to produce an unpleasant effect.

Cecily : A most distasteful one.

Gwendolen : But we will not be the first to speak.

Cecily : Certainly not.

Gwendolen : Mr. Worthing, I have something very particular to ask you. Much depends on your reply.

Cecily : Gwendolen, your common sense is invaluable. Mr. Moncrieff, kindly answer me the following question. Why did you pretend to be my guardian's brother ?

Algernon : In order that I might have an opportunity of meeting you.

Cecily (to GWENDOLEN*)* : That certainly seems a satisfactory explanation, does it not ?

Gwendolen : Yes, dear, if you can believe him.

Cecily : I don't. But that does not affect the wonderful beauty of his answer.

Gwendolen : True. In matters of grave importance, style, not sincerity is the vital thing. Mr. Worthing, what explanation can you offer to me for pretending to have a brother ? Was it in order that you might have an opportunity of coming up to town to see me as often as possible ?

Jack : Can you doubt it, Miss Fairfax ?

Gwendolen : I have the gravest doubts upon the subject. But I intend to crush them. This is not the moment for German scepticism. (*Moving to* CECILY.) Their explanations appear to be quite satisfactory, especially Mr. Worthing's. That seems to me to have the stamp of truth upon it.

Cecily : I am more than content with what Mr. Moncrieff said. His voice alone inspires one with absolute credulity.

Gwendolen : Then you think we should forgive them ?

Cecily : Yes. I mean no.

Gwendolen : True ! I had forgotten. There are principles

at stake that one cannot surrender. Which of us should tell them ? The task is not a pleasant one.

Cecily : Could we not both speak at the same time ?

Gwendolen : An excellent idea ! I always speak at the same time as other people. Will you take the time from me ?

Cecily : Certainly.

> GWENDOLEN *beats time with uplifted finger.*

Gwendolen and Cecily (speaking together) : Your Christian names are still an insuperable barrier. That is all !

Jack and Algernon (speaking together) : Our Christian names ! Is that all ? But we are going to be christened this afternoon.

Gwendolen (to JACK*) :* For my sake you are prepared to do this terrible thing ?

Jack : I am.

Cecily (to ALGERNON*) :* To please me you are ready to face this fearful ordeal ?

Algernon : I am !

Gwendolen : How absurd to talk of the equality of the sexes ! Where questions of self-sacrifice are concerned, men are infinitely beyond us.

Jack : We are. (*Clasps hands with* ALGERNON.)

Cecily : They have moments of physical courage of which we women know absolutely nothing.

Gwendolen (to JACK*) :* Darling.

Algernon (to CECILY*) :* Darling !

> *They fall into each other's arms.*

> *Enter* MERRIMAN. *When he enters he coughs loudly, seeing the situation.*

Merriman : Ahem ! Ahem ! Lady Bracknell.

Jack : Good heavens !

> *Enter* LADY BRACKNELL. *The couples separate in alarm.* *Exit* MERRIMAN.

Lady Bracknell : Gwendolen ! What does this mean ?

Gwendolen : Merely that I am engaged to be married to Mr. Worthing, mamma.

Lady Bracknell : Come here. Sit down. Sit down immediately. Hesitation of any kind is a sign of mental decay in the young, of physical weakness in the old. (*Turns to* JACK.) Apprised, sir, of my daughter's sudden flight by her trusty maid, whose confidence I purchased by means of a small coin, I followed her at once by a luggage train. Her unhappy father is, I am glad to say, under the impression that she is attending a more than usually lengthy lecture by the University Extension Scheme on the Influence of a permanent income on Thought. I do not propose to undeceive him. Indeed I have never undeceived him on any question. I would consider it wrong. But, of course, you will clearly understand that all communication between yourself and my daughter must cease immediately from this moment. On this point, as indeed on all points, I am firm.

Jack : I am engaged to be married to Gwendolen, Lady Bracknell !

Lady Bracknell : You are nothing of the kind, sir. And now, as regards Algernon ! . . . Algernon !

Algernon : Yes, Aunt Augusta.

Lady Bracknell : May I ask if it is in this house that your invalid friend Mr. Bunbury resides ?

Algernon (stammering) : Oh ! No ! Bunbury doesn't live here. Bunbury is somewhere else at present. In fact, Bunbury is dead.

Lady Bracknell : Dead ! When did Mr. Bunbury die ? His death must have been extremely sudden.

Algernon (airily) : Oh ! I killed Bunbury this afternoon. I mean poor Bunbury died this afternoon.

Lady Bracknell : What did he die of ?

Algernon : Bunbury ? Oh, he was quite exploded.

Lady Bracknell : Exploded ! Was he the victim of a revolutionary outrage ? I was not aware that Mr. Bunbury was interested in social legislation. If so, he is well punished for his morbidity.

Algernon : My dear Aunt Augusta, I mean he was found out ! The doctors found out that Bunbury could not live, that is what I mean—so Bunbury died.

Lady Bracknell : He seems to have had great confidence in the opinion of his physicians. I am glad, however, that he made up his mind at the last to some definite course of action, and acted under proper medical advice. And now that we have finally got rid of this Mr. Bunbury, may I ask, Mr. Worthing, who is that young person whose hand my nephew Algernon is now holding in what seems to me a peculiarly unnecessary manner ?

Jack : That lady is Miss Cecily Cardew, my ward.

LADY BRACKNELL *bows coldly to* CECILY.

Algernon : I am engaged to be married to Cecily, Aunt Augusta.

Lady Bracknell : I beg your pardon ?

Cecily : Mr. Moncrieff and I are engaged to be married, Lady Bracknell.

Lady Bracknell (with a shiver, crossing to the sofa and sitting down) : I do not know whether there is anything peculiarly exciting in the air of this particular part of Hertfordshire, but the number of engagements that go on seems to me considerably above the proper average that statistics have laid down for our guidance. I think some preliminary inquiry on my part would not be out of place. Mr. Worthing, is Miss Cardew at all connected with any of the larger railway stations in London ? I merely desire information. Until yesterday I had no idea that there were any families or persons whose origin was a Terminus.

JACK *looks perfectly furious, but restrains himself.*

Jack (in a clear, cold voice) : Miss Cardew is the granddaughter of the late Mr. Thomas Cardew of 149 Belgrave Square, S.W. ; Gervase Park, Dorking, Surrey ; and the Sporran, Fifeshire, N.B.

Lady Bracknell : That sounds not unsatisfactory. Three addresses always inspire confidence, even in tradesmen. But what proof have I of their authenticity ?

Jack : I have carefully preserved the Court Guides of the period. They are open to your inspection, Lady Bracknell.

Lady Bracknell (grimly) : I have known strange errors in that publication.

Jack : Miss Cardew's family solicitors are Messrs. Markby, Markby, and Markby.

Lady Bracknell : Markby, Markby, and Markby ? A firm of the very highest position in their profession. Indeed I am told that one of the Mr. Markby's is occasionally to be seen at dinner-parties. So far I am satisfied.

Jack (very irritably) : How extremely kind of you, Lady Bracknell ! I have also in my possession, you will be pleased to hear, certificates of Miss Cardew's birth, baptism, whooping-cough, registration, vaccination, confirmation, and the measles ; both the German and the English variety.

Lady Bracknell : Ah ! A life crowded with incident, I see ; though perhaps somewhat too exciting for a young girl. I am not myself in favour of premature experiences. (*Rises, looks at her watch.*) Gwendolen ! the time approaches for our departure. We have not a moment to lose. As a matter of form, Mr. Worthing, I had better ask you if Miss Cardew has any little fortune ?

Jack : Oh ! about a hundred and thirty thousand pounds in the Funds. That is all. Good-bye, Lady Bracknell. So pleased to have seen you.

Lady Bracknell (sitting down again) : A moment, Mr. Worthing. A hundred and thirty thousand pounds ! And in the Funds ! Miss Cardew seems to me a most attractive young lady, now that I look at her. Few girls of the present day have any really solid qualities, any of the qualities that last, and improve with time. We live, I regret to say, in an age of surfaces. (*To* CECILY) : Come over here, dear. (CECILY *goes across.*) Pretty child ! your dress is sadly simple, and your hair seems almost as Nature might have left it. But we can soon alter all that. A thoroughly experienced French maid produces a really marvellous result in a very brief space of time. I remember recommending one to young Lady Lancing, and after three months her own husband did not know her.

Jack : And after six months nobody knew her.

Lady Bracknell (glares at JACK *for a few moments. Then bends, with a practised smile, to* CECILY) : Kindly turn round, sweet child. (CECILY *turns completely round.*) No, the side view is what I want. (CECILY *presents her profile.*) Yes, quite as I expected. There are distinct social possibilities in your profile. The two weak points in our age are its want of principle and its want of profile. The chin a little higher, dear. Style largely depends on the way the chin is worn. They are worn very high, just at present. Algernon !

Algernon : Yes, Aunt Augusta !

Lady Bracknell : There are distinct social possibilities in Miss Cardew's profile.

Algernon : Cecily is the sweetest, dearest, prettiest girl in the whole world. And I don't care twopence about social possibilities.

Lady Bracknell : Never speak disrespectfully of Society, Algernon. Only people who can't get into it do that. (*To* CECILY) : Dear child, of course you know that Algernon has nothing but his debts to depend upon. But I do not approve of mercenary marriages. When I married Lord Bracknell I had no fortune of any kind. But I never dreamed for a moment of allowing that to stand in my way. Well, I suppose I must give my consent.

Algernon : Thank you, Aunt Augusta.

Lady Bracknell : Cecily, you may kiss me !

Cecily (kisses her) : Thank you, Lady Bracknell.

Lady Bracknell : you may also address me as Aunt Augusta for the future.

Cecily : Thank you, Aunt Augusta.

Lady Bracknell : The marriage, I think, had better take place quite soon.

Algernon : Thank you, Aunt Augusta.

Cecily : Thank you, Aunt Augusta.

Lady Bracknell : To speak frankly, I am not in favour of long engagements. They give people the opportunity of finding out each other's character before marriage, which I think is never advisable.

Jack : I beg your pardon for interrupting you, Lady Bracknell, but this engagement is quite out of the question. I am Miss Cardew's guardian, and she cannot marry without my consent until she comes of age. That consent I absolutely decline to give.

Lady Bracknell : Upon what grounds may I ask ? Algernon is an extremely, I may almost say an ostentatiously, eligible young man. He has nothing, but he looks everything. What more can one desire ?

Jack : It pains me very much to have to speak frankly to you, Lady Bracknell, about your nephew, but the fact is that I do not approve at all of his moral character, I suspect him of being untruthful.

ALGERNON and CECILY *look at him in indignant amazement.*

Lady Bracknell : Untruthful ! My nephew Algernon ? Impossible ! He is an Oxonian.

Jack : I fear there can be no possible doubt about the matter. This afternoon during my temporary absence in London on an important question of romance, he obtained admission to my house by means of the false pretence of being my brother. Under an assumed name he drank, I've just been informed by my butler, an entire pint bottle of my Perrier-Jouet, Brut, '89 ; wine I was specially reserving for myself. Continuing his disgraceful deception, he succeeded in the course of the afternoon in alienating the affections of my only ward. He subsequently stayed to tea, and devoured every single muffin. And what makes his conduct all the more heartless is, that he was perfectly well aware from the first that I have no brother, that I never had a brother, and that I don't intend to have a brother, not even of any kind. I distinctly told him so myself yesterday afternoon.

Lady Bracknell : Ahem ! Mr. Worthing, after careful consideration I have decided entirely to overlook my nephew's conduct to you.

Jack : That is very generous of you, Lady Bracknell. My own decision, however, is unalterable. I decline to give my consent.

Lady Bracknell (to CECILY*) :* Come here, sweet child. (CECILY *goes over.*) How old are you, dear ?

Cecily : Well, I am really only eighteen, but I always admit to twenty when I go to evening parties.

Lady Bracknell : You are perfectly right in making some slight alteration. Indeed, no woman should ever be quite accurate about her age. It looks so calculating. . . . (*In a meditative manner.*) Eighteen, but admitting to twenty at evening parties. Well, it will not be very long before you are of age and free from the restraints of tutelage. So I don't think your guardian's consent is, after all, a matter of any importance.

Jack : Pray excuse me, Lady Bracknell, for interrupting you again, but it is only fair to tell you that according to the terms of her grandfather's will Miss Cardew does not come legally of age till she is thirty-five.

Lady Bracknell : That does not seem to me to be a grave objection. Thirty-five is a very attractive age. London society is full of women of the very highest birth who have, of their own free choice, remained thirty-five for years. Lady Dumbleton is an instance in point. To my own knowledge she has been thirty-five ever since she arrived at the age of forty, which was many years ago now. I see no reason why our dear Cecily should not be even still more attractive at the age you mention than she is at present. There will be a large accumulation of property.

Cecily : Algy, could you wait for me till I was thirty-five ?

Algernon : Of course I could, Cecily. You know I could.

Cecily : Yes, I felt it instinctively, but I couldn't wait all that time. I hate waiting even five minutes for anybody. It always makes me rather cross. I am not punctual myself, I know, but I do like punctuality in others, and waiting, even to be married, is quite out of the question.

Algernon : Then what is to be done, Cecily ?

Cecily : I don't know, Mr. Moncrieff.

Lady Bracknell : My dear Mr. Worthing, as Miss Cecily states positively that she cannot wait till she is thirty-five—a remark which I am bound to say seems to me to show a some-what impatient nature—I would beg of you to reconsider your decision.

Jack : But my dear Lady Bracknell, the matter is entirely in your own hands. The moment you consent to my marriage with Gwendolen, I will most gladly allow your nephew to form an alliance with my ward.

Lady Bracknell (*rising and drawing herself up*) : You must be quite aware that what you propose is out of the question.

Jack : Then a passionate celibacy is all that any of us can look forward to.

Lady Bracknell : That is not the destiny I propose for Gwendolen. Algernon, of course, can choose for himself. (*Pulls out her watch.*) Come dear,—(GWENDOLEN *rises*)—we have already missed five, if not six, trains. To miss any more might expose us to comment on the platform.

Enter DR. CHASUBLE.

Chasuble : Everything is quite ready for the christenings.

Lady Bracknell : The christenings, sir ! Is not that somewhat premature ?

Chasuble (*looking rather puzzled, and pointing to* JACK *and* ALGERNON) : Both these gentlemen have expressed a desire for immediate baptism.

Lady Bracknell : At their age ? The idea is grotesque and irreligious ! Algernon, I forbid you to be baptized. I will not hear of such excesses. Lord Bracknell would be highly displeased if he learned that that was the way in which you wasted your time and money.

Chasuble : Am I to understand then that there are to be no christenings at all this afternoon ?

Jack : I don't think that, as things are now, it would be of much practical value to either of us, Dr. Chasuble.

Chasuble : I am grieved to hear such sentiments from you, Mr. Worthing. They savour of the heretical views of the Anabaptists, views that I have completely refuted in four of my unpublished sermons. However, as your present mood seems to be one peculiarly secular, I will return to the church at once. Indeed, I have just been informed by the pew-opener that for the last hour and a half Miss Prism has been waiting for me in the vestry.

Lady Bracknell (*starting*) : Miss Prism ! Did I hear you mention a Miss Prism ?

Chasuble : Yes, Lady Bracknell. I am on my way to join her.

Lady Bracknell : Pray allow me to detain you for a moment. This matter may prove to be one of vital importance to Lord Bracknell and myself. Is this Miss Prism a female of repellent aspect, remotely connected with education ?

Chasuble (somewhat indignantly) : She is the most cultivated of ladies, and the very picture of respectability.

Lady Bracknell : It is obviously the same person. May I ask what position she holds in your household ?

Chasuble (severely) : I am a celibate, madam.

Jack (interposing) : Miss Prism, Lady Bracknell, has been for the last three years Miss Cardew's esteemed governess and valued companion.

Lady Bracknell : In spite of what I hear of her, I must see her at once. Let her be sent for.

Chasuble (looking off) : She approaches ; she is nigh.

Enter Miss Prism *hurriedly.*

Miss Prism : I was told you expected me in the vestry, dear Canon. I have been waiting for you there for an hour and three-quarters. (*Catches sight of* LADY BRACKNELL, *who has fixed her with a stony glare.* MISS PRISM *grows pale and quails. She looks anxiously round as if desirous to escape.*)

Lady Bracknell (in a severe, judicial voice) : Prism ! (MISS PRISM *bows her head in shame.*) Come here, Prism ! (MISS PRISM *approaches in a humble manner.*) Prism ! Where is that baby ? (*General consternation. The* CANON *starts back in horror.* ALGERNON *and* JACK *pretend to be anxious to shield* CECILY *and* GWENDOLEN *from hearing the details of a terrible public scandal.*) Twenty-eight years ago, Prism, you left Lord Bracknell's house, Number 104 Upper Grosvenor Street, in charge of a perambulator that contained a baby of the male sex. You never returned. A few weeks later, through the elaborate investigations of the Metropolitan police, the perambulator was discovered at midnight standing by itself in a remote corner of Bayswater. It contained the manuscript of a three-volume novel of more than usually revolting sentimentality. (MISS PRISM *starts in involuntary indignation.*) But the baby was not there. (*Every one looks at* MISS PRISM.) Prism ! Where is that baby ? (*A pause.*)

Miss Prism : Lady Bracknell, I admit with shame that I do not know. I only wish I did. The plain facts of the case are these. On the morning of the day you mention, a day that is for ever branded on my memory, I prepared as usual to take the baby out in its perambulator. I had also with me a somewhat old, capacious hand-bag, in which I had intended to place the manuscript of a work of fiction that I had written during my few unoccupied hours. In a moment of mental abstraction, for which I never can forgive myself, I deposited the manuscript in the basinette, and placed the baby in the hand-bag.

Jack (who has been listening attentively) : But where did you deposit the hand-bag ?

Miss Prism : Do not ask me, Mr. Worthing.

Jack : Miss Prism, this is a matter of no small importance to me. I insist on knowing where you deposited the hand-bag that contained that infant.

Miss Prism : I left it in the cloak-room of one of the larger railway stations in London.

Jack : What railway station ?

Miss Prism (quite crushed) : Victoria. The Brighton line. *(Sinks into a chair.)*

Jack : I must retire to my room for a moment. Gwendolen, wait here for me.

Gwendolen : If you are not too long, I will wait here for you all my life.

 Exit JACK *in great excitement.*

Chasuble : What do you think this means, Lady Bracknell ?

Lady Bracknell : I dare not even suspect, Dr. Chasuble. I need hardly tell you that in families of high position strange coincidences are not supposed to occur. They are hardly considered the thing.

 Noises heard overhead as if some one was throwing trunks about. Every one looks up.

Cecily : Uncle Jack seems strangely agitated.

Chasuble : Your guardian has a very emotional nature.

Lady Bracknell : This noise is extremely unpleasant. It sounds as if he was having an argument. I dislike arguments of any kind. They are always vulgar, and often convincing.

Chasuble (looking up) : It has stopped now. *(The noise is redoubled.)*

Lady Bracknell : I wish he would arrive at some conclusion.

Gwendolen : This suspense is terrible. I hope it will last.

 Enter JACK *with a hand-bag of black leather in his hand.*

Jack (rushing over to MISS PRISM*)* : Is this the hand-bag, Miss Prism ? Examine it carefully before you speak. The happiness of more than one life depends on your answer.

Miss Prism (calmly) : It seems to be mine. Yes, here is the injury it received through the upsetting of a Gower Street omnibus in younger and happier days. Here is the stain on the lining caused by the explosion of a temperance beverage, an incident that occurred at Leamington. And here on the lock, are my initials. I had forgotten that in an extravagant mood I had had them placed there. The bag is undoubtedly mine. I am delighted to have it so unexpectedly restored to me. It has been a great inconvenience being without it all these years.

Jack (in a pathetic voice) : Miss Prism, more is restored to you than this hand-bag. I was the baby you placed in it.

Miss Prism (amazed) : You ?

Jack (embracing her) : Yes . . . mother !

Miss Prism (recoiling in indignant astonishment) : Mr. Worthing, I am unmarried !

Jack : Unmarried ! I do not deny that is a serious blow. But after all, who has the right to cast a stone against one who has suffered ? Cannot repentance wipe out an act of folly ? Why should there be one law for men, and another for women ? Mother, I forgive you. (*Tries to embrace her again.*)

Miss Prism (still more indignant) : Mr. Worthing, there is some error. (*Pointing to* LADY BRACKNELL) : There is the lady who can tell you who you really are.

Jack (after a pause) : Lady Bracknell, I hate to seem inquisitive, but would you kindly inform me who I am ?

Lady Bracknell : I am afraid that the news I have to give you will not altogether please you. You are the son of my poor sister, Mrs. Moncrieff, and consequently Algernon's elder brother.

Jack : Algy's elder brother ! Then I have a brother after all. I knew I had a brother ! I always said I had a brother ! Cecily,—how could you have ever doubted that I had a brother ! (*Seizes hold of* ALGERNON.) Dr. Chasuble, my unfortunate brother. Miss Prism, my unfortunate brother. Gwendolen, my unfortunate brother. Algy, you young scoundrel, you will have to treat me with more respect in the future. You have never behaved to me like a brother in all your life.

Algernon : Well, not till to-day, old boy, I admit. I did my best, however, though I was out of practice. (*Shakes hands.*)

Gwendolen (to JACK) : My own ! But what own are you ? What is your Christian name, now that you have become some one else ?

Jack : Good heavens ! . . . I had quite forgotten that point. Your decision on the subject of my name is irrevocable, I suppose ?

Gwendolen : I never change, except in my affections.

Cecily : What a noble nature you have, Gwendolen !

Jack : Then the question had better be cleared up at once. Aunt Augusta, a moment. At the time when Miss Prism left me in the hand-bag, had I been christened already ?

Lady Bracknell : Every luxury that money could buy, in-

24*

cluding christening, had been lavished on you by your fond and doting parents.

Jack : Then I was christened ! That is settled. Now, what name was I given ? Let me know the worst.

Lady Bracknell : Being the eldest son you were naturally christened after your father.

Jack (irritably) : Yes, but what was my father's Christian name ?

Lady Bracknell (meditatively) : I cannot at the present moment recall what the General's Christian name was. But I have no doubt he had one. He was eccentric, I admit. But only in later years. And that was the result of the Indian climate, and marriage, and indigestion, and other things of that kind.

Jack : Algy ! Can't you recollect what our father's Christian name was ?

Algernon : My dear boy, we were never even on speaking terms. He died before I was a year old.

Jack : His name would appear in the Army Lists of the period, I suppose, Aunt Augusta ?

Lady Bracknell : The General was essentially a man of peace, except in his domestic life. But I have no doubt his name would appear in any military directory.

Jack : The Army Lists of the last forty years are here. These delightful records should have been my constant study. (*Rushes to bookcase and tears the books out.*) M. Generals . . . Mallam, Maxbohm, Magley, what ghastly names they have—Markby, Migsby, Mobbs, Moncrieff ! Lieutenant 1840, Captain, Lieutenant-Colonel, Colonel, General 1869, Christian names, Ernest John. (*Puts book very quietly down and speaks quite calmly.*) I always told you, Gwendolen, my name was Ernest, didn't I ? Well, it is Ernest after all. I mean it naturally is Ernest.

Lady Bracknell : Yes, I remember now that the General was called Ernest. I knew I had some particular reason for disliking the name.

Gwendolen : Ernest ! My own Ernest ! I felt from the first that you could have no other name !

Jack : Gwendolen, it is a terrible thing for a man to find out suddenly that all his life he has been speaking nothing but the truth. Can you forgive me ?

Gwendolen : I can. For I feel that you are sure to change.

Jack : My own one !

Chasuble (to Miss Prism*) :* Lætitia ! (*Embraces her.*)

Miss Prism (enthusiastically) : Frederick ! At last !

Algernon : Cecily ! (*Embraces her.*) At last !

Jack : Gwendolen ! (*Embraces her.*) At last !

Lady Bracknell : My nephew, you seem to be displaying signs of triviality.

Jack : On the contrary, Aunt Augusta, I've now realized for the first time in my life the vital Importance of Being Earnest.

TABLEAUX

CURTAIN.

P. G. WODEHOUSE (1881–   ) *started
by writing school stories, but turned eventually
to those joyously irresponsible tales of gilded
youth which are a refuge for sufferers from a
prosaic world.   He has a long list of novels
and short stories to his credit, but he has done
nothing more popular than the launching of
Jeeves upon an admiring public.   Jeeves
becomes more and more in demand, and
readers of this story will understand why.*

THE ORDEAL OF YOUNG TUPPY

"WHAT-HO, Jeeves ! " I said, entering the room where he
waded knee-deep in suit-cases and shirts and winter
suitings, like a sea-beast among rocks. " Packing ? "

" Yes, sir," replied the honest fellow, for there are no secrets
between us.

" Pack on ! " I said approvingly. " Pack, Jeeves, pack with
care. Pack in the presence of the passenjare." And I rather
fancy I added the words " Tra-la ! " for I was in merry mood.

Every year, starting about the middle of November, there is
a good deal of anxiety and apprehension among owners of the
better-class of country-house throughout England as to who will
get Bertram Wooster's patronage for the Christmas holidays.
It may be one or it may be another. As my Aunt Dahlia says,
you never know where the blow will fall.

This year, however, I had decided early. It couldn't have
been later than Nov. 10 when a sigh of relief went up from a dozen
stately homes as it became known that the short straw had been
drawn by Sir Reginald Witherspoon, Bart., of Bleaching Court,
Upper Bleaching, Hants.

In coming to the decision to give this Witherspoon my custom,
I have been actuated by several reasons, not counting the fact
that, having married Aunt Dahlia's husband's younger sister,
Katherine, he is by way of being a sort of uncle of mine. In the
first place, the Bart. does one extraordinarily well, both browsing
and sluicing being above criticism. Then, again, his stables
always contain something worth riding, which is a consideration.
And, thirdly, there is no danger of getting lugged into a party
of amateur Waits and having to tramp the countryside in the rain,
singing, " When Shepherds Watched Their Flocks By Night."
Or for the matter of that, " Noel ! Noel ! "

All these things counted with me, but what really drew me to Bleaching Court like a magnet was the knowledge that young Tuppy Glossop would be among those present.

I feel sure I have told you before about this black-hearted bird, but I will give you the strength of it once again, just to keep the records straight. He was the fellow, if you remember, who, ignoring a lifelong friendship in the course of which he had frequently eaten my bread and salt, betted me one night at the Drones that I wouldn't swing myself across the swimming-bath by the ropes and rings and then, with almost inconceivable treachery, went and looped back the last ring, causing me to drop into the fluid and ruin one of the nattiest suits of dress-clothes in London.

To execute a fitting vengeance on this bloke had been the ruling passion of my life ever since.

" You are bearing in mind, Jeeves," I said, " the fact that Mr. Glossop will be at Bleaching ? "

" Yes, sir."

" And, consequently, are not forgetting to put in the Giant Squirt ? "

" No, sir."

" Nor the Luminous Rabbit ? "

" No, sir."

" Good ! I am rather pinning my faith on the Luminous Rabbit, Jeeves. I hear excellent reports of it on all sides. You wind it up and put it in somebody's room in the night watches, and it shines in the dark and jumps about, making odd, squeaking noises the while. The whole performance being, I should imagine, well calculated to scare young Tuppy into a decline."

" Very possibly, sir."

" Should that fail, there is always the Giant Squirt. We must leave no stone unturned to put it across the man somehow," I said. " The Wooster honour is at stake."

I would have spoken further on this subject, but just then the front door bell buzzed.

" I'll answer it," I said. " I expect it's Aunt Dahlia. She 'phoned that she would be calling this morning."

It was not Aunt Dahlia. It was a telegraph-boy with telegram. I opened it, read it, and carried it back to the bedroom, the brow a bit knitted.

" Jeeves," I said. " A rummy communication has arrived. From Mr. Glossop."

" Indeed, sir ? "

"I will read it to you. Handed in at Upper Bleaching. Message runs as follows :

"*When you come to-morrow, bring my football boots. Also, if humanly possible, Irish water-spaniel. Urgent. Regards. Tuppy.*"

"What do you make of that, Jeeves ? "

"As I interpret the document, sir, Mr. Glossop wishes you, when you come to-morrow, to bring his football boots. Also, if humanly possible, an Irish water-spaniel. He hints that the matter is urgent, and sends his regards."

"Yes, that's how I read it, too. But why football boots ? "

"Perhaps Mr. Glossop wishes to play football, sir."

I considered this.

"Yes," I said. "That may be the solution. But why would a man, staying peacefully at a country-house, suddenly develop a craving to play football ? "

"I could not say, sir."

"And why an Irish water-spaniel ? "

"There again I fear I can hazard no conjecture, sir."

"What *is* an Irish water-spaniel ? "

"A water-spaniel of a variety bred in Ireland, sir."

"You think so ? "

"Yes, sir."

"Well, perhaps you're right. But why should I sweat about the place collecting dogs—of whatever nationality—for young Tuppy ? Does he think I'm Santa Claus ? Is he under the impression that my feelings towards him, after that Drones Club incident, are those of kindly benevolence ? Irish water-spaniels, indeed ! Tchah ! "

"Sir ? "

"Tchah, Jeeves."

"Very good, sir."

The front door bell buzzed again.

"Our busy morning, Jeeves."

"Yes, sir."

"All right. I'll go."

This time it was Aunt Dahlia. She charged in with the air of a woman with something on her mind—giving tongue, in fact, while actually on the very doormat.

"Bertie," she boomed, in that ringing voice of hers which cracks window-panes and upsets vases, " I've come about that young hound, Glossop."

"It's quite all right, Aunt Dahlia," I replied soothingly.

" I have the situation well in hand. The Giant Squirt and the Luminous Rabbit are even now being packed."

" I don't know what you're talking about, and I don't for a moment suppose you do, either," said the relative somewhat brusquely, " but, if you'll kindly stop gibbering, I'll tell you what I mean. I have had a most disturbing letter from Katherine. About this reptile. Of course, I haven't breathed a word to Angela. She'd hit the ceiling."

This Angela is Aunt Dahlia's daughter. She and young Tuppy are generally supposed to be more or less engaged, though nothing definitely Morning Posted yet.

" Why ? " I said.

" Why what ? "

" Why would Angela hit the ceiling ? "

" Well, wouldn't you, if you were practically engaged to a fiend in human shape and somebody told you he had gone off to the country and was flirting with a dog-girl ? "

" With a what was that, once again ? "

" A dog-girl. One of these dashed open-air flappers in thick boots and tailor-made tweeds who infest the rural districts and go about the place followed by packs of assorted dogs. I used to be one of them myself in my younger days, so I know how dangerous they are. Her name is Dalgleish. Old Colonel Dalgleish's daughter. They live near Bleaching."

I saw a gleam of daylight.

" Then that must be what his telegram was about. He's just wired, asking me to bring down an Irish water-spaniel. A Christmas present for this girl, no doubt."

" Probably. Katherine tells me he seems to be infatuated with her. She says he follows her about like one of her dogs, looking like a tame cat and bleating like a sheep."

" Quite the private Whipsnade, what ? "

" Bertie," said Aunt Dahlia—and I could see her generous nature was stirred to its depths—" one more crack like that out of you, and I shall forget that I am an aunt, and hand you one."

I became soothing. I gave her the old oil.

" I shouldn't worry," I said. " There's probably nothing in it. Whole thing no doubt much exaggerated."

" You think so, eh ? Well, you know what he's like. You remember the trouble we had when he ran after that singing-woman.'"

I recollected the case. You will find it elsewhere in the archives. Cora Bellinger was the female's name. She was studying for Opera, and young Tuppy thought highly of her.

Fortunately, however, she punched him in the eye during Beefy Bingham's clean, bright entertainment in Bermondsey East, and love died.

"Besides," said Aunt Dahlia. "There's something I haven't told you. Just before he went to Bleaching, he and Angela quarrelled."

"They did?"

"Yes. I got it out of Angela this morning. She was crying her eyes out, poor angel. It was something about her last hat. As far as I could gather, he told her it made her look like a Pekingese, and she told him she never wanted to see him again in this world or the next. And he said 'Right ho!' and breezed off. I can see what has happened. This dog-girl has caught him on the rebound, and, unless something is done quick, anything may happen. So place the facts before Jeeves, and tell him to take action the moment you get down there."

I am always a little piqued, if you know what I mean, at this assumption on the relative's part that Jeeves is so dashed essential on these occasions. My manner, therefore, as I replied, was a bit on the crisp side.

"Jeeves's services will not be required," I said. "I can handle this business. The programme which I have laid out will be quite sufficient to take young Tuppy's mind off love-making. It is my intention to insert the Luminous Rabbit in his room at the first opportunity that presents itself. The Luminous Rabbit shines in the dark and jumps about, making odd, squeaking noises. It will sound to young Tuppy like the Voice of Conscience, and I anticipate that a single treatment will make him retire into a nursing-home for a couple of weeks or so. At the end of which period he will have forgotten all about the bally girl."

"Bertie," said Aunt Dahlia, with a sort of frozen calm. "You are the Abysmal Chump. Listen to me. It's simply because I am fond of you and have influence with the Lunacy Commissioners that you weren't put in a padded cell years ago. Bungle this business, and I withdraw my protection. Can't you understand that this thing is far too serious for any fooling about? Angela's whole happiness is at stake. Do as I tell you, and put it up to Jeeves."

"Just as you say, Aunt Dahlia," I said stiffly.

"All right, then. Do it now."

I went back to the bedroom.

"Jeeves," I said, and I did not trouble to conceal my chagrin, "you need not pack the Luminous Rabbit."

" Very good, sir."

" Nor the Giant Squirt."

" Very good, sir."

" They have been subjected to destructive criticism, and the zest has gone. Oh, and, Jeeves."

" Sir ? "

" Mrs. Travers wishes you, on arriving at Bleaching Court, to disentangle Mr. Glossop from a dog-girl."

" Very good, sir. I will attend to the matter and will do my best to give satisfaction."

That Aunt Dahlia had not exaggerated the perilous nature of the situation was made clear to me on the following afternoon. Jeeves and I drove down to Bleaching in the two-seater, and we were tooling along about half-way between the village and the Court when suddenly there appeared ahead of us a sea of dogs and in the middle of it young Tuppy frisking round one of those largish, corn-fed girls. He was bending towards her in a devout sort of way, and even at a considerable distance I could see that his ears were pink. His attitude, in short, was unmistakably that of a man endeavouring to push a good thing along ; and when I came closer and noted that the girl wore tailor-made tweeds and thick boots, I had no further doubts.

" You observe, Jeeves ? " I said a in a low, significant voice.

" Yes, sir."

" The girl, what ? "

" Yes, sir."

I tootled amiably on the horn and yodelled a bit. They turned—Tuppy, I fancied, not any too pleased.

" Oh, hullo, Bertie," he said.

" Hullo," I said.

" My friend, Bertie Wooster," said Tuppy to the girl, in what seemed to me rather an apologetic manner. You know—as if he would have preferred to hush me up.

" Hullo," said the girl.

" Hullo," I said.

" Hullo, Jeeves," said Tuppy.

" Good afternoon, sir," said Jeeves.

There was a somewhat constrained silence.

" Well, good-bye, Bertie," said young Tuppy. " You'll be wanting to push along, I expect."

We Woosters can take a hint as well as the next man.

" See you later," I said.

" Oh, rather," said Tuppy.

I set the machinery in motion again, and we rolled off.

" Sinister, Jeeves," I said. " You noticed that the subject was looking like a stuffed frog ? "

" Yes, sir."

" And gave no indication of wanting us to stop and join the party ? "

" No, sir."

" I think Aunt Dahlia's fears are justified. The thing seems serious."

" Yes, sir."

" Well, strain the brain, Jeeves."

" Very good, sir."

It wasn't till I was dressing for dinner that night that I saw young Tuppy again. He trickled in just as I was arranging the tie.

" Hullo ! " I said.

" Hullo ! " said Tuppy.

" Who was the girl ? " I asked, in that casual, snaky way of mine—off-hand, I mean.

" A Miss Dalgleish," said Tuppy, and I noticed that he blushed a spot.

" Staying here ? "

" No. She lives in that house just before you come to the gates of this place. Did you bring my football boots ? "

" Yes. Jeeves has got them somewhere."

" And the water-spaniel ? "

" Sorry. No water-spaniel."

" Dashed nuisance. She's set her heart on an Irish water-spaniel."

" Well, what do you care ? "

" I wanted to give her one."

" Why ? "

Tuppy became a trifle haughty. Frigid. The rebuking eye.

" Colonel and Mrs. Dalgleish," he said, " have been extremely kind to me since I got here. They have entertained me. I naturally wish to make some return for their hospitality. I don't want them to look upon me as one of those ill-mannered modern young men you read about in the papers who grab everything they can lay their hooks on and never buy back. If people ask you to lunch and tea and what not, they appreciate it if you make them some little present in return."

" Well, give them your football boots. In passing, why did you want the bally things ? "

" I'm playing in a match next Thursday."

" Down here ? "

" Yes. Upper Bleaching *versus* Hockley-cum-Meston. Apparently it's the big game of the year."

" How did you get roped in ? "

" I happened to mention in the course of conversation the other day that, when in London, I generally turn out on Saturdays for the Old Austinians, and Miss Dalgelish seemed rather keen that I should help the village."

" Which village ? "

" Upper Bleaching, of course."

" Ah, then you're going to play for Hockley ? "

" You needn't be funny, Bertie. You may not know it, but I'm pretty hot stuff on the football field. Oh, Jeeves."

" Sir ? " said Jeeves, entering right centre.

" Mr. Wooster tells me you have my football boots."

" Yes, sir. I have placed them in your room."

" Thanks. Jeeves, do you want to make a bit of money ? "

" Yes, sir."

" Then put a trifle on Upper Bleaching for the annual encounter with Hockley-cum-Meston next Thursday," said Tuppy, exiting with swelling bosom.

" Mr. Glossop is going to play on Thursday," I explained as the door closed.

" So I was informed in the Servants' Hall, sir."

" Oh ? And what's the general feeling there about it ? "

" The impression I gathered, sir, was that the Servants' Hall considers Mr. Glossop ill advised."

" Why's that ? "

" I am informed by Mr. Mulready, Sir Reginald's butler, sir, that this contest differs in some respects from the ordinary football game. Owing to the fact that there has existed for many years considerable animus between the two villages, the struggle is conducted, it appears, on somewhat looser and more primitive lines than is usually the case when two teams meet in friendly rivalry. The primary object of the players, I am given to understand, is not so much to score points as to inflict violence."

" Good Lord, Jeeves ! "

" Such appears to be the case, sir. The game is one that would have a great interest for the antiquarian. It was played first in the reign of King Henry the Eighth, when it lasted from noon till sundown over an area covering several square miles. Seven deaths resulted on that occasion."

" Seven ! "

" Not inclusive of two of the spectators, sir. In recent years, however, the casualties appear to have been confined to broken limbs and other minor injuries. The opinion of the Servants' Hall is that it would be more judicious on Mr. Glossop's part were he to refrain from mixing himself up in the affair."

I was more or less aghast. I mean to say, while I had made it my mission in life to get back at young Tuppy for that business at the Drones, there still remained certain faint vestiges, if vestiges is the word I want, of the old friendship and esteem. Besides, there are limits to one's thirst for vengeance. Deep as my resentment was for the ghastly outrage he had perpetrated on me, I had no wish to see him toddle unsuspiciously into the arena and get all chewed up by wild villagers. A Tuppy scared stiff by a Luminous Rabbit—yes. Excellent business. The happy ending, in fact. But a Tuppy carried off on a stretcher in half a dozen pieces—no. Quite a different matter. All wrong. Not to be considered for a moment.

Obviously, then, a kindly word of warning while there was yet time, was indicated. I buzzed off to his room forthwith, and found him toying dreamily with the football boots.

I put him in possession of the facts.

" What you had better do—and the Servants' Hall thinks the same," I said, " is fake a sprained ankle on the eve of the match."

He looked at me in an odd sort of way.

" You suggest that, when Miss Dalgleish is trusting me, relying on me, looking forward with eager, girlish enthusiasm to seeing me help her village on to victory, I should let her down with a thud ? "

I was pleased with his ready intelligence.

" That's the idea," I said.

" Faugh ! " said Tuppy—the only time I've ever heard the word.

" How do you mean, Faugh ? " I asked.

" Bertie," said Tuppy, " what you tell me merely makes me all the keener for the fray. A warm game is what I want. I welcome this sporting spirit on the part of the opposition. I shall enjoy a spot of roughness. It will enable me to go all out and give of my best. Do you realize," said young Tuppy, vermilion to the gills, " that She will be looking on ? And do you know how that will make me feel ? It will make me feel like some knight of old jousting under the eyes of his lady. Do you suppose that Sir Lancelot or Sir Galahad, when there was a tourney scheduled for the following Thursday, went and pretended they had sprained their ankles just because the thing was likely to be a bit rough ? "

" Don't forget that in the reign of King Henry the Eighth——"

" Never mind about the reign of King Henry the Eighth. All I care about is that it's Upper Bleachings' turn this year to play in colours, so I shall be able to wear my Old Austinian shirt. Light blue, Bertie, with broad orange stripes. I shall look like something, I tell you."

" But what ? "

" Bertie," said Tuppy, now becoming purely ga-ga, " I may as well tell you that I'm in love at last. This is the real thing. I have found my mate. All my life I have dreamed of meeting some sweet, open-air girl with all the glory of the English countryside in her eyes, and I have found her. How different she is, Bertie, from these hot-house, artificial London girls ! Would they stand in the mud on a winter afternoon, watching a football match ? Would they know what to give an Alsatian for fits ? Would they tramp ten miles a day across the fields and come back as fresh as paint ? No ! "

" Well, why should they ? "

" Bertie, I'm staking everything on this game on Thursday. At the moment, I have an idea that she looks on me as something of a weakling, simply because I got a blister on my foot the other afternoon and had to take the bus back from Hockley. But when she sees me going through the rustic opposition like a devouring flame, will that make her think a bit ? Will that make her open her eyes ? What ? "

" What ? "

" I said ' What ? ' "

" So did I."

" I meant Won't it ? "

" Oh, rather."

Here the dinner-gong sounded, not before I was ready for it.

Judicious inquiries during the next couple of days convinced me that the Servants' Hall at Bleaching Court, in advancing the suggestion that young Tuppy, born and bred in the gentler atmosphere of the Metropolis, would do well to keep out of local disputes and avoid the football field on which these were to be settled, had not spoken idly. It had weighed its words and said the sensible thing. Feeling between the two villages undoubtedly ran high, as they say.

You know how it is in these remote rural districts. Life

tends at times to get a bit slow. There's nothing much to do in the long winter evenings but listen to the radio and brood on what a tick your neighbour is. You find yourself remembering how Farmer Giles did you down over the sale of your pig, and Farmer Giles finds himself remembering that it was your son, Ernest, who bunged the half-brick at his horse on the second Sunday before Septuagesima. And so on and so forth. How this particular feud had started, I don't know, but the season of peace and goodwill found it in full blast. The only topic of conversation in Upper Bleaching was Thursday's game, and the citizenry seemed to be looking forward to it in a spirit that can only be described as ghoulish. And it was the same in Hockley-cum-Meston.

I paid a visit to Hockley-cum-Meston on the Wednesday, being rather anxious to take a look at the inhabitants and see how formidable they were. I was shocked to observe that practically every second male might have been the Village Blacksmith's big brother. The muscles of their brawny arms were obviously strong as iron bands, and the way the company at the Green Pig, where I looked in incognito for a spot of beer, talked about the forthcoming sporting contest was enough to chill the blood of any one who had a pal who proposed to fling himself into the fray. It sounded rather like Attila and a few of his Huns sketching our their next campaign.

I went back to Jeeves with my mind made up.

" Jeeves," I said, " you, who had the job of drying and pressing those dress-clothes of mine, are aware that I have suffered much at young Tuppy Glossop's hands. By rights, I suppose, I ought to be welcoming the fact that the Wrath of Heaven is now hovering over him in this fearful manner. But the view I take of it is that Heaven looks like overdoing it. Heaven's idea of a fitting retribution is not mine. In my most unrestrained moments I never wanted the poor blighter assassinated. And the idea in Hockley-cum-Meston seems to be that a good opportunity has arisen of making it a bumper Christmas for the local undertaker. There was a fellow with red hair at the Green Pig this afternoon who might have been the undertaker's partner, the way he talked. We must act, and speedily, Jeeves. We must put a bit of a jerk in it and save young Tuppy in spite of himself."

" What course would you advocate, sir ? "

" I'll tell you. He refuses to do the sensible thing and slide out, because the girl will be watching the game and he imagines, poor lizard, that he is going to shine and impress her. So we must employ guile. You must go up to London to-day, Jeeves, and to-morrow morning you will send a telegram, signed 'Angela,' which will run as follows. Jot it down. Ready? "

" Yes, sir."

" ' So sorry—— ' . . ." I pondered. " What would a girl say, Jeeves, who, having had a row with the bird she was practically engaged to because he told her she looked like a Pekingese in her new hat, wanted to extend the olive-branch? "

" ' So sorry I was cross,' sir, would, I fancy, be the expression."

" Strong enough, do you think? "

" Possibly the addition of the word ' darling ' would give the necessary verisimilitude, sir."

" Right. Resume the jotting. ' So sorry I was cross, darling . . .' No, wait, Jeeves. Scratch that out. I see where we have gone off the rails. I see where we are missing a chance to make this the real tabasco. Sign the telegram not ' Angela ' but ' Travers.' "

" Very good, sir."

" Or, rather, ' Dahlia Travers.' And this is the body of the communication. ' Please return at once.' "

" ' Immediately ' would be more economical, sir. Only one word. And it has a stronger ring."

" True. Jot on, then. ' Please return immediately. Angela in a hell of a state.' "

" I would suggest ' Seriou ly ill,' sir."

" All right. ' Seriously ill.' ' Angela seriously ill. Keeps calling for you and says you were quite right about hat.' "

" If I might suggest, sir—— ? "

" Well, go ahead."

" I fancy the following would meet the case. ' Please return immediately. Angela seriously ill. High fever and delirium. Keeps calling your name piteously and saying something about a hat and that you were quite right. Please catch earliest possible train. Dahlia Travers.' "

" That sounds all right."

" Yes, sir."

" You like that ' piteously '? You don't think ' incessantly ' ? "

" No, sir. ' Piteously ' is the *mot juste*."

" All right. You know. Well, send it off in time to get here at two-thirty."

" Yes, sir."

" Two-thirty, Jeeves. You see the devilish cunning? "

" No, sir."

" I will tell you. If the telegram arrived earlier, he would get it before the game. By two-thirty, however, he will have started for the ground. I shall hand it to him the moment there is a lull in the battle. By that time he will have begun to get some idea of what a football match between Upper Bleaching and Hockley-cum-Meston is like, and the thing ought to work like magic. I can't imagine any one who has been sporting awhile with those thugs I saw yesterday not welcoming any excuse to call it a day. You follow me ? "

" Yes, sir."

" Very good, Jeeves."

" Very good, sir."

You can always rely on Jeeves. Two-thirty I had said, and two-thirty it was. The telegram arrived almost on the minute. I was going to my room to change into something warmer at the moment, and I took it up with me. Then into the heavy tweeds and off in the car to the field of play. I got there just as the two teams were lining up, and half a minute later the whistle blew and the war was on.

What with one thing and another—having been at a school where they didn't play it and so forth—Rugby football is a game I can't claim absolutely to understand in all its niceties, if you know what I mean. I can follow the broad, general principles, of course. I mean to say, I know that the main scheme is to work the ball down the field somehow and deposit it over the line at the other end, and that, in order to squelch this programme, each side is allowed to put in a certain amount of assault and battery and do things to its fellow-man which, if done elsewhere, would result in fourteen days without the option, coupled with some strong remarks from the Bench. But there I stop. What you might call the science of the thing is to Bertram Wooster a sealed book. However, I am informed by experts that on this occasion there was not enough science for any one to notice.

There had been a great deal of rain in the last few days, and the going appeared to be a bit sticky. In fact, I have seen swamps that were drier than this particular bit of ground. The red-haired bloke whom I had encountered in the pub paddled up and kicked off amidst cheers from the populace, and the ball went straight to where Tuppy was standing, a pretty colour-scheme in light blue and orange. Tuppy caught it neatly, and hoofed it back, and it was at this point that I understood that an Upper Bleaching *versus* Hockley-cum-Meston game had certain features not usually seen on the football field.

For Tuppy, having done his bit, was just standing there, looking modest, when there was a thunder of large feet and the red-haired bird, galloping up, seized him by the neck, hurled him to earth, and fell on him. I had a glimpse of Tuppy's face, as it registered horror, dismay, and a general suggestion of stunned dissatisfaction with the scheme of things, and then he disappeared. By the time he had come to the surface, a sort of mob-warfare was going on at the other side of the field. Two assortments of sons of the soil had got their heads down and were shoving earnestly against each other, with the ball somewhere in the middle.

Tuppy wiped a fair portion of Hampshire out of his eye, peered round him in a dazed kind of way, saw the mass-meeting and ran towards it, arriving just in time for a couple of heavy-weights to gather him in and give him the mud-treatment again. This placed him in an admirable position for a third heavy-weight to kick him in the ribs with a boot like a violin-case. The red-haired man then fell on him. It was all good, brisk play, and looked fine from my side of the ropes.

I saw now where Tuppy had made his mistake. He was too dressy. On occasions such as this it is safest not to be con-spicuous, and that blue and orange shirt rather caught the eye. A sober beige, blending with the colour of the ground, was what his best friends would have recommended. And, in addition to the fact that his costume attracted attention, I rather think that the men of Hockley-cum-Meston resented his being on the field at all. They felt that, as a non-local, he had butted in on a private fight and had no business there.

At any rate, it certainly appeared to me that they were giving him preferential treatment. After each of those shoving-bees to which I have alluded, when the edifice caved in and tons of humanity wallowed in a tangled mass in the juice, the last soul to be excavated always seemed to be Tuppy. And on the rare occasions when he actually managed to stand upright for a moment, somebody—generally the red-haired man—in-variably sprang to the congenial task of spilling him again.

In fact, it was beginning to look as though that telegram would come too late to save a human life, when an interruption occurred. Play had worked round close to where I was stand-ing, and there had been the customary collapse of all concerned, with Tuppy at the bottom of the basket, as usual ; but this time, when they got up and started to count the survivors, a sizable cove in what had once been a white shirt remained on the ground. And a hearty cheer went up from a hundred patriotic throats as the news spread that Upper Bleaching had drawn first blood.

The victim was carried off by a couple of his old chums, and the rest of the players sat down and pulled their stockings up and thought of life for a bit. The moment had come, it seemed to me, to remove Tuppy from the *abattoir*, and I hopped over the ropes and toddled to where he sat scraping mud from his wish-bone. His air was that of a man who has been passed through a wringer, and his eyes, what you could see of them, had a strange, smouldering gleam. He was so crusted with alluvial deposits that one realized how little a mere bath would ever be able to effect. To fit him to take his place once more in polite society, he would certainly have to be sent to the cleaner's. Indeed, it was a moot point whether it wouldn't be simpler just to throw him away.

" Tuppy, old man," I said.

" Eh ? " said Tuppy.

" A telegram for you."

" Eh ? "

" I've got a wire here that came after you left the house."

" Eh ? " said Tuppy.

I stirred him up a trifle with the ferrule of my stick, and he seemed to come to life.

" Be careful what you're doing, you silly ass," he said, in part. " I'm one solid bruise. What are you gibbering about ? "

" A telegram has come for you. I think it may be important."

He snorted in a bitter sort of way.

" Do you suppose I've time to read telegrams now ? "

" But this one may be frightfully urgent," I said. " Here it is."

But, if you understand me, it wasn't. How I had happened to do it, I don't know, but apparently, in changing the upholstery, I had left it in my other coat.

" Oh, my gosh," I said, " I've left it behind."

" It doesn't matter."

" But it does. It's probably something you ought to read at once. Immediately, if you know what I mean. If I were you, I'd just say a few words of farewell to the murder-squad and come back to the house right away."

He raised his eyebrows. At least, I think he must have done, because the mud on his forehead stirred a little, as if something was going on underneath it.

" Do you imagine," he said, " that I would slink away under

her very eyes ?   Good God !   Besides," he went on, in a quiet, meditative voice, " there is no power on earth that could get me off this field until I've thoroughly disembowelled that red-haired bounder.   Have you noticed how he keeps tackling me when I haven't got the ball ? "

" Isn't that right ? "

" Of course it's not right.   Never mind !   A bitter retribution awaits that bird.   I've had enough of it.   From now on I assert my personality."

" I'm a bit foggy as to the rules of this pastime," I said. " Are you allowed to bite him ? "

" I'll try, and see what happens," said Tuppy, struck with the idea and brightening a little.

At this point, the pall-bearers returned, and fighting became general again all along the Front.

There's nothing like a bit of rest and what you might call folding of the hands for freshening up the shop-soiled athlete. The dirty work, resumed after this brief breather, started off with an added vim which it did one good to see.   And the life and soul of the party was young Tuppy.

You know, only meeting a fellow at lunch or at the races or loafing round country-houses, and so forth, you don't get on to his hidden depths, if you know what I mean.   Until this moment, if asked, I would have said that Tuppy Glossop was, on the whole, essentially a pacific sort of bloke, with little or nothing of the tiger of the jungle in him.   Yet here he was, running to and fro with fire streaming from his nostrils, a positive danger to traffic.

Yes, absolutely.   Encouraged by the fact that the referee was either filled with the spirit of Live and Let Live or else had got his whistle choked up with mud, the result being that he appeared to regard the game with a sort of calm detachment, Tuppy was putting in some very impressive work.   Even to me, knowing nothing of the finesse of the thing, it was plain that if Hockley-cum-Meston wanted the happy ending they must eliminate young Tuppy at the earliest possible moment.   And I will say for them that they did their best, the red-haired man being particularly assiduous.   But Tuppy was made of durable material.   Every time the opposition talent ground him into the mire and sat on his head, he rose on stepping-ston s of his dead self, if you follow me, to higher things.   And in the end it was the red-haired bloke who did the dust-biting.

I couldn't tell you exactly how it happened, for by this time the shades of night were drawing in a bit and there was a dollop of mist rising, but one moment the fellow was hareing along, apparently without a care in the world, and then suddenly Tuppy had appeared from nowhere and was sailing through the air at his neck. They connected with a crash and a slither, and a little later the red-haired bird was hopping off, supported by a brace of friends, something having gone wrong with his left ankle.

After that, there was nothing to it. Upper Bleaching, thoroughly bucked, became busier than ever. There was a lot of earnest work in a sort of inland sea down at the Hockley end of the field, and then a kind of tidal wave poured over the line, and when the bodies had been removed and the tumult and the shouting had died, there was young Tuppy lying on the ball. And that, with exception of a few spots of mayhem in the last five minutes, concluded the proceedings.

I drove back to the Court in rather what you might term a pensive frame of mind. Things having happened as they had happened, there seemed to me a goodish bit of hard thinking to be done. There was a servitor of sorts in the hall, when I arrived, and I asked him to send up a whisky-and-soda, strongish, to my room. The old brain, I felt, needed stimulating. And about ten minutes later there was a knock at the door, and in came Jeeves, bearing tray and materials.

" Hullo, Jeeves," I said, surprised. " Are you back ? "

" Yes, sir."

" When did you get here ? "

" Some little while ago, sir. Was it an enjoyable game, sir ? "

" In a sense, Jeeves," I said, " yes. Replete with human interest and all that, if you know what I mean. But I fear that, owing to a touch of carelessness on my part, the worst has happened. I left the telegram in my other coat, so young Tuppy remained in action throughout."

" Was he injured, sir ? "

" Worse than that, Jeeves. He was the star of the game. Toasts, I should imagine, are now being drunk to him at every pub in the village. So spectacularly did he play—in fact, so heartily did he joust—that I can't see the girl not being all over him. Unless I am greatly mistaken, the moment they meet, she will exclaim ' My hero ! ' and fall into his bally arms."

" Indeed, sir ? "

I didn't like the man's manner. Too calm. Unimpressed. A little leaping about with fallen jaw was what I had expected my words to produce, and I was on the point of saying as much when the door opened again and Tuppy limped in.

He was wearing an ulster over his football things, and I wondered why he had come to pay a social call on me instead of proceeding straight to the bathroom. He eyed my glass in a wolfish sort of way.

" Whisky ? " he said, in a hushed voice.

" And soda."

" Bring me one, Jeeves," said young Tuppy. " A large one."

" Very good, sir."

Tuppy wandered to the window and looked out into the gathering darkness, and for the first time I perceived that he had got a grouch of some description. You can generally tell by a fellow's back. Humped. Bent. Bowed down with weight of woe, if you follow me.

" What's the matter ? " I asked.

Tuppy emitted a mirthless.

" Oh, nothing much," he said. " My faith in woman is dead, that's all."

" It is ? "

" You jolly well bet it is. Women are a wash-out. I see no future for the sex, Bertie. Blisters, all of them."

" Er—even the Dogsbody girl ? "

" Her name," said Tuppy a little stiffly, " is Dalgleish, if it happens to interest you. And, if you want to know something else, she's the worst of the lot."

" My dear chap ! "

Tuppy turned. Beneath the mud, I could see that his face was drawn and, to put it in a nutshell, wan.

" Do you know what happened, Bertie ? "

" What ? "

" She wasn't there."

" Where ? "

" At the match, you silly ass."

" Not at the match ? "

" No."

" You mean, not among the throng of eager spectators ? "

" Of course I mean not among the spectators. Did you think I expected her to be playing ? "

" But I thought the whole scheme of the thing——"

" So did I. My gosh ! " said Tuppy, laughing another of those hollow ones. " I sweat myself to the bone for her sake. I allow a mob of homicidal maniacs to kick me in the ribs and stroll about on my face. And then, when I have braved a fate worse than death, so to speak, all to please her, I find that she didn't bother to come and watch the game. She got a phone-call from London from somebody who said he had located an Irish water-spaniel, and up she popped in her car, leaving me flat. I met her just now outside her house, and she told me. And all she could think of was that she was as sore as a sunburnt neck because she had had her trip for nothing. Apparently it wasn't an Irish water-spaniel at all. Just an ordinary English water-spaniel. And to think I fancied I loved a girl like that. A nice life-partner she would make ! ' When pain and anguish wring the brow, a ministering angel thou '——I don't think ! Why, if a man married a girl like that and happened to get stricken by some dangerous illness, would she smooth his pillow and press cooling drinks on him ? Not a chance ! She'd be off somewhere trying to buy Siberian eel-hounds. I'm through with women."

I saw that the moment had come to put in a word for the old firm.

" My cousin Angela's not a bad sort, Tuppy," I said, in a grave elder-brotherly kind of way. " Not altogether a bad egg, Angela, if you look at her squarely. I had always been hoping that she and you . . . and I know my Aunt Dahlia felt the same."

Tuppy's bitter sneer cracked the top-soil.

" Angela ! " he woofed. " Don't talk to me about Angela. Angela's a rag and a bone and a hank of hair and an A1 scourge, if you want to know. She gave me the push. Yes, she did. Simply because I had the manly courage to speak out candidly on the subject of that ghastly lid she was chump enough to buy. It made her look like a Peke, and I told her it made her look like a Peke. And instead of admiring me for my fearless honesty she bunged me out on my ear. Faugh ! "

" She did ? " I said.

" She jolly well did," said young Tuppy. " At four-sixteen p.m. on Tuesday the seventeenth."

" By the way, old man," I said, " I've found that telegram."

" What telegram ? "

" The one I told you about."

" Oh, that one ? "

" Yes, that's the one."

" Well, let's have a look at the beastly thing."

I handed it over, watching him narrowly. And suddenly, as he read, I saw him wobble. Stirred to the core. Obviously.

" Anything important ? " I said.

" Bertie," said young Tuppy in a voice that quivered with strong emotion, " my recent remarks *re* your cousin Angela. Wash them out. Cancel them. Look on them as not spoken. I tell you, Bertie, Angela's all right. An angel in human shape, and that's official. Bertie, I've got to get up to London. She's ill."

" Ill ? "

" High fever and delirium. This wire's from your aunt. She wants me to come up to London at once. Can I borrow your car ? "

" Of course."

" Thanks," said Tuppy, and dashed out.

He had only been gone about a second when Jeeves came in with the restorative.

" Mr. Glossop's gone, Jeeves."

" Indeed, sir ? "

" To London."

" Yes, sir ? "

" In my car. To see my cousin Angela. The sun is once more shining, Jeeves."

" Extremely gratifying, sir."

I gave him the eye.

" Was it you, Jeeves, who 'phoned to Miss What's-her-bally-name about the alleged water-spaniel ? "

" Yes, sir."

" I thought as much."

" Yes, sir ? "

" Yes, Jeeves, the moment Mr. Glossop told me that a Mysterious Voice had 'phoned on the subject of Irish water-spaniels, I thought as much. I recognized your touch. I read your motives like an open book. You knew she would come buzzing up."

" Yes, sir."

" And you knew how Tuppy would react. If there's one thing that gives a jousting knight the pip, it is to have his audience walk out on him."

" Yes, sir."

" But, Jeeves."

" Sir ? "

" There's just one point. What will Mr. Glossop say when he finds my cousin Angela full of beans and not delirious ? "

" The point had not escaped me, sir. I took the liberty of ringing Mrs. Travers up on the telephone and explaining the circumstances. All will be in readiness for Mr. Glossop's arrival."

"Jeeves," I said, "you think of everything."

"Thank you, sir. In Mr. Gossop's absence, would you care to drink this whisky-and-soda?"

I shook the head.

"No, Jeeves, there is only one man who must do that. It is you. If ever any one earned a refreshing snort, you are he. Pour it out, Jeeves, and shove it down."

"Thank you very much, sir."

"Cheerio, Jeeves!"

"Pip-pip, if I may use the expression."